BUSINESS/SCIENCE/TECHNOLOGY DIVISION
CHICAGO PUBLIC LIBRARY
400 SOUTH STATE STREET
CHICAGO, IL 60605

R00357 72349

The
Chicago Public Library

REFERENCE

THE CUPOLA AND ITS OPERATION

THIRD EDITION

1965

Published by the American Foundrymen's Society

Golf and Wolf Roads, Des Plaines, Illinois

TS
231
.A5
1954

Copyright 1965 by
The American Foundrymen's Society
(Incorporated)
Des Plaines, Illinois

Printed in The United States of America

The American Foundrymen's Society as a body is not responsible for the statements and opinions advanced in this publication. Nothing contained in any publication of the American Foundrymen's Society is to be construed as granting any right, by implication or otherwise, for manufacture, sale or use in connection with any method, apparatus or product covered by Letters Patent, nor as insuring anyone against liability for infringement of Letters Patent.

THE CHICAGO PUBLIC LIBRARY
THE CHICAGO PUBLIC LIBRARY
JUL 28 1969 D

CHICAGO PUBLIC LIBRARY
BUSINESS / SCIENCE / TECHNOLOGY
400 S. STATE ST. 60605

Presentation and Appreciation

We wish to express our thanks and appreciation to the predecessors of the present *Cupola Advisory Committee* and to the individual authors who compiled the 1946 and 1954 editions of THE CUPOLA AND ITS OPERATION. Details of the work of previous groups are included in the preface of those editions.

The book was first published with the *committee* under the guidance of Mr. R. G. McElwee. The second edition was published after the *committee* had been reactivated for that purpose. Mr. H. Bornstein accepted the chairmanship of the *committee* in 1953; his organizing ability and personal enthusiasm were largely responsible for the complete and up-to-date handbook published at that time.

Continuing developments in the many phases of cupola technology and changes in the objectives of cupola operation indicated the need for revision. To prepare for the revision, the book was reviewed by the individual committee members to determine corrections and additions needed. At a meeting in the fall of 1962 a plan of revision was developed and assignments were made.

The *Editorial Subcommittee* met in December 1963 to review all manuscripts. Members participating were H. A. Deane, W. W. Levi, H. Bornstein and H. W. Gorman. Mr. S. C. Massari, *Technical Director of AFS,* took an active part in this and other work of the *committee.* Valuable help and cooperation were received from G. G. Petterson, *AFS Publications Editor,* who was responsible for preparing the book for publication.

Most of the contributors to this third edition of the *Cupola Handbook* are members of the *Cupola Advisory Committee:*

H. W. GORMAN, *Chairman*	General Castings Corporation (1949-64 Allis-Chalmers Mfg. Company)
M. H. HORTON, *Vice-Chairman*	Deere & Company
R. A. BAUER	Acme Steel Company
H. N. BOGART	Ford Motor Company
H. BORNSTEIN	Retired
R. CARLSON	American Cast Iron Pipe Company
R. A. CLARK	Metals Division, Union Carbide Corp.
H. A. DEANE	Campbell, Wyant & Cannon Foundry Company
T. GISZCZAK	Central Fdy. Div., General Motors Corp.

J. A. HAVNEN	Burnham Corporation
W. R. JAESCHKE	Consultant
C. F. JOSEPH	Consultant, Miller & Company
D. E. KRAUSE	Gray Iron Research Institute
W. W. LEVI	Consultant
H. W. LOWNIE JR.	Battelle Memorial Institute
D. MATTER	Ohio Ferro Alloys Corporation
M. D. NEPTUNE	James B. Clow & Sons
W. A. QUENELLE	Central Foundry Company
J. E. REHDER	Canada Iron Foundries (1952-64)
B. I. STERN	Lakey Foundry Corporation
H. H. WILDER	Vanadium Corporation of America

In addition to the work of the *committee,* invaluable assistance was given by these men, without whose help the book would not have been complete. G. Krumlauf, Republic Steel Corp., prepared the *Pig Iron* chapter; he received suggestions on the manuscript from E. C. Mathis, retired, and E. J. Burke, Hanna Furnace Corp. Prof. H. L. Womochel, University of Michigan, rewrote the chapter *Metallurgy of the Cast Irons.* Chapters on *Emissions Control* and *Safe Practices* were prepared by H. J. Weber, *AFS SH&AP Director.* Prof. C. R. Loper Jr., University of Wisconsin, was responsible for the material in the chapter entitled *Temperature Measuring.* T. E. Barlow, International Minerals & Chemical Corp., revised the *Refractories* chapter. Aiding committee members in the *Scrap* chapter revision were L. H. Brogley, International Harvester Co., and W. R. Hohl, General Motors Corp., and in creating the *Basic Slag Cupola* chapter, G. F. Thomas, International Nickel Co., formerly of Deere & Co.

In revising THE CUPOLA AND ITS OPERATION an endeavor has been made to produce a comprehensive reference for this widely used melting medium. The material in this book has been prepared by men who are recognized authorities in their particular fields, who have drawn from their own researches or from sources considered reliable for the data presented. In some areas the material is entirely new; other aspects required minor revision.

While all material contained herein has been carefully reviewed by the *Cupola Advisory Committee* and a special *editorial committee* it is recognized that the information in this book may lead to different interpretations, in accordance with varied personal experiences and plant equipment. Any comments, suggestions or corrections the reader has to offer will be of value in preparing a subsequent edition. Such comments should be addressed to the *Technical Director,* AFS International Headquarters, Golf and Wolf Roads, Des Plaines, Illinois 60016.

H. W. Gorman, *Chairman*
Cupola Advisory Committee
AMERICAN FOUNDRYMEN'S SOCIETY

Frontispiece : 17th century foundry gun manufacture.

Contents

OPERATIONS

PRIMITIVE METHOD OF SMELTING ORE

Introduction

THE EVOLUTION OF THE CUPOLA (Chapter 1*) emphasizes the age and maturity of this widely used melting medium. . . . Many of the earlier workers showed considerable imagination. The more fanciful trimmings have been shorn away under the pressure of experience.

For several decades the basic design of the cupola underwent no radical changes. There has been a steady growth in its use and an increasing desire for a better understanding of the manner in which it does its job. This has led to the development of improved devices and refinements to permit closer control and measurement of the factors that determine its behavior.

These developments have earned for the cupola an eminent position as a melting medium. Outstanding are its thermal efficiency, low initial cost, low operating cost and, above all, its versatility. To illustrate the latter, cupolas operating commercially in this country range in hourly output from two tons to fifty tons, in heats from two hours a day to several successive days – all making irons that cover a host of compositions designed to meet the demands inherent in the application of cast iron parts in virtually all segments of industry.

There is no basis for fearing for the future of the cupola. On the contrary, with the increasing application of sound principles of process control and further basic scientific knowledge, the cupola can be expected to turn out more and better controlled metal at lower cost.

Cupola technology is currently enjoying a healthy spate of fresh ideas. Old and new objectives, such as heated blast, long sustained melting campaigns, the effect of basic slags, etc., are receiving attention on a large and intrepid scale. No doubt many improved usages will come from these efforts. The basis for optimism lies in the fact that the underlying cause of this evolutionary spurt is recognition of the need for close control of all the operational factors that determine the behavior of the cupola. Similar attention to the melting of irons in standard cupolas, which for some time to come will account for the bulk of gray iron production, will undoubtedly assure rich rewards.

The sections of this 1965 edition of THE CUPOLA AND ITS OPERATION – *Equipment, Materials, Operations* – treat present cupola practices of proven merit.

*Historical résumé (with some revision) of the 1954 edition's *History of the Cupola* based on the 1947 Charles Edgar Hoyt Lecture by the late J. T. MacKenzie of American Cast Iron Pipe Co.

History

CUPOLA is diminutive of the Latin *cupa,* meaning cask as shown in Figs. 1.1 and 1.2.

The cupola is a refractory lined cavity with necessary openings at the top for the escape of gasses and for charging the stock, and at the bottom for entry of the air blast and for drawing off molten iron and slag. It is an efficient melting furnace.

A bed of fuel is laid in the cupola and ignited. Then alternate layers of metal and fuel are charged (Fig. 3.3) and the blast is turned on. If a few simple laws are followed, melting begins quickly and can be continued for a long time.

The cupola is used for almost all gray iron melting, for some copper and nonferrous alloys, for most rock wool production, and as the primary melting unit for much of the malleable iron manufactured.

It is melter of considerable tonnage of pig, scrap and spiegeleisen for transfer to open hearth furnaces.

In 1963 there were 2817 cupolas in the gray iron foundries of the United States and Canada.

CUPOLA TYPES

The patent (Fig. 1.4) of John Wilkinson is dated June 2, 1794. Actually it was intended as an improvement on the old forge used for centuries as a melting furnace. The result was a melting unit instead and the modern cupola, with which Wilkinson commonly is associated, developed along these lines.

There is evidence that bellows driven cupolas (Fig. 1.1) have been used for centuries by itinerant foundrymen in China for mending broken cooking utensils.

Fig. 1.1. An early (1789) French iron foundry.

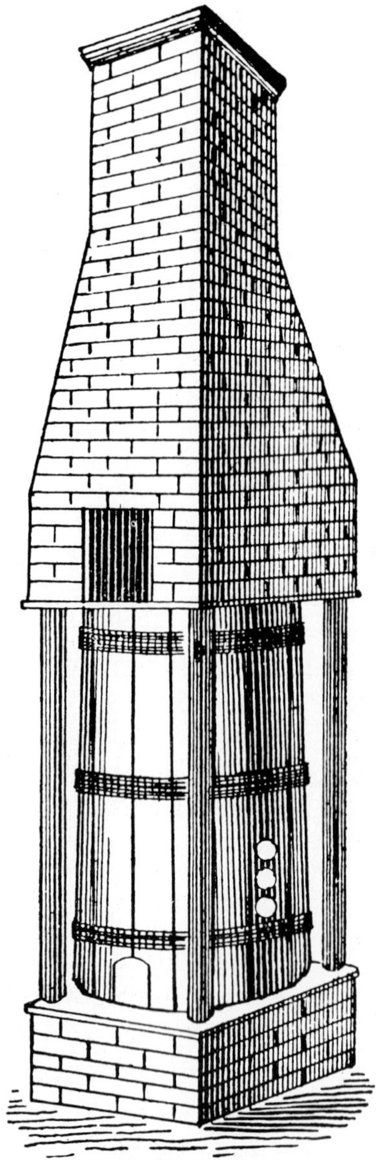

Fig. 1.2. Old style stave cupola.

Small cupolas have been ingeniously designed for special purposes. W. J. Keep made one in sections and mounted it on wheels (Fig. 1.3).

Scrap parts and an oil drum were welded by our armed forces to make a cupola (Fig. 1.5) in New Guinea during World War II.

For repairing trolley tracks (Fig. 1.6), J. W. Paxson built a special cupola with blower. It had a shield to prevent damage to the trolley wire.

Fig. 1.3. W. J. Keep's cupola. Sections 18 in. deep; about 27 in. outside diameter.

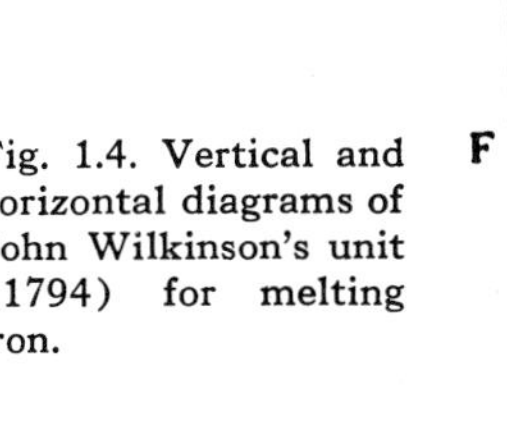

Fig. 1.4. Vertical and horizontal diagrams of John Wilkinson's unit (1794) for melting iron.

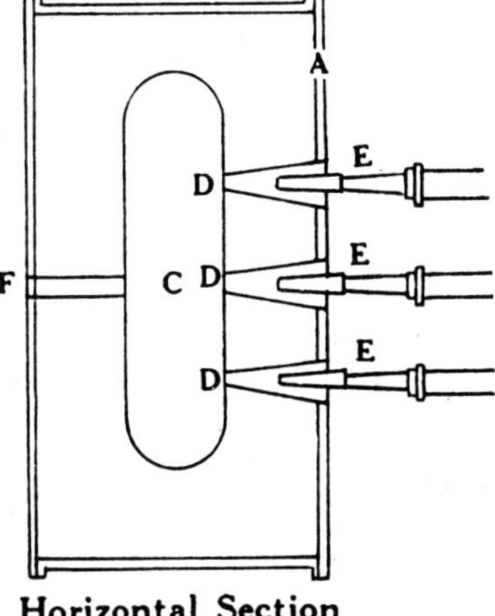

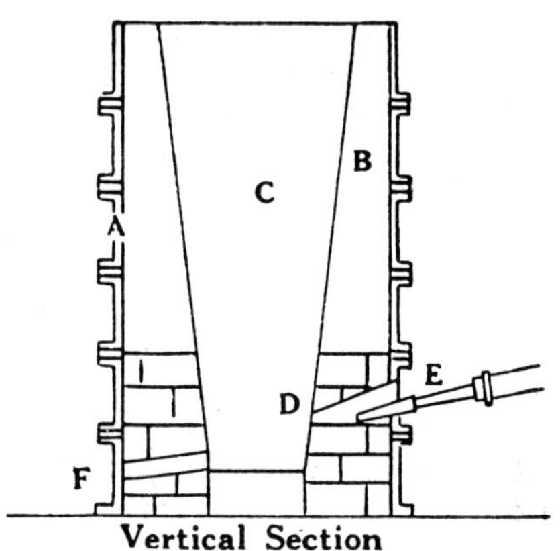

T. D. West, an energetic experimenter, designed a combined cupola and crucible furnace (Fig. 1.7) for experimental melts. His repeat results were not satisfactory so he contrived the comparative fusion cupola (Fig. 1.9) for melting one kind of iron in one side and another iron in the other. He had assumed that conditions would be the same. He employed the center tuyere.

The Shaw-Walker cupolette is ingenious. It has an inside diameter of about 2 ft and is only 2 ft high above the tuyeres, with a blower similar to a small hair drier in each tuyere. A cover over the top, with a hole about 6 in. diameter, radiates the heat downward and helps force the blast to the center. Batch melting of 100 to 200 lb iron at frequent intervals and temperatures of 2600 F (1425 C) and higher are features of this small unit.

Heights extend from the 2 ft stack cupolette to some cupolas now taller than 66 ft.

Of a 50 ft stack employed in Germany, Dr. Richard A. Moldenke reported, "It melted hot iron but it's doubtful extreme height had anything to do with it."

Diameters range from 5 in. to a modern 15 ft giant melting 55 tons/hr.

Cupolas have been made square and rectangular to oval and round. Circular is the shape almost universally in use today.

The oval cupola (Fig. 1.8, from 1882 *American Foundry Practice* by T. D. West) was designed to give better penetration of the blast in larger sizes. Brickwork is complex but the idea sound. Difficulty was overcome by making the furnace link shaped (two half circles with a rectangular section between them). Today's cupolas achieve blast penetration with protruding tuyeres.

At a large pipe plant there were three 40 ton cupolas consisting of two 72 in. semicircles with a 30 x 72 in. rectangular section. Standard firebrick shapes thus were available for lining.

Experiments have altered the vertical cross-section. E. Kirk thought a lamp chimney shape like the Grandall (Fig. 1.10) was ideal. Later he favored a straight lining or slight bosh, the Zippler arrangement (Fig. 1.12). Another curious shape was the reservoir cupola (Fig. 1.11), with three courses of odd shaped firebrick.

The greatest interest in structural details has been shown in the tuyeres. Some of these are in referred to illustrations. The most successful of unusual tuyeres is the Zippler (Fig. 1.12). According to Kirk, this worked well so long as Zippler ran the cupola.

Fig. 1.5. Simple cupola constructed from an oil drum and scrap parts welded by U.S. armed forces in the field.

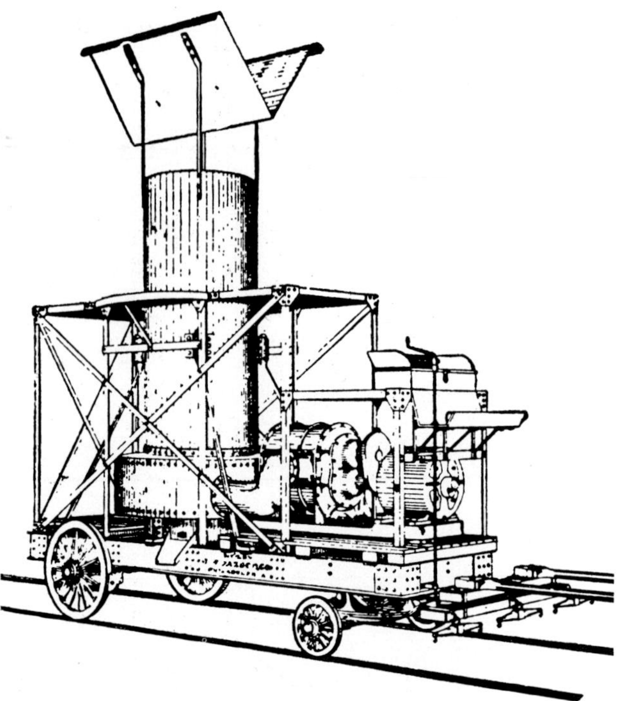

Fig. 1.6. **Paxson special truck and track cupola used in melting iron for connecting the ends of rails for trolley roads.**

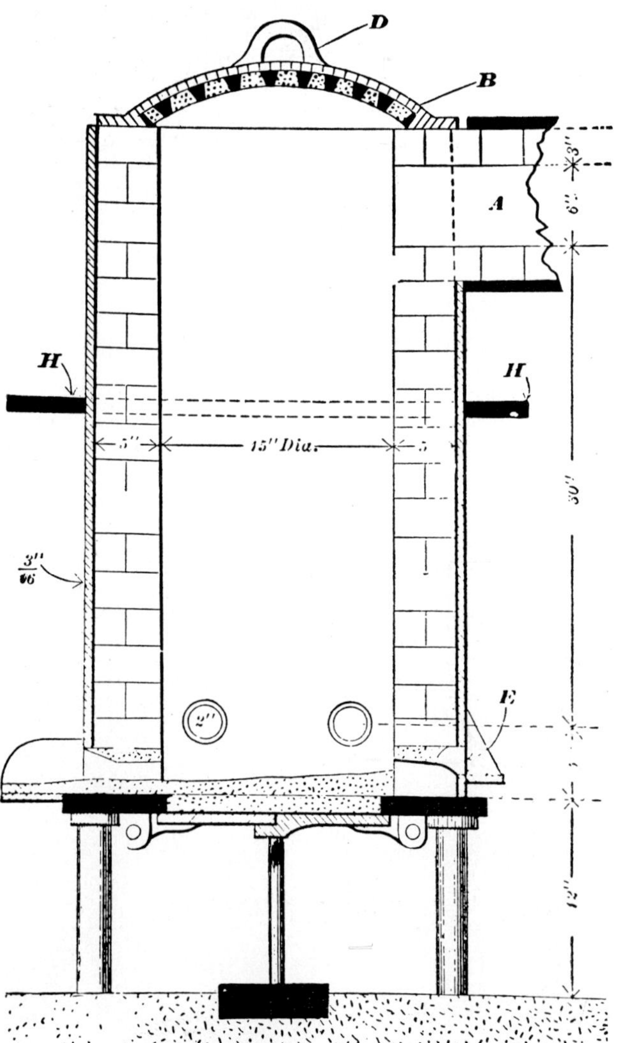

Fig. 1.7. **West's combined cupola and crucible furnace.**

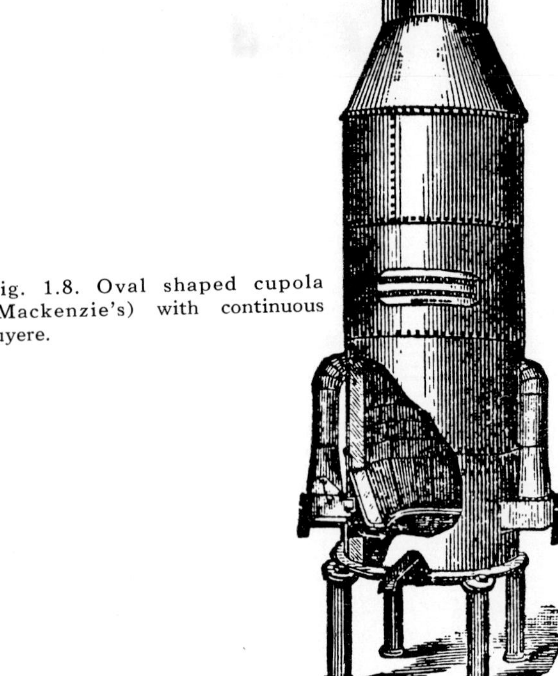

Fig. 1.8. Oval shaped cupola (Mackenzie's) with continuous tuyere.

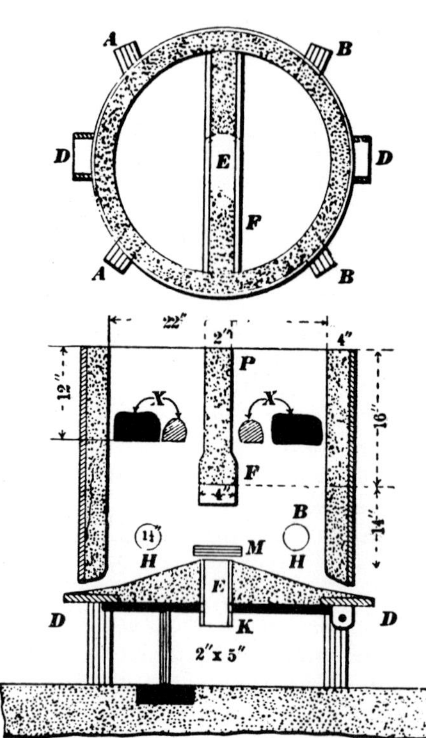

Fig. 1.9. **West's comparative fusion test cupola.**

The modern tuyere employed to the greatest extent is shown in Fig. 2.6. Hurst illustrates tuyeres in Fig. 1.13. Others are Figs. 1.14, 1.15, and the Watt cupola (Fig. 1.16), a good melter, Kirk said. Also shown is the Knoeppel (Fig. 1.19), practically a continuous lower tuyere with high upper tuyeres. Kirk thought this system successful on some large cupolas.

Regarding one of the first continuous tuyeres, the cupola by Mackenzie (Fig. 1.8), Kirk wrote:

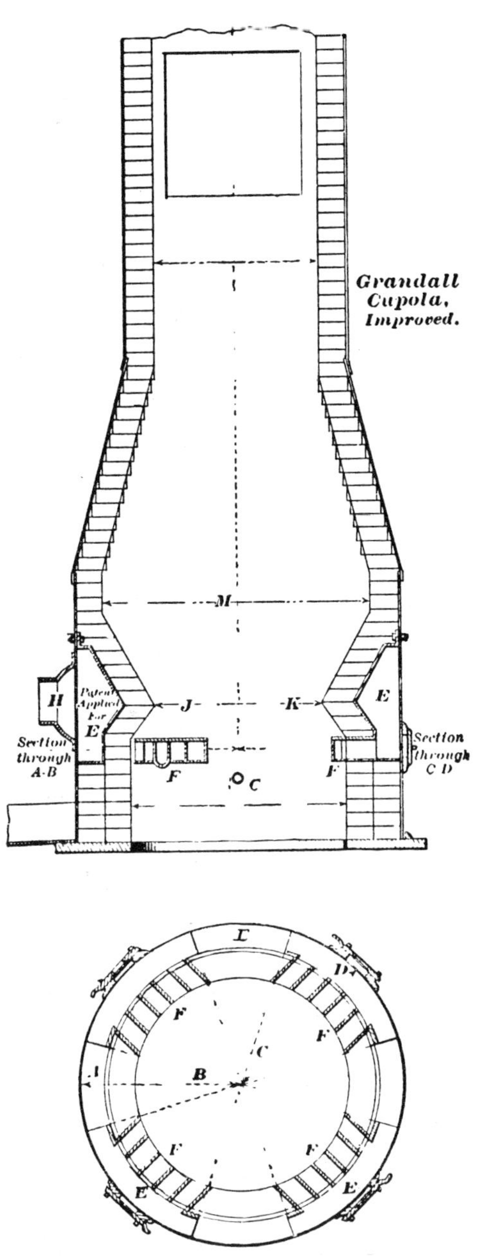

Fig. 1.10. Vertical and horizontal sections of the Grandall lamp chimney cupola.

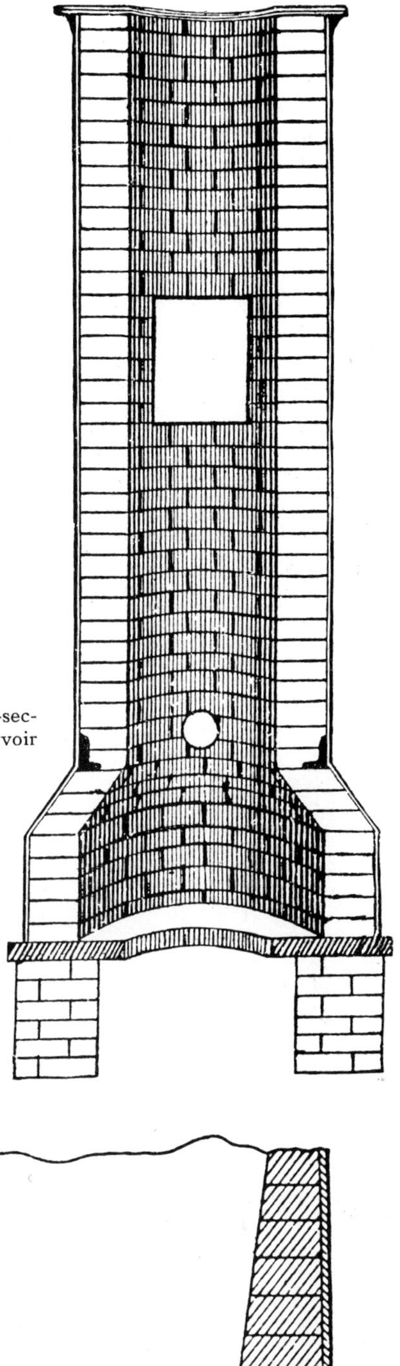

Fig. 1.11. Cross-section of the reservoir cupola.

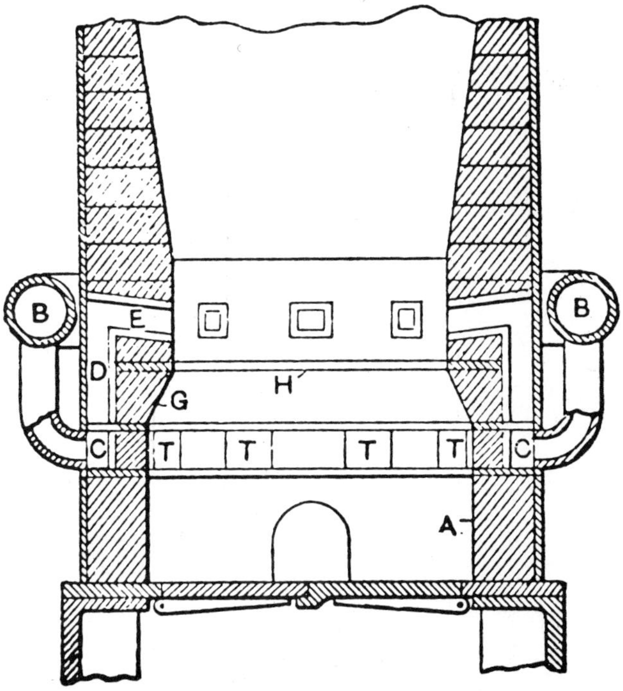

"Before these improvements were made cupolas melted very slow, and it was the practice to put on the blast just after the noon hour and melt all afternoon. From four to five hours were commonly required to melt any ordinary heat.

"Molders generally stopped molding when the blast was put on, and a great deal of valuable time was lost waiting for iron. To prevent this loss of time Mr. Mackenzie, a practical molder and founder of Newark, N.J., conceived the idea of melting a heat in two hours, and designed the Mackenzie cupola, which, when first introduced, was known as the two-hour cupola.

"This cupola, I believe, was the first cupola patented in this country, and it presented a number of new features in cupola construction.

Fig. 1.12. Cross-section of Zippler cupola showing tuyere arrangement and complex brickwork.

"The old theory of driving blast to the center of the cupola by force of the blower and the small tuyeres was entirely abandoned, and the theory of supplying a sufficient volume of blast to fill the cupola adopted. Cast-iron tuyere boxes were bolted to the castings for the attachment of blast pipes, and blast was delivered to the cupola from an inside belt air chamber and continuous tuyere. The air chamber which was formed by an apron riveted at the top to the cupola shell was entirely open at the bottom, giving unlimited space for escape of blast into the cupola.

"This was a complete change from the old theory of putting blast into a cupola with great force, and revolutionized the theory of melting. This cupola gave excellent results, and was adopted by all the leading foundrymen of the time, and many of them are still in use, and continue to give good results in melting when properly managed.

"But this cupola has its objectionable features, the greatest of which is its tendency to bridge and bung up when not properly managed. This tendency to bridge is due to a large extent to the cupola being boshed by the inside air chamber, and the blast being supplied to it just at the point of the lower angle of the bosh. The blast passes up over the bosh before it becomes heated, causing a chilling of cinder and slag at this point, and the building-out of the lining with a very hard substance that is difficult to remove, and careless or incompetent melters frequently permit the lining to grow at this point until the melting capacity of the cupola is reduced one-half, and the smaller ones frequently bridge before they are in blast more than an hour when the lining is permitted to get out of shape.

"Much better results might have been obtained from this cupola had the inventor furnished, to be hung up near the cupola for the guidance of the melter, a framed diagram or blueprint, showing the proper shape for lining of the bosh and melting zone when the lining was new and as it burned away; but such a diagram was never furnished, and I have frequently seen melters running these cu-

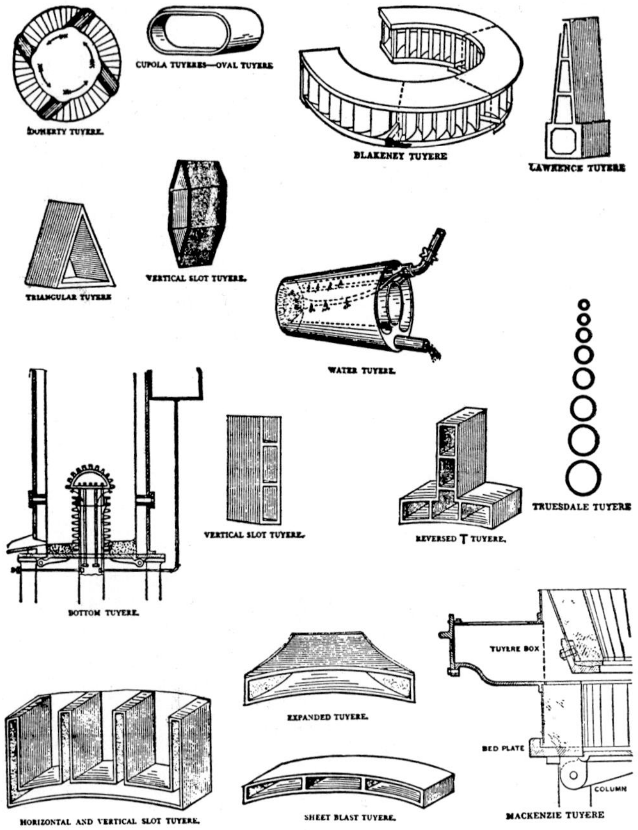

Fig. 1.13. Tuyere types and shapes used in foundry cupolas.

Fig. 1.14. Block used for Watt cupola tuyere.

Fig. 1.15. Section with tuyere plates attached.

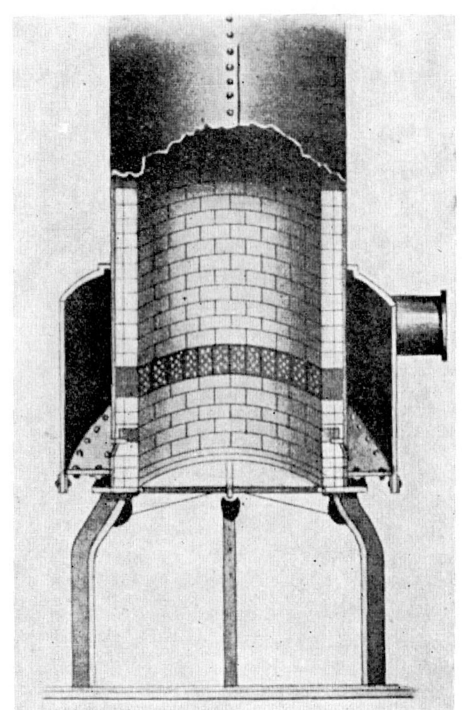

Fig. 1.16. Cutaway view of a cupola fitted with Watt tuyeres.

polas who did not have the least idea of the shape the lining should be put in when repairing it for a heat, having never seen one when newly lined or in shape."

Thus Mackenzie obviated the need for penetration on large cupolas by the oval shape already discussed.

Several cupolas have been built lately with water cooled copper tuyeres protruding some inches from the lining. The Philipon cupola in Belgium is the first of these brought to our attention, and is reported to be quite a successful operating unit.

The furnace most generally used in the last half of the nineteenth century was the Colliau (Fig. 1.17). Later it was built by J. W. Paxson (internal view Fig. 1.18). The Newton (Fig. 1.20) was another good cupola along the plain lines of the Colliau.

The Ireland (Fig. 1.21), one of the first attached forehearths shown in the literature (circa 1890), was among the popular cupolas in England and in Europe. The tuyere system is complicated and difficult to maintain. It was replaced by a plain cupola of the Colliau type before 1929.

Two other interesting ones are the Magill (Fig. 1.23), with its expensive refractory tile tuyere construction,

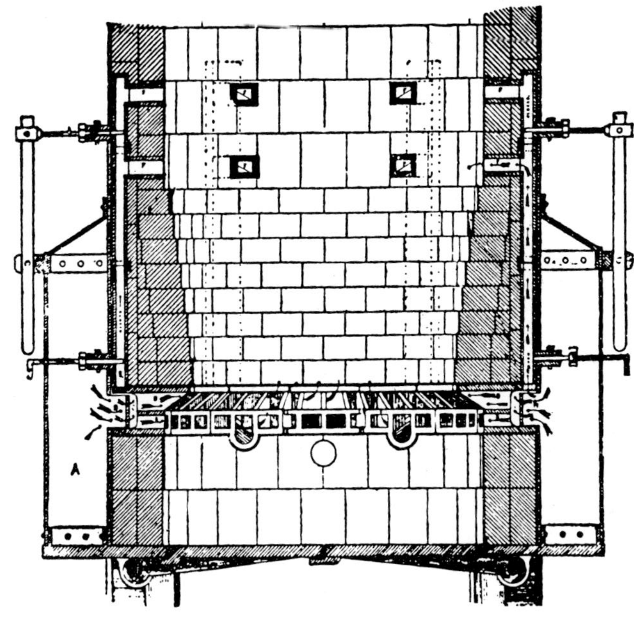

Fig. 1.19. Cross-section showing Knoeppel system of tuyeres.

Fig. 1.17. The Colliau cupola.

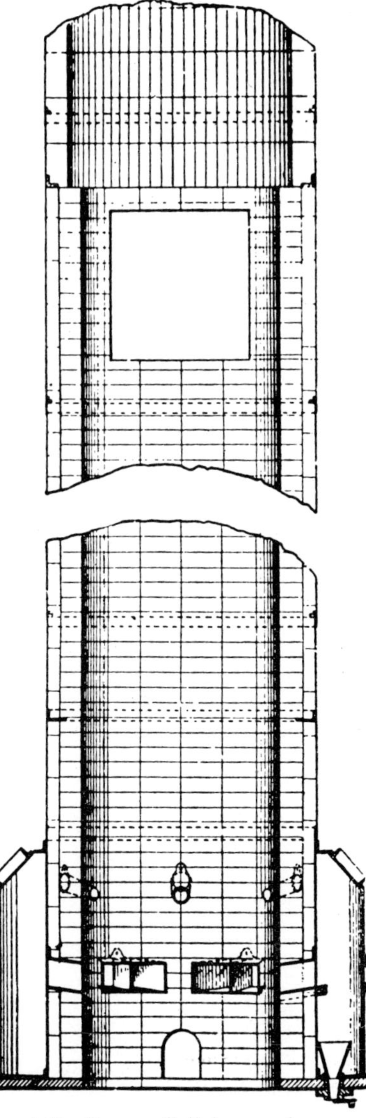

Fig. 1.18. Paxson-Collaiu cupola.

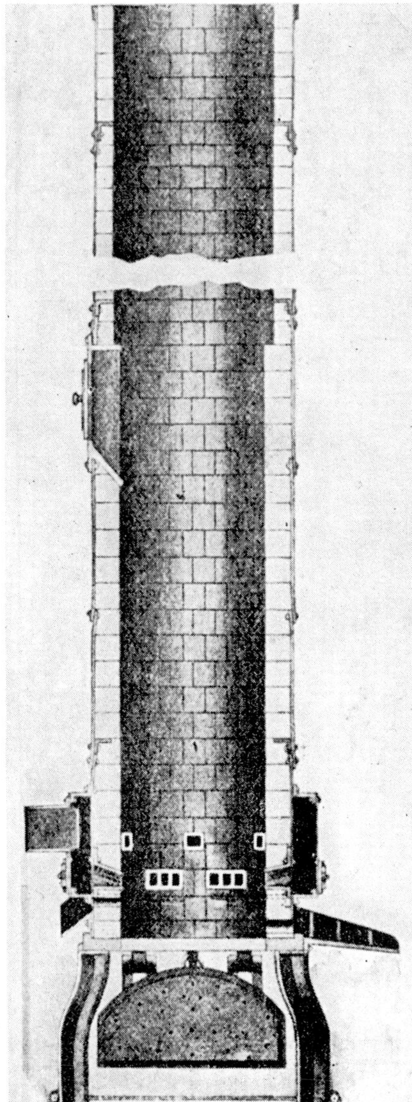

Fig. 1.20. The Newton cupola.

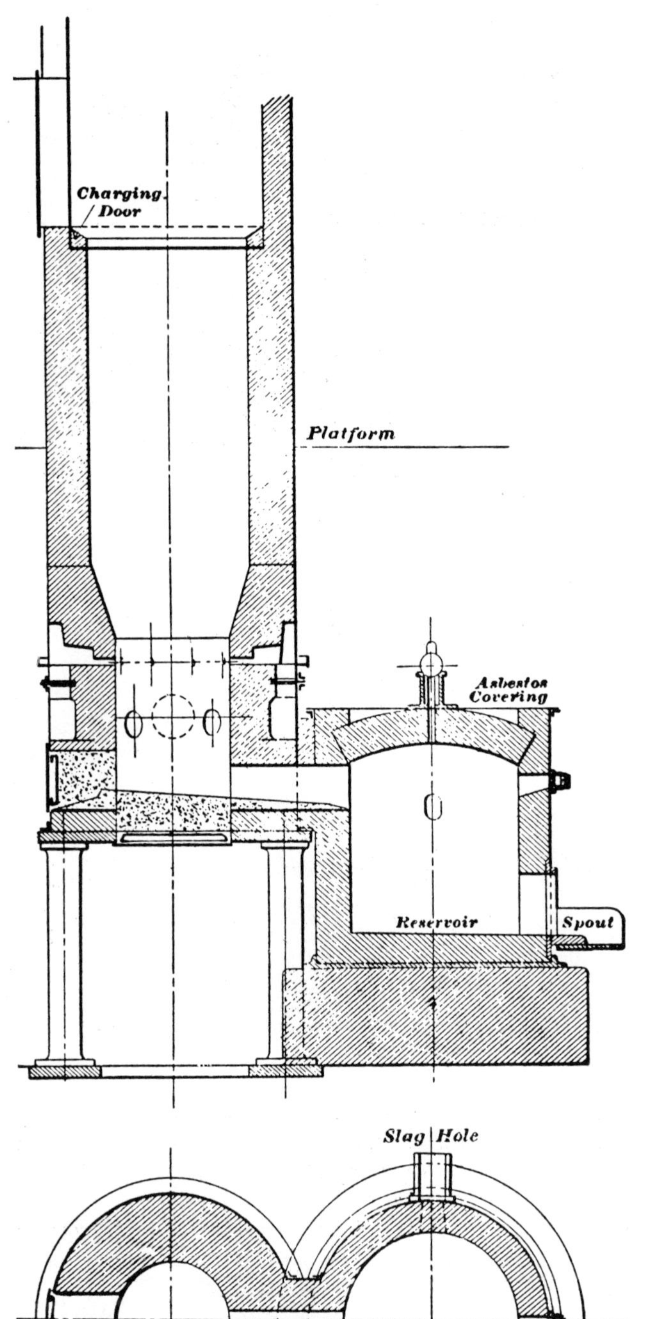

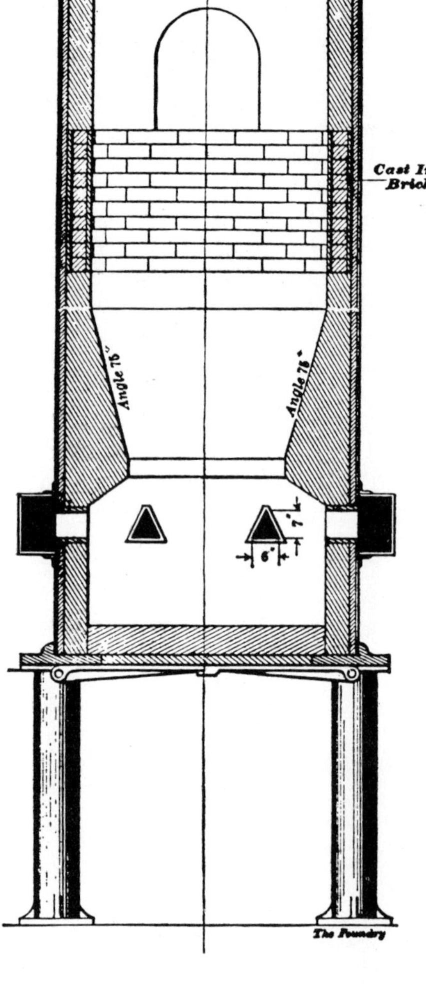

Fig. 1.22. Grove cupola section.

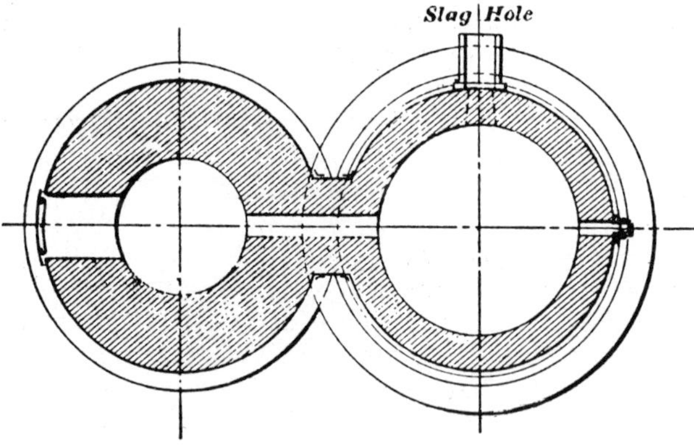

Fig. 1.21. Plan and end views of the Ireland cupola.

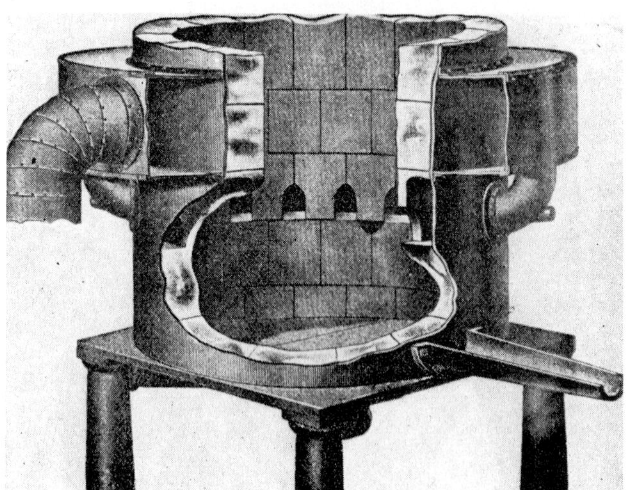

Fig. 1.23. Magill patent cupola.

and the Grove, with triangular tuyeres and cast iron bricks at the charging door (Fig. 1.22).

Figure 1.24 is the Greiner cupola. About 300 were used in Europe. Coke saving was at least 20 per cent; in some cases even 40 and 50 per cent, Kirk reported. The Stewart, made in Scotland, was of similar construction.

Figure 1.25 is the section of the Greiner-Erpf. (Alex Moore said of this: "A number of pop-gun tuyeres at different heights with which to vaccinate the monoxide as it tries to leave by the fire escape without a permit from the Board of Health.") There is striking similarity to the Poumay cupola (Fig. 1.26) which was patented years later. Many Poumays were operating in England and on the Continent with apparently good results as late as 1929.

The Sheehan cupola (Fig. 1.27) frankly and boldly

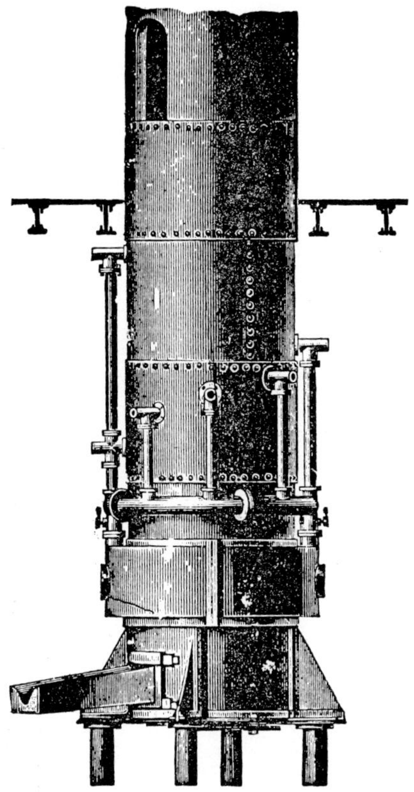

Fig. 1.24. Greiner coke saving cupola.

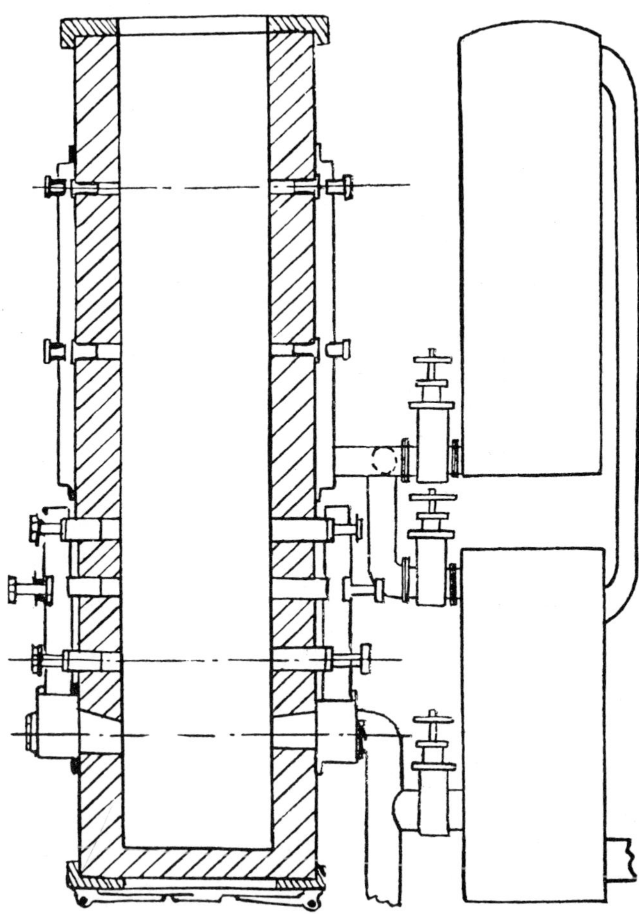

Fig. 1.25. Arrangement of auxiliary tuyeres described in Greiner and Erpf patent specifications.

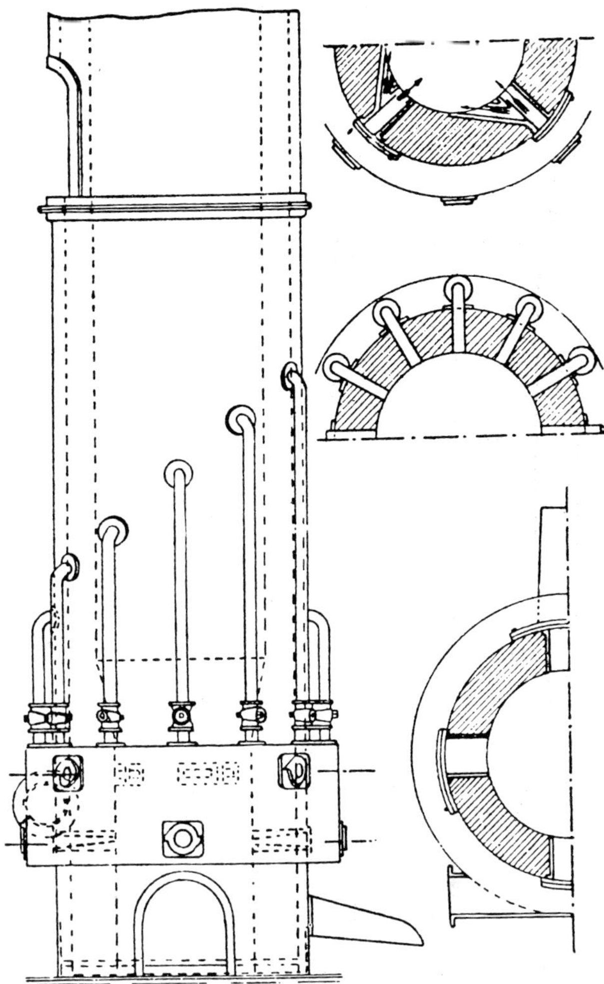

Fig. 1.26. Poumay system of secondary air injection through spiral row of small openings.

puts in two sets of tuyeres and proposes to melt with the upper row and superheat with the lower. Sheehan claims it can reduce silicon from silica in the reaction zone between tuyeres.

The latest attempt to accomplish the recovery of some of the carbon monoxide heat loss is the balaced blast cupola of the British Cast Iron Research Association (Fig. 1.29). It is said to differ from the previous examples by having the relative amounts of air admitted at the several levels adjusted to give a maximum of carbon monoxide at the bottom and a minimum at the top. Most of the users report excellent results. A useful feature of this cupola is the provision of valves by which the bottom tuyeres may be cut off one or two at a time and any accumulation of slag melted away. One user reports regular heats of 30 hr.

Many attempts have been made to recover the waste heat, both sensible and latent, in the blast itself. Cameron (Fig. 1.28) tried to cool the refractories on one side and heat them on the other. Olivo (Fig. 1.30) tried to add the heat of the gas escaping from the slag hole. Holland (Fig. 1.32) in 1890 tried one type of heat exchanger above the charging door, and Zoller tried another one (Fig. 1.31). There are several reasons for the failure of this type of cupola. There must be considerable carbon monoxide in the gas to give a flame hot enough to heat the blast; the flame is usually slow in developing; and the mechanical upkeep, due to oxidation of the structure and to stresses due to repeated heating and cooling, is high; also, the structure is accessible only with difficulty.

Frauenknecht (Fig. 1.33) tried by-passing some of the hot gases around the preheating zone through the downcomer pipes, thus heating the blast instead of the stack—the upkeep must have been a problem. Baillot in 1908 (Fig. 1.34) ran the blast through a ring-shaped metal box in the stack but the heat from so small a contact must not have been considerable. Coplan improved the Baillot construction by increasing the size of the ring which he made of heat-resisting alloy and lowering it much closer to the melting zone. He also put vanes in the ring to make the blast pass three or four times around the box. Warping of the boxes was the chief problem.

Moore tried verticle box type castings (Fig. 1.35) made of ingot mold gray iron. The box, weighing over

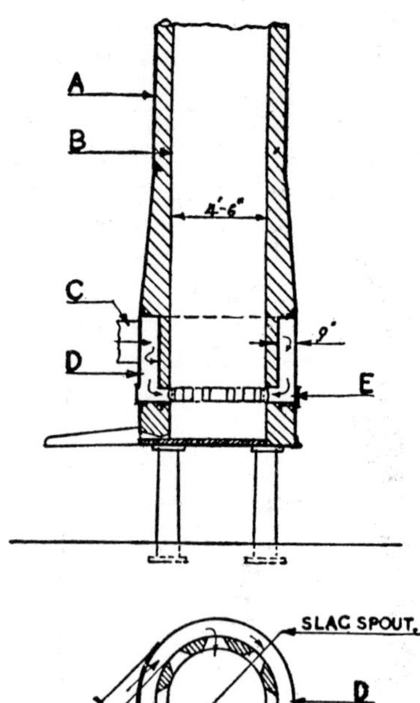

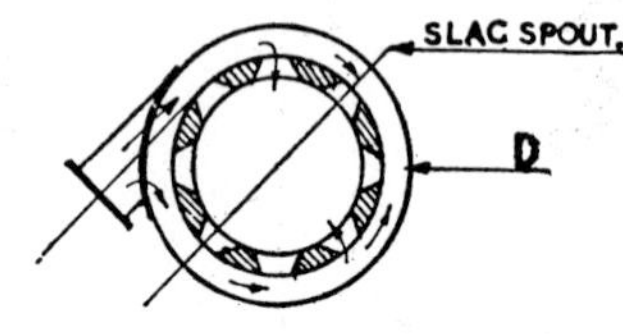

Fig. 1.28. Cameron hot blast cupola.

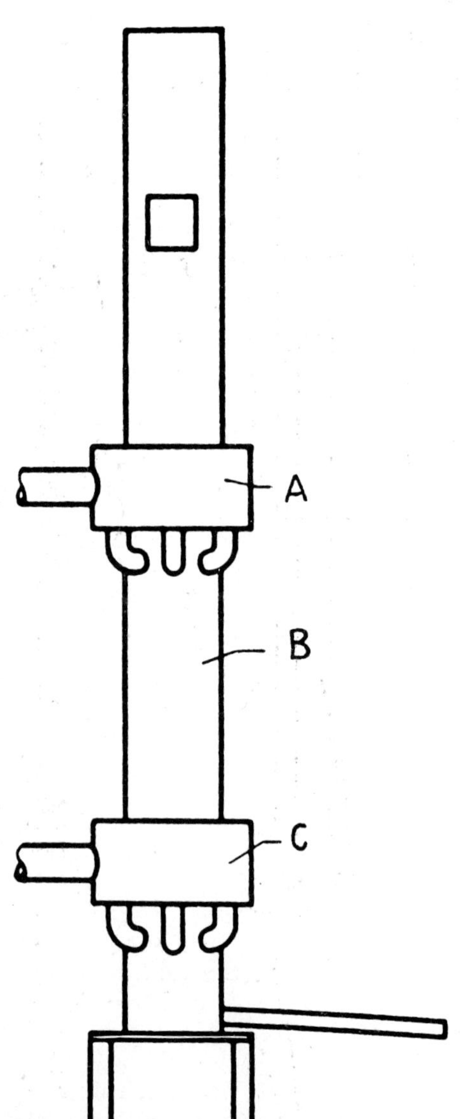

Fig. 1.27. Sheehan cupola with two sets of tuyeres: A. melting zone, C. superheating zone, B. reaction column.

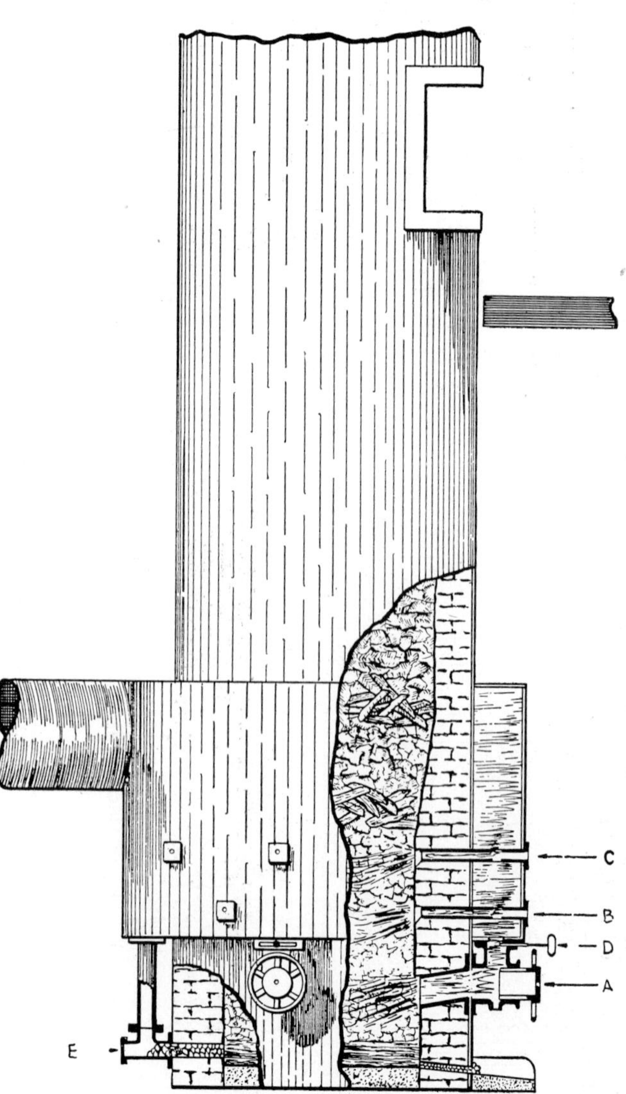

Fig. 1.29. General arrangement of the balanced blast cupola.

3000 lb, gradually grew and cracked (on cooling) at a point opposite the top bustle pipe (no. 1 in Fig. 1.35).

They lasted from 25 to 125 heats of 16 to 20 hr; the blast temperature was raised about 200 F. Two high-nickel-chrome boxes were tried but they warped badly during about the fifth heat and tore loose at the top connection. Barr and Holmes then designed the tubular construction shown in Fig. 1.38. These tubes are connected at the top by U-bends with a piston ring fit so there is no restraint lengthwise.

Plain cast iron pipe was used first, but 25-20 chrome-nickel steel was later used and well over 100 heats of 16 to 20 hr were obtained. The temperature rise on this type is of the order of 250 F. This scheme was later abandoned in favor of an external heater for the blast.

The Griffin hot blast (Fig. 1.37) is the most widely used and generally successful scheme yet devised for using both sensible and the latent heat of the cupola gas. A large portion of the gases is exhausted at a point a few feet below the charging door and burned in the heat exchanger where the blast is heated to 600 F. The only trouble with this unit, that has come to the author's attention, is the upkeep of the heat exchanger, although due to the size and cost of an installation it would hardly be justified except for a large operation and long heats.

An obvious way to get a hot blast is to heat it. A good heat exchanger and any kind of fuel can be used.

George Fischer, Ltd., Schaffhausen, Switzerland, made the installation shown in Fig. 1.36 on small cupolas of 24-39 in. internal diameter. Gas firing achieved 1100 F (593 C) blast temperature.

With air heated to 1100 F, the combination operates efficiently on 6 to 8 per cent coke. By using less

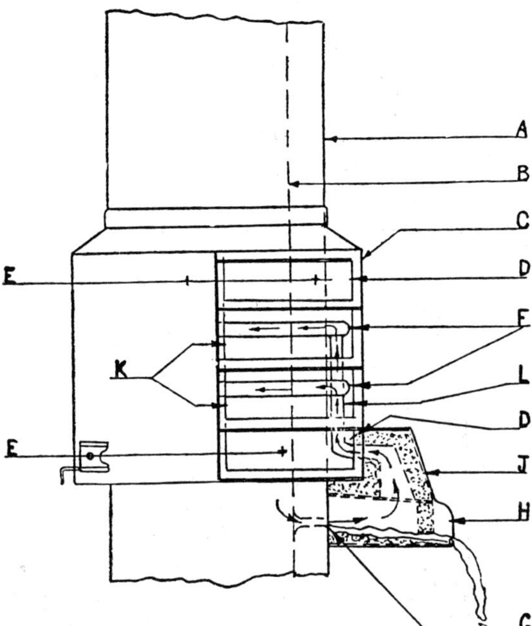

Fig. 1.30. Olivo hot blast cupola.

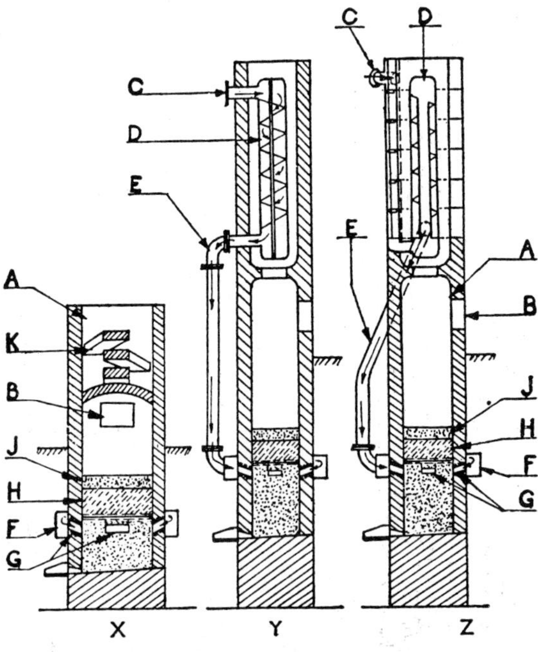

Fig. 1.31. Zoller hot blast cupola.

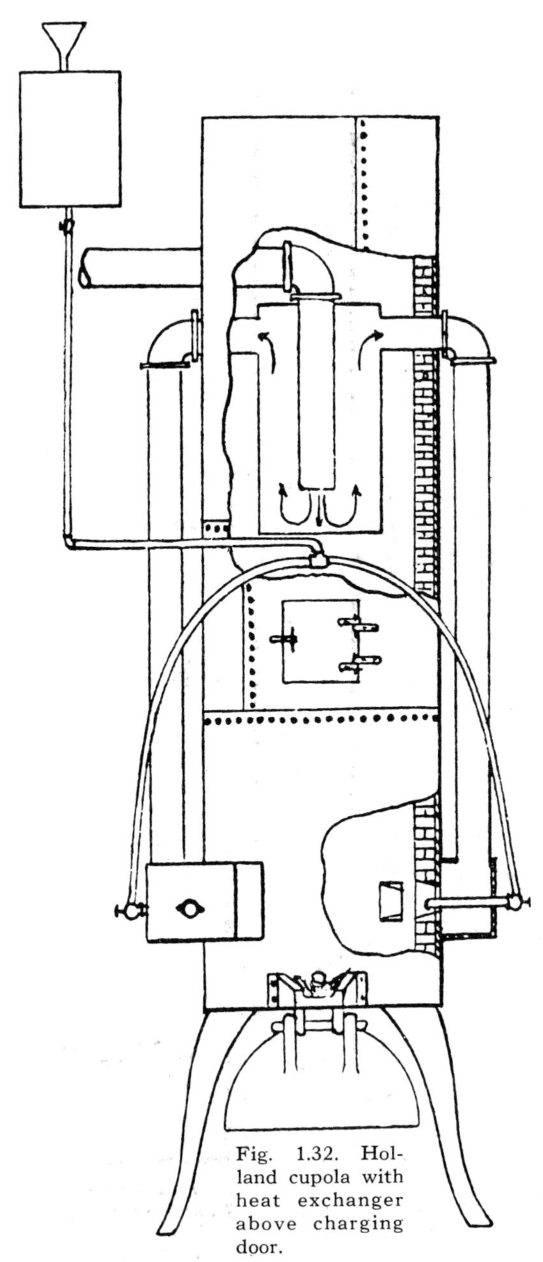
Fig. 1.32. Holland cupola with heat exchanger above charging door.

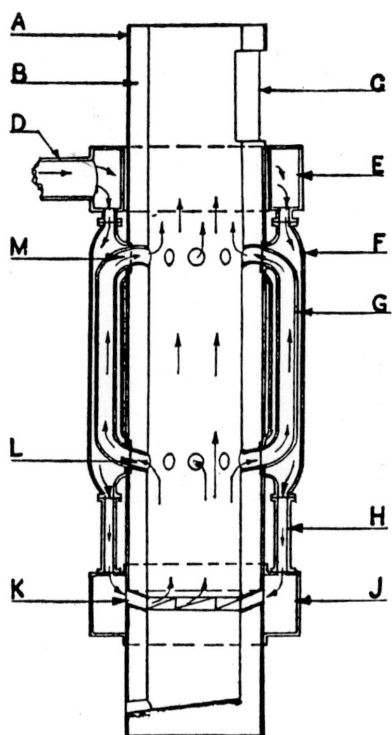

Fig. 1.33. Frauenknecht hot blast cupola.

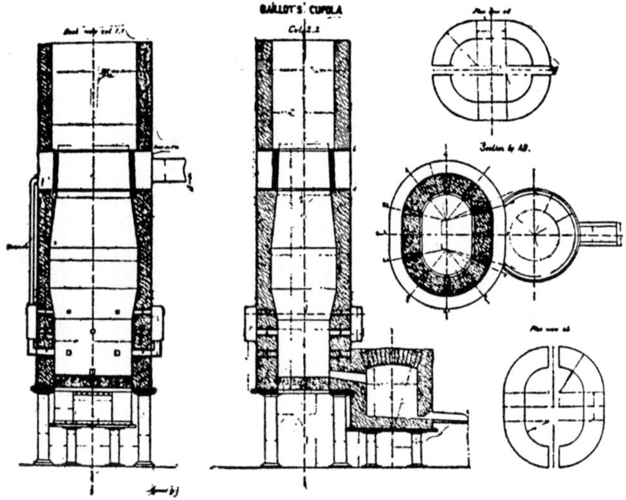

Fig. 1.34. Baillot hot blast cupola.

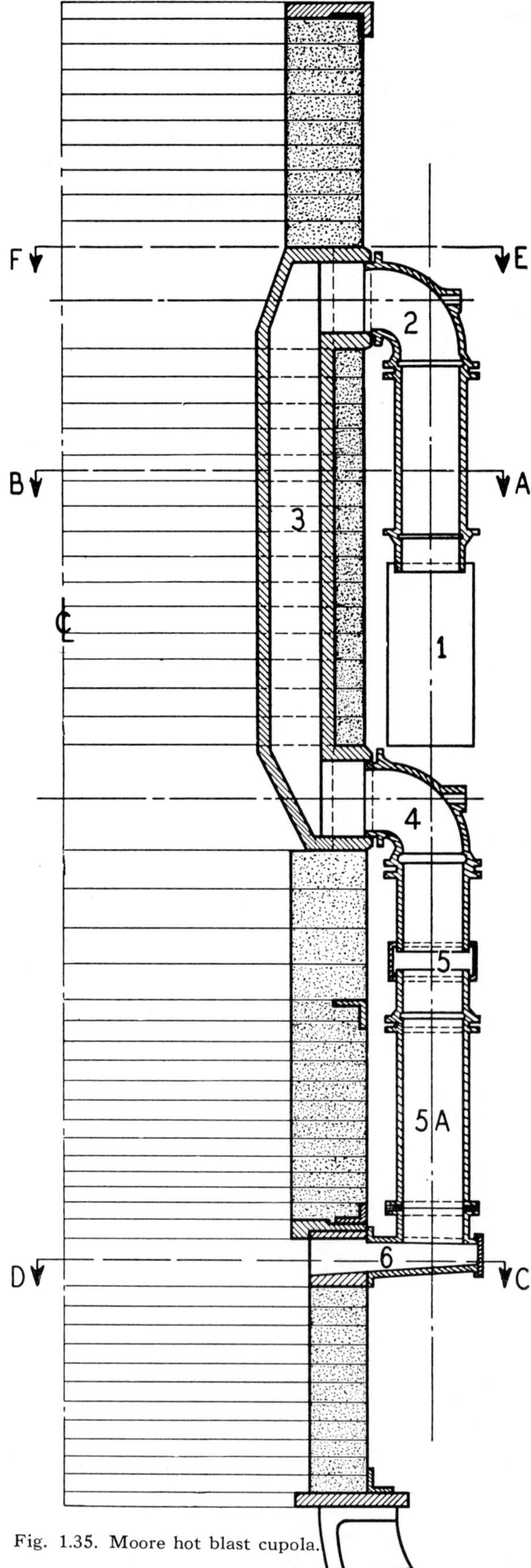

Fig. 1.35. Moore hot blast cupola.

coke not enough blast is required to bring in the necessary heat, and if excess blast is used the iron is severely oxidized. The efficiency of the whole unit is stated to be 59 per cent. The blast temperature is above that of the ignition point of the coke, so there is no danger of blowing out the fire. The tonnage is therefore relatively high and, due to the small amount of coke used, sulfur pick-up is low.

The Schürmann cupola (Fig. 1.39) was tried to some extent in Germany but it seems to be just another cupola for the history books now. It is a reversing regenerator, but the slag, coke, iron, etc. was destructive to the checker brick since it was blown right across the melting zone. The latest proposal is due to E. Longden (Fig. 1.40). This is a revival of the old idea of blowing fuel into the tuyeres with the blast. Part of the air goes through a gas producer *E* and the oxygen is converted to carbon monoxide; this then passes through the inner pipe and is mixed with the rest of the blast at the tuyeres. It does not look promising for the same principle has been tried with gas, tar, oil, and powdered coal,

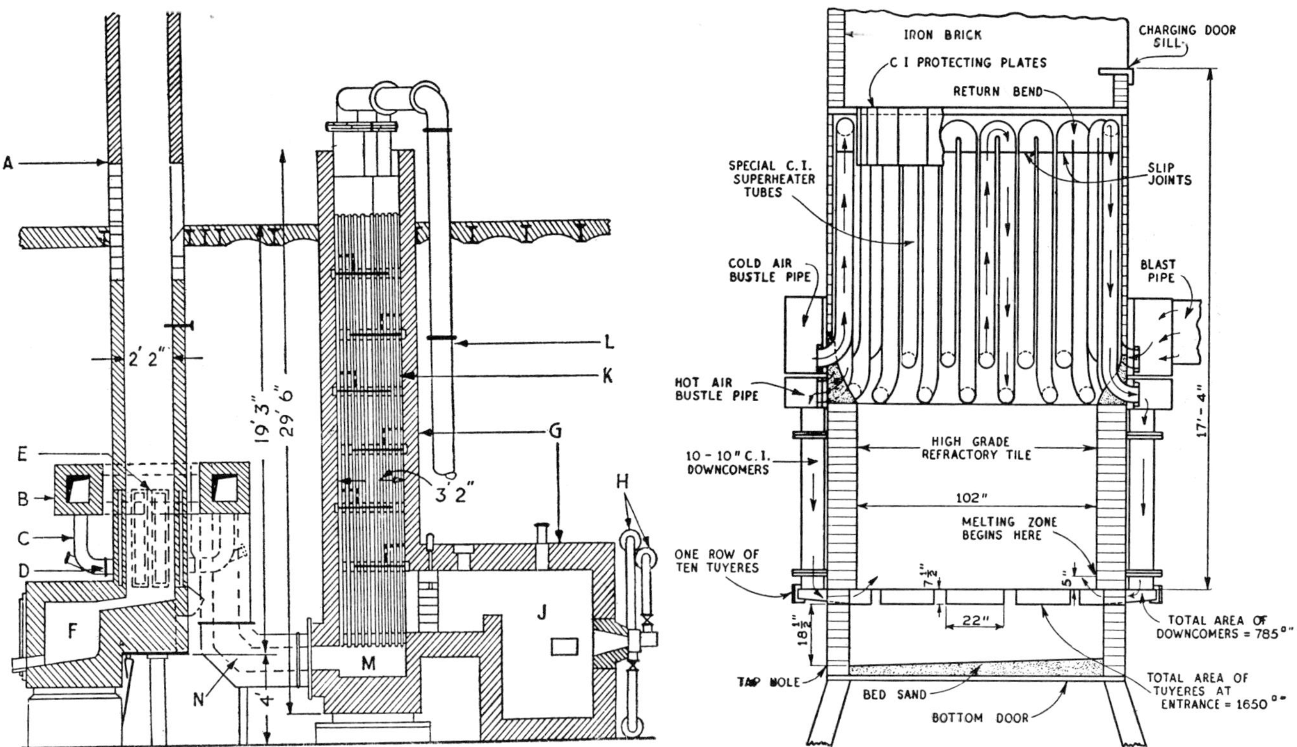

Fig. 1.36. Piwowarsky hot blast cupola.

Fig. 1.38. Improved Moore system (102 in. cupola shown).

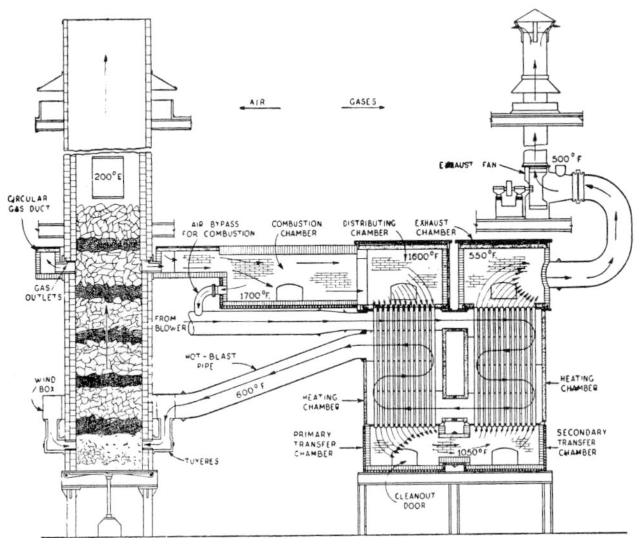

Fig. 1.37. Diagram of Griffin hot blast equipment.

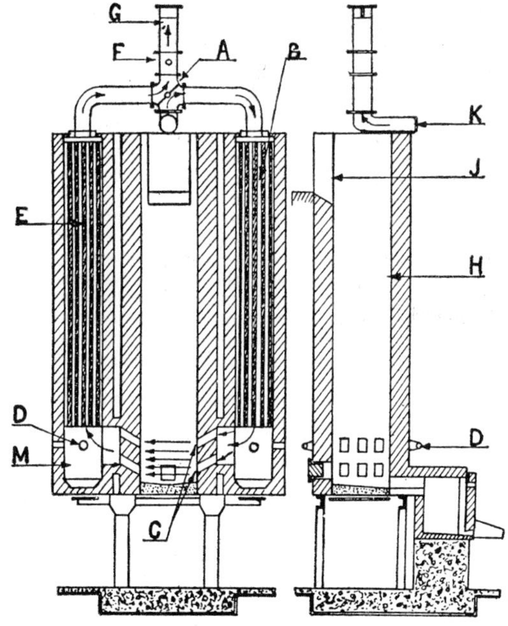

Fig. 1.39. Schurmann hot blast cupola: H. cupola shaft, J. charging door, K. cold air from blower, A. reversing valve, B & E. preheater, C. main tuyeres, D. small secondary air boosting tuyeres to the chamber, M. distributing and secondary combustion chamber, F. throttle valve, G. outlet chimney.

but all have been abandoned. It was reported that an explosion destroyed the last cupola that was blowing powdered coal into the tuyeres.

In addition to heating the blast, the advantages of which are clearly proven practically and theoretically sound, other expedients have been tried such as the utterly unsound scheme of recirculating the gas, and/or blowing steam into the tuyeres—both of which were done on the irrational assumption that the temperature in the melting zone was too high and that these devices would spread it out. Drying the blast, which is also reasonable from a heat balance standpoint, was tried early—soon after the experiments on the iron blast furnace proved successful. It was abandoned for a long time and only recently revived for making piston rings, and has since been reported of value with other castings where the close control of chilling tendency is important.

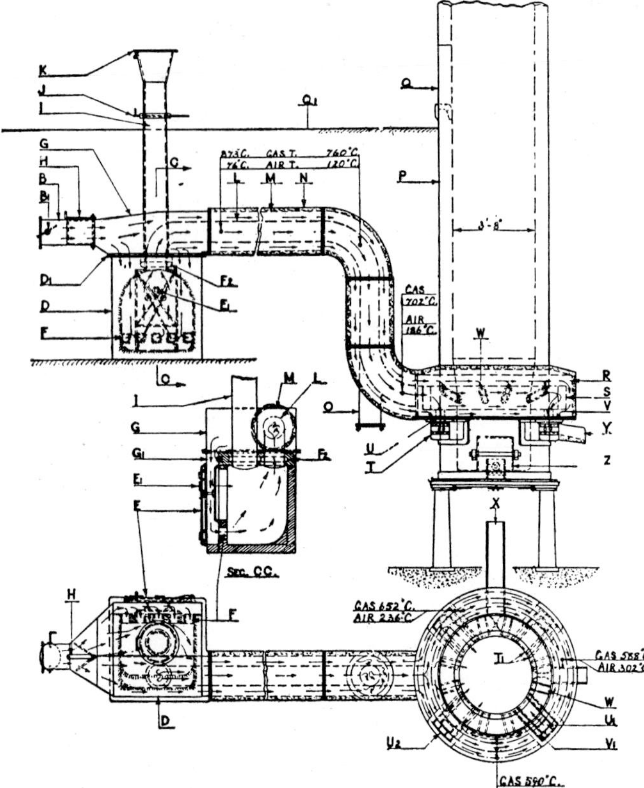

Fig. 1.40. Longden hot blast cupola.

However, some experiments seemed to show that water sprayed into the tuyeres did for a time increase the temperature of the molten metal. E. Piwowarsky explained this phenomenon on the basis of improved heat transfer due to the hydrogen in the gas. Undoubtedly, some moisture is necessary to catalyze combustion, but the weight of evidence seems to show that about three grains per cu. ft. is the best value and that the cupola suffers if the moisture is in excess of this amount. It is probably true that most castings are not sufficiently sensitive to chill to justify the cost of dry blast, and that the small amount of coke necessary to compensate for ordinary excess moisture is economical.

Pulsating blast has been stated superior to steady blast, according to some work done in France, but in the writer's plant where sometimes a fan with its steady blast and sometimes an epicycloidal blower with its pulsations are used, no significant differences have been observed.

Wartime developments in cheap oxygen offer some hope of improvement by enrichment and some experiments are now under way along this line. It will depend on whether the higher temperature developed can be put into the iron or whether it will merely result in richer gas. It may turn out to be the best solution of the problem of the decline in coke quality.

An examination was made of TRANSACTIONS volumes of the American Foundrymen's Association and early issues of *The Foundry*.

W. J. Keep (Fig. 1.42) conducted a Question and Answer column in *The Foundry*. E. Kirk was a frequent contributor.

T. D. West advocated center tuyeres. Dr. Richard Moldenke (Fig. 1.41) was secretary of the American Foundrymen's Association from 1900 until 1914.

These grand men of the foundry did wonders for the development of the cupola and the understanding of its operation.

There were still many who derided the chemist in the foundry. Some good humorous verses passed through the pages of *The Foundry* only 50 years ago on that subject. Much activity was under way in the matter of standard samples for the analysis of pig iron. Actual temperatures are notably absent from their discussions of actual data, nothing about volume except that it was sometimes mentioned as blower capacity. The chief subjects of debate were coke ratios, upper tuyeres, the relative virtues of anthracite coal and coke, and later beehive and byproduct coke, and the effect of the weather on melting.

Kirk understood the space theory of melting in 1877, long before Moldenke and Belden's tests proved it, and stated that the piece of coke-piece of iron theory of charging was based on the belief that melting took place all the way up the stack. He mentions the case of light coke; instead of increasing the coke, reduce the amount of iron in the charge instead. This may be the reason for some of the problems with poor coke today. Outerbridge showed clearly in 1906 the advantage of silicon added to the ladle. W. J. Keep explained the reason for preferring wet coke after the bed was made; the water prevented to some extent the formation of carbon monoxide and, since there is always excess heat in the stack, it would pay to have a shower bath for the coke pile.

Granted good construction, adequate blowing equipment, with pressure gages and volume control—all readily available today—a good refractory lining is the first concern of the melter. Long ago, the importance of good brick laid close together was appreciated, but even so a new lining will sometimes leak at the joints and run a hot spot. A good practice is to lay the melting zone of smaller size brick than the rest of the stack, and after drying daub this for the first heat just as for subsequent heats.

The fundamental importance of the bed was recognized by all of the old masters and it can not be over-emphasized today. If the bed is properly "lit-off" and of the correct height for the size and quality of the coke and the volume of blast, the subsequent charges of iron and coke control, mainly, the temperature of the iron and the melting rate. If the bed is too high a little time and coke is wasted, but if the bed is too low oxidation may be heavy and the whole heat lost. Subsequent charges of coke must maintain the correct height of bed. If too much is used, the only result is waste of time, coke and power. If insufficient coke is used the iron begins to oxidize, the slag gets out of control, tuyeres stop up, refractories burn out and, unless caught in time, the heat may be stopped. Poor coke, an error in weighing, forgetting a charge of coke, one-sided charging, or not enough flux to keep the slag fluid are the chief causes of such occurrences.

John Doyle said in 1905 (*The Foundry*) that "a high melting ratio is like the pot of gold at the end

Fig. 1.41. Dr. Richard Moldenke, AFS Past Secretary.

Fig. 1.42. Sketch of W. J. Keep.

of the rainbow—it had better be let alone rather than searched for." Kirk said in 1904—it is "lots cheaper to buy scrap than to make it."

Much stress has been laid since the Moldenke-Belden tests on the shape of the bed and the thickness of the melting zone found in those tests. Belden's tests were run at fairly low blast volume, and P. H. Wilson proved by tests that the shape shown by Belden, an inverted cone, is gradually flattened out and then actually reversed as the blast volume is increased. F. K. Vial has proved that a 12-in. coke charge is not too thick for normal operation. This is not inconsistent with the 4-in. zone found by Belden for, as would be expected and lately proven by Rambush and Taylor, the size of the coke decreases rapidly as it goes down the stack—furthermore the coke used up as monoxide never gets there so the two figures probably mean the same thing.

The following selections from *"Cupola Scraps"* of E. Kirk appear pertinent even to this day:

"Often a melter 'don't know' why the cupola is working badly, because if he knew he would be discharged for carelessness."

"A bad light-up makes a bad heat. The bed must be burned evenly or it will not melt evenly."

"Don't burn up the bed before charging the iron."

"A new cupola always effects a great saving in fuel, but it is often hard to find the fuel (saved) at the end of the year. A little more practical knowledge in managing the old cupola will often enable the foundrymen to find the fuel saved and the price of the new cupola besides."

"If you go into the foundry when the heat is being melted and find the tap hole almost closed, the spout all bunged and the melter picking at the spout with a tap bar and running a rod into the tap hole a yard or so, in his efforts to get the iron out, and remark to him: 'You are having some trouble with your cupola today,' he will say: 'Yes, we have some very bad coke today!' or, 'We are melting some dirty pig iron or scrap today, sir!' He never thinks: 'We have a very poor melter today, sir!' "

And last but not least —

"Less fuel is generally required to melt iron in the foundry office than is required to melt it in a cupola."

CHAPTER 2

Conventional Cupola

The cupola is a vertical shaft type furnace, consisting of a cylindrical steel shell lined with refractory materials and equipped with a windbox and tuyeres for the admission of air. A charging opening is provided at an upper level for the introduction of melting stock and fuel. Near the bottom are holes and spouts for removal of molten metal and slag.

One of the outstanding features of such a vertical shaft furnace is that the ascending gases come into intimate contact with the descending melting stock, and a direct and efficient exchange of heat from the hot gases to the melting stock takes place. The descending fuel replaces that burned from the original coke bed and maintains the height of this bed.

Greater understanding of these inherent features accounts for the continued popularity of the cupola and the rejection of radical changes in design.

To meet varied requirements, the conventional cupola is manufactured in the standard sizes shown in Table 2.1. The ratings in this table are average and generally conservative for American practice. Some variations may be found in plants operating with special metal conditions or special techniques.

DESIGN AND CONSTRUCTION

The Shell

The cupola stack or shell is fundamentally a steel casing to contain and support the refractory lining, wind and tuyere boxes, tuyeres, roof hood and spark arrester. Figure 2.1 is an outline showing features of the conventional cupola.

The shell consists of heavy steel plates rolled into cylindrical sections, and riveted, bolted or welded together with downward-lapping joints for protection against weather. The top of the stack is reinforced with an angle-iron ring, riveted onto the shell in such a manner as to afford protection against rain seepage between lining and shell.

Lower or body section is substantially built to support the load of the upper sections. Shelf segments are bolted to the inside of the shell at regularly spaced intervals for supporting the lining. The stack of the cupola extends through the roof with sufficient height to comply with local fire codes, usually a minimum of 10 ft above the roof or adjoining peaks. It is sometimes carried further to provide more naural draft at the charging opening, or to provide additional space to permit complete combustion of the gases above the charged column.

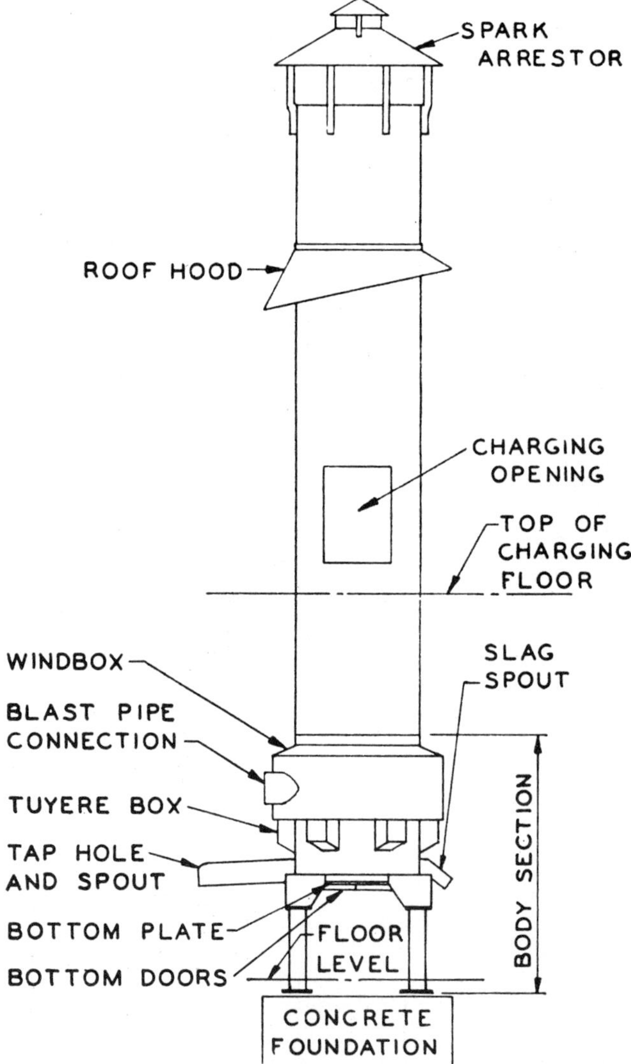

Fig. 2.1. Sketch of conventional cupola shows many parts.

If cupola gases are drawn into the foundry buildings it is due to a partial vacuum in the buildings created by an exhaust system. This condition should be corrected by relieving the partial vacuum rather than attempting to overcome it with a cupola stack of unreasonable height.

Foundation

A suitable foundation for the cupola and its charged load should be provided. A diagram giving the dimensions for the top of the foundation is usual-

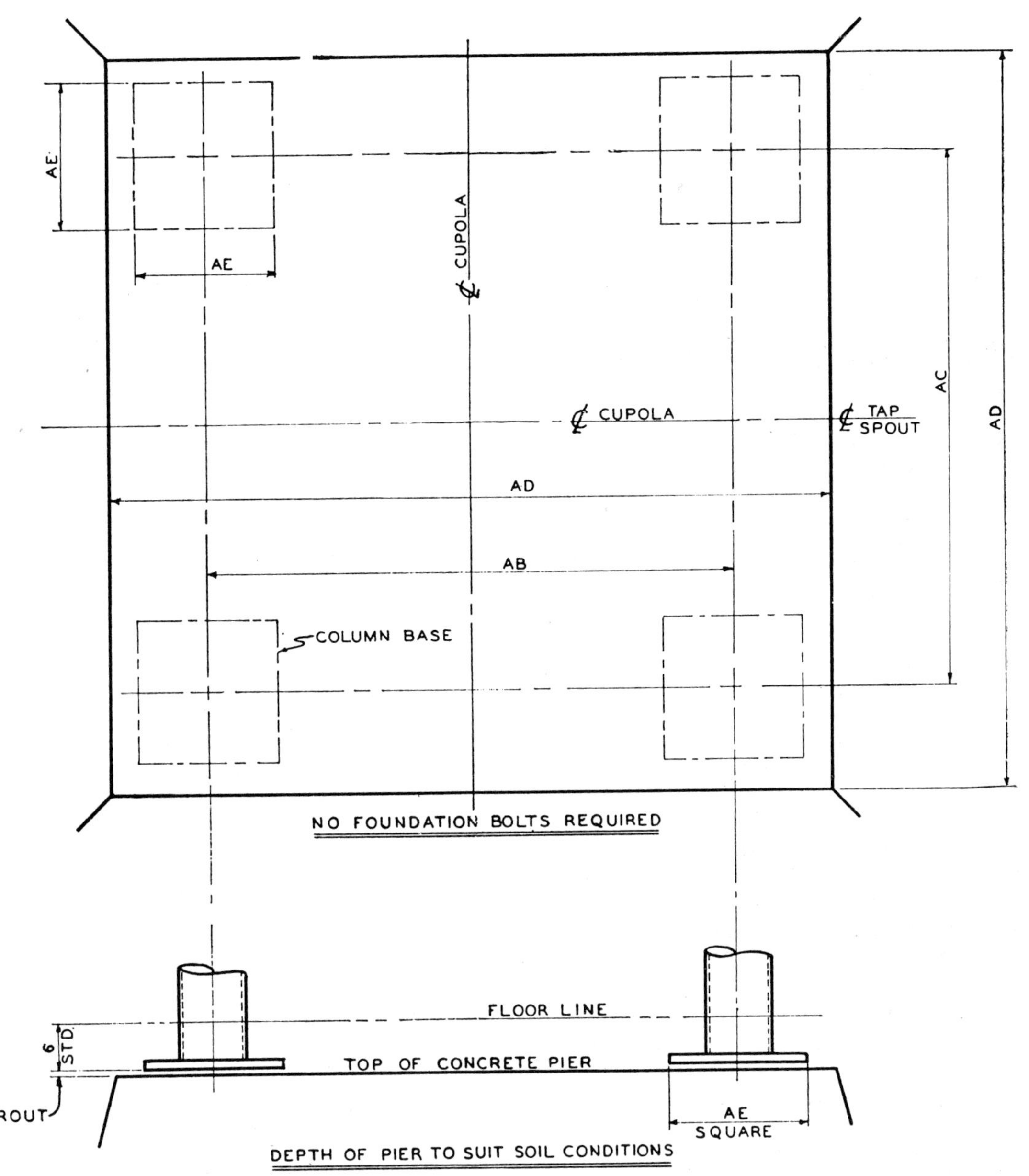

CUPOLA SIZE	SHELL DIAM.	AB	AC	AD	AE	WEIGHT PER FOOT	TOTAL WEIGHT
1	32	3'-0	2'-11¾	4'-6	12	265	22000
2	36	3'-0	3'-1½	4'-10	16	340	27000
2½	41	3'-5	3'-6	5'-4	16	395	37000
3	46	3'-10	3'-11	5'-9	16	435	43000
3½	51	4'-3	4'-2	6'-2	16	475	49000
4	56	4'-8	4'-4	6'-8	18	525	57000
5	63	5'-1	5'-1	7'-1	18	960	77000
6	66	5'-5	5'-0¾	7'-5	19	1015	85000

CUPOLA SIZE	SHELL DIAM.	AB	AC	AD	AE	WEIGHT PER FOOT	TOTAL WEIGHT
7	72	5'-10	5'-10	8'-0	19	1105	96000
8	78	6'-6	6'-3¾	8'-8	20	1205	110000
9	84	7'-0	6'-10¾	9'-2	20	1285	122000
9½	90	7'-6	7'-2¾	9'-8	20	1385	136000
10	96	8'-0	7'-8¾	10'-2	20	1430	155000
11	102	8'-6	8'-6	10'-8	20	1530	210000
12	108	9'-0	9'-0	12'-0	2'-0	1655	230000

TOTAL WEIGHTS ARE BASED ON CUPOLAS 45'-0 HIGH. FOR EACH ADDITIONAL FOOT OF UPPER STACK ADD WEIGHT PER FOOT AS SHOWN IN TABLE. WEIGHTS ARE BASED ON RECOMMENDED CHARGE LEVELS AND STANDARD LINING THICKNESS.

Fig. 2.2. Drawing of cupola foundation, with dimension chart.

TABLE 2.1. **RANGE OF SIZES AND OPERATING RECOMMENDATIONS FOR CONVENTIONAL CUPOLAS**

Cupola Size	Shell Dia.	Minimum Thickness of Lower Lining,* in.	Dia. Inside Lining, in.	Area Inside Lining, sq. in.	Melting Rate†† Tons per Hour With Iron/Coke (After Bed) Ratios of 6	8	10	12	Bed Coke Height Above Tuyeres, in.**	Coke and Iron Charges, lb Coke	Iron 6/1	8/1	10/1	12/1	Limestone, lb	Air Thru Tuyeres, cfm	Suggested Blower Selection*** cfm	Discharge Pressure, oz
1	32	4½	23	415	1	1½			36-42	35	210	280			7	940	1040	16
2	36	4½	27	572	1¾	2¼			36-42	45	270	360			9	1290	1430	16
2½	41	7	27	572	1¾	2¼			36-42	45	270	360			9	1290	1430	16
3	46	7	32	804	2½	3¼	4		40-46	65	390	520	650		13	1810	2000	16†
3½	51	7	37	1075	3¼	4¼	5¼		40-46	85	510	680	850		17	2420	2700	16-20†
4	56	7	42	1385	4	5½	7		42-48	110	660	880	1110		22	3100	3450	20-24
5	63	9	45	1590	4½	6¼	8		42-48	130	780	1040	1300		26	3600	4000	20-24
6	66	9	48	1809	5½	7¼	9	10¾	45-51	145	870	1160	1450	1740	29	4100	4500	24-28
7	72	9	54	2290	7	9¼	11½	13¾	45-51	185	1100	1480	1850	2220	37	5200	5750	24-32
8	78	9	60	2827	9	11¼	14	17	45-51	225	1350	1800	2250	2700	45	6400	7100	24-32
9	84	9	66	3421	10½	13¾	17	20½	45-51	275	1650	2200	2750	3300	55	7700	8600	24-32
9½	90	9	72	4071	12¼	16¼	20¼	24½	47-53	325	1950	2600	3250	3900	65	9200	10200	28-36
10	56	9	78	4778	15	19	23¾	28¾	47-53	385	2300	3080	3850	4600	77	10700	11900	28-36
11	102	12	78	4778	15	19	23¾	28¾	47-53	385	2300	3080	3850	4600	77	10700	11900	28-40
12	108	12	84	5542	17	22¼	27¾	33¼	47-53	445	2670	3560	4450	5400	89	12500	13900	32-40

*Use heavier linings for long heats.

***When auxiliary equipment is added to blast system or when piping is long or intricate, more pressure capacity may be required.

††Under normal conditions metal temperatures will decrease as iron to coke ratio increases. Select coke ratio on basis of foundry operational characteristics, i.e., charging bucket, size and quality of coke and scrap, charging door height, etc.

**Bed coke height varies as square root of blast pressure. Height in in. $= 10.5\sqrt{P} + 6$ in. (P = windbox pressure in oz).

†When air weight control is used, recommend blowers with 20 oz discharge pressure.

†††Table based on coke consumption rate of one lb/sq in./hr. Because blast rates allow for possible blast leakage, melting rates are conservative for blast rates given.

ly supplied by the manufacturer. However, the concrete footing should rest on hardpan, and the depth will depend on soil conditions.

The top of the foundation should be kept 6 in. below the foundry floor level, allowing for fill with sand or other heat insulating material for protection of the concrete footing. It is not necessary to bolt the cupola legs to the foundation. Representative plan and dimension chart for foundations is in Fig. 2.2.

Body Section

The body section consists of the supporting legs, base structure and bottom plate, bottom doors, and windbox section of the stack, as shown in Fig. 2.3.

The bottom plate is of heavy steel with a circular opening of a size to conform with the lining dimensions. The bottom plate is substantially reinforced with heavy beams, angles and gusset plates. It is also fitted with hinge angles for hanging of the bottom doors.

The cupola legs are of steel column construction and should be filled with reinforced concrete. These legs are bolted to the underside of the heavy beams of the base structure. Cupola legs vary in height according to local requirements, but the minimum height should allow free swing of the bottom doors, and convenience for removal of the cupola drop.

The drop-bottom type door was about the first American improvement to the original solid-bottom cupola. The bottom doors are of semi-circular shape, made of cast iron heavily ribbed, and perforated to permit escape of gases. One door is lipped to form a support for the other door when the doors are propped into operating position. The door props may be solid steel bars of 1½-in. diameter or more, or a combination of two screw props and one solid bar prop may be used. A suitable solid base for the props should be provided. A cast iron base with bosses cast-on to align with the bosses on the lipped bottom door may be purchased with the cupola from the manufacturer. The bosses position the screw props so that they will be plumb and most effective in supporting the load on the bottom doors. A long, tapered wedge is provided for driving under the middle solid prop.

Figure 2.4 shows prop base casting and props. A small winch is effective to raise bottom doors (Fig. 2.5).

The lower or first section of the cupola stack is welded securely, inside and outside, to the bottom plate. The windbox, tuyere boxes, slag and tap spouts are attached to this section. The windbox and tuyere boxes are of ample cross-sectional area and welded securely to the body section to eliminate blast leakage that was formerly the case with riveted construction. The top of the windbox is of conical shape, to avoid accumulation of and corrosion by cupola cinder.

A blast pipe connection is incorporated in the windbox design and located near the top. It may be a single, tangential or radial, or of double top entrance pattern. Blast piping of simple design is the least expensive to replace when failure occurs. Replacement of an elaborate blast pipe system is sometimes delayed because of the expense involved, and cupola operational control suffers during the period that the faulty piping is continued in service.

The bottom level of the windbox is above the level of the tuyeres and thereby avoids accumulation of iron and slag as was the case in earlier designs when the windbox rested on the bottom plate. This level also makes it more convenient to install light-up torch ports, kindling tuyeres and slag and tap spouts.

Tuyere boxes or elbows connect the windbox chamber to the tuyere openings in the shell. The tuyere elbows are suitably equipped with large peep and hand holes, covers with ground joints, and locking devices that permit the covers to be quickly opened and closed and held tightly against blast leakage.

Tuyeres

The conventional cupola is supplied with a system of tuyeres amply large to provide easy delivery of the combustion air to the coke bed. Tuyere ratio

Fig. 2.3. Body section of a conventional cupola.

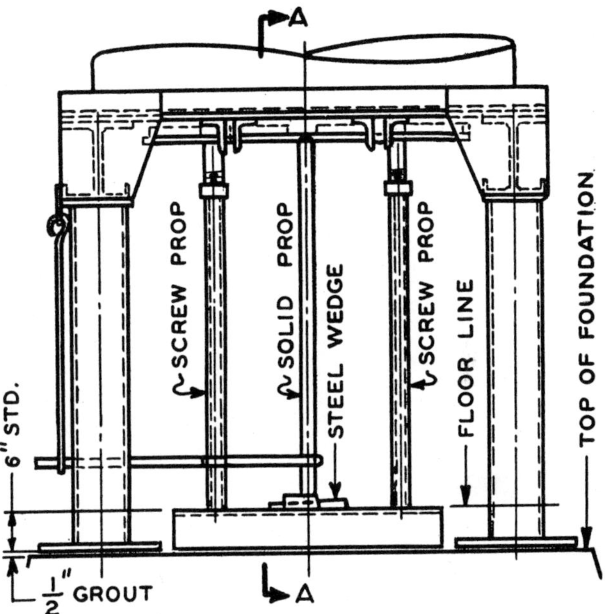

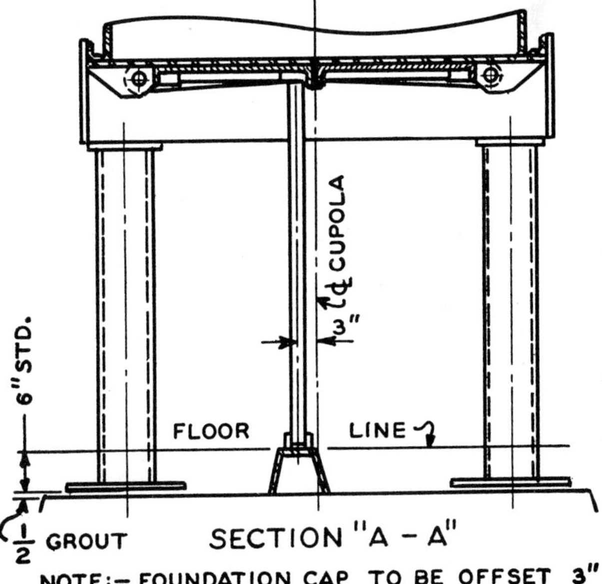

Fig. 2.4. Sketches of cupola bottom door props and base.

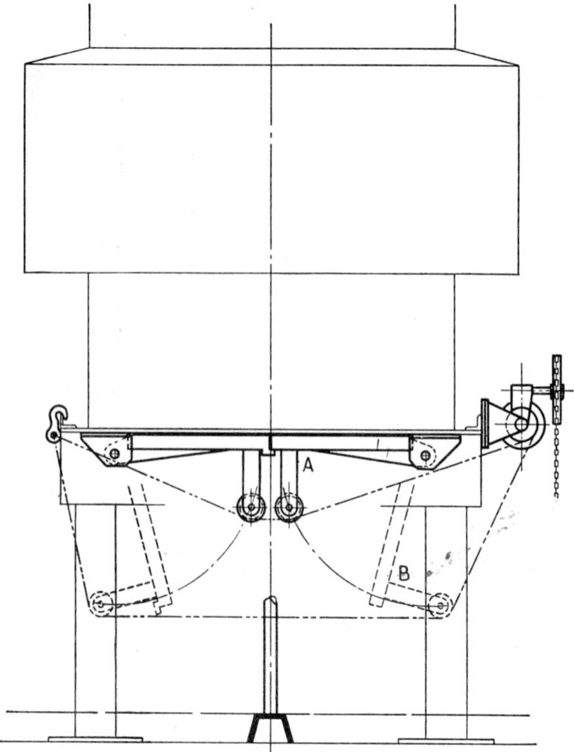

Fig. 2.5. Sketch of cupola bottom door hoist.

is a common term used to denote the ratio of the sum of the area of the tuyeres at their smallest cross-sectional area, to the cross-sectional area of the cupola. This ratio is generally of the order of 1 to 4, or 25 per cent. Tuyeres and tuyere areas are about the most controversial subject of cupola discussions. In actual operation, tuyeres may be found ranging from 1/10 to as much as 1/3 of the cupola area. They may be round, square or rectangular, and of the individual box or continuous types.

However, the effective area which is inherent within the cupola and which determines what the cupola pressure will be, is equivalent to only 1½ per cent of the cupola area. Therefore, in a cupola having a tuyere area of 1/6 the cupola area, the tuyere area is still about 10 times as great as the bottleneck within the cupola.[1]

The size and design of tuyeres is frequently overemphasized, and actually far greater benefits will result from correction of faulty practice than from a change in tuyere design or size. Correct stock distribution will correct many of the difficulties attributed to tuyeres.[2]

The simplest tuyeres with good practice will produce good results and for that reason most manufacturers supply tuyeres of simple design.[3]

The tuyeres shown in Fig. 2.6 consist of cast iron bottom plates, cast iron spacers and cast iron cover plates. The bottom plates and cover plates are made up in segments of a circle for ease of handling. The cover plates are also in two rings, an outer and a smaller inner ring, that can be easily replaced without disturbing the outer ring and backup lining. The thought in this design is to provide tuyeres that are amply large for each particular cupola and afford the greatest ease of installation and replacement.

Upper tuyeres are another American development, and they aid in maintaining clean operating conditions for rapid melting on long heats. They have demonstrated their advantage when fuel and charging stock are of low grade. A discussion of the balanced blast cupola appears at the end of this chapter.

At least one tuyere should be of the safety type, provided with a small channel 1½ or 2 in. below the normal tuyere level.

Should slag and iron rise to an unsafe level, the channel of the safety tuyere (Fig. 2.6) has a fusible plate that will melt through easily.

Some conventional cupola tuyeres are equipped with gates or valves.[4] When these gates are air-pressure tight and the gate closed tightly, slag bridging in front of the tuyere may be melted away by the heat of the coke bed in the absence of the blast.

However, to be effective the gates must close tight and the tuyeres be of the individual type. The deslagging of tuyeres by this practice would not be effective with the continuous type tuyere.

The gates may be operated manually in a definite sequence and schedule, or equipped to operate automatically in a set pattern. Schedules for de-slagging tuyeres usually allow from 5 to 10 min for the time one or more tuyeres are closed for the de-slagging action.

Tuyeres are set high enough to provide ample well capacity; also 4 to 6-in. clearance above the slag hole, so that the slag need not rise into the chilling zones immediately adjacent to the tuyeres. This tuyere height may be from 20 in. above the bottom plate on small cupolas to 28 in. or even higher on large cupolas.

Data in Table 2.2 may be used to estimate well holding capacity. These data are based on 46 per cent of well space being available for molten iron.

Tap and Slag Spouts

The well portion of a cupola has tap and slag spouts (Fig. 2.6), a simple arrangement for intermittent tapping and back slagging; also for continuous tapping through a sized taphole and back slagging.

Continuous tapping also may be achieved by a front slagging spout as shown in Figs. 2.8 and 2.7 (chart

TABLE 2.2. **APPROXIMATE HOLDING CAPACITY OF CUPOLA WELL**

Dia. Inside Lining, in.	Approx. Holding Capacity Cupola Well, lb
23	570
27	820
32	1160
37	1540
42	1990
45	2280
48	2610
54	3390
60	4050
66	4910
72	5840
78	6840
84	7960

(Based on 12 in. average depth of metal — distance sand bottom to slag spout)

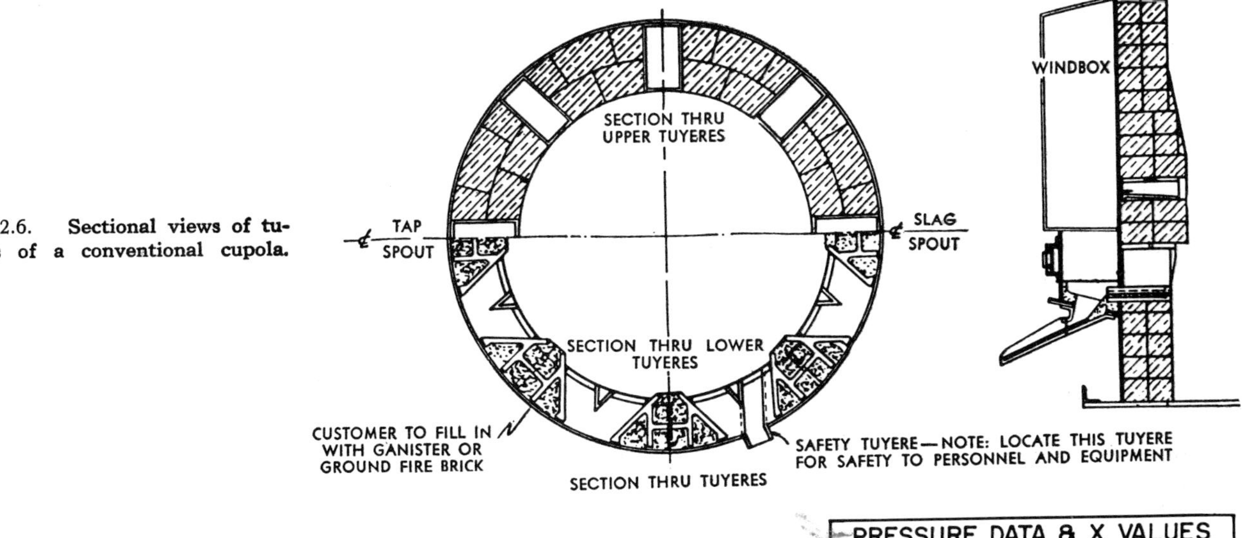

Fig. 2.6. **Sectional views of tuyeres of a conventional cupola.**

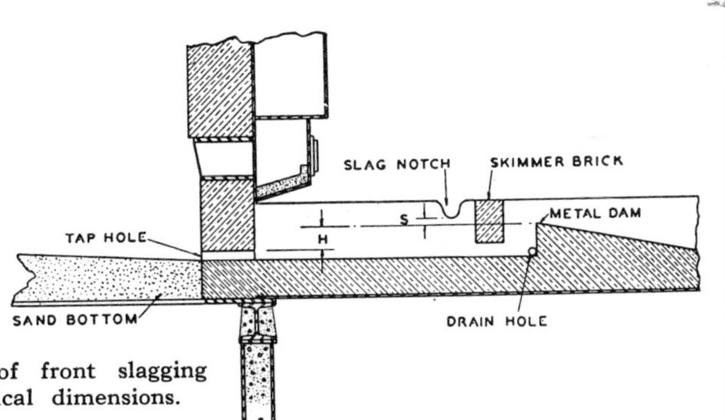

PRESSURE DATA & X VALUES

WINDBOX (W)	CUPOLA (C)	X (W)	X (C)
BALANCED-BLAST CUPOLA			
22 OZ.	15 OZ.	6.0 IN.	4.3 IN.
19 OZ.	12 OZ.	5.2 IN.	3.5 IN.
14 OZ.	9.5 OZ.	4.0 IN.	2.9 IN.
CONVENTIONAL CUPOLA			
21.5 OZ.	18 OZ.	5.9 IN.	5.0 IN.
16 OZ.	13 OZ.	4.5 IN.	3.7 IN.
13.5 OZ.	10.5 OZ.	3.9 IN.	3.1 IN.
10 OZ.	8 OZ.	3.0 IN.	2.5 IN.

Fig. 2.7. Cross-section of front slagging spout and table of critical dimensions.

shows critical dimensions of the spout for varying operating pressures).

Figure 2.9 is a line drawing of another type of spout for continuous tapping and back slagging. It is similar in theory to the front slagging spout except that in this case the dam must be high enough to prevent slagging through the tap hole and no slag skimmer is necessary. This type of spout may be suitable for operation with basic slags, for the slag volume held in the well will vary in a direct ratio with the operating pressure and melting rate.[5]

Charging Openings

The conventional cupola has a charging opening. In the hand charged cupola this opening is relatively low to conform with the existing charging deck. Frequently this height was only about 14 ft from bottom plate to the charging opening sill, and much sensible heat was lost to the atmosphere.

For hand charging there is one or more of these openings, just large enough to introduce the charged materials. The small openings have cast iron doors designed to hold a refractory lining.

For mechanical charging the opening is usually set at a higher level to allow more efficient absorption of the heat from the ascending hot gases. The effective height of the cupola is really the height from the top of the tuyeres to the top of the charged column. However, since tuyere heights do not vary greatly, it has been more common to refer to the effective height of a cupola as the height from the bottom plate to the charge opening sill. This height may vary from 15 ft on small diameter cupolas to 25 ft on cupolas of large diameter. A generally accepted average is 21 ft, and at this height little sensible heat is wasted.

For mechanically charged cupolas the charge openings are larger, faced with cast iron frames, and the stack suitably reinforced with structural beams. Only in special cases are they equipped with doors or other types of heat shields.

Upper Stack

To protect against fire, there is a space between the cupola stack and the building roof structure. This area is sheltered by the roof hood (Fig. 2.1).

The conventional cupola is also equipped with a spark arrestor, a double-cone arrangement of heavy perforated steel plate supported by durable cast iron

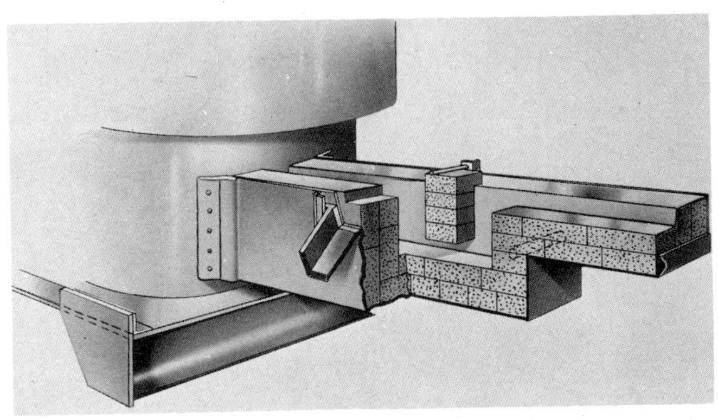

Fig. 2.8. Cutaway view of front slagging spout.

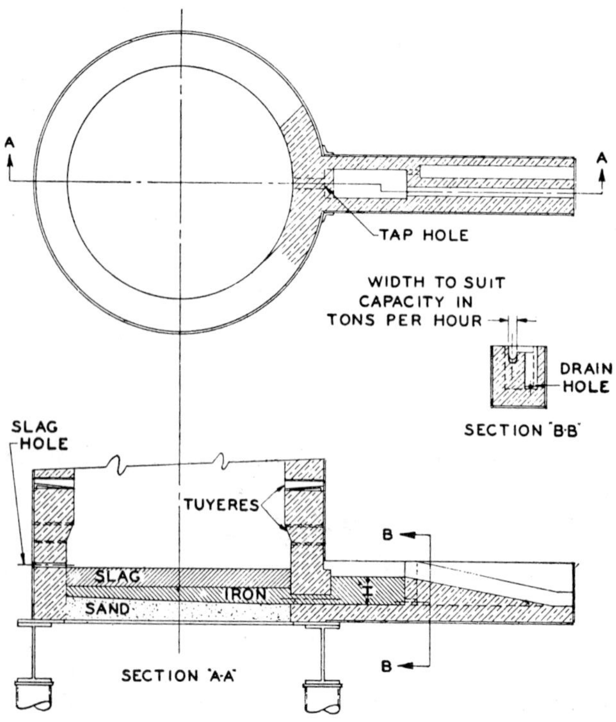
A
A
TAP HOLE
WIDTH TO SUIT
CAPACITY IN
TONS PER HOUR
DRAIN
HOLE
SECTION 'B-B'
SLAG
HOLE
TUYERES
B
SLAG
IRON
SAND
SECTION 'A-A'
B
NOTE-DIM. H WILL BE OF SIMILAR RELATIONSHIP TO CUPOLA OPERATING PRESSURES AS IN TABLE FOR FRONT SLAG SPOUTS WITH THE EXCEPTION THAT IN ORDER TO PREVENT FRONT SLAGGING DIM. H MUST BE INCREASED BY AT LEAST 50%

Fig. 2.9. Top view and section of continuous tapping spout with back slagging.

legs. This spark arrestor reduces the fire hazard of cupola sparks, but does not prevent cinders and fly ash from accumulating on adjacent roofs, nor does it remove undesirable conditions from the waste gases.

Special equipment is available for cleaning cupola waste gases, but not as standard equipment of the conventional cupola.

A windbox pressure gage is part of the standard equipment of a conventional cupola, and a suitable pipe connection on the top of the windbox is provided for its connection.

ERECTING CUPOLA

The conventional cupola is usually shipped with the body section as one piece, but with legs to be attached in the field. The balance of the cupola stack is shipped in 10-ft sections so constructed as to provide for downward lapping joints as protection against weather. Erecting a cupola is a relatively simple job, which some foundrymen prefer to do with their own plant force.

Erection may be accomplished by using two or three chain hoists suspended from the charging floor, A-frames, or gin poles (if erected outdoors). Stack sections are numbered for erection, like numbers joining. Match-mark numbers start at the top of the cupola. The top, or number one section of stack is placed in position and raised high enough to slide the next section into place. Old automobile leaf type springs are very helpful in fitting one section of stack in another. The spark arrester is placed on the roof and should be bolted onto the cupola as it is being raised through the roof opening.

Section two fits inside section one. Now section one should be riveted or bolted to section two. Holes are all punched from uniform templates to facilitate assembly. All sections may be either bolted or riveted. If bolts are used, they should be turned up tight with heads on the inside. The body or windbox section fits outside the joining stack section. Note location of safety spout to be certain it is properly located for safety of personnel and accessory equipment.

The charging opening may be located at any desired point by turning the stack until proper position is obtained.

The cupola is hoisted, with body section high enough to admit columns, which are loosely bolted to body section. The columns, previously filled with reinforced concrete, are set on wedges in position desired, allowing ½-in. for grouting. The cupola is lowered until it rests on the foundation and the bolts are tightened, making certain that the cupola columns are in proper position.

The slag and tap spouts, pressure gage and blast piping should then be connected to the body section.

REFERENCES

1. Reese, D. J. "Cupola Operation," AFS Transactions, vol. 46 (1938).
2. Carter, Sam, and Carlsen, Ralph. "Acid Cupola Slags and Some Relationships to Melting Conditions" AFS Transactions, vol. 61, p. 527 (1953).
3. Mulcahy, Bernard P. "How to Use the Cupola," *Foundry*, Jan. 1952, p. 152.
4. "Auto-Slagging Twin Tuyeres," *Foundry Trade Journal*, Aug. 6, 1953, p. 175.
5. Levi, W. W. "Operation of the Cupola," AFS Transactions, vol. 58, p. 1 (1950).

CHAPTER 3

Special Cupolas Accessories

The conventional acid lined cupola has been the traditional melting unit in the foundry industry ever since its inception.

Over the years, much thought has been given to the principles involving the operation, and many refinements and modifications in the form of mechanization and the addition of numerous accessories have been introduced. However, these efforts have been directed largely towards improving the control and efficiency of the conventional cupola and, although in themselves gratifying, have not overcome some of the major inherent limitations of the process.

The basic principles and design involved remain the same and, consequently, we are still handicapped in our ability to govern oxidation rates and metal-slag reactions so as to substantially eliminate melting losses and perform such metallurgical refinements as desulfurization, deoxidation, etc.

These deficiencies constitute an additional handicap in that they limit the degree to which low cost raw materials such as scrap iron and steel scrap can be used, necessitating substantial amounts of expensive pig iron in order to meet carbon and sulfur requirements.

Furthermore, it is frequently not recognized that present cast iron specifications are governed, at least to some extent, by the ability of the cupola to produce rather than by ideal metallurgical requirements.

Coupled with the foregoing limitations is the fact that the overwhelming majority of cupolas in use today are limited in their ability to operate for periods much over 18 hr due to excessive refractory

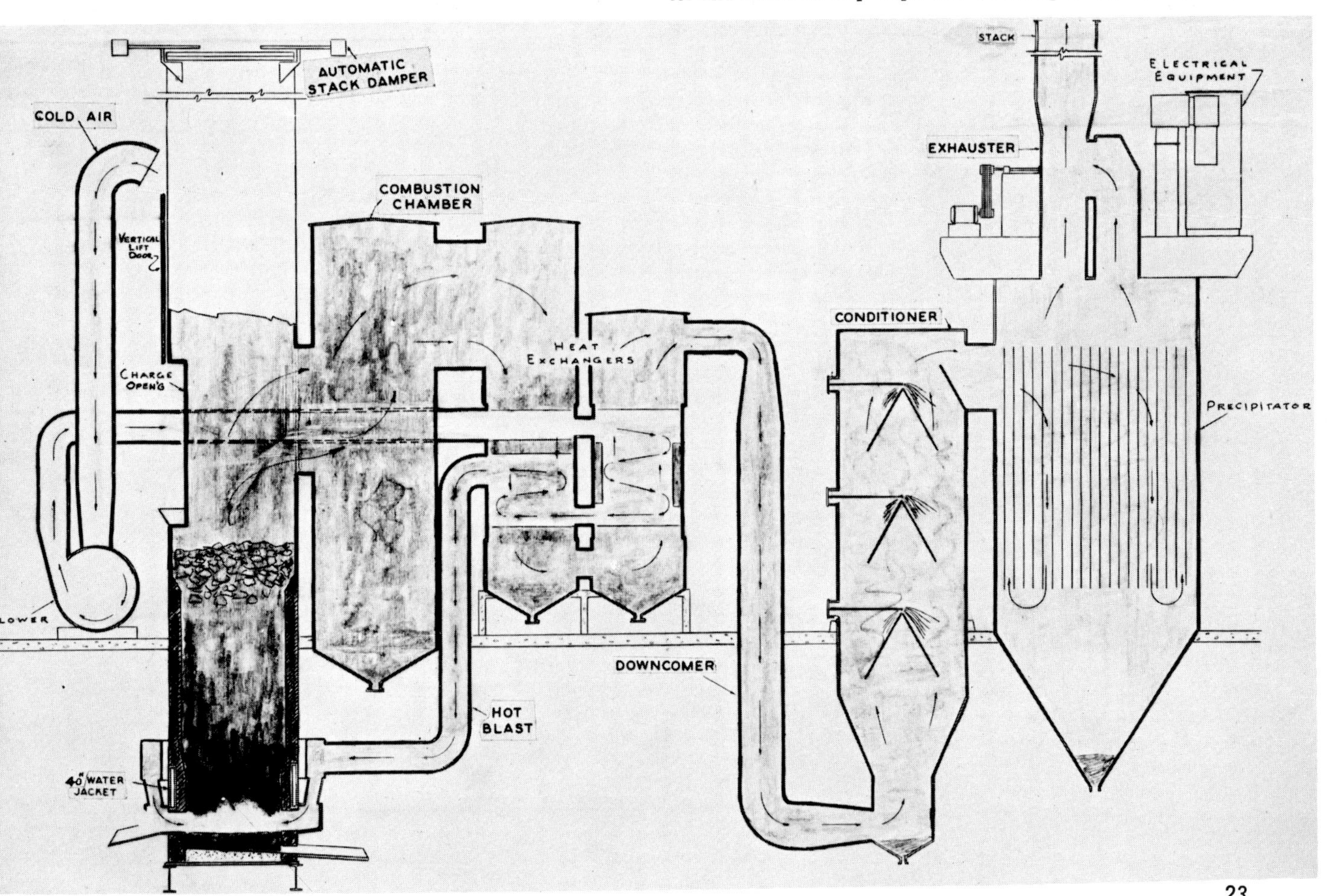

Fig. 3.1. **Diagrammatic sketch of side-charged acid-lined front-slagging cupola. The installation includes automatic stack dampers, internal sectional water jacket, blast recuperator and electrostatic precipitator. (Whiting Corp., Harvey, Ill.)**

erosion, thereby necessitating the installation of duplicate units whenever continuity of metal supply is a requirement, as is the case in most production foundries.

These limitations have not been looked upon in the past as a serious handicap, but rather an established fact. The rapid progress made in foundry metallurgy during the past decade, coupled with steadily rising costs of raw materials and labor, have brought about requirements which are beyond the capability of the present cupola.

This is especially the case in the production of new special purpose ferrous cast materials where the need for such requirements as low sulfur, high carbon and close control of oxidation has been pointed out in many articles written for the technical and trade press.

Extensive research during the past few years in this country and abroad has resulted not only in improved designs but in the development of cupolas which are capable of control and purification on a plane approaching that of batch-type metallurgical units.

It is the purpose of this chapter to describe these developments and their ability to overcome past deficiencies, and resolve the problems created by new and increased demands.

MODIFICATION OF ACID TYPE CUPOLAS

Although this chapter is primarily concerned with new types of cupolas, the latest developments in design and operation of some conventional acid lined cupolas are of sufficient significance to warrant their inclusion under the heading of "Special Cupolas." Two ultra-modern installations have been selected to demonstrate the progress made in this field.

Side Charged Acid Cupola

Design. Figure 3.1 shows a diagrammatic sketch of an installation incorporating the latest thinking in connection with a side-charged acid-lined front-slagging cupola. This installation is composed of a conventional cupola stack (102 in.) which has been modified to include automatic stack dampers. In addition, the shell is fitted with an internal sectional water jacket extending upward 36 in. from the tuyere level. Although the stack is side-charged by means of a skip hoist, a counterbalanced sliding door operating vertically permits the closing of the opening between charges.

A blast recuperator consisting of a combustion chamber and a heat exchanger for preheating the incoming blast, as well as a conditioner and an electrostatic precipitator for the removal of solid particle matter from the effluent gases completes the unit.

Operation. In the operation of this cupola an acid lining in the form of brick or monolithic covers the coolers to a depth of about 8 in. at the start. Although the water coolers appreciably decrease the rate of refractory erosion, it is interesting to note that towards the end of a full day's campaign only a thin layer of

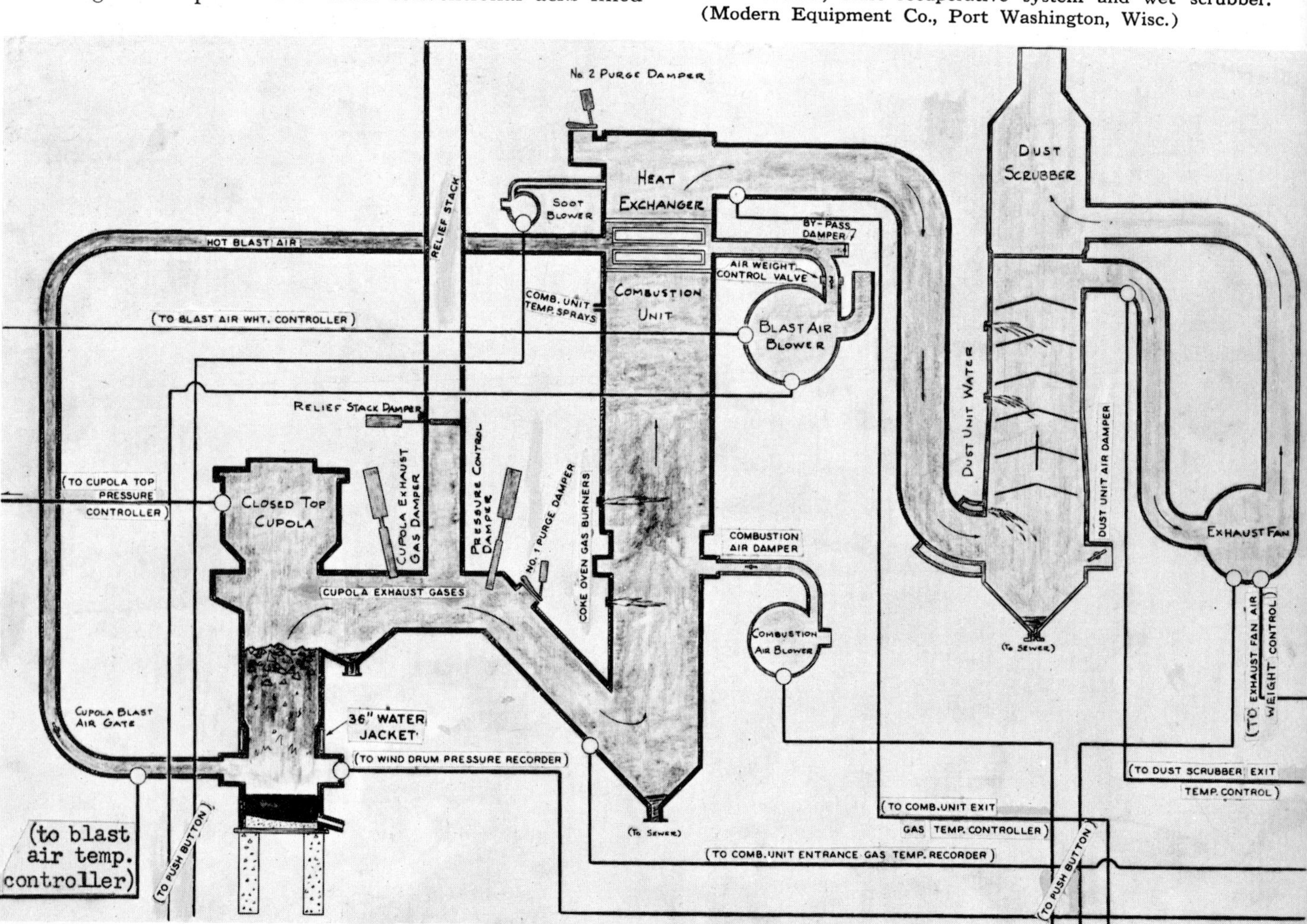

Fig. 3.2. Top-charged acid-lined cupola fitted with internal water coolers, blast recuperative system and wet scrubber. (Modern Equipment Co., Port Washington, Wisc.)

refractory or slag covers the coolers, and that this layer remains fairly constant once equilibrium has been reached. However, no attempt is made to operate this installation in excess of 18 hr.

The effluent gases from the cupola are burned in the combustion chamber and then passed through the heat exchanger, thereby preheating the incoming blast air to a temperature of 600 F maximum. The products of combustion from the recuperator then go through a water vapor conditioning chamber for the purpose of cooling and ionization prior to entering the electrostatic precipitator. In this latter unit the remaining fines are precipitated out of the exhaust gasses, the coarser particles having settled in the bottoms of the various prior components of the system through gravity. Each one of these components is fitted with a hopper which, by means of automatic valves, continuously discharges the solids collected into a sluicing system.

The complete unit operates under a slight negative pressure controlled by means of an exhaust fan in conjunction with the precipitation unit.

All the various control mechanisms for the installation are interlocked and operated from a central control board.

Top Charged Acid Cupola

Design. Figure 3.2 shows a diagrammatic sketch of an installation which has been further modified in that the unit is fully enclosed and that the charging is performed through the top of the stack rather than through the conventional side opening. This is accomplished by means of a pair of refractory lined lids covering the top, which are activated in the horizontal plane by means of hydraulic units at the time of charging. The mechanism of charging involves the use of a specially designed cylindrical cone bottom bucket, the lower end of which is fitted with a plastic weighted curtain extending below the bucket and creating a seal in a cylindrical water trough on top of the cupola when in charging position.

Operation. The various steps in charging the cupola involve filling the bucket and elevating the same by means of a skip hoist. While in travel, a steel cover is automatically placed on top of the bucket to form the upper seal. When in charging position, the lower part of the bucket is sealed by the curtain. The sliding doors are next opened, the cone lowered, and the charge dropped into the stack. Following this, the cone is raised, the sliding doors closed, and the bucket picked up by the skip hoist. The mechanism involved seals the cupola from the outside during operation.

In a manner similar to the previous unit, this cupola is also fitted with internal water coolers which are covered with refractory.

The effluent gases from the cupola are passed into the combustion chamber of a recuperative system, but may also be by-passed into the open through a relief stack. This system differs from the one previously described in that the combustion chamber and heat exchanger are combined in one unit. From the recuperator the products of combustion go through a vertical wet scrubber for the removal of fines, and are then exhausted into the atmosphere by means of a blower. The various units of the system are again provided with automatically discharging collection hoppers in which the coarser particles are separated out.

Summary. The benefits derived from the innovations incorporated in these installations are to be found in decreased melting losses as a result of improved control, and increased efficiency through better utilization of the fuel, as well as decreased refractory consumption. In addition, the methods adopted for cleaning the waste gases have reduced the ejection of objectionable dust particles into the open by about 95 per cent.

DEVELOPMENTS IN CUPOLA DESIGN

Although the installations described in the foregoing constitute a distinct departure from conventional design and incorporate many new and interesting features, they are still limited in their scope by the basic principles involved. Consequently, they do not permit the freedom in choice of raw materials dictated by rapidly changing economic and supply conditions nor the control of such chemical and metallurgical reactions as deoxidation and desulfurization necessitated by requirements in the new field of special purpose cast materials.

Before discussing the modifications to cupola designs and operational techniques which have been necessary to overcome present limitations, it may be helpful at this point to review briefly the general mechanism of combustion and indicate the modifications to gas and metal/slag reactions required in order to resolve the problems at hand.

Metallurgical Reactions

It is a well-known fact that inside of the cupola various zones of reaction exist, and that the relative degree of control exercised over these reactions governs the quality of the end product. Of more importance, however, in connection with the present problems, is the fact that by proper procedures these reactions may be modified and altered so as to perform a variety of metallurgical functions not generally associated with conventional cupola operations.

In examining the conditions inside the cupola, it will be found that four definite zones exist. From top to bottom these are:

a) Preheat Zone
b) Reduction Zone
c) Oxidation Zone
d) Metal/Slag Reaction Zone

In the following discussion, the gas phase of the reactions involved will be considered first in order to establish the proper sequence.

When the air enters the cupola through the tuyeres (Fig. 3.3), the oxygen of this air combines with the carbon of the incandescent coke to form carbon dioxide; i.e., $C + O_2 = CO_2$ (+14,550 Btu/lb Carbon).

The exothermic nature of this reaction results in the liberation of the large amounts of heat required for the melting operation.

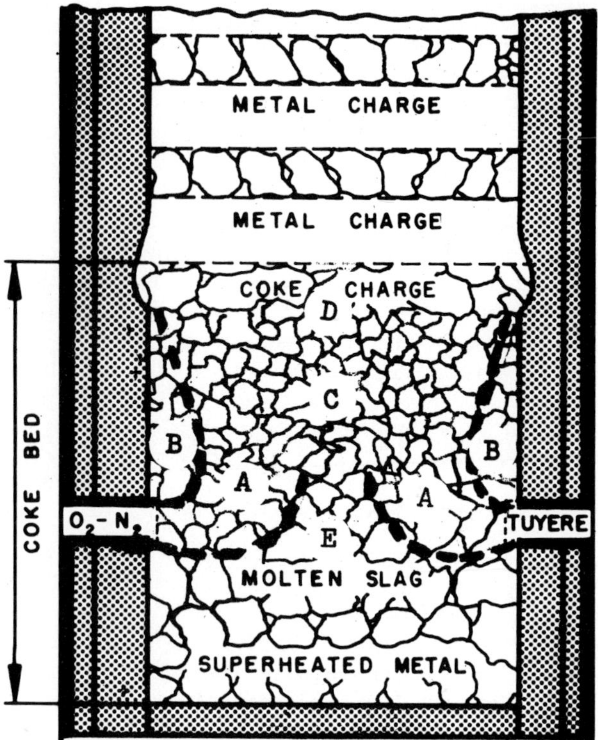

Fig. 3.3. Cross-section of cupola showing reaction areas.
A — $O_2 + CO_2$
B — Area high in O_2
C — $CO + CO_2$
D — High $CO:CO_2$ ratio
E — High $CO:CO_2$ ratio

In the presence of excess carbon at the proper temperature, however, CO_2 is not stable, but will rapidly pick up an additional carbon atom to form carbon monoxide, i.e., $CO_2 + C = 2CO$ (−5,850 Btu per pound of carbon).

In view of the oxidizing and heat liberating nature of the CO_2 reaction, and the reducing and heat absorbing nature of the CO reaction, it becomes evident that the control of such pertinent factors as melting rate, temperature, metallic losses, carbon, etc., depends to a great degree upon our ability to govern the extent and relative level of the areas in the cupola where these reactions predominate, as well as the speed with which they reach completion and the degree of such completion.

However, a number of variables are involved which influence these reactions. Therefore, in order to determine what corrective measures and modifications may be required to present cupola practice, a clear understanding of these variables is necessary.

It must be recognized that the combustion behavior of carbon in the cupola is not entirely dependent on chemical considerations, but is also influenced by physical factors such as temperature, coke size, wind velocity, relative coke to air ratio, etc.

Combustion Factors

In order for combustion to occur, intimate contact must first be established between the carbon and the oxygen. Once this condition is at hand, the resultant CO_2 reaction proceeds, first at chemical reaction rates, but as more heat is liberated, thereby increasing the temperature, the speed of the reaction increases and becomes more and more dependent upon the physical factors involved. For instance, the influence of variations in coke size becomes evident by the fact that the smaller the coke, the larger is the surface area of reactive carbon and the shorter is the time required to reach temperature. Consequently, smaller coke size increases the reaction rate. Similarly, increased wind velocity results in a lowering of the temperature because of the cooling effect on the coke, thereby decreasing the reaction rate.

The conditions surrounding the CO reaction are governed by similar variables. Beginning at the upper level of the oxidation zone where high temperatures are at hand, the reaction proceeds first at a very rapid rate, depending largely upon the physical factors at hand. The endothermic nature of this reaction, coupled with the rapid transfer of heat to the descending burden, gradually lowers the temperature of the gas phase and, consequently, the reaction rate, until a point is finally reached where the reaction ceases. The composition of the gas phase, i.e., the relative $CO:CO_2$ ratio at this point represents that of the effluent gases and is an important indicator of the conditions inside the cupola.

Having established the manner in which carbon and oxygen react with each other in the cupola, it can now be concluded that on the basis of an initially balanced iron-coke-air ratio:

a) Increasing the air volume at a constant coke ratio results in lower $CO:CO_2$ ratio, increased melting rate but colder metal.
b) Increasing the amount of coke at constant air volume results in higher $CO:CO_2$ ratio, decreased melting rate but hotter metal.
c) Decreasing the coke size at constant coke to air ratio results in higher $CO:CO_2$ ratio, increased melting rate but colder metal.
d) Increasing the blast temperature at constant coke to air ratio results in higher $CO:CO_2$ ratio, increased melting rate and hotter metal.

In analyzing the foregoing factors, it is apparent that by proper manipulation, the gas phase of the operation can be regulated so as to produce a variety of conditions required for specific metallurgical functions. However, the degree to which this can be accomplished depends, as already pointed out, on our ability to control the rate of reaction, as well as the extent of the areas where they predominate.

Referring again to the sectional view of the cupola shown in Fig. 3.3, it will be seen that the combustion does not progress uniformly across the cupola, but that different conditions exist between the center and the outside as a result of the resistance of the coke to the free flow of the air and the upward direction of the gas phase, as well as the cooling effect produced.

Immediately in front of the tuyeres $CO_2 + O_2$ exist, but whereas towards the center and slightly upward the reaction rapidly reaches completion, an area high in free oxygen remains just above the tuyeres and extends up along the wall. Although this zone always produces oxidation, it follows that large areas of free oxygen exaggerate this condition. Considering metallic losses and the severe refractory erosion produced by high iron oxide slags, it is evident that our efforts must be directed toward restricting the sphere of influence of O_2 and CO_2. Much can be accomplished in this direction by promoting high reaction rates through increased amounts of coke and higher blast temperature, thereby shortening the reaction zone, but certain modifications to the tuyere design are also indicated.

Turning for a moment to the reduction zone, it will be seen that the relative composition of the gas phase in this zone, i.e., the $CO:CO_2$ ratio, and the extent of the area of the same is entirely a function of the conditions established in the combustion zone, and accordingly governed thereby.

In the area below the tuyere level, reducing conditions predominate because of high temperatures and the absence of free oxygen. Consequently, the oxidation of the metallics encountered in the combustion zone is reversed to some extent in this area. The degree of such reversal depends upon the relative $CO:CO_2$ ratio, which is largely governed by the combustion zone, and the time of exposure to the reducing gas, i.e., the depth of the well.

Additional Factors Involved

It is a well-known fact that higher carbon pick-up can more readily be attained in cupolas operating with basic slags than with acid. This is probably due to the rapid fluxing and removal of the ash in the coke, which is acid in nature, thereby increasing the available active carbon surface area. In addition, the non-wetting character of basic slags relative to coke further promotes this condition. The degree of carbon pick-up therefore becomes a function of the basicity of the slag in addition to previous considerations.

From this, it must be concluded that modifications to the cupola are desired which will allow the use of entirely synthetic slags, which can be governed to perform specific functions without the danger of contamination from lining erosion and uncontrolled amounts of metallic oxides.

In addition to greatly improved carbon control, this type of operation will make possible substantial desulfurization, which is predicated on operating with truly basic slags. This will constitute a decided advantage over the conventional acid cupola where little can be done relative to sulfur, the amount of which, therefore, primarily becomes a function of the sulfur in the coke and, to some extent, the metallics. Much has been said about the use of fairly high amounts of limestone in acid cupolas for sulfur removal, but such practice is limited in its scope and carries with it the penalty of a decided increase in lining erosion.

According to Rocca, Grant and Chipman, the mechanism involved in the removal of sulfur is a two-stage reaction in which:

a) The metallic sulfides from the metal first dissolve in the slag until equilibrium is reached between the amounts in the slag and the metal, i.e.,

$$FeS \text{ (metal)} \rightleftarrows FeS \text{ (slag)}$$

b) These sulfides then react with the lime in the slag to form iron oxide and calcium sulfide, i.e.,

$$FeS + CaO \rightleftarrows FeO + CaS$$

As this latter reaction can only take place when an excess of calcium oxide is present, and the iron oxide content of the slag is low, the significance of the conditions outlined in the foregoing becomes evident.

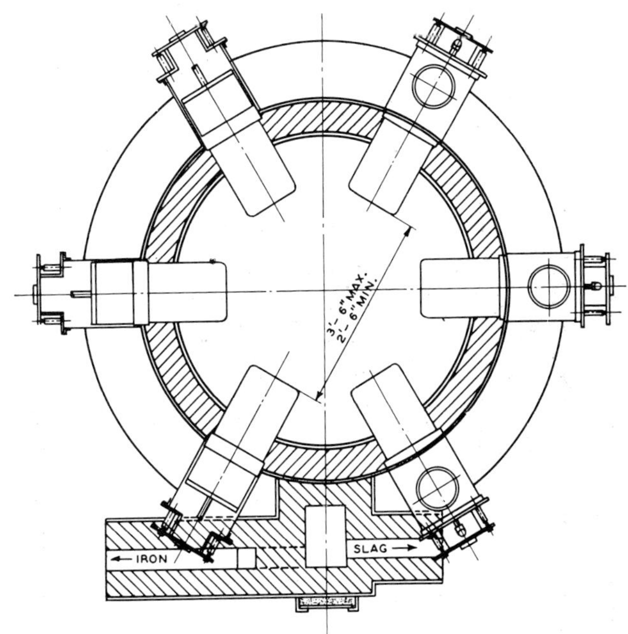

Fig. 3.4. **Water-cooled projecting tuyeres used to confine combustion reaction to a concentrated area.**

However, it must be pointed out that an adequate depth of such slag maintained at a constant high temperature and fluidity is necessary in order to insure the required metal to slag and slag to coke reactions. Careful consideration must therefore be given to the well depth as well as to the refractory.

Summary. In light of the foregoing discussion, it becomes apparent that by certain modifications to design and operational technique, present limitations can be overcome and conditions established which will resolve the problems created by new and increased demands.

These demands may again be summarized as follows:

1) Ability to meet analytical specifications with low cost raw materials such as scrap iron or steel.
2) Ability to perform effective desulfurization regardless of the raw materials.
3) Ability to control oxidation to a point of minimum metallic losses and as may be required in the manufacture of new special purpose cast irons.
4) Ability to operate over extended periods without requiring internal repair.

The modifications to operational technique and design indicated must thus be in a direction which will permit:

a) A concentrated combustion zone able to produce very high temperatures.
b) Complete freedom in formulating the slag composition.
c) Maintaining the slag depth at a constant predetermined level.
d) Continuous tapping.
e) Extended operation unhampered by present refractory limitations.

Discussion. In order to confine the combustion reaction to a concentrated area and thereby minimize the zone of free oxygen, the application of projecting tuyeres is indicated (Fig. 3.4). Such tuyeres, which generally are made of copper and, of necessity, water cooled, permit the introduction of the air at any predetermined distance from the center. Consequently, a more concentrated combustion (i.e., higher reaction temperature) is accomplished and the area of free oxygen is greatly reduced.

Projecting water cooled tuyeres have been made of cast iron, steel and copper. Steel up to 4 in. protrusion is effective. Copper proves to be best and most successful at all distances.

Copper tuyeres have been fabricated and cast. Cast tuyeres must be free of sand in the water circulating area to be used successfully.

Water consumption usually will be 15-25 gallons/min. Tuyere failures are caused by poor water distribution, interruptions in water source and lack of back pressures on the tuyere. Because of the amount of water being used, tuyere failures cannot be detected readily by a water temperature rise.

The quickest detection that can be made is to feel the water at the tuyere water outlet and note if there is an occasional surge and slight temperature rise. Water can be put in the top or the bottom of the tuyere. Most installations have bottom inlets.

A tuyere failure can be determined by the blackening of the coke in front of the tuyere and a gradual loss in metal temperature. However, if the temperature loss is not great the tuyere still can operate. If the water has too much effect it usually is shut off and the melt continued.

In developing the water cooled liningless cupola, it was necessary to form the combustion zone by protruding and inclining the tuyeres, obtaining proper blast velocities and contouring the cupola shell.

Fleming[1] noted that in a hot blast cupola 500 C (932 F) of 34 in. dia., 85-115 feet/sec blast velocities produced the best results. Löbbecke[2] points out that, as blast velocities increased and tuyere inclination increased, metal temperature improved chemical analysis and removed the secondary melting zone which had occurred at lower tuyere inclinations and lower blast velocities. Blast velocities ranging from 68-525 feet/sec were covered and tuyere inclinations ranged from 0-12.5 deg. in a cupola of 36.5 in. dia. Best results were obtained at 10-12.5 deg. tuyere inclination and 219.8 to 375 ft/sec blast velocities.

These experiments were to produce a cupola that has a combustion zone efficient from the center of the cupola. A cupola may have the proper tuyere blast velocities, inclination and protrusion but if the proper distribution of coke and metal charge is not obtained difficulties can occur with metal temperature, chemical analysis and the buildup of skulls above the metal zone and around the tuyeres. Sidewall wind travel can produce this condition that can be avoided by maintaining a high density against the cupola walls and a loose center.

Tuyere protrusions have varied in the different installations. Fleming found that protrusions of 2¼ coke diameters were satisfactory if the coke diameter was 8 per cent of the cupola diameter. A deep protrusion can create high oxidation losses with poor metal temperatures. As the protrusion is decreased apparently the blast velocities have to be increased. Tuyeres have protruded in most cases to obtain a distance of 30-33 in. from tuyere nose to tuyere nose.

Factual data on the effect of tuyere protrusion is limited but in most cases 4-9 in. from the lining usually is used, greater distances if the cupola shell is used as the starting point. No protrusion in a liningless cupola usually produces a double melt zone. This phenomenon does not seem to change with variations of blast velocity.

Many cupolas installed with straight sidewall shells perform excellently provided there is proper water distribution the full length of the shell. Thin shells of ⅝-in. have been used successfully. Cracking has occurred in thicknesses of one in. or more.

Temperature losses by use of water on the shell have been negligible in some cases and high in other installations. The rate of slag build up, retention and composition can influence the loss of heat. The cupola shell diameter and melting rate also can influence the heat losses in a properly designed and charged cupola.

Improvements can be obtained in an acid lined cupola with cold or hot blast by following the same procedures as for the hot blast liningless cupola. Results will not be as great but are noticeable. Such cupolas with deep cupola wells can obtain good car-

Fig. 3.5. Balanced blast cupola — design and arrangement of tuyeres. A) lower or main tuyeres; B and C) adjustable auxilliary tuyeres; D) slide valve; E) lighting-up tuyeres.

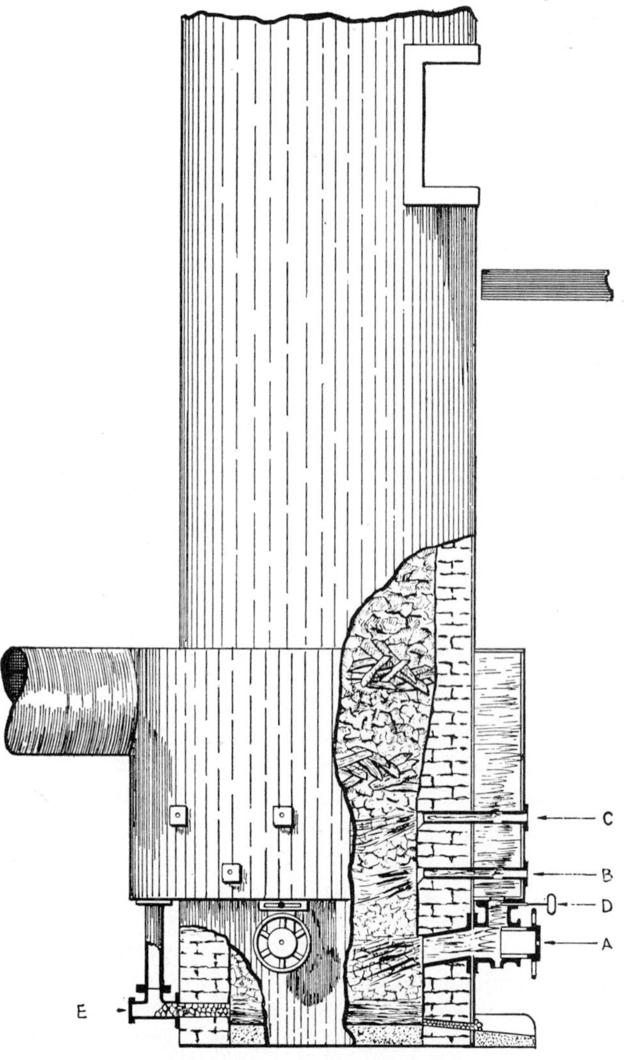

bon pick up which allows greater use of steel or cheap materials in the charge.

The need for high CO:CO_2 ratios in order to promote carbon pick-up and reducing conditions is usually met by increasing the amount of coke. This added cost, however, can be substantially minimized by the adoption of hot blast. Tests have shown that whereas the maximum flame temperature for cold blast is around 3600 F, temperatures of over 4000 F can be reached by preheating the blast to about 1000 F. The resultant increase in reaction rate reduces the amount of coke necessary to achieve the required reaction temperature.

Ability to adjust the slag to any predetermined composition, whether acid, neutral or basic, necessitates the elimination of uncontrollable contaminants, such as normally produced by refractory erosion, metallic oxides, etc. This can best be accomplished by the judicious application of water cooling to the melting zone, and preferably also to the well.

It will be found that water, properly used, constitutes an excellent refractory and permits the elimination of conventional lining materials in the melting zone, which are automatically replaced by a thin layer of slag coating the inside wall. Consequently, no contamination is derived from the melting zone. As for the well area, it has been found that a neutral material such as graphite, in conjunction with water cooling, gives excellent results and operational life.

Coupled with the ability to control the composition of the slag must also be the ability to control the volume, temperature, and viscosity, if effective desulfurization and deoxidation are to be accomplished. It is obvious that the depth of the well must be adjusted so as to allow adequate time for the required slag-coke and metal-coke reactions. However, the depth must not be so great as to cause undue heat losses with a resultant lowering of the slag and metal temperatures, nor must the slag level be so close to the tuyeres as to cause reoxidation. The latter condition, aside from its detrimental effect on the reactivity of the slag, frequently leads to excessive foaming.

The slag level, and consequently the volume, can best be controlled by means of a conventional siphon box, thereby necessitating the use of forehearths.

Aside from the advantages listed, it becomes obvious that the application of water cooling permits continuous operation over extended periods, as refractory problems are largely eliminated.

Conclusions

Considering all factors involved, it may thus be concluded that the best approach to the problems at hand, found to date, is the application of water cooling, and that such an installation should preferably consist of a closed-top cupola equipped with fully cooled melting zone and well, projecting tuyeres, continuous tapping device and high temperature hot blast.

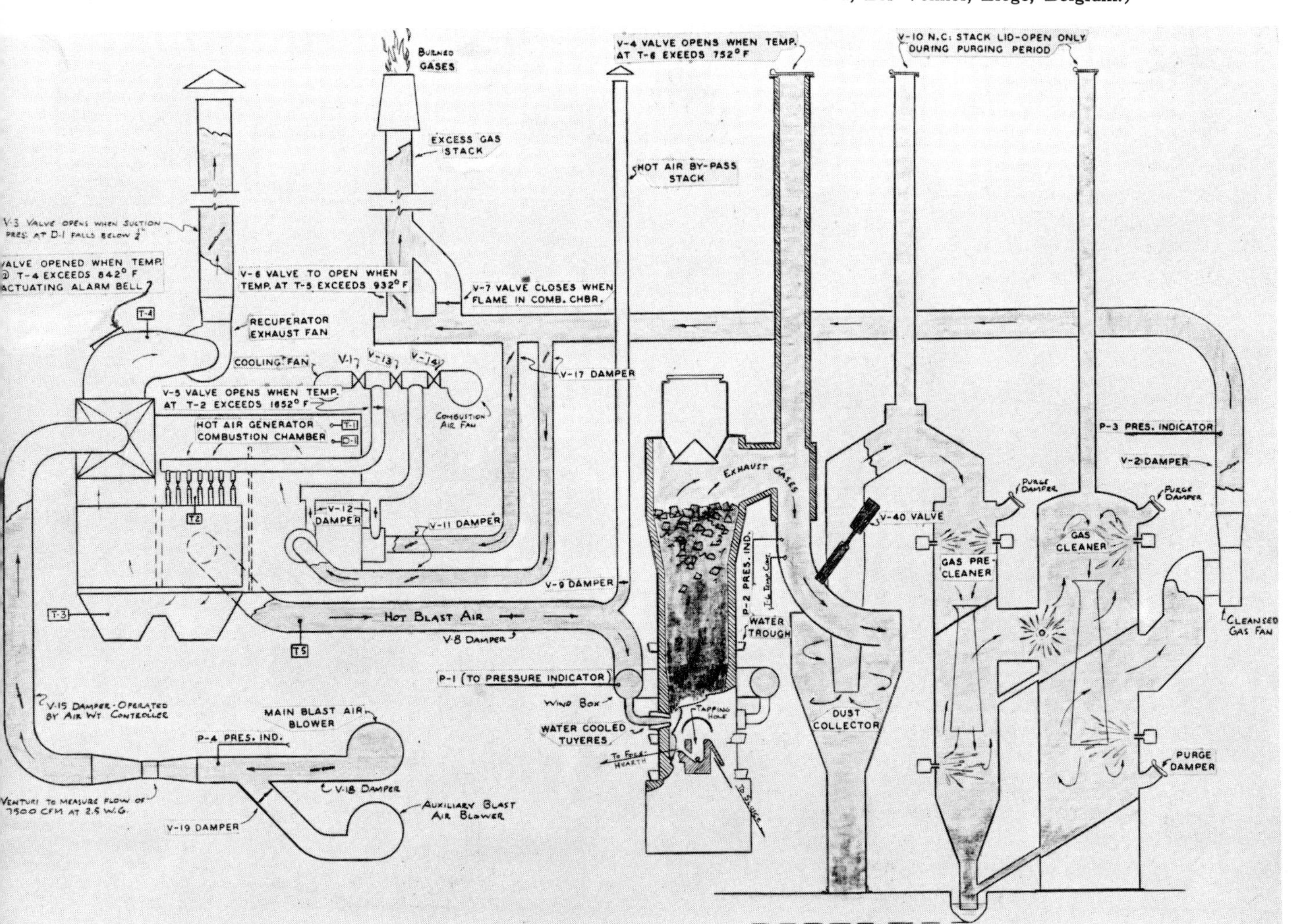

Fig. 3.6. Diagrammatic sketch of closed-top, externally water-cooled metallurgical blast cupola. (Compagnie Generale des Conduite d'Eau, Les Vennes, Liege, Belgium.)

It may further be concluded that such a cupola will meet present carbon specifications with high steel charges (up to 100 per cent) with the added advantage of low phosphorus, and permits very effective desulfurization. In addition, the economy of operation compares favorably with present practice, and therefore does not limit the application to specialty irons but offers advantages in the manufacture of commercial gray iron.

BALANCED BLAST CUPOLA

The balanced blast cupola was developed by the British Cast Iron Research Association and patented in England, United States and other countries. The purpose of this development was to improve the quality of cupola melted metal and reduce coke consumption by improving combustion efficiency.

Its main features are the arrangement and design of the tuyeres (Fig. 3.5). Three rows of tuyeres are used, all equipped with valves for regulating or balancing the distribution of the blast at the different levels of the combustion zone. The main tuyeres are further equipped with slide gates that can shut the blast off tightly from individual tuyeres for short periods of time during the melt, to permit melting away of the bridging at those tuyeres.
By operating these shut-off gates, singly or in groups, in regular sequence, the cupola is kept quite free from bridging at these tuyeres. Uniformly high combustion efficiency is possible with resulting high melting rates. These special tuyeres, with a suitable windbox, can be applied to existing and new cupolas.

In the United States these cupolas have been particularly successful in pipe foundries, melting at high rates and with low coke consumption. In these foundries, where the temperature requirement ranges from 2675 to 2500 F, and obtained with coke consumption as low as 125 lb per ton of melt, melting rates are correspondingly high, one 78 in. ID balanced blast cupola melting as much as 44 tons per hr. In other foundries where metal temperature requirements are higher, coke consumption ranges from 150 to 200 lb per ton, with metal temperatures up to about 2800 F.

On recent installations of the balanced blast cupola in the United States, the original design of slide gates on the main tuyeres has been replaced with specially built butterfly gates that may be operated manually, or mechanically by an automatic electrical time control system.

WATER COOLED CUPOLAS

Various types of water cooled cupolas have been developed in the United States and abroad. Although the same in principle, they differ in the method adopted for cooling, which may be accomplished either by internal water jackets or a series of tubes, or by a blanket of water flowing down the outside of the shell. Opinions differ as to the merit of these two systems, but it is believed that the external method, because of its simplicity, presents fewer operating problems. However, it must be pointed out that both types have given excellent results over several years of operation.

Closed Top Externally Water Cooled Cupola[3]

The installation in Figs. 3.6, 3.7 and 3.8 was selected to demonstrate operation of the features outlined in the foregoing conclusions.

As will be seen in Fig. 3.8, the cupola shell is of an

Fig. 3.7. General layout and charging system for metallurgical blast cupola shown in Fig. 3.6.

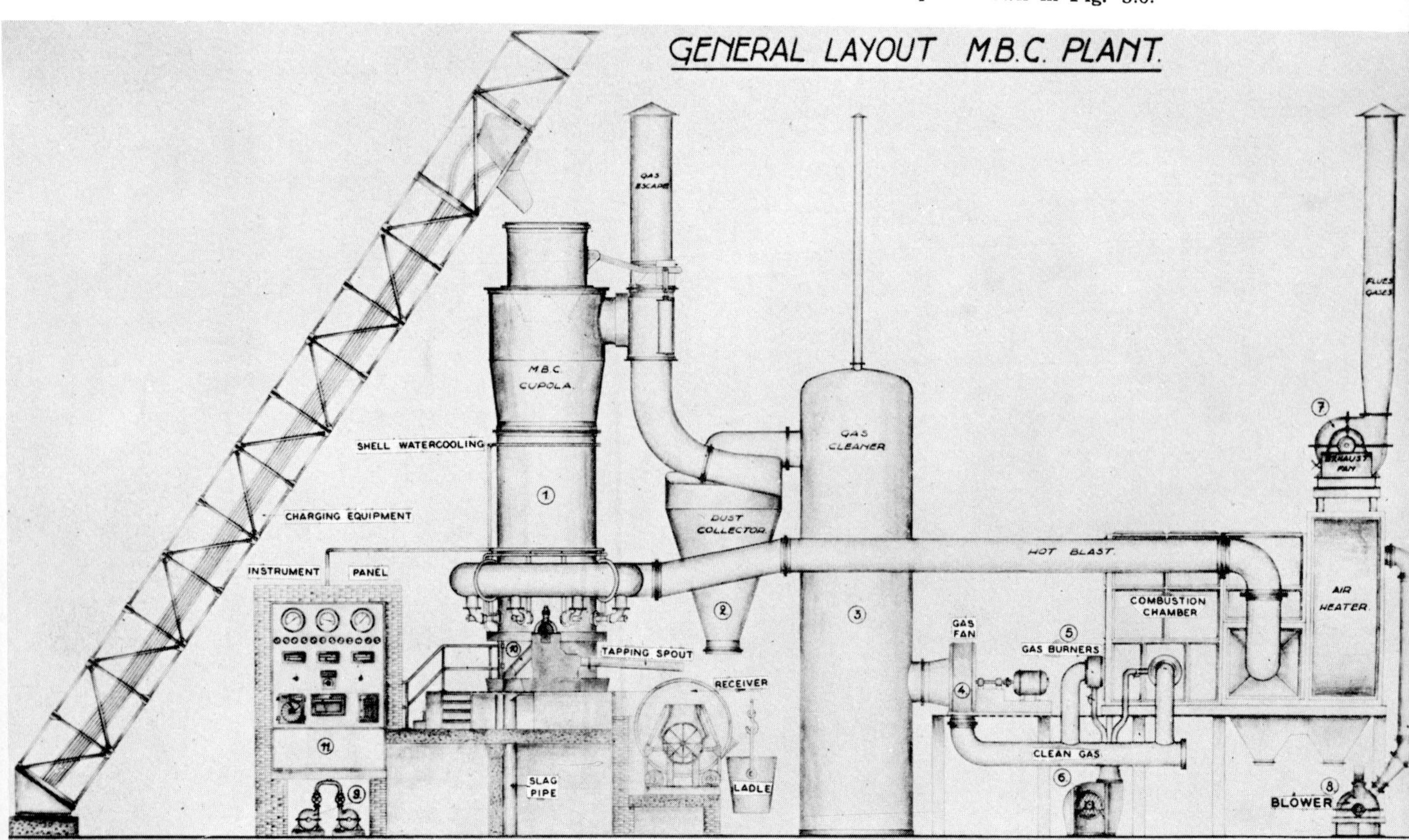

all-welded construction (heavy gage rolled plate $1\frac{1}{4}$ in. thick), mounted on a solid concrete foundation. A side door in the well area replaces conventional drop-bottom doors, and serves to clean out remaining coke and slag at the end of the melting campaign, and also permits entrance for the purpose of inspection and repair.

The top of the cupola is composed of a bell and hopper arrangement, similar to blast furnace construction except that the upper end is sealed by a hinged lid hydraulically activated by means of a lever arm, instead of the conventional upper bell.

The tuyere arrangement, as will be seen, consists of eight projecting water-cooled copper tuyeres connected to a brick lined bustle pipe.

The cupola shell is water-cooled by means of a heavy spray from a perforated pipe encircling the unit, forming a solid blanket flowing down the outside. This water is collected in a trough at the tuyere level. A second perforated pipe located under this trough supplies the water required for cooling the well area.

Refractory. The upper portion of the cupola stack is lined with conventional brick. The reduction, melting, and combustion zone requires no refractories. However, the practice has been to coat this area with a thin insulating layer of a high carbonaceous or dolomitic material, either rammed or sprayed-in prior to starting the campaign. The purpose of this is to arrive at proper reaction temperatures faster and thereby higher initial metal temperature.

The refractory used in the well consists of a high carbonaceous material, either monolithic or in the form of carbon blocks.

Continuous metal tapping and slag removal is accomplished by means of a siphon arrangement based on conventional principles. The cooling water from the tuyeres is used to disintegrate the slag.

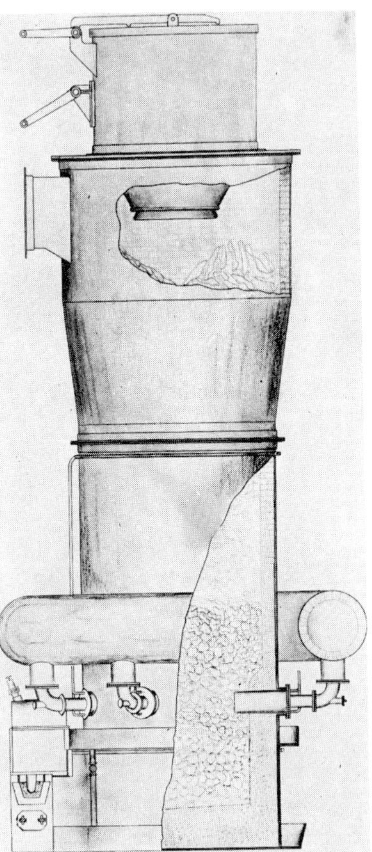

Fig. 3.8. View of cupola shell, closed top and tuyere arrangement of installation shown in Fig. 3.6.

Operation. In the operation of the cupola the charging is accomplished by means of a skip hoist, equipped with a tilting bucket (Fig. 3.7). As the bucket reaches the charging position, the top lid is automatically opened and the charge deposited into the hopper. Immediately following this, the lid is closed and the bell lowered, permitting the charge to enter the stack proper.

The effluent gases (see schematic diagram, Fig. 3.6) leave the cupola through an opening located below the bell, and may either be by-passed through a stack to the atmosphere or directed to a dry dust collector of the cyclone type, by means of a water-cooled slide valve located in the duct between the stack and the collector. In this latter unit the coarse particles carried through by the gas are removed, prior to entering a two-stage wet scrubber involving a pre- and post-conditioning technique, where the major portion of the remaining fines is removed. The clean gas is burned in the combustion chamber of the recuperator and serves to heat the blast air to a temperature of 1000 F. The cupola operates under a slight positive pressure which is regulated by means of a suction blower at the exit end of the scrubber.

Fig. 3.9. Sectional view of open top, drop bottom door, continuous tapping cold blast cupola. (Glamorgan Pipe and Foundry Co., Lynchburg, Va.)

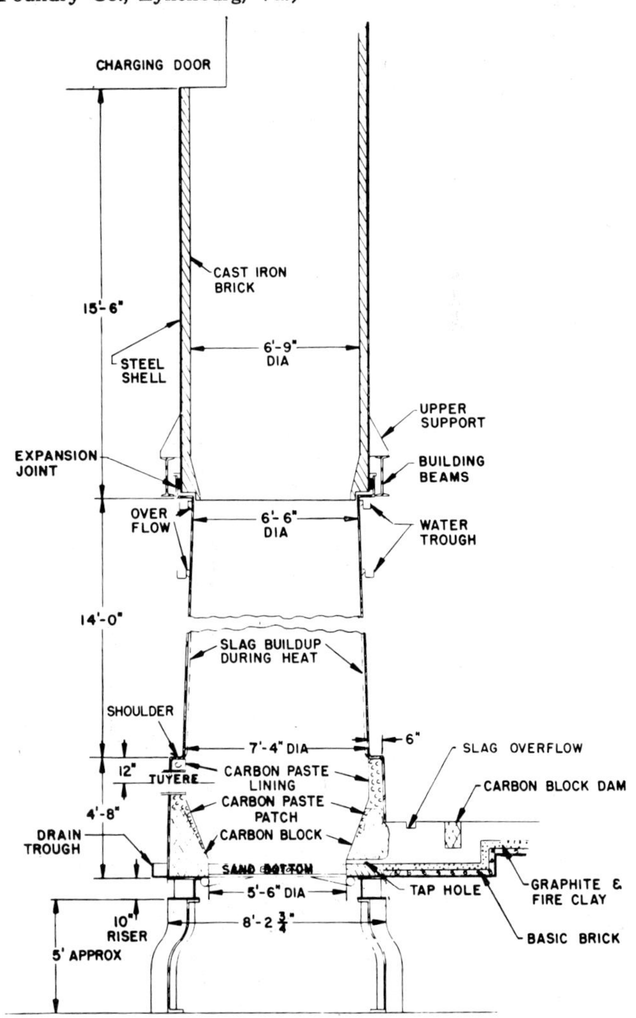

Summary. A number of installations of this general type, including some with conventional drop-bottom doors rather than the permanent bottom design, have been in operation over a period of several years involving both acid and basic practice. Usually, the cupolas operate on a basis of five consecutive 16-hr shifts, but on several occasions operations covering several weeks have been successfully carried out without necessitating shutdowns for internal repair. At the end of each shift, the cupola is banked for the night by first draining out all slag and metal and then adding a few charges of coke.

The advantages claimed for this type of operation are:

a) Excellent control of reactions permitting the use of low cost raw materials.
b) A wide latitude in the selection of slags, thereby allowing effective desulfurization.
c) Ability to operate with low-grade high-sulfur cokes without detrimental effect on the final results.

In addition, the principle of cleaning the gases prior to their use in the recuperative system greatly diminishes maintenance problems.

Open Top Externally Water Cooled Cupola

Figure 3.9 shows a sectional view of an open top, drop bottom door, continuous tapping cold blast cupola. As will be noticed, this cupola is supported on columns in the customary manner. The bottom portion of the stack is formed by a conical structure composed of a lower section, 4 ft. 8 in. high, containing the well and conventional tuyeres, and an upper stepped-in section, 14 ft. high, forming the melting zone. The continuation of the stack is a cylindrical shell independently supported and connected with the lower portion by means of an expansion joint. Although the refractory used in the well area is of similar type as in the previous unit, no refractory is used in the combustion or melting zone. The portion of the cupola above the conical section is lined with cast iron blocks.

The cone shaped portion of the shell involving the melting zone and the well is cooled by a water curtain produced by continuously overflowing two water troughs encircling the shell. This water, after completing its function, is collected in a drain trough and used to flush the slag. In the operation of this cupola approximately 150 gal of water per minute is applied to the shell when the cupola is lighted, and this is increased to about 260 gal when melting begins. At that time the temperature rise of the water is about 90 F. After a short period a slag coating about one inch thick is formed on the inside of the unlined portion of the shell, thereby acting as an insulation. The volume of water is then reduced to about 220 gal per minute with a temperature rise of about 70 F.

This particular installation represents a design which originated in France and has been adopted by an Eastern foundry for the manufacture of centrifugal cast pipe. In the interest of economy, and in order to circumvent certain raw material shortages, it was desirable for this foundry to use the highest possible percentage of ordinary commercially purchased scrap iron. As this type of scrap had always been found to

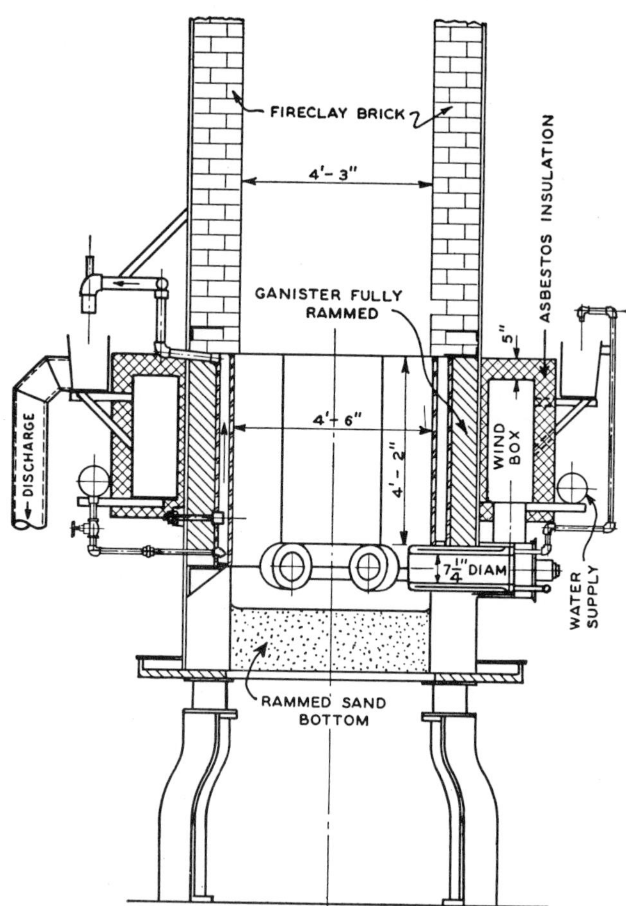

Fig. 3.10. Internal water cooling is accomplished in this cupola by means of built-in water jackets. (Ford Motor Co., Dearborn, Mich.)

contain an appreciable amount of steel, such practice would be restricted if dependent upon conventional operation, in view of the carbon and sulfur requirements which called for 3.65/3.75 per cent and 0.09 per cent maximum, respectively. Although these could possibly have been met by operating a conventional basic lined cupola, economy of operation dictated the use of a water-cooled cupola.

Some open top cupolas have an external shell, encompassing the operating shell. Coverage is maintained from the tuyere area to a distance above the melt zone. Water can be siphoned from the bottom of the tank or can be removed at a controlled rate. If a hot area develops, increased water flow could be taken from the exit in the area or flow in other areas reduced for more cooling of the area involved.

This type construction has some bad features. More maintenance is needed to secure proper cooling. Since the tank is open on top, fine material tends to build up in the bottom of the tank next to the shell. It is imperative that cleanout holes be used regularly. The enclosing shell does not allow visual observation of the operating shell. A leak will cause the wall of water to flow into the operating cupola. Cupolas so equipped, however, can allow water interruptions and have been held from 15 minutes to one-half hour without burn-through occurring.

Some new cupolas have been put in operation without conventional windboxes. Piping is direct to each tuyere from the main blower pipe. With proper air

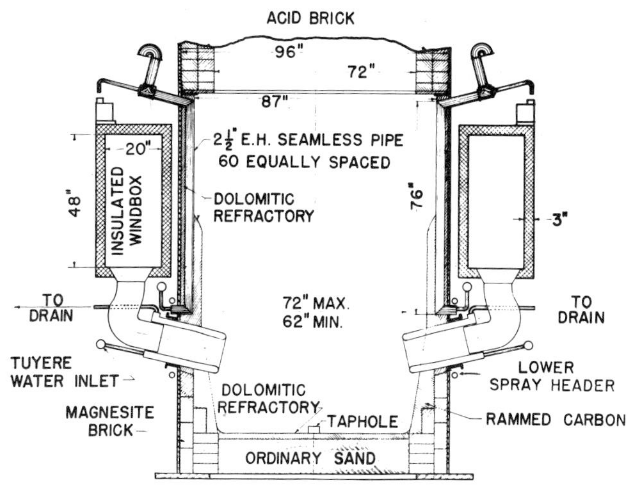

Fig. 3.11. The cooling arrangement in this basic lined cupola is a series of closely spaced water tubes extending upward from the tuyeres. (Lynchburg Foundry Co., Lynchburg, Va.)

distribution there has been good cupola performance. Not requiring windbox supports has eased construction problems.

Other than allowing the use of cheaper material in the metal charge, less refractory consumption and labor costs, and chemical control due to a stabilized melting zone, water cooling permits some existing cupolas to be converted to increase melting rates. Thus increased production has been obtained in the foundry cupola on one shift to offset the necessity of going to two shifts at lower melt rate.

Acid slag operated cupolas, with water cooled shells 700-1000 F (370-540 C) hot blast, deep cupola wells and protruding tuyeres are successfully operated with 60 per cent steel and returns in the carbon ranges of 3.30 to 3.60 per cent; metal temperature of 2800-2900 F (1537-1593 C) in coke ratio 6.5-7.5 to 1. Following a normal pattern coke ratio will increase as steel is reduced.

Internally Water Cooled Cupolas

Internal water cooling can be achieved by using either built-in water jackets or a series of closely spaced water tubes.

Figure 3.10 shows a sectional view of a cupola with built-in water jackets. This construction has been used extensively in Europe in connection with acid as well as basic operation. Experience in this country, however, has indicated that external water cooling is equally effective and simplifies the problem of converting a conventional stack to a water-cooled cupola. In connection with acid practice, the purpose of such water jackets has been primarily to effect economy by minimizing refractory requirements. One such installation, however, has been in use in a British foundry over a period of several years, involving basic operation.[4]

The installation in Fig. 3.11 incorporates a series of closely spaced water tubes extending upward 76 in. from tuyere level.

This cooling arrangement has worked excellently in daily production melting iron for centrifugal castings, as well as the low-sulfur type for manufacture of nodular cast iron.

Details of the operation of this unit are in the Basic Slag Cupola Chapter 26, and Reference[5], W. W. Levi.

Fuel Economics

Additional attempts to improve fuel economics of the cupola have had some success in the United States, Europe and Russia.[6] Articles cover the use of natural gas, and oil injection.

Most of the work follows that in the U.S. Natural gas was used as an auxiliary fuel with coke and as a complete means of melting metal in a cupola. Experiments by the University of Wisconsin indicate results were best when gas was used as an added fuel.

Report of a gas assisted 30 in. cupola[7] shows that gas successfully can be used in an operating cupola with some economical returns (Figs. 3.12, 3.13, 3.14, 3.15).

Injecting oil through tuyeres[8] was done by B.C.I. R.A. on an experimental basis. Loss of temperature, lower carbon levels and lower melting rates occurred in gray iron melt. However, tests conducted on a cupola producing a malleable base iron for duplexing indicated that a coke savings could be obtained.

Fig. 3.12. Cupola equipped with gas burners which operate independent of air for coke. (Ohio Products Co., Orrville, Ohio)

Fig. 3.13. Gas assisted cupola: two air blowers separate air supply for combustion of coke and gas. Each blower has own set of controls.

Fig. 3.14. Gas assisted cupola: front slagger allows slag to stream into drum of water for easy disposal.

Fig. 3.15. Hot iron being poured from receiving ladle in front of gas assisted cupola.

Endeavoring to utilize cheap and abundant steel scrap, experiments were conducted on cold and hot blast conventional cupolas using low air pressure to inject graphite into the melting zone through the tuyeres. Published results[9] indicate good carbon control, with minor loss in temperature and melt rate. Physical properties of the metal followed those of normal carbon equivalent gray iron. Injection rates were varied in order to determine recovery data, rate of carbon increase and control of the injection process.

Results of these tests and others run in the U.S. indicate that 25 to 50 lb of graphite is used per ton of metal. Normal consumption appears to be 25 to 30 lb/ton. As the steel increases in the charge the affinity for the graphite is increased. Thus a high C.E. input in the metallic cupola charger is not conducive to good graphite recovery.

The equipment for graphite injection consists of a pressurized tank containing graphite. Flow meters and pressure gages are incorporated on the tank. A set orifice at the bottom receives graphite from the tank at the rate pressure is metering it out. The graphite enters a rubber hose connected to a lance which enters the cupola tuyeres and extends to the tip of the tuyere.

Chip injectors have been designed for mounting on the cupola to blow cast iron chips into the melting zone. The installation usually is mounted 20 to 36 in. above and between conventional tuyeres. Two or more units have been placed on a cupola. Line pressures from 80-120 lb have been used and the injection interval varied from 8 to 30 sec. Pounds/injection will vary according to size of chips but usually will be 10-20 lb per shot. Injection rates that exceed 10 per cent of the metal charge will produce silicon losses and loss in temperature. Most operators have found extra coke is required for chip injectors. Ten to 20 tons of chips per day have been consumed without affecting the cupola operation or physical properties of the metal.

Computers to determine the metal charge and sequence of charging are available. Only a few foundries are using computers for this purpose.

Many devices indicate charge level height and contribute to better cupola operation and control. These range from nuclear devices, and photoelectric cells to simple mechanical levers.

The special cupolas and the auxiliary equipment decrease metal cost and cupola operating expense. Special cupolas have proved practical and auxiliary equipment is relatively low cost.

REFERENCES

1. D. Fleming, *The Controlled Slag Hot Blast Cupola,* AFS Transactions, vol. 66 (1958) p. 113.
2. E. L. W. Löbbecke, *From Conventional Lined Cupola to Liningless Hot Blast Cupola,* The British Foundryman, vol. 51 (1958) p. 331.
3. R. Doat, M. A. DeBock, *Metallurgical Blast Cupola,* AFS Transactions, vol. 60 (1952) p. 44.
4. E. S. Renshaw, *Basic Cupola Melting and its Possibilities,* AFS Transactions, vol. 59 (1951) p. 20.
5. W. W. Levi, *Melting Iron in a Basic Lined Water Cooled Cupola,* AFS Transactions, vol. 60 (1952) p. 740.
6. G. I. Kletskin et al., Russian Castings Production, January 1961.
7. R. F. Dalton, *Gas Assisted Cupola,* Modern Castings, vol. 44, no. 4 (October 1963) p. 54.
8. H. J. Leyshon, R. B. Coates, *Effect of Injecting Fuel Oil through the Tuyeres of a Cold Blast Cupola,* British Cast Iron Research Association Journal, vol. 10 (1962) p. 181.
9. Leyshon, Coates, K. E. L. Nicholas, *Graphite Injection through the Tuyeres of a Cold Blast Cupola,* B.C.I.R.A. Journal, vol 9 (1961) p. 189.

CHAPTER 4

Mechanical Charging

Many cupolas are still charged by hand. However, more and more foundries are installing mechanical charge make-up and charging equipment because of the advantages and savings to be realized.

No one today wants the job of hand charging the cupola. It is a hard and disagreeable job in winter or summer, rain or shine, snow or hail, and the average workingman today is not looking for that kind of a job. The old-time foundryman believed that hand charging was the best and only way to distribute the stock in the cupola properly.

Today it is difficult to find anyone who is doing a good job of hand charging. Experience has shown that mechanical charging equipment, properly selected to fit the conditions of the foundry, will do a better job of charging.

Great improvements have been made in mechanical charging equipment and charging buckets in recent years. Today there is a wide selection of charging equipment available. It is only necessary to select the equipment best adapted to the conditions of a particular foundry.

COMPLETE MECHANICAL HANDLING

No one type of charging equipment may be considered as providing an optimum solution for ideally serving all charging conditions. The scope of operations, selection of adequate equipment and the physical arrangement of each piece of equipment to provide the most economical and practical installation is a problem that should be handled by a capable foundry engineer.

Mechanical charging operations should be considered as including every step, from the receipt of raw materials in the foundry yard, the procedure for making up and weighing charges, to the final delivery of materials to the cupola. Each move and all handling of material should be accomplished mechanically if at all possible. With a complete mechanical charging system it is possible to make up and charge from 20 to 50 tons of material per hour with a crew of two to three men.

The advantages afforded by complete mechanization of the unloading, storing, weighing, making up and charging operations over the method of manual handling are as follows:

a) Reduces labor requirements:
   A comparison of labor for unloading material from railroad cars by manual labor and by mechanical means is given in the following figures:[1]

Unloading 30-ton car of coke	Man-hours/Ton
Manual labor	0.8
Crane with grab bucket	0.1
Unloading 50-ton car of pig iron	
Manual labor	0.64
Crane with magnet	0.06
Unloading 35-ton car of scrap	
Manual labor	0.69
Crane with magnet	0.057

b) Improves working conditions by:
   1) Eliminating all manual labor on the hot charging deck.
   2) Minimizing manual work in the yard.
c) Provides more favorable conditions for good supervision, and most of the operations may be supervised from the ground level.
d) Eliminates the necessity for an expensive charging deck.
e) Affords more efficient cupola operation with the higher charge level of stock and more uniform and accurately prepared charges.

YARD CRANE AND STOCK YARD

In all mechanized charging systems a yard crane, properly selected to meet the user's requirements, is a necessity. The type most commonly used is a three-motor overhead traveling crane (similar to Fig. 4.1) equipped with a motor-operated grab bucket for unloading coke and limestone, and a magnet for unloading metal and making up metal charges. For small cupolas operating at low tonnage a crane with

Fig. 4.1. Overhead traveling crane used in stock yard for charge make-up.

a relatively short span can be used. It is rarely necessary to exceed an 80-ft span even for the larger sizes of cupolas. Every effort should be made to store all charge ingredients as closely as possible to the make-up hoppers.

In some installations, because of unusual yard conditions or limitations, crawler-type cranes (Fig. 4.2) have been used for yard service. This type of crane is satisfactory for small foundries, but is generally too slow for handling larger tonnages where a fast cycle is required.

In order to have the most practical arrangement of yard facilities, due consideration must be given to the number of men employed, the method of unloading incoming materials, the method of delivering material from the yard to the charging floor, and the amount of coke and metallics carried in storage prior to the proposed mechanization.

In addition to the foregoing items, it is important to have the dimensions of the yard, the location of railroad tracks, all dimensions of the cupolas and cupola buildings and the electric power available for operating the cranes and charging equipment. Careful attention should be given to the layout of unloading and yard storage facilities in order to achieve ease and economy of handling materials.

Raw materials may be stored in the yard in concrete walled bins, in steel hoppers and in open heaps. Figure 4.3 shows a covered yard where scrap is stored in open piles on the ground. Figures 4.4 and 4.5 are partially covered yards where materials are stored in concrete bins.

WEIGHT OF MATERIALS

To aid the operator in determining the amount of space required for storing materials the following information is offered. The weight of pig iron, scrap, coke and limestone varies with the size, section, etc., of each piece. A good average figure to be used for determining charging bucket and weigh hopper sizes is 110 lb/cu ft for metallics, 27 lb/cu ft for coke, and 100 lb/cu ft for limestone.

Where raw materials are unloaded from railroad

Fig. 4.2. Crawler-type cranes are used for yard service in some installations.

Fig. 4.3. Covered stock yard equipped with overhead cranes. Scrap is stored in open piles.

Fig. 4.4. Partially covered yard with concrete bins for material storage.

Fig. 4.5. Overhead crane in partially covered storage area equipped with concrete storage bins.

cars by the magnet and grab bucket and placed in conically shaped piles in the storage yard, the following area requirements should be considered:

Limestone In Open Piles

Weight, tons	Volume, cu ft	Yard Space Required, sq ft
1	20	27
3	60	56.5
5	100	79.5

Coke In Open Piles

Weight, tons	Volume, cu ft	Yard Space Required, sq ft
5	370	177
10	740	284
20	1480	444
30	2220	582

STORAGE FACILITIES

When planning the raw materials storage yard some thought should be given to providing covered storage. The benefits that may be derived from covered storage are:

a) Affords a means of protecting labor during adverse weather conditions.
b) Eliminates loss due to a slow-up of operations that may be caused by adverse weather conditions.
c) Prevents coke and stone from becoming water soaked.

The storage of pig iron and scrap in bins constructed of either steel plate or concrete retaining walls offers some advantages over the system of placing material in unrestricted piles in the open yard. The advantages are:

a) Different grades and classes of materials may be definitely separated and identified for use in making up charges.
b) A better appearance in storage yard is achieved.
c) Less yard area is required.

Before deciding upon the yard storage space needed, a careful study should be made of all the factors that determine the maximum amount of raw materials necessary for uninterrupted production.

These factors are:

a) Proposed tonnage output of finished castings.
b) Maximum rate of stock depletion to meet production requirements.
c) Elapsed time for delivery of raw materials from the supplier's plant to the foundry yard.

For maintaining accurate control of the physical and chemical qualities of cast metals it is recommended that a suitable marking system for identifying grades of pig iron and scrap be adopted. The marking system should be set up so that the different grades of pig iron and scrap and the materials as received in each shipment may be readily identified. The system should also include a record of the quantities of materials on hand.

CHARGE MAKE-UP EQUIPMENT

Many factors must be given consideration before selection of the most practical system of charge make-up is made. The factors to be considered are:

a) Size of cupola.
b) Number of hours the cupola will operate each day.
c) Iron to coke ratio.
d) Physical condition of scrap.
e) Maximum tonnage to be melted each hour.
f) Local conditions such as location of buildings and railroad tracks.
g) Quality of the cast product.
h) Grade and size of largest pieces of scrap.

The facilities required for a fully mechanized charge make-up system may include the main and auxiliary items of equipment indicated in the following list:

a) Loading and trimming platform.
b) Metal weigh hoppers.
c) Coke and limestone weigh hoppers.
d) Scales.
e) Vibrating feeders and screeners.
f) Coke and limestone storage bins.
g) Bucket transfer car.
h) Roller conveyors.

Fig. 4.6. **Iron trimming platform serves to support the metal batch weigh hopper, and as a storage place for stock used to trim the charge.**

Fig. 4.7. **Metal batch weigh hoppers are of heavy construction, and are suspended from hopper suspension scales.**

i) Magnet.
j) Grab bucket.

A description of each of the items of equipment mentioned is given in the following paragraphs.

Loading and Trimming Platforms

A trimming platform serves a dual purpose. It supports the metal batch weigh hopper which weighs all the metal ingredients and serves as a convenient storage place for pig iron and scrap which are used to trim the charge (Fig. 4.6). If an excess of pig iron or scrap is brought up with the magnet, the materials not used are deposited on the trimming platform. If the crane operator has not brought up quite enough material, an additional amount is taken from the platform to make up the desired charge weight. This practice makes it possible to speed up the make-up operation by eliminating the necessity of the crane making another trip to the stock pile for two or three pigs or a few pounds of scrap.

Fig. 4.8. Movable type coke and limestone weigh hopper is mounted on transfer car.

Metal Weigh Hoppers

Metal batch weigh hoppers (Fig. 4.7) are constructed of heavy steel plate, amply reinforced with structural shapes, and are suspended from heavy duty hopper suspension scales. The scale mechanism is designed to withstand the shock of heavy metal pieces dropping from the magnet. Usually a complete metal charge is made up in the hopper and then dropped into the charging bucket, which is stationed directly below the hopper.

It is important to select a hopper that is large enough to hold one complete charge, with a 10 or 15 per cent allowance on the volume to take care of large pieces or a possible future increase in the size of the metal charge. Metal hoppers are usually fitted with a loading funnel to facilitate loading from the magnet, and an apron to direct the charge into the charging bucket, thus eliminating spillage.

It is important also to select a weigh hopper that will discharge the material vertically into the charging buckets in order to obtain the best possible distribution of stock in the cupola. Chute loading devices, where the material is delivered to the bucket by an inclined chute, should be avoided since they tend to load the bucket unevenly.

Fig. 4.9. Suspended type weigh hopper for coke and limestone.

It is recommended that the light bulky scrap material be placed in the hopper first to protect the equipment from the impact of the heavy material.

Coke and Limestone Weigh Hoppers

Coke and limestone weigh hoppers usually are smaller in size and lighter in construction than metal weigh hoppers since they are not required to handle pig iron and scrap. If space permits, it is recommended that separate hoppers be provided for weighing the coke and stone. The weigh hoppers should be of capacities suitable for the job of weighing the charges accurately. The scale dial should be graduated in small increments to make weighing operations more exact.

Coke and limestone hoppers may be stationary or movable. They can be mounted on small transfer cars (Fig. 4.8) or suspended as a lorry (Fig. 4.9). Existing conditions and the duty cycle will determine the most practical arrangement.

Scales

The hopper suspension type scale is most commonly used for mechanized charge make-up systems. Weigh hoppers are suspended from the scale beams for batch weighing. Scales are available in various capacities, and the beams and levers can be made to fit a wide range of hopper sizes. It is extremely important to select a dial large enough so that the crane operator can tell at a glance when the proper amount of any given ingredient has been deposited in the hopper. When vibrating feeders are used for carrying coke and limestone from the storage bins to the weigh hopper, the scale can be equipped with an automatic cut-off device which stops the feeders when the desired weight of material has been delivered to the hopper.

Platform scales are used in some installations where manual charge make-up is employed. Platform scales can be arranged to accommodate wheelbarrows, one or two charging buckets or some type of transfer buggy. Scale platform can be mounted at grade level for use with a wheelbarrow or transfer buggy. Where charging buckets are on the platform and it is desirable to have the top of the bucket at grade level, the platform is placed in a pit below grade.

Many accessories are available to facilitate the charge make-up operation. The dial can be equipped with a light which is helpful if the scale is indoors in a poorly lighted location. Adjustable snap markers can be attached to the dial to facilitate reading of weights. In some cases an additional remote dial is desirable or necessary. A print weigh device which stamps the weight of the charge on a paper ticket or sheet is also available and simplifies the work of recording the weights during the charging operations. A typical hopper scale is in Fig. 4.10.

Fig. 4.10. Typical hopper type scale with snap markers attached to dial to assist in reading weights.

Vibrating Feeders and Screeners

Vibrating feeders are used in some installations for delivering coke and limestone from the storage bins to the weigh hopper. The feeders are actuated by a push button and can be arranged to stop automatically when the desired weight of materials has been delivered to the weigh hopper.

It is common practice to equip the coke feeder with a grizzly to screen the coke and remove particles that are considered too small to go into the cupola. These small particles, commonly called coke breeze, fall through the bars on the grizzly and are directed to a tote box or hopper by means of a chute attached to the feeder. The bars on the grizzly section can be spaced to screen out different size particles, depending on the requirements of the user.

Coke and Limestone Storage Bins

In almost all mechanized make-up and charging systems, coke and limestone storage bins are required. The bins are filled by means of clamshell buckets, or by a system consisting of a track hopper and a belt conveyor or an elevator. The storage bin most commonly used is a two-section bin, in which coke is stored in the larger section and limestone in the smaller section. Separate air or hydraulically operated gates are used at the lower section of the bin to discharge the coke and stone separately in predetermined quantities. Hydraulic gates are recommended because of the possibility of freezing in air lines in some sections of the country.

Multiple bins (Fig. 4.11) are desirable in order to unload and store several carloads of coke without the necessity of storing on the ground and then rehandling, thus causing excessive breakage of coke. In no case should the coke storage capacity be less than 1½ carloads. If the coke and stone storage bin is outside in an open yard, covers should be provided for the bin.

It is worthy of mention at this time that no ideal way has yet been developed for handling coke by mechanical means without incurring a certain amount of breakage. For this reason, some highly mechanized foundries still resort to fork handling of coke.

Bucket Transfer Car and Scale Car

For crane type charging systems, some means must be employed to transport the charging buckets from the make-up area to the pick-up point under the charging crane. An electric motor driven two-bucket transfer car (Fig. 4.12) is used in most installations of this kind. The car is equipped with an operator's platform, and the operator rides with the car and also operates the gates on the weigh hoppers and hooks the bucket onto the hook of the charging crane.

A variety of arrangements is available, but the car described is the most popular. The bucket transfer car can be arranged for remote control, or a gasoline or diesel motor can be used in place of an electric motor. Cars for transporting single buckets are available, but are not generally recommended.

In some make-up systems it is found desirable or convenient to weigh all charged materials on the car, and a scale transfer car (Fig. 4.13) is used for this purpose. The scale employed is similar in de-

Fig. 4.11. Multiple bins for storage of coke and limestone.

sign to the hopper-type scale, and the cabinet and dial are mounted on the car.

The one disadvantage of the scale transfer car is that small metal pieces become lodged under the scale platform and interfere to some extent with the operation of the scale.

Roller Conveyors

In some installations it has been found necessary to use roller conveyors to position the charging buckets. While satisfactory systems of gravity or power-driven conveyors are available, they are generally used only because of unusual yard layouts or dimensional limitations. In most installations, some type of bucket transfer car has been found more suitable. A typical section of roller conveyer is in Fig. 4.14.

Lifting Magnets

Electric lifting magnets are available in round and rectangular shapes and in various lifting capacities. The duty cycle and the size of the opening in the weigh hopper or charging bucket must be considered when selecting the magnet.

Lifting capacities of the various sizes of magnets are shown in the accompanying table.

Electric Lifting Magnets

Diameter, in.	39	45	55	65
Net. Weight, lb	2450	3500	7500	11100
Head Room Required, in.	41	41	53	57
Average Current at 230 Volts	19.5	31	51	73
Generator Capacity Required (KW)	5	10	15	25
Size of Duplex Flexible Cable	No. 8	No. 8	No. 4	No. 4
Average Lifting Capacity, lb				
Billets and Slabs	25,000	38,000	50,000	70,000
Skull Cracker Ball	12,000	16,000	23,000	38,000
Machine Cast Pig from Cars	800	1,420	2,900	4,000
Machine Cast Pig from Stock Pile	875	1,580	3,000	4,400
No. 1 Heavy Melting Steel Scrap	875	1,580	3,000	4,400
No. 2 Melting Steel	650	1,000	1,900	2,800
No. 1 Machinery Scrap, Cast Iron	600	900	1,600	2,300
Cast Iron Borings	600	1,000	1,900	2,900
Steel Turnings	300	450	950	1,700

Coke and Limestone Handling Equipment

Coke is a friable material, and excessively rough, or just excessive handling will result in coke breakage. The extent of the damage done will depend on the type of equipment employed, the frequency with which the coke passes through crushing phases of the system, and the strength of the coke.

Handling coke carefully by hand fork has been disappearing from practice in mechanized foundries. As shown under item a) at the beginning of this chapter, at least eight times as much labor is involved in unloading a car of coke by hand fork as compared to that required when using a yard crane equipped with a grab bucket.

Where cranes are available, the grab bucket represents a very small additional equipment investment, and can be economically used for unloading much of the bulk material received at foundries, including the cupola coke and limestone. If the coke is of average cupola coke strength and handled only once by the grab bucket, breakage has not been considered serious in foundries where this method has been employed for periods of 25 years and longer.

Where coke can be received by container cars and the coke delivered directly to the storage and make-up hoppers by overhead crane, handling costs are low and breakage is held to a minimum (Fig. 4.15).

Track hopper and inclined conveyor belt is another method of handling coke mechanically and economically (Fig. 4.16). Skip buckets and even bucket elevators are sometimes used.

Whatever handling system is employed should be capable also of handling the limestone.

Inasmuch as any mechanical system will cause some coke breakage, it is advisable to provide suitable service hopper capacity and schedule shipments so that rehandling of the coke is unnecessary. Screens for removal of coke fines may be incorporated in most systems.

Fig. 4.13. Gasoline driven transfer car equipped with scale.

Fig. 4.12. Electric motor driven transfer car has capacity for two charging buckets.

Fig. 4.14. Section of power driven roller conveyor used to position charging buckets.

Scrap Sizing Tools

The use of adequate tools for the preparation of scrap is an item that should not be overlooked by the operator.

A skull cracker for handling by the crane magnet to break up the large pieces of scrap, and a shear or oxyacetylene apparatus for cutting the large pieces of steel scrap to a size suitable for charging are tools that should be included with the charge make-up equipment.

CHARGE MATERIALS

With mechanical charging, as in hand charging, it is extremely important that all materials to be charged be carefully selected for size and analysis, and that all materials be accurately weighed. It is recommended that a record be made of the weight of all materials that go into the charge. A typical cupola melting log appears as Fig. 20.8. It is common practice to weigh all the metal in the charge in one weigh hopper, and the coke and stone in a separate hopper. Generally speaking, all materials are placed in one charging bucket for delivery to the cupola charging opening.

TYPES OF CHARGING BUCKETS

Importance of Bucket Design

Probably the most important single item in a mechanical charging system is the charging bucket. There are several different types of charging buckets available to meet any condition and to handle almost any size material. Careful consideration should be given to the selection of the charging bucket in order to achieve the best possible results, both from the standpoint of handling materials economically and obtaining the best possible metallurgical control over the melting process in the cupola.

The types of charging buckets generally in use are:

a) Side dump skip bucket.
b) Single leaf hinged bottom bucket.
c) Double leaf hinged bottom bucket.
d) Cone bottom bucket.

Fig. 4.15. Coke containers are handled directly from car to storage and make-up hoppers.

Types of buckets are described in the following paragraphs.

1. Side Dump Bucket (Fig. 4.17)

Advantages:

a) Can do a fair job of distributing the charge in small cupolas.
b) Practically any type or size of scrap can be charged.
c) The vertical or inclined skip using the side dump type bucket is less expensive than other types of chargers.

Disadvantages:

a) Coke and metal charges will be thrown to the far side of the cupola, causing the charge to pile higher on one side. This condition results in blast channeling and the impact of the charge against the lining tends to be destructive.
b) Small sized materials, like the limestone, segregate and tend to drop off the discharge end of the bucket and concentrate on the near side of the cupola. This segregation creates excessive fluxing of the lining on that side and increases the tendency for bridging at the tuyeres on the far side.

2. Leaf Hinged Bottom Buckets (Fig. 4.18)

The single and double leaf hinged bottom charging buckets are widely used for cupola charging where large size metal scrap makes it necessary to have a bucket with a full open bottom.

Advantages:

a) Full volume capacity for any given size of bucket.
b) Manual labor is not required to hook and unhook the bucket from the skip carriage.
c) There is no stem interference with the scrap and pig delivery to the bucket by the make-up magnet.
d) Gives more uniform distribution of charge material than the side-dump bucket.

Disadvantages:

a) It is possible that the latch may be tripped accidentally and the full load be prematurely discharged.
b) The entire charge is suddenly dropped from

Fig. 4.16. Track hopper and inclined conveyor belt handle coke to storage hopper.

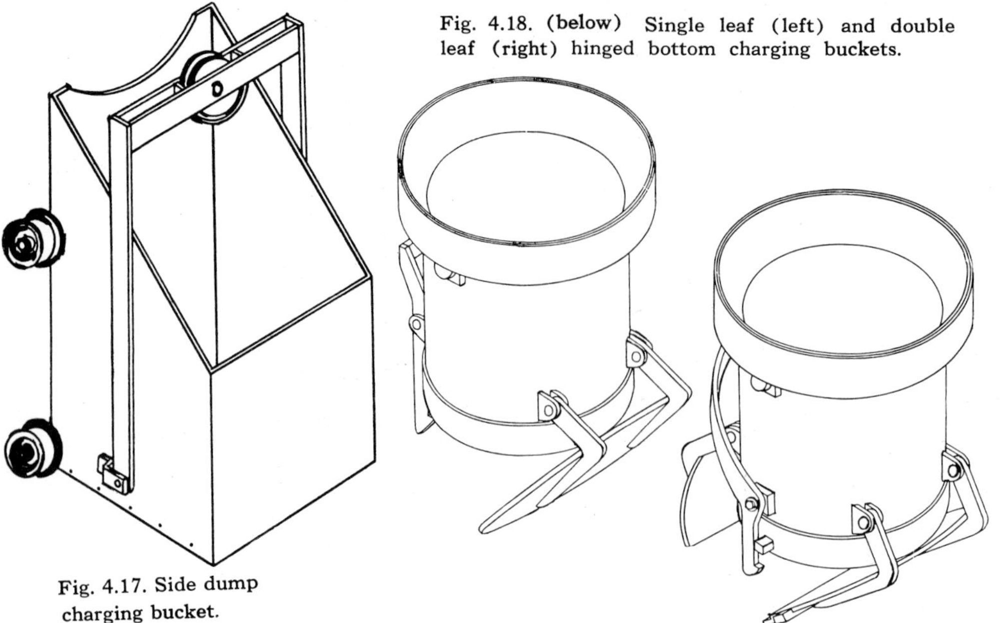
Fig. 4.17. Side dump charging bucket.

Fig. 4.18. (below) Single leaf (left) and double leaf (right) hinged bottom charging buckets.

the charging door level with considerable impact and possible damaging effect on the bed coke.

c) A tendency to pack the charge tightly at the center of the stack and loosely around the circumference, thus permitting a blast channeling around the cupola lining.

3. Cone Bottom Bucket

The cone bottom type of charging bucket is generally preferred over all other methods of charge handling where the size of material can be controlled, and for most efficient cupola operation.

4. Full Cone Bottom Bucket (Fig. 4.19)

Advantages:

a) This type of bucket does an excellent job of distributing the stock in the cupola. The charge is tight around the circumference of the cupola and more open in the center. This results in better penetration of the blast and more uniform melting across the entire area of the cupola. The cone bottom bucket does a job mechanically that formerly was accomplished by the best hand charging practice.

b) The cone bottom bucket, in common with several other types, can be discharged in a very simple manner by using a wishbone shaped casting (Fig. 4.20) attached to the shell of the cupola. It is only necessary for the crane man to place the bucket on the wishbone casting and lower the cone. No latches or trip lines are employed.

c) The load is suspended from the bottom, which means there is no chance of premature discharge of the stock. This is an important safety feature.

d) The charging crane operator can dribble the stock from the bucket by moving the cone up and down; or with a hydraulically controlled cone bottom skip hoist bucket, the speed at which the cone is lowered can be adjusted.

e) This type of bucket can be used with stationary and swivel type skip hoists (Fig. 4.19) as well as various types of crane chargers.

Disadvantages:

a) The stem in the center of the bucket attached to the top of the cone interferes to some extent with the delivery of some kinds of material into the bucket with magnet loading.

b) The diameter of the bucket must be sufficiently less than the inside diameter of cupola at the charging door to allow space for discharging the materials.

c) The volume of the cone itself represents a loss in capacity of the charging bucket.

d) Tangled scrap and large pieces do not have free delivery from the cone bottom bucket.

e) When material is discharged from the cone bottom bucket it impinges on the sides of the cupola, which is necessarily somewhat hard on the lining at the charging zone. This is usually cared for by installing 4 to 6 ft of cast iron blocks at the charging location.

Perhaps the disadvantage listed under d) should really be classed as an advantage because it must be admitted that any piece of scrap which will not discharge readily through the cone bottom bucket should not be charged in the cupola. All particular operators recognize that good cupola operation makes it desirable, and in most cases imperative, that the larger pieces of scrap be broken before they are charged in the cupola.

In view of the popularity of the cone bottom charging bucket, a description of the manner in which the bucket is supported in the cupola is considered appropriate.

The bucket is supported by the wishbone or forked shaped casting, illustrated in Fig. 4.20. The wishbone rests on brackets located at several points at a predetermined distance above the charging opening sill. The cone bottom bucket is provided with a projecting flange around the top which comes to rest on

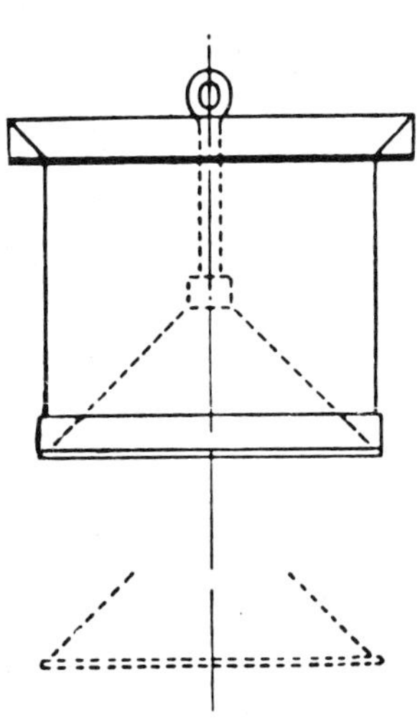

Fig. 4.19. Full cone bottom controlled charging bucket diagram (above) and used with skip hoist (left).

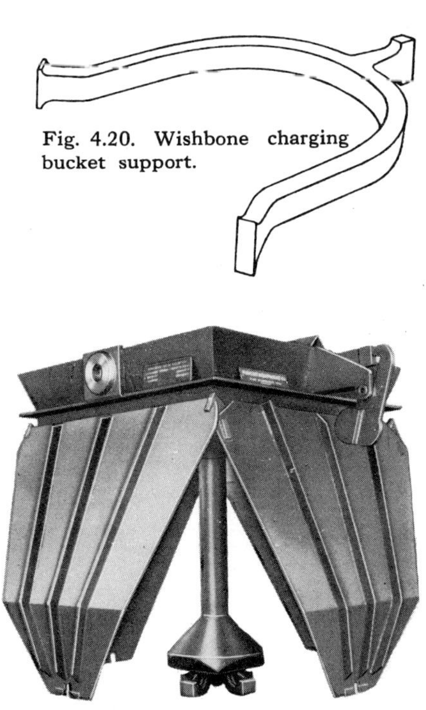

Fig. 4.20. Wishbone charging bucket support.

Fig. 4.21. Small cone orange peel bucket. The four doors normally closed are in open position to show details of the cone and steel spider.

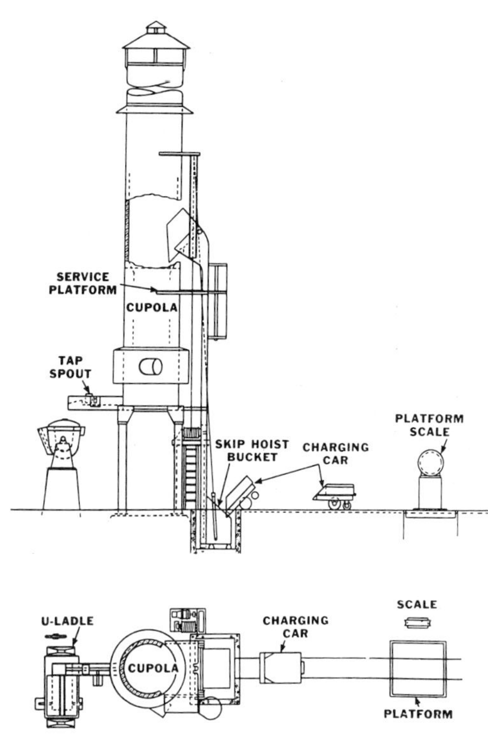

Fig. 4.22. Vertical skip hoist with side discharge bucket.

the wishbone when the bucket is delivered into the cupola and lowered into position for discharging by the crane operator.

5. Orange Peel Bucket (Fig. 4.21)

This small cone bucket with its four orange peel type doors combines the good features of bottom drop and cone type buckets to make it practical for charging the large diameter cupola.

As the doors swing open from the four sides, large pieces – cylinder blocks, piston ring sprues, bailed scrap and other bulky materials – clear readily and spread evenly.

MECHANICAL CHARGING EQUIPMENT

The first mechanical equipment consisted of four-wheeled cars which were loaded by hand in the stock yard and pushed by two or three men to an elevator which raised the cars to the charging floor. At this level two or three other men pushed the car to the cupola where an electric, pneumatic or hydraulic mechanism raised the rear end of the car and allowed the charge materials to spill into the cupola. As demands for increased production grew it was necessary to speed up the charging operation, and out of the early and rather crude methods several types of improved equipment have been developed. Today this equipment is classified under two general types: skip-hoist and crane-type chargers.

SKIP TYPE CHARGERS

Skip type chargers may be divided into five general types:

1) Vertical skip with side discharge bucket.
2) Inclined skip with side discharge bucket.
3) Stationary inclined skip hoist.
4) Swivel type inclined skip hoist.
5) Heavy duty skip with charging cars.

1) *Vertical Skip Hoist with Side Discharge Bucket*

The vertical skip hoist is the least expensive of all cupola chargers and is used principally for small cupolas. This is the simplest of all mechanical systems. In this unit there is one bucket which is part of the machine, and is raised and lowered by a cable attached to an electric hoist. The bucket is mounted on wheels which travel on a vertical track, curved at the top so that the bucket is automatically tilted forward when it reaches the charging door and its contents dumped into the cupola.

The bucket may be filled at floor level by means of wheelbarrows, mechanical loader, or by hand. The usual practice is to place the iron charges first, then the coke and flux material, with the result that all materials are thoroughly mixed when they reach the melting zone. Figure 4.22 shows a typical setup.

2) *Inclined Skip with Side Discharge Bucket*

The inclined skip hoist is illustrated in Fig. 4.23. Basically, the design and function of the inclined skip hoist is similar to that of the vertical skip except that the structural runway is in an inclined position. The track is inclined to permit operation of the charger under conditions where installation of a vertical charger is not possible. For example, the space at the rear of the cupola may be needed for work associated with cupola operation, or space immediately back of the cupola is occupied by a building or other plant facilities that cannot conveniently be removed.

3) *Stationary Inclined Skip Hoist with Bottom Discharge Bucket*

This type of skip is designed to serve the larger sizes of cupolas, and consists of an inclined structural track which is fitted with a bucket carriage to carry the charging bucket from the loading point to the

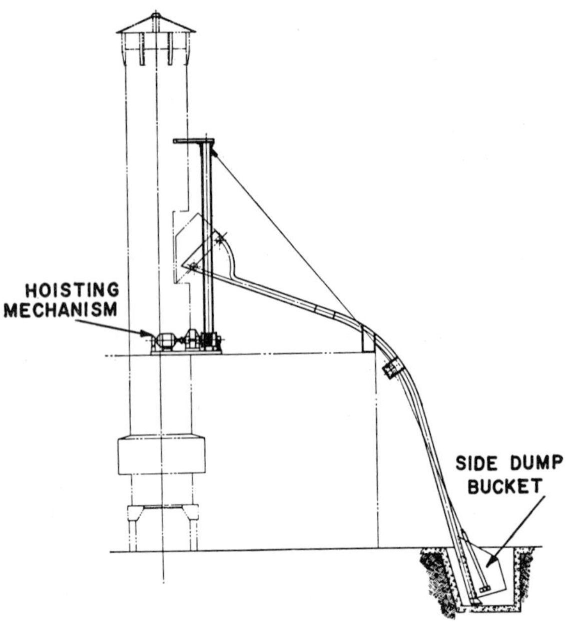

Fig. 4.23. Inclined side dump skip charger.

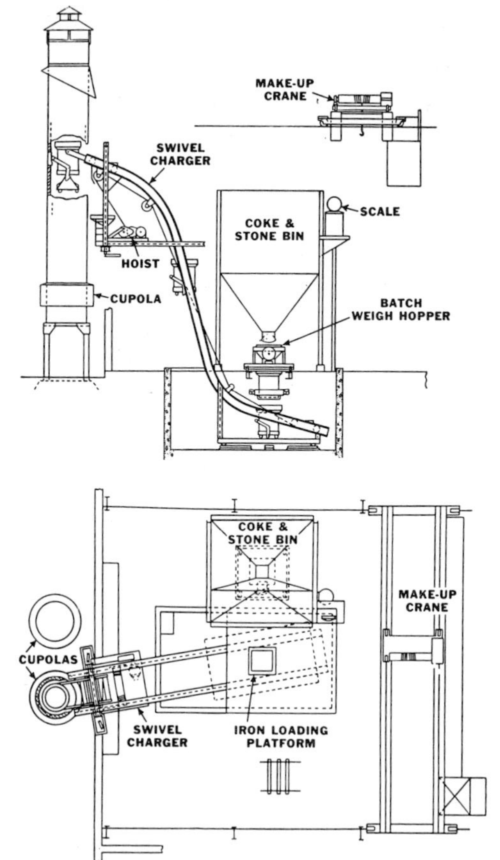

Fig. 4.24. Swivel type inclined skip hoist charger.

charging opening. The angle of incline of the track is governed by the distance from the loading point to the cupola. With this type of charger the loading point can be out in the stock yard under the crane runway, and the cupolas can be inside of the building.

The span of this type charger usually varies from 40 to 100 ft, depending on existing conditions. Buckets may be either double leaf or single leaf quick-release type, or full cone bottom hydraulically controlled discharge type. A bucket closing device automatically closes and latches the bottom of the bucket as it returns for the next charge under the charge make-up hopper. The lower end of the charger track may be set at grade level, or in a pit below grade depending on the space available above the charge make-up and trimming platform.

4) *Swivel Type Inclined Skip Hoist with Bottom Discharge Bucket*

The inclined swivel type skip hoist (Fig. 4.24) is of the same design as the stationary type except that it is pivoted at the lower end, and designed so that the upper end swivels on a curved track to serve two, three or more cupolas. Swiveling from one cupola to another may be either manual or electric powered; and when electric powered, the push button control can be provided with an automatic indexing arrangement, which will permit charging any two cupolas in simultaneous operation.

5) *Special Heavy Duty Skip Hoist*

The heavy duty skip hoist (illustrated in Fig. 4.25) is used where heavy and unusual types of scrap are to be charged. The charger consists of a structural inclined runway, elevator platform on which rails are mounted, a heavy charging car and hoisting mechanism. The charging car is loaded in the yard, pushed onto the platform and securely locked to the rails. The elevator platform tips through an angle of about 90 degrees when it reaches the top of the runway, discharging the material over the lip of the car and into the cupola. This type of charger serves one cupola and is being used successfully in car wheel foundries. This type of charger is also used for large diameter cupolas in special steel mill duplexing operations where large tonnages are handled.

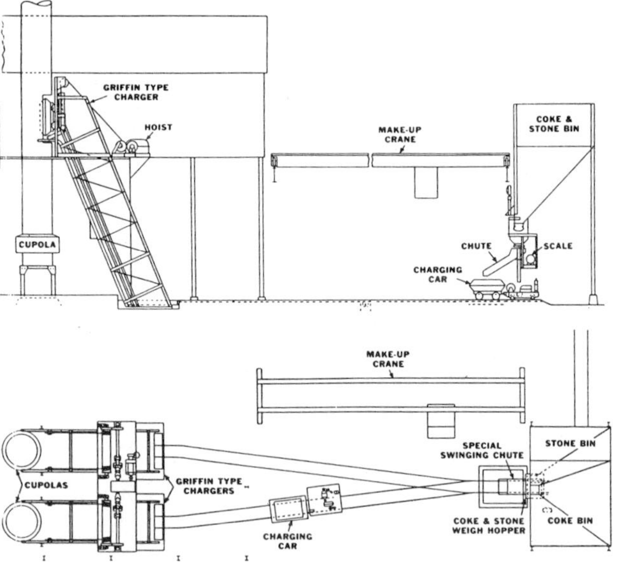

Fig. 4.25. Special heavy duty skip charger.

CRANE TYPE CHARGERS

This general classification covers a variety of forms all based on the use of bottom discharge buckets. Crane type chargers are available to suit almost any existing condition. The most popular type of bucket used with crane chargers is the full cone bottom type, which has an extended rim at the top of the bucket that rests on a wishbone shaped bucket support in the cupola. The outer shell is supported by the wishbone and the cone bottom is lowered, allowing the charge to dribble out. With this arrangement a single hoist is used. If a double hoist is used, one line carries or supports the bucket, while the other holds the bucket bottom closed during travel and opens the bucket bottom after arrival at the discharge position. A wishbone support is not required

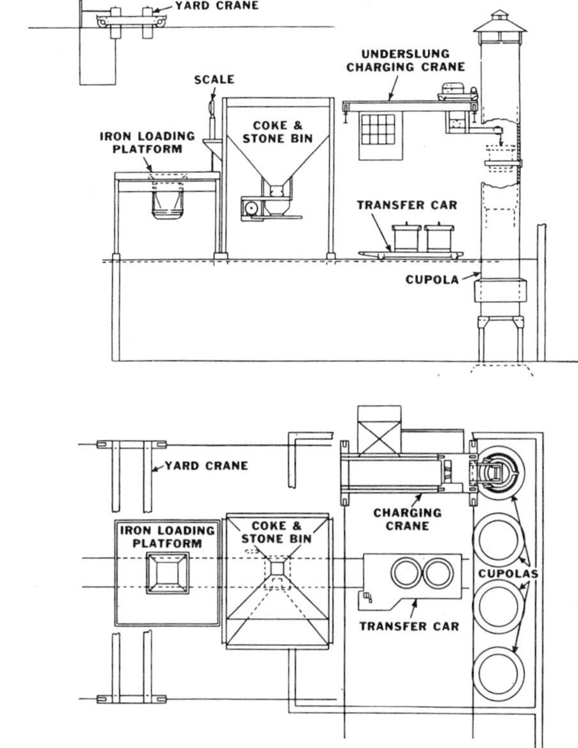

Fig. 4.26. **Underslung type crane charging system.**

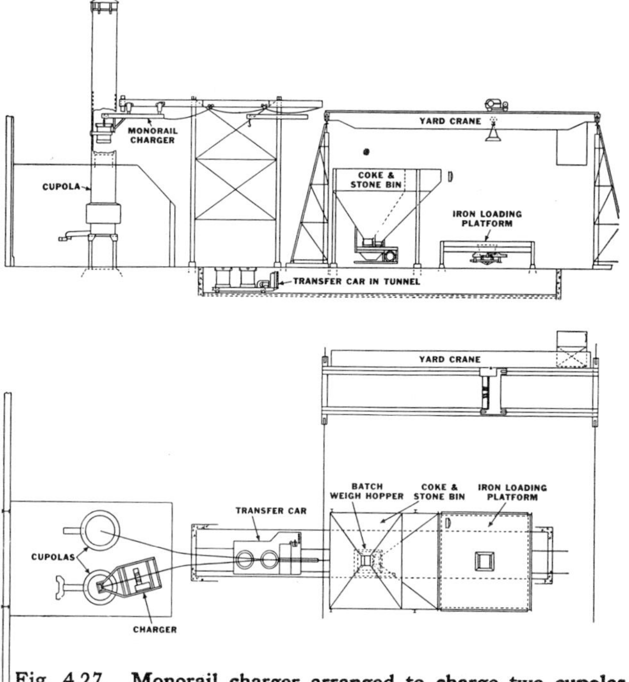

Fig. 4.27. **Monorail charger arranged to charge two cupolas.**

when a double hoist is used on the charging crane.

Crane type charging equipment is available in many forms and permits considerable choice to suit the specific requirements of any given job. In general they may be classed as follows:

1) Underslung type
2) Monorail type
3) Horseshoe type
4) Gantry type
5) Jib crane type
6) Overhung type

1) *Underslung Type*

This equipment operates on a runway parallel to the cupolas at a height just clearing the charging doors. It may be used to service any number of cupolas.

While the cone bottom bucket is generally used, this type of charger design is sufficiently flexible to permit the use of many types of buckets or combinations of different types.

In charging the crane bridge is aligned with the cupola (Fig. 4.26), and the bucket is carried into the charging door on a boom attached to the trolley. This boom reaches into the cupola under the crane runway girder.

Underslung chargers are the most popular of all crane types because of their flexibility, permitting them to be adapted to a wide variety of conditions.

2) *Monorail Type*

This type of charger travels on a monorail track from the cupola to the make-up point in the yard below. Switches in the track permit this type of charger to serve more than one cupola (Fig. 4.27). The track may be straight or curved, as desired, when the loading point is not in a direct line with the charging opening. With this type of charger the loading or pick-up point can be in close to the cupola or at some remote point in the yard.

3) *Horseshoe Type*

The horseshoe type charger shown in Fig. 4.28 was developed to serve a single cupola, and has all the advantages of crane type charging. It is readily adapted to unusual building conditions, and where the make-up point is at considerable distance from the cupola. This charger operates on a fixed narrow-

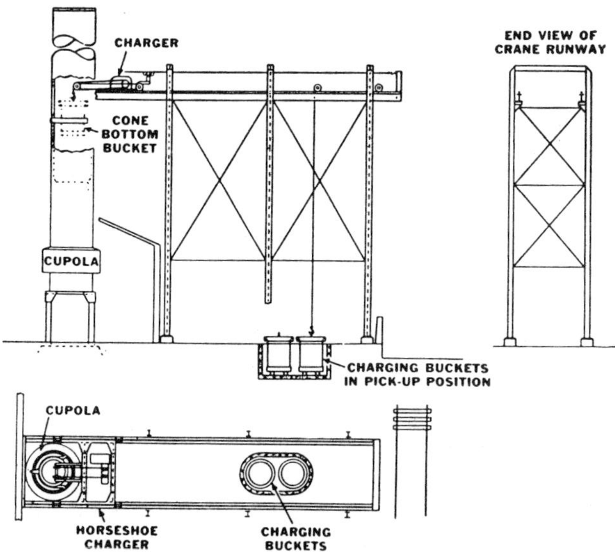

Fig. 4.28. **Horseshoe type crane charging system.**

gage runway, and the operation is usually controlled from a remote control station.

It uses cone bottom buckets in most cases, although other types of bottom discharge buckets can be employed.

4) *Gantry Type Chargers*

The gantry type shown in Fig. 4.29 was developed for use where headroom is limited—usually on an existing charging floor. It generally employs cone bottom buckets, but has the flexibility of crane type chargers, permitting the use of other types of bottom discharge buckets. With this type charger the charging buckets are hoisted from the pick-up point at grade level through a wall in the charging floor.

5) *Jib Crane Type*

A jib crane charger, shown in Fig. 4.30, may serve either one of two cupolas. It has a motorized hoist,

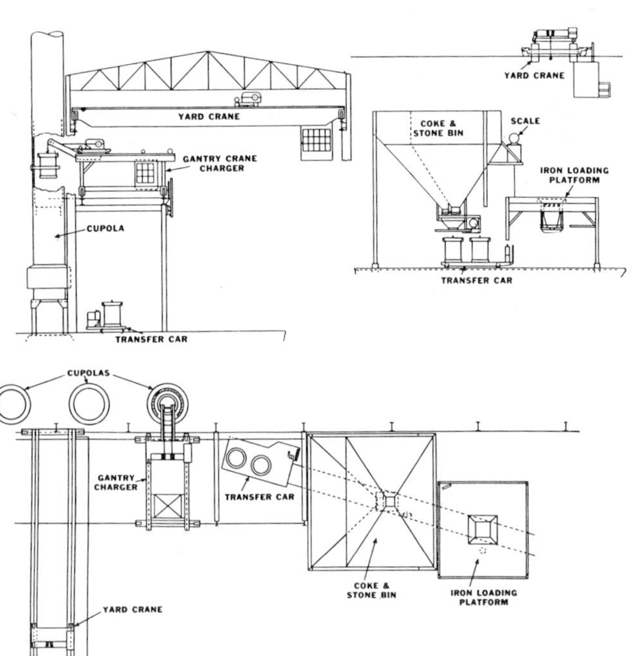

Fig. 4.29. **Gantry crane type charging system.**

and most units have a motorized slewing mechanism to swing the bucket into the cupola after the bucket has been elevated.

This type of charger is usually the least expensive of the crane type, but is the most difficult to control accurately because of the momentum of the loaded bucket being suspended from an extended boom.

6) *Overhung Type Chargers*

The overhung type crane charger (Fig. 4.31) like the underslung type can serve two or more cupolas. This type of charger is applied where the crane runway is relatively low. The overhung boom brings the bucket in over the crane rail, thus making it possible to gain additional height for the cupola charging door sill.

Other special arrangements of crane type chargers are available, but they are special in nature and are designed especially to fit very unusual conditions. For example, in a few special cases a combination charging and yard crane is used. This unit has two trolleys, or a single special trolley with a double hoist. One hoist is used for the magnet to make up charges, and the other is used to handle the charging bucket. A unit of this kind will fit certain special conditions only where an extended duty cycle is used, since it is obvious that a charge must be made up and deposited in the cupola before the next charge can be prepared.

A feature that has been used in a few crane charger installations is the retractable wishbone, which is a bucket support attached to the crane rather than the cupola. The retractable wishbone is controlled from the crane cab and is extended under the flanges of the bucket after the bucket has been raised to its highest point. The use of this unit avoids continuous exposure of the wishbone to the cupola heat.

GENERAL

Charging cranes are usually equipped with control cabs, but they can be designed for push-bottom operation from a remote control station. A cab is strongly recommended because it will enable the operator to see what is happening when the bucket is discharged and to speed up the charging operation.

In a few installations the crane charger has been arranged for complete automatic control from a single push button. At this writing automatic operation of charging cranes is in the pioneering stage.

DISCUSSION

From time to time ideas are advanced for the control of the blast in a cupola. Some of these ideas involve the use of specially designed tuyeres; others deal with windbox design.

Actually, if the problem is given a little thought it will be apparent that the blast will travel the line of least resistance, and since the actual resistance to

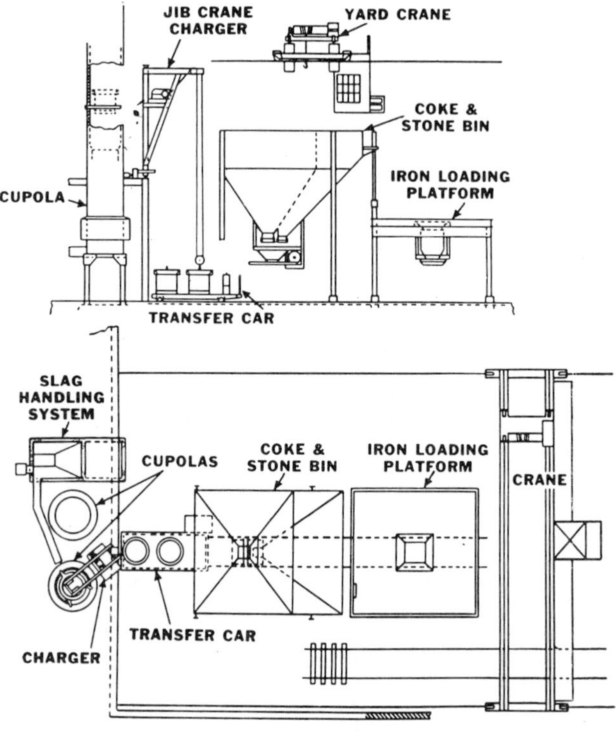

Fig. 4.30. **Jib crane charging system may serve one or two cupolas.**

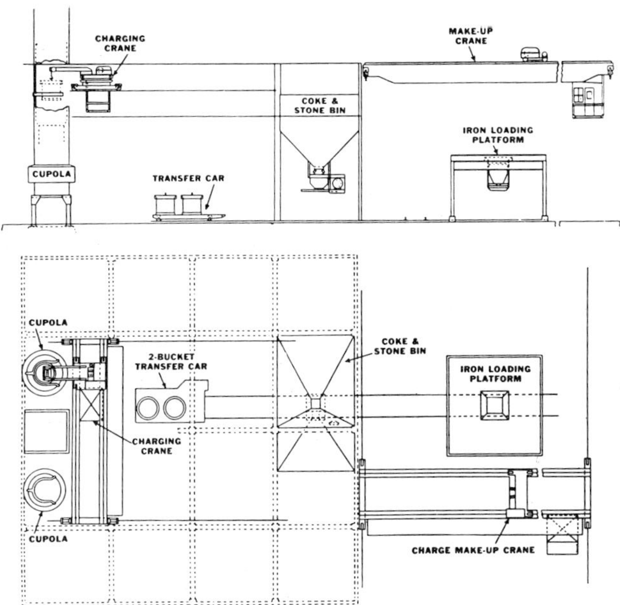

Fig. 4.31. **Charging system with overhung type crane.**

the blast is the coke bed and the super-imposed charges of metal and coke, it follows that the proper distribution of these materials within the cupola, promoting uniform resistance, will result in the most uniform blast distribution and most uniform melting rate over the full cross section of the cupola.

By proper distribution of the charging stock is meant concentration of the least permeable material uniformly around the cupola next to the lining, with the lighter, more open material in the center. The object of this is to induce better penetration by the blast and to prevent channeling of the blast at the lining, in this way causing more uniform flow of the blast and hot gases across the full cross section of the cupola.

Blast furnace operators have recognized this fact for years, and realize that to obtain this uniform flow or distribution of the hot gases they must charge their furnaces uniformly dense at furnace wall or lining, with increasing permeability toward the center of the stack. Hence the development and almost universal application of the rotating top for blast furnaces.

Proper distribution of charged materials in a cupola can be accomplished by mechanical means. Careful study and consideration should be given to the selection of make-up and charging equipment to achieve the best possible results.

ACKNOWLEDGMENT

Photographs and drawings of cupola charging equipment were provided through the courtesy of the Whiting Corp., Harvey, Ill., and the Grindle Corp., also of Harvey, Ill.

REFERENCES

1. Gregg, A. W., "Mechanization for the Small Foundry," *Foundry,* August, 1948.

2. The Electric Controller & Mfg. Co., Cleveland, Ohio, Bulletin No. 900.

3. Whiting Corp., Harvey, Ill., Bulletin 237R

4. Publication by American Iron & Steel Institute, New York.

CHAPTER 5

Forehearths
Ladles

FOREHEARTHS

A forehearth is any vessel interposed between the cupola spout and the distributing or pouring ladle. In a broad sense there are two types, namely, the non-tilting type and the tilting type. There is a variety of designs for each of the two types. The most common and presently popular name for the forehearth is a mixing ladle. However, this name is misleading because the forehearth is used to perform other functions also, which will be mentioned later in this chapter.

NON-TILTING FOREHEARTHS

The non-tilting type forehearth is disappearing from the foundry scene rather rapidly, primarily because it is not as flexible as the tilting type. In view of the fact that there are few non-tilting types in use, only a brief description will be offered.

In design the non-tilting forehearth is usually either a round vertical shell, or a box type with vertical sides. The vessel is refractory lined, and a refractory lined cover can be employed to retain the heat. Because it does not tilt, a fixed connection to the cupola can be made by means of the cupola spout.

The metal can be slagged in the cupola proper, the cupola spout, or the forehearth. Slag spouts are provided at the point of slag removal. Generally the tap hole is located at the bottom to assure clean metal. With the addition of an internal dam, to facilitate continuous tapping or desulfurizing, the metal flow-off channel is located at the top metal line. In this event a draining spout must be provided to drain the metal at the end of a particular operating cycle (Figs. 5.1 and 5.2).

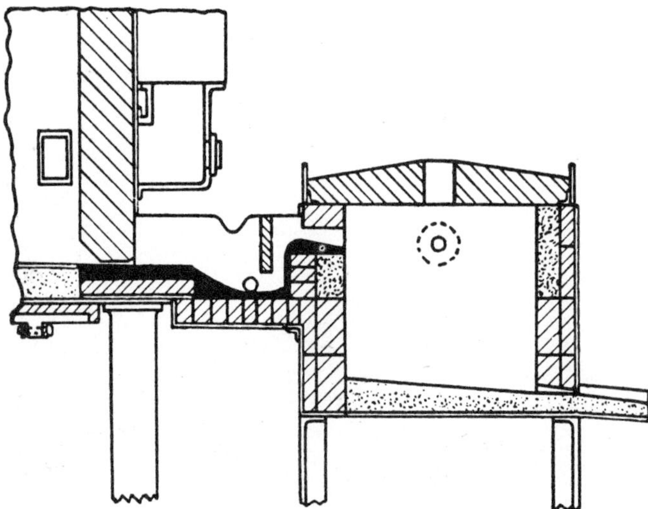

Fig. 5.1. **Sectional view of cupola forehearth arranged for continuous flow of iron from cupola, with separation of slag and intermittent tapping from forehearth.**

TILTING FOREHEARTHS

The popular forehearth is of the tilting type. The means for tilting can be a forked shank operated by hand (now out-moded and generally considered unsafe), or a gearing, usually the worm and worm-wheel arrangement, for hand operation. Electric motors and hydraulic cylinders have been adapted to do the tilting mechanically.

Tilting forehearths generally follow three designs. The least used is the elliptical shaped having straight vertical sides; the oldest design is the round type with either tapered or straight sides, with the greatest shell dimension being in the vertical direction; the most popular is the round bottom type with straight horizontal lines, and the greatest shell dimension being in the horizontal direction. The latter is divided into two groups; namely, the cylindrical forehearth and the U-shaped forehearth.

The elliptical, straight sided or tapered sided may be covered, but usually are not because it is difficult to maintain an opening through which metal can flow continually. The cylindrical and the U-shaped always are covered to reduce radiation losses from the surface of the metal.

Tilting type forehearths are equipped with teapot spouts whereby the metal is drawn from the bottom, insuring clean metal. Draining spouts are not re-

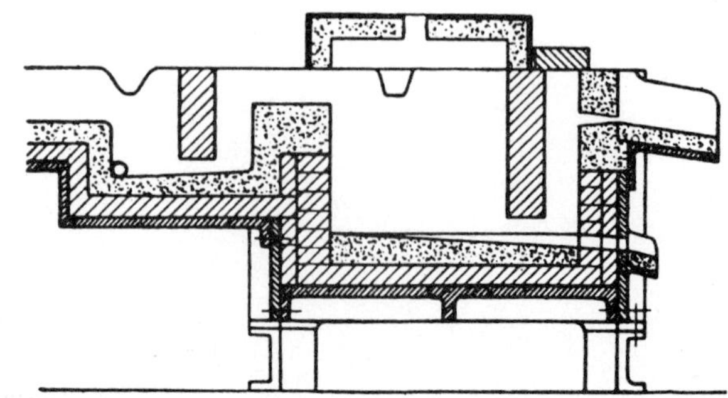

Fig. 5.2. **Sectional view of cupola forehearth arranged for continuous flow of iron from cupola with slag separation and continuous delivery of iron at forehearth spout.**

quired because the forehearth can be tilted forward so that all of the metal can be drained. Slag notches are usually provided.

Nearly all present-day applications of the forehearth employ either the cylindrical or the U-shaped design. Of the two, the cylindrical is stronger structurally because the tops of the sides are part of the cylinder and cannot spread as easily as the straight sides of the U-shaped design. The U-shape is less difficult to line.

Suspension Method

The most common method of suspending the tilting forehearth is to place the trunnions into bearings connected to stands. These stands can be fastened directly to the floor, in which case the forehearth cannot be moved and is repaired in place.

Many times the stands are fastened to a truck equipped with wheels operating on an industrial track, so that one forehearth can serve one or more cupolas, or it can be moved to one side for repair (Fig. 5.3).* In more recent applications the stands have been mounted on skids so that an overhead crane or a fork lift truck can place the forehearth in a relining or repair area away from the cupola. Some forehearths are suspended from overhead members. While this does not allow for removal, operators are easily able to keep the floor clean.

Lining

Judgment must be used as to the thickness of the lining, considering heat losses and the amount of metal passing through the forehearth.

For smaller tonnages a minimum of 4 in. of lining, including insulation, would suffice. For heavy daily tonnages and long heats a maximum of 11 in., including the insulation, would be advantageous. Rammed linings have been reported to give longer life because the elimination of joints reduces the area for attack and erosion. Lining life can vary greatly depending on the type of refractory used, the care with which it is installed, dried and preheated prior to service, temperature of metal and the frequency of ladle use. A service life of 8000 to 12,000 tons in 3 to 4 months is possible with daily patching. A sharp decrease in lining life may be expected when desulfurizing is practiced.

Preheating

A thorough preheating to about the operating temperature is very important. The length of preheat time will depend on the fuel used, capacity and position of burner, and thickness of lining. A heavily lined ladle will require more preheating than one with less lining. The time may vary anywhere from 1½ to 3½ hr.

The simple portable type torch is usually inserted through the metal-receiving opening. Many times this is removed too soon before the metal is tapped from the cupola, and much heat is lost from the lining. It is advisable to have burners mounted permanently on the ladle in such a position they will not interfere with the flow of the metal. The flame can then be left burning until the ladle is nearly full. After a forehearth has been filled and is thoroughly heated the metal drop through it varies from 50 to 100 degrees (Fig. 5.4).

In recent years a few tilting forehearths, usually with shallow baths, have been equipped with pulverized coal burners in order to hold a uniform temperature, and also to keep the temperature drop to an absolute minimum. This type of fuel and burner preheats the ladle and remains burning throughout the melting operation.

Much effort and money is spent melting the metal so that it leaves the cupola spout at high temperature. Improper preheating of the forehearth and insufficient lining will lose this temperature very rapidly. Reduced temperature at the forehearth spout reduces the effective pouring time, thereby increasing pouring costs. It is important, therefore, that sufficient thought be given to the proper selection of forehearths.

FOREHEARTH FUNCTIONS

The functions of the forehearths are to:

a) Serve as a means of evening out metal composition (mixing).
b) Serve for temporary storage of metal (holding).
c) Permit an intermediate treatment of metal, (desulfurizing).

Either the non-tilting or tilting type forehearth can perform the foregoing functions. The cylindrical

Fig. 5.3. U-shaped forehearth mounted on truck.

Fig. 5.4. Burners for preheating are permanently mounted in forehearth cover.

Fig. 5.5. Straight sided, geared, covered and insulated distributing ladle pouring into tapered, covered pouring ladle.

* Illustrations in this chapter were provided through courtesy of Modern Equipment Co., and other sources.

and the U-shaped forehearths in the tilting group are the best suited. The reason for this is that the metal enters the top at one end and leaves the bottom at the other end through the teapot spout. The fact that the metal moves from one end to the other and from the top to the bottom insures mixing action, which is desirable for desulfurizing and also for mixing or evening out the composition of the metal.

Mixing

In order to properly carry out the first function, namely, evening out metal composition, the forehearth should hold approximately a 15-min supply of metal, or ¼ of the hourly melting rate of the cupola. Six minute's holding capacity is about the minimum, and advised only when very light castings must be poured at relatively high temperatures. For heavy castings and lower pouring temperatures forehearths may hold as much as a 30-min supply. The metal from a group of charges will mix to give uniformity. If desired, this forehearth can also be used for the addition of alloys which are usually placed into the molten stream in the cupola spout. This type of forehearth is also called a mixing ladle.

Holding

The capacity of the forehearth required to serve for temporary storage of metal depends entirely on local conditions. The pouring requirements may not be uniform or the metal distributing time may vary. The cupola melting rate could vary. The effect these variations have on a smooth operation can be minimized or eliminated. The amount of the variations will determine the size required for sufficient capacity to allow constant melting under varying metal distributing and pouring conditions. This type of forehearth is also referred to as a holding ladle.

Desulfurizing

The thickness of lining and capacity are important when selecting equipment to perform the third function, namely, permit an intermediate treatment of metal, such as desulfurizing. The amount of sulfur reduction required and the amount of desulfurizing material such as soda ash used certainly must be considered and, of course, may vary. It is a safe rule to allow a 12-min holding time for efficient desulfurizing practice. A forehearth for this purpose is usually referred to as a desulfurizing ladle.

In general, the forehearth, whether it be a non-tilting or tilting type, lends itself to continuous tapping from the cupola and attendant continuous slagging, both of benefit from an operating standpoint.

LADLES

A ladle is any vessel in which molten metal can be conveyed, or from which it can be poured into other ladles, molds, ingots or pigs. The two purposes for which ladles are used are distributing and pouring.

The distributing ladle receives its metal either directly from a cupola spout or from the spout of a forehearth. From there the metal is conveyed to and poured into pouring ladles.

A pouring ladle is any ladle used to pour metal into molds, ingots, etc. (Fig. 5.5).

Conveying Metal

The pouring ladle does not necessarily receive its metal from a separate distributing ladle. In the event that only small molds are to be poured, and the pouring areas are close to the melting unit, small pouring ladles may receive molten iron directly from the cupola or forehearth. For smaller molds hotter metal must be poured, and the elimination of an extra metal transfer from a distributing ladle is desirable.

Whenever the molds to be poured are sufficiently large to require a large pouring ladle, it is not uncommon for the pouring ladle to be taken from the pouring area to receive its metal directly from either the cupola or forehearth.

In small and medium sized jobbing foundries it is general practice to serve pouring ladles up to about 600-lb capacity with hand pushed distributing ladles carrying a maximum of about 1200 lb of metal. The capacity of the distributing ladle may vary. If at all possible the capacity of the distributing ladles should be in even multiples of the pouring ladles to be served so that part of the metal will not have to be pigged or taken back to the cupola. The size of the distributing ladle is governed by the amount a man can push on an overhead monorail, usually about 1200 lb under favorable operating conditions. It requires about one minute to push such a ladle 200 ft.

In large and highly mechanized foundries where there is a greater demand for metal, overhead cranes or electric hot-metal carriers convey large distributing ladles. The ladle size is governed by the ability of pouring ladles to take metal from the large distributing ladles. For general snap-flask molds the metal should not be held over 3 to 7 min from the time the ladle leaves the cupola or forehearth spout until the last metal is poured into the pouring ladle. When large castings are poured this holding time can be increased.

There are three basic types of ladles:

1. Straight sided
2. Tapered side (usually called tapered ladles)
3. Cylindrical (Fig. 5.6).

In addition to the basic type, choice must be made of these features in ladle equipment:

1) Spout or pouring method—
   a. Conventional pouring lip (seldom used on cylindrical ladles).
   b. Teapot spout (Fig. 5.6).
   c. Bottom pour (Fig. 5.7); not used on cylindrical ladles.
2) Means of tilting ladle—
   a. Vertical lever, hand tilt. (Maximum capacity about 600 lb for pouring with tapered and straight side ladles; cylindrical ladles 750 lb.)
   b. Forked shank, hand tilt. (Maximum capacity about 1000 lb for pouring with tapered and straight side ladles; cylindrical ladles about 1500 lb. Gearings are recommended.)
   c. Gearing. (Usually the worm and wormwheel type, either hand operated or motor driven.

Maximum capacity about 40 tons on tapered and straight side ladles on which gearing is used.)

   d. Crane hook tilt. (Used on ladles 35 or more tons; sometimes used on smaller bottom pour ladles.)

3) Heat retention features–
   a. Cover (Fig. 5.6) (It is not practical usually to have covers on ladles under 250 lb capacity. From refractory and operating standpoints covers are not usually furnished on tapered or straight side ladles over 5000 lb capacity. Never used on bottom pour ladles.)
   b. Insulation (Fig. 5.6). Usually on cylindrical ladles above 5000 lb capacity; recommended for distributing ladles having holding time over 5 min; generally used on pouring ladles subject to long metal holding time.

4) Suspension member–
   a. Square bail (Figs. 5.5 and 5.6). Best suited for all ladles and capacities; Recommended as pouring device suspension for ladles up to 1000 lb capacity; required for strength for all ladles over 5 ton capacity.
   b. V-bail (Fig. 5.7). Can be used for any type ladle up to 10,000 capacity.
   c. Stands (fasten to ladle trunnions).

5) Special features–
   a. Multiple spouts.
   b. Special ladle bowl (to provide mold clearance; to reach sprues located a long distance from edge of mold; to fit under existing cupola or forehearth spouts).
   c. Special lips (to reach sprues located long distance from edge of a mold).

Straight Sided and Tapered Ladles

The straight sided and taper sided ladles have much in common, and in most cases they could be interchanged. The main advantage of the tapered ladle is that it affords more room, due to its small bottom diameter, in areas where molds are set close together. The tapered sides facilitate easy removal of the lining. The advantage of the straight sided ladle is that it is easy to line with standard shapes, allowing the brick joints to come into close and uniform contact with each other. These ladles are usually furnished with a conventional pouring lip which draws metal directly off the top of the ladle. Either of these two types can be equipped with teapot spouts or bottom pour mechanism (Fig. 5.7) to draw clean metal off the bottom of the ladle. Most squeezer molds are poured with tapered type ladles (Fig. 5.5).

Cylindrical Ladle

The cylindrical ladle has advantages over tapered and straight sided ladles for pouring medium and small molds. A minimum of effort is required to operate it because the shell and refractory actually rotate about the metal. The spout travels through a minimum distance between the start of pour and the point at which the last metal leaves the spout. This minimizes the metal drop and also requires less raising of the ladle during the pouring.

The distance through which the spout moves is about 40 degrees less than the spout of a standard tapered or straight sided ladle of the same capacity. The small diameter allows the ladle to be drawn up close to the mold or, if desired, on top of the mold so that distant sprues can be reached with a minimum metal drop.

Teapot spouts are used to assure clean metal. Figure 5.8 shows how a standard cylindrical ladle can be used to pour a mold with the sprue in a specific location, which could not be poured by a standard tapered or straight sided ladle. The disadvantage of the cylindrical ladle is that it is more difficult to line. Pre-shaped refractories have been developed making lining less difficult. Some cylindrical ladles have end plates that are completely removable, which aids the lining procedure.

Ladle Selection

Distributing ladles may be any of the three types of ladles previously mentioned, but regardless of type they are usually equipped with conventional pouring lips. A refractory lined cover is used for maximum heat retention. In the event that metal is held over

Fig. 5.6. Cylindrical, geared, covered and insulated ladle with square bail. Cover is in open position. Teapot spout is to be built into lining.

Fig. 5.7. V-bail, taper sided, open, geared bottom pour ladle.

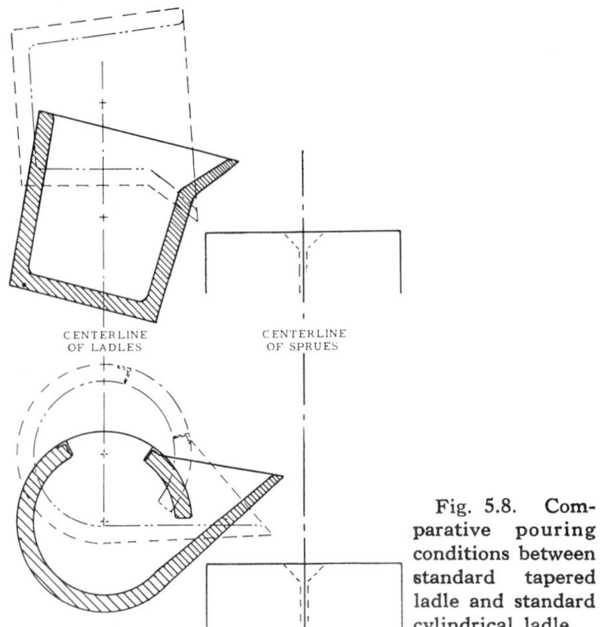

Fig. 5.8. Comparative pouring conditions between standard tapered ladle and standard cylindrical ladle.

5 min, insulation placed in back of the regular lining should be used (Fig. 5.5).

Insulating brick are rather delicate and, unless care is exercised, are destroyed when refractory linings are replaced. The replacement of the insulating brick under these conditions becomes expensive, and many foundries replace them with regular refractory, thereby giving them a thick, heavy lining. Laying insulated shapes with air-setting cement and coating the inner surface with a good graphite blacking wash before applying the refractory should help to protect them when a ladle is relined.

The type and capacity of a pouring ladle for a given group of molds is an important consideration. Greatest care must be exercised in the light and medium squeezer molds. Care must be taken to choose a ladle for quick and easy manipulation, and of a capacity that permits pouring the contents without excessive loss of temperature.

Continually pigging that portion of the metal which is too cold to pour is not economical. To hold this cooled-off metal, called the heel, until a new hot batch is received is not good practice, because it will chill the next ladle of iron. It is more economical to have a group of ladles with different capacities so that the proper ladle can be selected for a group of molds or for pouring on particular days, rather than to pour small molds with oversized ladles.

When the molds are placed on conveyors care must be taken to have a ladle with a proper spout to pour a variety of sprue positions from a more or less fixed line of pouring. Molds set out on a floor allow more flexibility in pouring. The ladle selected would be either a tapered covered or a cylindrical covered. Of these, the cylindrical is better adapted to meet difficult pouring situations as far as metal drop and sprue locations are concerned. It also requires less effort to operate.

The maximum capacity for either in this light and medium squeezer mold range is about 400 lb of metal, and the tilting method best suited is a vertical lever, hand tilt, because the action is direct and fast and the operator is sensitive to the pouring action.

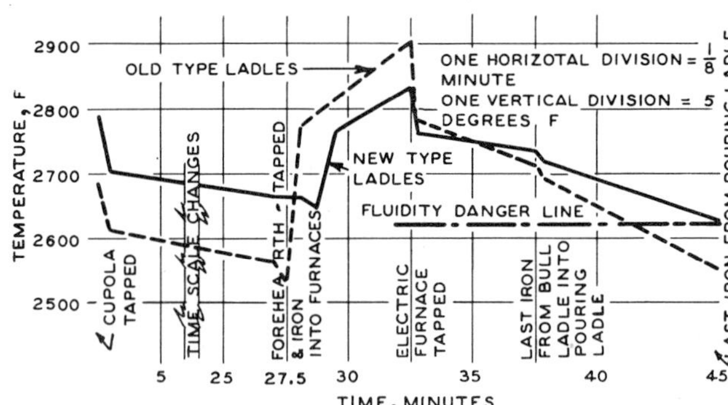

Fig. 5.9. Time-temperature curves showing temperatures of iron from time it is tapped from cupola to time last iron is poured from pouring ladle, including period of superheating in electric furnace.

As an example, an average of about 1½ lb per sec, including all motions from the start of actual pouring to the finish of actual pouring, is the approximate pouring rate on light squeezer molds placed on a floor. A 225-lb ladle suspended from a crane bridge and a rigid member with a variable lift would require about 2½ min to pour, and would pour off 25 molds of 9 lb each. Pouring rates can vary greatly depending on local conditions.

Conserving Heat

The selection of ladles for distributing and pouring is a study in conserving heat. An unnecessary transfer of metal may lower the temperature 50 to 75 F. Losses of temperature in all ladles are those absorbed by the ladle lining and those lost by radiation from the ladle. Linings should be as heavy as good economy permits for a particular kind of operation. This may be anywhere from ¼-in. in a hand ladle to as much as 6 in. in a large steel foundry ladle. Heavy linings absorb more heat than thin linings, but once they are heated to service temperature and held close to that temperature the loss by radiation may be as much as 50 per cent less than for the thinly lined ladles.

All ladles should be preheated and thoroughly dried, and kept close to service temperature by good scheduling of metal delivery. The more quickly a ladle is refilled the less will be the loss of temperature. During lunch periods or other shutdowns it would be advisable to place ladles under preheating torches. For continuous pouring schedules ladle linings as heavy as 3 or 3½ in. can be used with 500-lb capacity pouring ladles. The preheating of heavily lined ladles may not be justified if they are used intermittently or for short periods of about 1 hr.

Ladle covers reduce the temperature losses from the metal surface and also retain heat during a delay in service schedules. A very important present-day consideration, however, is that covers protect pourers from the intense heat, permitting them to work more efficiently. The covered ladles, a means of mechanically carrying, lowering and raising a ladle, have greatly improved working conditions and resulted in a savings and the opportunity to obtain better workers (Figs. 5.5 and 5.9).

REFERENCES

Clark, Ralph A., "Gray Iron Heat Conservation," AMERICAN FOUNDRYMAN, Oct., 1951.

Joseph, Carl F., "Measuring and Controlling Temperatures and Fluidity," AFS TRANSACTIONS, vol. 44, p. 103 (1936).

CHAPTER 6

Blowing
Blast Control

BLOWING EQUIPMENT

Selection of proper equipment to supply "blast" air to a foundry cupola is of utmost importance to every foundryman. Because of its unlimited supply, there may be a tendency to feel that air is not a costly nor important factor. Nevertheless, when it is realized that the weight of air required in cupola operation is of the same order as the weight of the iron charges, it is apparent that very careful consideration should be given, not only to the quantity of air, but also to the means of delivering it to the cupola and the method of controlling its supply.

Analysis of Requirements

Before attempting to select proper blast equipment for cupola service, a thorough study of the local operating conditions should be made. Each cupola installation has its own distinctive features and should, therefore, be analyzed independently to arrive at the best selection of type and size of equipment. In different cases, the selection may perhaps be different, even though the size of cupola and melting rate may be the same. Therefore, in making the analysis, the following factors should be taken into consideration:

Factors Determining Air Volume and Pressure

1) Size and type of cupola.
2) Melting rate (normal and maximum).
3) Iron to coke ratio in charges (appreciably affected by preheating the blast and by the moisture content of the blast).
4) Type of iron required.
5) Temperature of iron at spout.
6) Height of coke bed and charges above tuyeres.
7) Size and quality of coke.

Factors Governing Selection of Blower

1) Maximum volume and pressure for maximum melting conditions.
2) Initial and operating costs.
3) Location of blower with reference to cupola.
4) Maximum temperature of air at blower inlet.
5) Method of drive.
6) Altitude of installation.

The procedure for calculating the quantity of air required for any given cupola installation is outlined very thoroughly in Chapter 33, and to some extent in Chapter 34. In this connection, too much attention cannot be given to providing sufficient capacity to meet maximum melting requirements.

The pressure required at the blower discharge is not so readily calculated. It is determined primarily by the maximum quantity of air to be forced through the melting zone area, the nature of the coke and metal charge, and the height of the charge above the tuyeres. The pressure requirements are also influenced by the tuyere and windbox design, the size, length and nature of the blower piping, and the use of heating and dehumidifying equipment for the cupola blast.

Table 24.1 lists some normal windbox pressures for various size cupolas under general conditions. Actual determination of pressure requirements for a cupola installation must be based on existing similar conditions modified by any difference in the factors previously listed.

CUPOLA BLOWER TYPES

Blowers employed generally for foundry cupola service are of three types: 1) the positive displacement or "lobular" blower; 2) the centrifugal or "turbo" blower; and 3) the fan blower, similarly designed, for low pressure conditions and short heats.

Positive Displacement Blowers

The positive displacement blower delivers a definite volume of air with each revolution of its lobes at any required pressure and against any resistance

Fig. 6.1. Positive displacement blower (phantom view).

set up inside the cupola, within the design limitations of the blower and its driving motor. At constant speed, it delivers an essentially *constant volume* at *varying pressures.* The power consumption, when the blower is operating at constant speed. varies directly with the blower discharge pressure, irrespective of the volume of air actually delivered to the cupola.

Centrifugal Blowers

The centrifugal blower delivers air at the design pressure by the centrifugal action of one or more relatively high-speed impellers, acting much in the same manner as a centrifugal pump. The action is not "positive," inasmuch as there is an open path from the discharge to the suction at all times. At constant speed, the centrifugal blower will deliver its design pressure *essentially constant* with *varying volumes,* and the power consumption will vary directly with the standard volume of air delivered.

Fan-Type Blowers

The fan blower operates according to the same principle as the centrifugal blower, but it is less intricately designed and its efficiency is lower.

Positive displacement and centrifugal blowers have their advantages for specific operating conditions, and the choice between the two types may depend upon the circumstances surrounding a particular installation as well as the dictates of experience. To assist in making a choice, a more detailed explanation of the characteristics of the three blower types is presented.

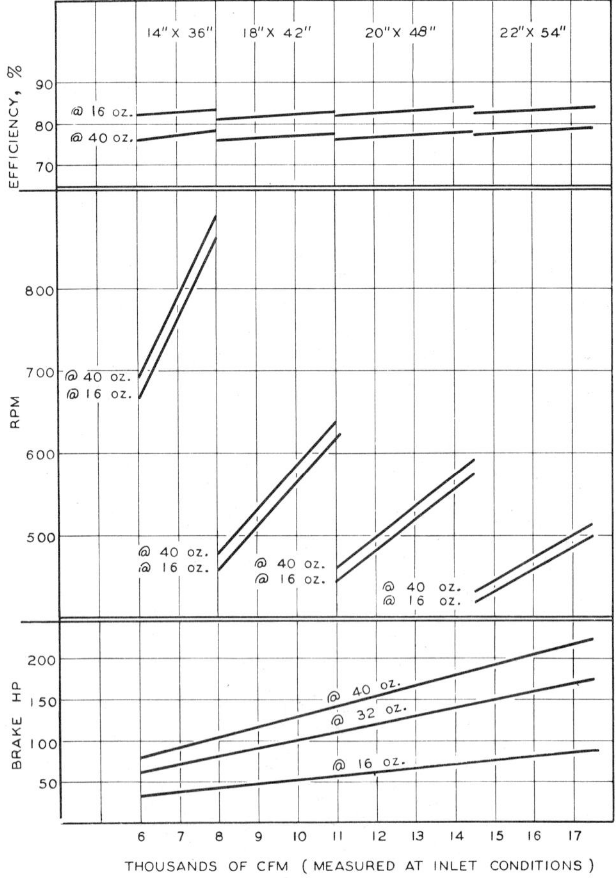

Fig. 6.2. **Characteristic curves for positive displacement blowers.**

CUPOLA BLOWER CHARACTERISTICS

Positive Displacement Blower

The positive displacement blower, illustrated in Fig. 6.1, consists of two lobe-shaped impellers, mounted on parallel shafts, which rotate in opposite directions within a suitable casing. The rotative relation of the impellers is maintained by external timing gears. The impellers do not touch each other or the casing and, therefore, internal lubrication is not required (Fig. 6.1). The impellers rotate at moderate speeds, generally from 200 to 500 rpm for large blowers, and up to 800 rpm for smaller blowers.

Typical performance curves for various positive displacement blowers when operated at different speeds are shown in Fig. 6.2.

It is important to note that a definite volume of air is displaced with each revolution, and that the air volume will be delivered positively against any resistance within the limits of structural strength of the blower and the horsepower of the driving motor. At constant speed, therefore, it will deliver an essentially constant volume regardless of varying operating pressure. Therefore, the speed to be selected is that which is required to deliver the volume of air calculated for the maximum desired melting rate, keeping in mind the fact that the actual quantity of air in standard cubic feet will be inversely proportional to the absolute temperature of inlet air. With certain types of humidity control equipment, the inlet air temperature may go to 110 F.

When cupola operation requires a lesser quantity of air, the excess is removed from the blast system through a variable butterfly valve on the piping between the blower and the cupola. This valve may be operated manually, but is usually operated automatically as outlined in the "Blast Control Equipment" section of this chapter.

If desired, the lesser quantity of air may be obtained and the efficiency of the blower itself improved by the use of a variable speed drive unit in connection with, or replacing, the multiple V-belt

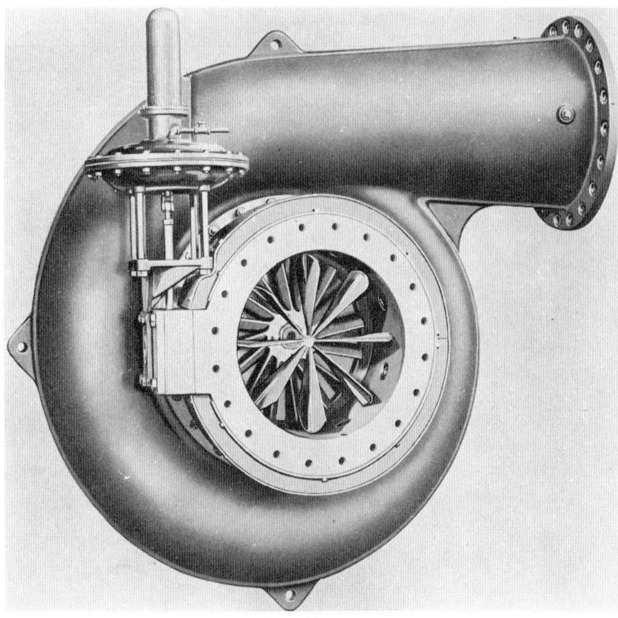

Fig. 6.3. Single stage centrifugal blower with automatically controlled inlet vanes.

drive for reducing the rpm to correspond with the lesser blast requirements. In most instances, however, the economies effected in the blower are practically offset by the losses in the variable speed drive.

Centrifugal Blower

The centrifugal blower may be the single stage (Fig. 6.3) or the multistage type.

Single-stage blowers consist essentially of a single impeller, which may be of the semi-enclosed or fully enclosed type, surrounded by a scroll or volute-shaped casing. The impeller is usually a single aluminum alloy casting, and the casing may be made of cast iron or fabricated from steel plates. This type blower usually is driven by a 3600 rpm electric motor, and may be of the overhung type, with the impeller mounted on an extension of the motor shaft, or it may be of the pedestal type, with its own shaft and bearings and direct-coupled to its driver.

Multistage blowers consist of two or more impellers, usually of the enclosed type, arranged in a suitable casing. Generally they are driven by an 1800 rpm electric motor, or the blower may have its own shaft and bearings with the motor and blower shafts connected by means of a flexible coupling.

The performance of a medium size single-stage 3600 rpm centrifugal blower is shown in Fig. 6.4. From the curves in Fig. 6.4, it will be noted that, with a practically constant motor speed, the discharge pressure of the blower is at a minimum when delivering the maximum quantity of air at the higher inlet air temperature. Considering that the maximum quantity of air delivered to the cupola will be proportional to the square root of the blower delivery pressure, and that the blower delivery pressure will vary inversely as the absolute temperature (barometric and relative humidity remaining constant), too much attention cannot be given to specifying a blower designed for adequate discharge pressure to supply a sufficient quantity of air (usually expressed in pounds) for maximum melting conditions. In this connection, it is well to note that with certain types of humidity control equipment for the blast, it is necessary to maintain an air temperature as high as 110 F leaving this equipment. Also, that with certain types of cupola blast heating equipment, the pressure loss through the heater unit will amount to as much as 7 oz.

When cupola operation requires less discharge pressure than that developed by the centrifugal blower, a butterfly or vane type gate is installed at the

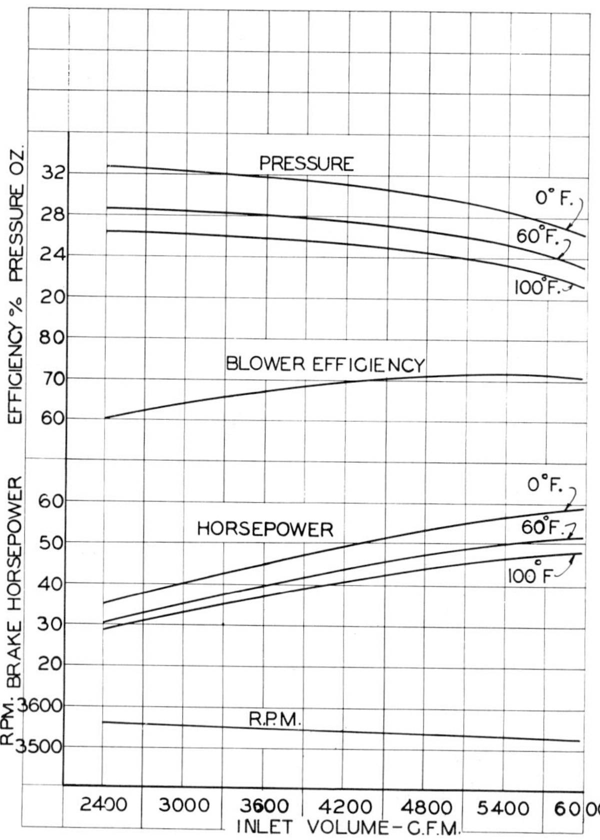

Fig. 6.4. Performance curves of single stage 3600 rpm centrifugal blower.

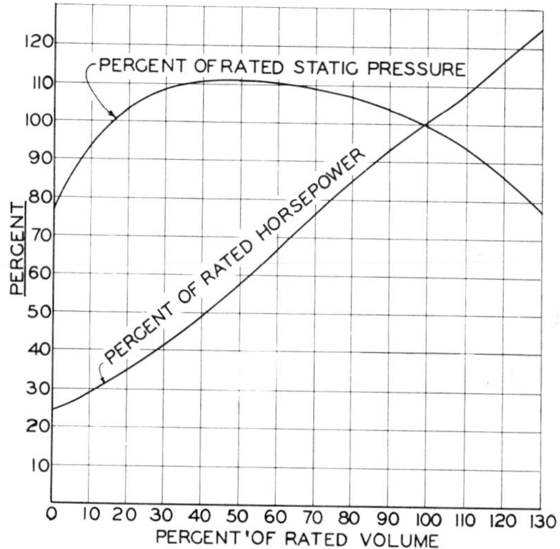

Fig. 6.5. Characteristic operating curves for fan blower.

Fig. 6.6. Fan blower to supply air for small cupolas.

blower discharge or inlet for reducing the windbox pressure to that required for the desired cupola operation.

Figure 6.3 shows a vane type blast gate mounted on the inlet of a single stage centrifugal blower. Shown also is an air motor for remote manual or automatic operation, also available for direct operation.

The rotating vanes are pitched so that air passing through is diverted in the direction of the blower rotation. This improves the blower efficiency appreciably, but the additional cost of this type gate as compared with the butterfly type is such that its use is warranted only on the larger size blowers. The range of practical operation for a centrifugal blower is from 50-100 per cent of its rating. The use of a vane type gate at the inlet will extend the lower range a few per cent.

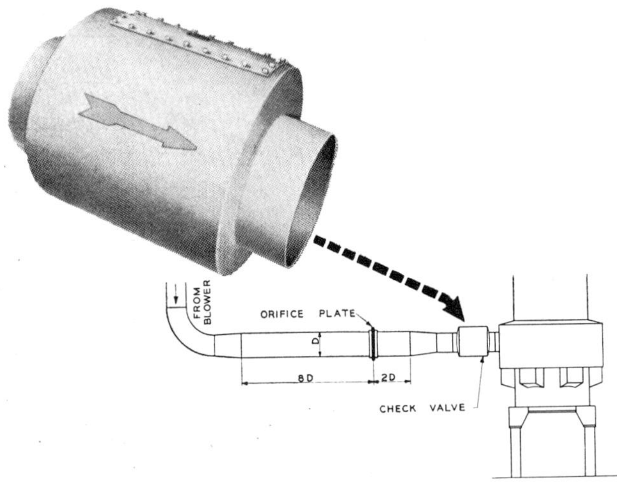

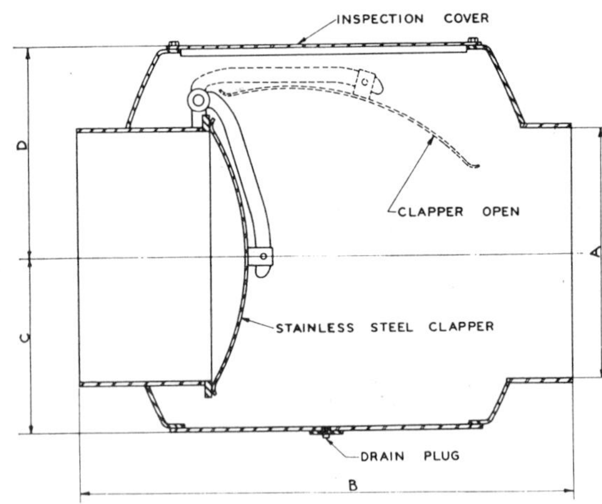

Pipe Size, in. A	B	C	D	Approx. Wt., lb
6	21½	4	5½	50
8	23½	5¼	7¼	75
10	25½	7	9	100
12	30	8	10	125
16	35½	11	13	165
20	41	13	15	215

Fig. 6.7. Top — Cupola blast line check valve and location diagram. Bottom — Dimensional sketch of check valve installation.

Fan Blower

The fan blower (Fig. 6.6) is used extensively to furnish the air supply for small cupolas where the operation is not continuous and low first cost is a prime consideration. It may be belt driven or direct-connected to the motor.

The operating characteristics are essentially the same as those of the centrifugal blower, as shown in Fig. 6.5, except that the pressure built up by the fan is considerably lower. The pressure varies with the density of the air and, therefore, the fan blower selected must be capable of building up the maximum pressure needed by the cupola on a hot day when the density of the air is low. When the cupola does not require the full pressure, or on cold days when a greater pressure is built up, the fan discharge is throttled to give the desired capacity. Figure 6.5 shows the operating characteristics of a fan blower.

AIR PIPING

After the blower has been selected, the piping arrangement should be given very careful consideration. To obtain the best flow characteristics and to keep friction at a minimum, the air piping between the blower and the cupola should be as straight and as short as possible, with a minimum number of elbows. It also is essential that the piping and all connections be as tight as possible, because a piping system that leaks will offset, at least partially, the advantages gained by the most careful selection of the blast equipment.

Round ductwork is preferable to square or rectangular, especially with the positive displacement blower as the pulsations tend to cause cracking at the corners that result in leaks.

To avoid any chance of carbon monoxide backing up into the ductwork and forming an explosive mixture, especially when hot blast or humidity control is used, a gravity check valve should be installed in the ductwork as it joins the cupola windbox (Fig. 6.7). Also, provisions should be made for venting the windbox during short shutdown periods when there is no blast pressure in the windbox (Fig. 6.8).

Some of the cupola manufacturers are now in a position to supply special flap valves between the windbox and each tuyere box that automatically close off the connection to the windbox and vent the tuyere to atmosphere as the windbox pressure drops to zero.

Fig. 6.8. Automatic vent for cupola windbox.

BLAST CONTROL EQUIPMENT

Until the second quarter of the Twentieth Century, the control of combustion air supplied to the cupola was manual and with the use of pressure gages. Windbox pressures were usually taken as an indication of the quantity of air being supplied to the cupola. Most foundries had a more less constant routine with reference to product and schedule, in relation to which normal operating pressures for the various charges and melting conditions were established.

A pressure gage, of the indicating or recording type, which measures air pressure in the windbox, was usually located so the cupola operator could easily read the scale or chart.

Many types of indicating gages were used for measuring windbox pressures. The most common and reliable was the mercury-column type. This instrument consists of a mercury-filled glass tube inserted in a hollow rectangular metal base with an adjustable graduated metal scale mounted behind it. The base is connected to the windbox. The pressure of the air in the windbox causes the mercury to rise in the tube to a corresponding height, which is read from the scale. Usually the scale is graduated in pounds per square inch (psi) and ounces per square inch (osi) and covers a 5 psi range.

A gage type indicator also is constructed to withstand the over-range of pressure which may exist in the cupola. Gages are of the diaphragm type, or the pressure is measured by a metal tube, usually 5 in. dia., mounted inside a case. The tube movement, changing with the pressure, is transferred to an indicating pointer through a suitable connecting link. The pointer moves over a dial scale graduated in ounces the required range.

The recording gage (Fig. 6.9) is similar to the indicating instrument in construction and may be mounted in a circular case of 10 or 12-in. diameter, or a rectangular case 12 x 14 in. In addition to the pressure tube, a chart and driving mechanism are provided to record graphically the variations of pressure.

Fig. 6.9. Pressure recorder gage, 12 in.

Recorded measurements of windbox pressures are more useful than indicating pressures because they show the trend and rate of change and supply a record for the analysis of operating experience.

With the advent of mass production and its demand for additional tonnages and various types of cupola iron with more uniform composition, it was imperative that control of the cupola operation be greatly improved. When it was realized that the quantity of air required in cupola operation is equal in weight to the iron charged, the first step in controlling the operation was by controlling the air supplied to the cupola by volume rather than windbox pressure.

VOLUME METERS

There are several standard methods of measuring the volume of air delivered to the windbox. Before equipment for automatically controlling the air supply of the cupola was developed, it was standard practice to place in the blast pipe a volume meter

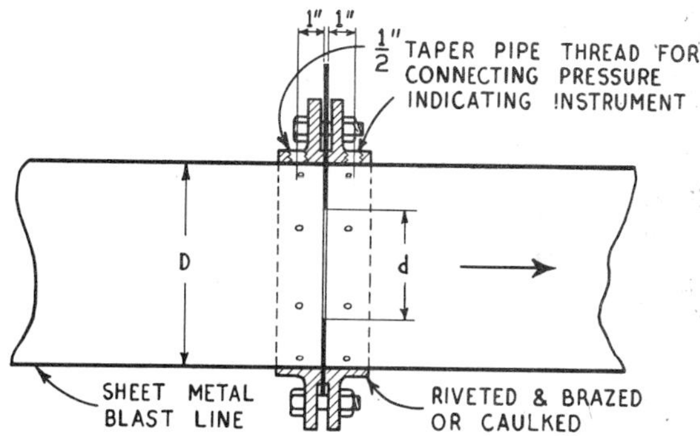

Fig. 6.10. Flange connection using orifice union. Pressure connection holes are 1 in. upstream and downstream, respectively, from orifice plate faces.

TABLE 6.1. VALUES OF E FOR FLANGE CONNECTIONS[1]

d/D*	E*	d/D	E	d/D	E
0.05	0.5985	0.30	0.6035	0.55	0.6403
0.06	0.5986	0.31	0.6040	0.56	0.6434
0.07	0.5987	0.32	0.6045	0.57	0.6468
0.08	0.5988	0.33	0.6051	0.58	0.6503
0.09	0.5989	0.34	0.6058	0.59	0.6541
0.10	0.5990	0.35	0.6065	0.60	0.6580
0.11	0.5991	0.36	0.6072	0.61	0.6622
0.12	0.5992	0.37	0.6081	0.62	0.6667
0.13	0.5994	0.38	0.6090	0.63	0.6714
0.14	0.5995	0.39	0.6099	0.64	0.6763
0.15	0.5996	0.40	0.6110	0.65	0.6815
0.16	0.5998	0.41	0.6121	0.66	0.6869
0.17	0.5999	0.42	0.6133	0.67	0.6928
0.18	0.6001	0.43	0.6147	0.68	0.6988
0.19	0.6002	0.44	0.6161	0.69	0.7052
0.20	0.6004	0.45	0.6176	0.70	0.7119
0.21	0.6006	0.46	0.6193	0.71	0.7189
0.22	0.6008	0.47	0.6210	0.72	0.7263
0.23	0.6010	0.48	0.6229	0.73	0.7340
0.24	0.6013	0.49	0.6250	0.74	0.7421
0.25	0.6016	0.50	0.6271	0.75	0.7505
0.26	0.6019	0.51	0.6294	0.76	0.7594
0.27	0.6023	0.52	0.6319	0.77	0.7687
0.28	0.6027	0.53	0.6345	0.78	0.7783
0.29	0.6031	0.54	0.6373	0.79	0.7884

*d = diameter of orifice in inches; D = inside diameter of blast pipe in inches; E = efficiency.

[1] Spink, L. K., *Principles and Practice of Flow Meter Engineering*, Sixth Edition, 1943, p. 66.

of the differential type consisting of two parts, a primary element and an instrument to measure the differential pressure created by it. The latter is related to the velocity and volume of the air flowing at the point of measurement. The simplest formulas by which these relations can be expressed are:

1) $$v = \sqrt{2gh}$$

in which

v = velocity in ft per sec
g = acceleration of gravity (32.15 ft per sec)
h = differential pressure

and

2) $$V = v \times 0.7854 \times D^2 \times 60$$

in which

V = volume in cu ft per min
v = velocity in ft per sec
D = inside diameter of pipe at point of measurement.

Primary Elements

Three types of primary elements are used: the orifice plate, the Pitot tube, and the Venturi tube. In all cases the primary element should be inserted in a straight portion of the blast pipe, and as far downstream as possible from any source of flow disturbance such as elbows or blast gates. It is immaterial whether the pipe is horizontal, vertical or inclined. When possible, the straight length of pipe selected should be at least ten pipe diameters upstream and five pipe diameters downstream from the primary element to insure accurate measurements. However, due to the size of the blast pipe used on cupolas and the physical layout of the average foundry, these ideal conditions can seldom, if ever, be realized. If 15 pipe diameters of straight pipe are not available, it is recommended that only one or two pipe diameters downstream from the primary element be allowed in order to obtain as much straight run upstream as possible. These conditions usually cannot be met in existing installations, and with the new larger installations with large diameter ductwork requiring excessively long runs, it is advisable to use straightening vanes for insuring accuracy that would be lost due to turbulence in the air stream. The location of straightening vanes in blast piping is shown in Figs. 6.20 and 6.21.

ORIFICE PLATE

The orifice plate is by far the most commonly used type of primary element. It consists simply of a flat plate with a circular square-edged hole machined in it, and is held between flanges which are installed in the blast pipe at the desired point of measurement. Since the hole in the plate is smaller than the inside diameter of the blast pipe, the velocity of the air flow is increased at this point. The resulting differential pressure across the plate is related to the flow in the blast pipe and serves as a measure of it. The orifice plate has constant accuracy, and it can be inspected without difficulty.

Connections to measure the differential pressure created by the orifice plate may be made directly to the flanges holding the plate or to the pipe at specified points, as follows: 1) flange connections—pressure connection holes are located directly in the flanges at distances of one inch upstream and downstream from the corresponding faces of the orifice plate, as shown in Fig. 6.10; 2) Vena contracta connections—the upstream connection is located one pipe diameter and the downstream connection one-half pipe diameter from the orifice plate, as shown in Fig. 6.11. These connections are used when orifice flanges are not available. They are used with standard flanges not tapped for pressure connection holes. Computations based on vena contracta connections check those of flange connections within commercial limits for practically all installations.

Orifice Calculations

$$Q = 5.648 \times E \times d^2 \times F_t \times \sqrt{h \times P}$$

in which

Q = cu ft per min (14.7 psi pressure and 60 F)
E = efficiency of orifice (Table 6.1)
d = diameter of orifice in inches
F_t = factor for temperature (Table 6.2)
h = pressure differential in inches of water
P = pressure in psi absolute (indicated pressure + 14.7 psi)
5.648 = basic orifice coefficient to which correction factor for any set of conditions may be applied.

TABLE 6.2. CORRECTION FACTOR FOR FLOWING TEMPERATURE[2] (F_t)

F°		F°		F°		F°	
1	1.0621	41	1.0188	81	0.9804	121	0.9460
2	1.0610	42	1.0178	82	0.9795	122	0.9452
3	1.0598	43	1.0168	83	0.9786	123	0.9444
4	1.0587	44	1.0158	84	0.9777	124	0.9436
5	1.0575	45	1.0148	85	0.9768	125	0.9428
6	1.0564	46	1.0138	86	0.9759	126	0.9420
7	1.0553	47	1.0128	87	0.9750	127	0.9412
8	1.0541	48	1.0118	88	0.9741	128	0.9404
9	1.0530	49	1.0108	89	0.9732	129	0.9396
10	1.0519	50	1.0098	90	0.9723	130	0.9388
11	1.0508	51	1.0088	91	0.9714	131	0.9380
12	1.0497	52	1.0078	92	0.9706	132	0.9372
13	1.0486	53	1.0068	93	0.9697	133	0.9364
14	1.0474	54	1.0058	94	0.9688	134	0.9356
15	1.0463	55	1.0049	95	0.9679	135	0.9348
16	1.0452	56	1.0039	96	0.9671	136	0.9340
17	1.0441	57	1.0029	97	0.9662	137	0.9332
18	1.0430	58	1.0019	98	0.9653	138	0.9325
19	1.0420	59	1.0010	99	0.9645	139	0.9317
20	1.0409	60	1.0000	100	0.9636	140	0.9309
21	1.0398	61	0.9990	101	0.9627	141	0.9301
22	1.0387	62	0.9981	102	0.9619	142	0.9294
23	1.0376	63	0.9971	103	0.9610	143	0.9286
24	1.0366	64	0.9962	104	0.9602	144	0.9278
25	1.0355	65	0.9952	105	0.9593	145	0.9270
26	1.0344	66	0.9943	106	0.9585	146	0.9263
27	1.0333	67	0.9933	107	0.9576	147	0.9255
28	1.0323	68	0.9924	108	0.9568	148	0.9248
29	1.0312	69	0.9915	109	0.9559	149	0.9240
30	1.0302	70	0.9905	110	0.9551	150	0.9232
31	1.0291	71	0.9896	111	0.9543	...	....
32	1.0281	72	0.9887	112	0.9534	...	.....
33	1.0270	73	0.9877	113	0.9526	...	.....
34	1.0260	74	0.9868	114	0.9518	...	.....
35	1.0250	75	0.9859	115	0.9509	...	.....
36	1.0239	76	0.9850	116	0.9501	...	.....
37	1.0229	77	0.9840	117	0.9493	...	.....
38	1.0219	78	0.9831	118	0.9485	...	.....
39	1.0208	79	0.9822	119	0.9476	...	.....
40	1.0198	80	0.9813	120	0.9468	...	.....

[2] Spink, L. K., "*Principles and Practice of Flow Meter Engineering,*" Sixth Edition, 1943, p. 104.

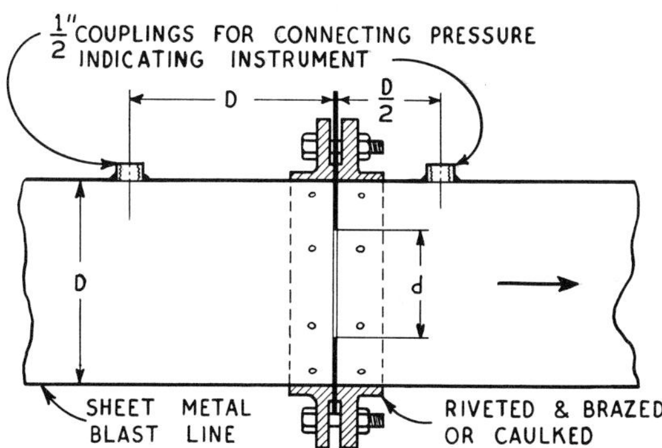

Fig. 6.11. Vena contracta connection using companion flanges.

PITOT TUBE

The Pitot tube was the first primary element used in volume meters applied to cupola operation. In general, a Pitot tube for indicating or recording flow consists of two members, one for indicating the sum of the static and kinetic or impact pressure at a point in a body of air in motion by registering the intensity of impact due to the interruption of a small portion of the flow, and the other for indicating only the static pressure (Fig. 6.12). Because the flow is determined for only one point in the blast line, the accuracy of volume measurement by the Pitot is not high, but for the same conditions the results are always comparable, and, therefore, commercially adequate.

There are many types of Pitot tubes, but the combined type is most convenient and is generally used. It consists of a tube within a tube, as shown in Fig. 6.13. The impact opening faces upstream and should be set at the center line of the pipe. The illustration shows one type of Pitot tube with different installations. In one case, the position of the tube is fixed with a jam nut, and in the other, a corporation cock and stuffing box are used. The latter arrangement permits easy adjustment of the position of the tube and removal of the tube for inspection and cleaning.

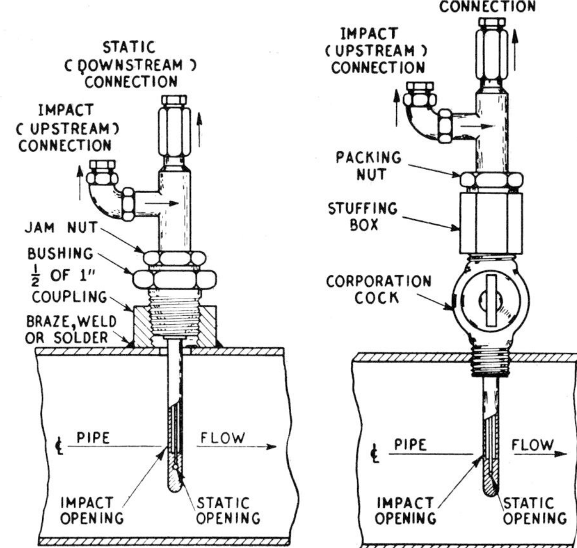

Fig. 6.13. Combined type Pitot tube. Two methods of installation are shown.

Pitot Tube Calculations

$$Q = 3.82 \times D^2 \times F_t \times \sqrt{h \times P}$$

in which

Q = cu ft per min (14.7 psi pressure and 60 F)
D = inside diameter of blast pipe in inches
F_t = factor for temperature (Table 6.2)
h = pressure differential in inches of water
P = pressure in psi absolute
3.82 = basic orifice coefficient (Foxboro) to which correction factors for any set of conditions may be applied.

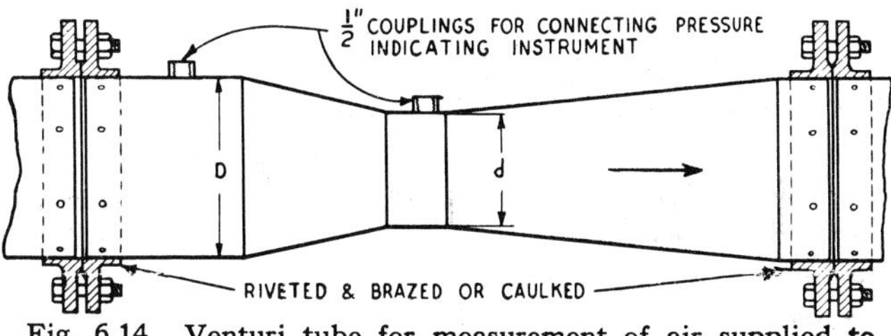

Fig. 6.14. Venturi tube for measurement of air supplied to the cupola.

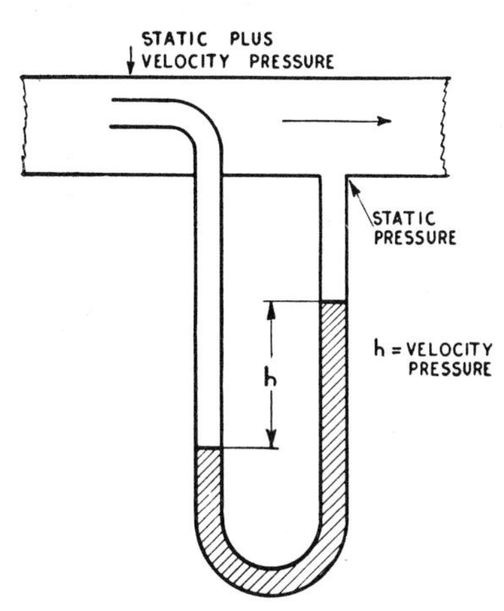

Fig. 6.12. Principle of the Pitot tube.

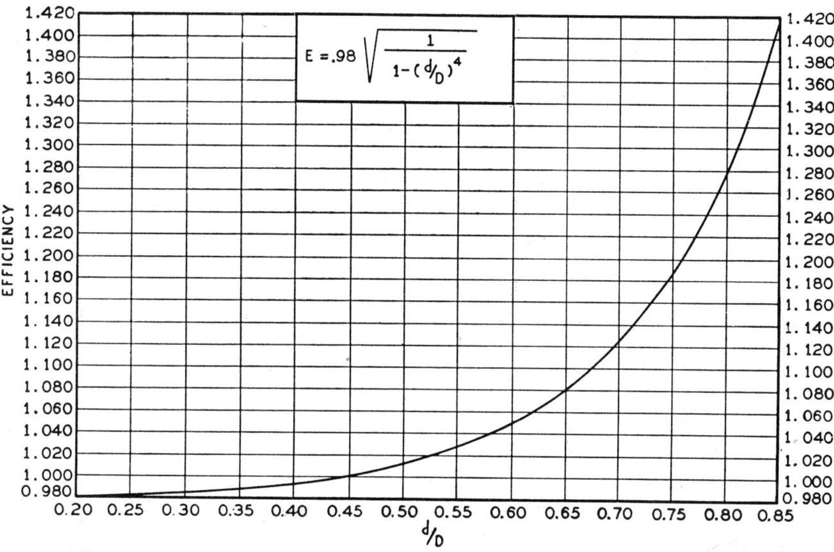

Fig. 6.15. Efficiency chart of Venturi meters. D = in. inside diameter of pipe line; d = in. throat diameter.

VENTURI TUBE

The Venturi tube is used as a primary element when increased capacity is required or when high pressure recovery is desirable. It combines in a single unit a short restricted member between two tapered sections, and is usually inserted in the blast pipe between two flanges. Its purpose is to accelerate the velocity of the air and temporarily reduce its static pressure, thus creating a pressure differential from which the rate of flow can be determined. Suitable pressure connections are provided for observing the difference in pressure at the inlet and in the restricted portion, or throat, as shown in Fig. 6.14. The Venturi tube, as applied to the measurement of air supplied to the cupola, is made of sheet metal, as shown in the illustration. Figure 6.15 is an efficiency chart of Venturi meters.

Venturi Tube Calculations

$$Q = 5.648 \times E \times \frac{d^2}{F_t} \times \sqrt{h \times P}$$

in which

Q = cu ft per min (14.7 psi pressure and 60 F)
E = efficiency (Fig. 6.15)
d = inside diameter of throat in inches
F_t = factor for temperature (Table 6.2)
h = pressure differential in inches of water
P = pressure in psi absolute

INSTRUMENTS FOR MEASURING DIFFERENTIAL PRESSURE

The instruments used with the primary elements are the indicating volume meter of the inclined column type, and the float or bell type indicator or recorder.

The inclined indicating gage consists of a liquid-containing glass tube installed at an angle, as shown in Fig. 6.16, so that for a small change in pressure a relatively large movement of the liquid in the tube will be effected. It is graduated directly in cu ft or lb of air per min. This instrument is generally used when the primary element is the Pitot tube in which the differential pressure created is small.

The manometer employed when the primary element is the orifice plate or the Venturi tube, consists of a U-tube containing mercury. A float is carried on the surface of the mercury in one leg. The movement of this float is transmitted through a system of links to indicate or record the differential pressure on a scale or chart, as shown in Fig. 6.19.

A modification of the mercury manometer has been developed to operate in applications where lower differentials are desirable. In the bell type construction, shown in Fig. 6.18, the high and low pressures from each side of the orifice are applied above and below a bell, the motion of which is opposed by a calibrated spring. Mercury is used around the bottom of the bell to seal the chambers above and below the bell. The movement of the bell, acting through a system of links, serves to indicate or record the differential pressure, or the related air volume in cu ft per min.

The instruments described in the foregoing were used primarily for indicating and recording the volume of air passing to the cupola. Cupola operation was greatly improved over that obtained when guided by windbox pressure only, but there still remained the necessity of manually operating the blast gates. This led to the development of additional features for flow instruments of the type whereby the instrument may be set for any desired quantity of air to be delivered to the cupola, and the instrument would automatically open or close the blast-controlling gate to maintain that quantity passing to the cupola.

AIR WEIGHT CONTROL

Further refinements in the cupola operation, resulting from control of the blast to the cupola, were obtained when it was felt advisable to supply the cupola with a predetermined constant quantity of oxygen. It is a well-known fact that for a given predetermined volume of air being supplied to the cupola, the actual quantity or weight of oxygen in

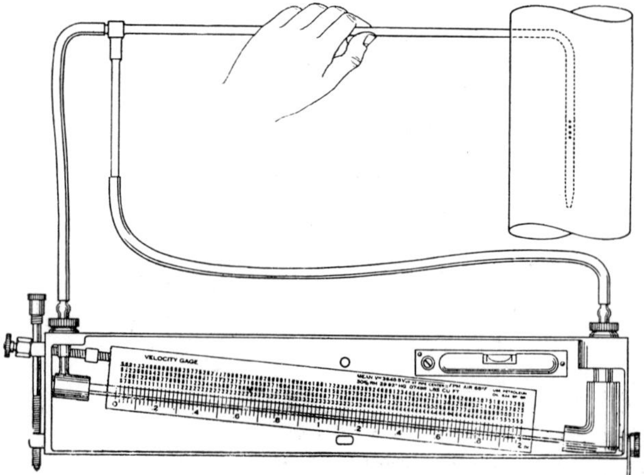

Fig. 6.16. Inclined indicating differential pressure gage.

Fig. 6.17. Bell type air weight controller.

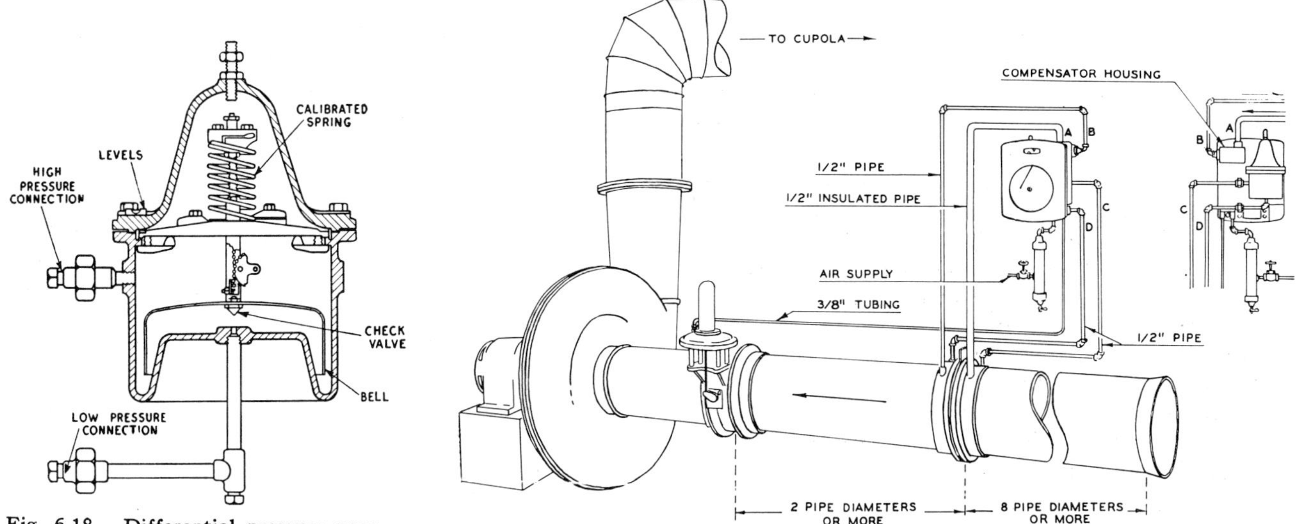

Fig. 6.18. Differential pressure gage — bell type.

Fig. 6.20. **Air weight controller installation on fan or centrifugal blower.**

that air will vary with the temperature and the atmospheric pressure. Where the air supply to the cupola is determined by volume or by windbox pressure, the actual quantity of oxygen available for combustion will vary, and uniform melting conditions will not be maintained. Modern equipment for controlling the cupola blast takes into account these varying conditions and provides a most convenient method for supplying a cupola for any predetermined constant quantity of oxygen within the range of the cupola blower and expressed in terms of standard cu ft, or lb of air, per min.

Two of the most satisfactory types of such equipment are the one which bases the control on the volume determined by an orifice plate or Venturi tube, and the other which is based on the electrical input to the blower motor.

Control Method Using Orifice Plate or Venturi Tube

This method of control measures the flow of air by means of an orifice plate or Venturi tube placed in the blast line to the cupola. The main control instrument is shown in Fig. 6.17. This instrument receives the differential pressure from the orifice or Venturi tube resulting from the flow of air in the blast line. This differential pressure is translated into recordings of air flow on the recording pen. In the translation, corrections for temperature and pressure of the air at the orifice are made, causing the pen to record the flow in standard cu ft of air (or pounds of air if preferred) per unit of time.

The control mechanism is guided by the position of the recording pen relative to the index pointer, and positions the valve controlling the flow to keep

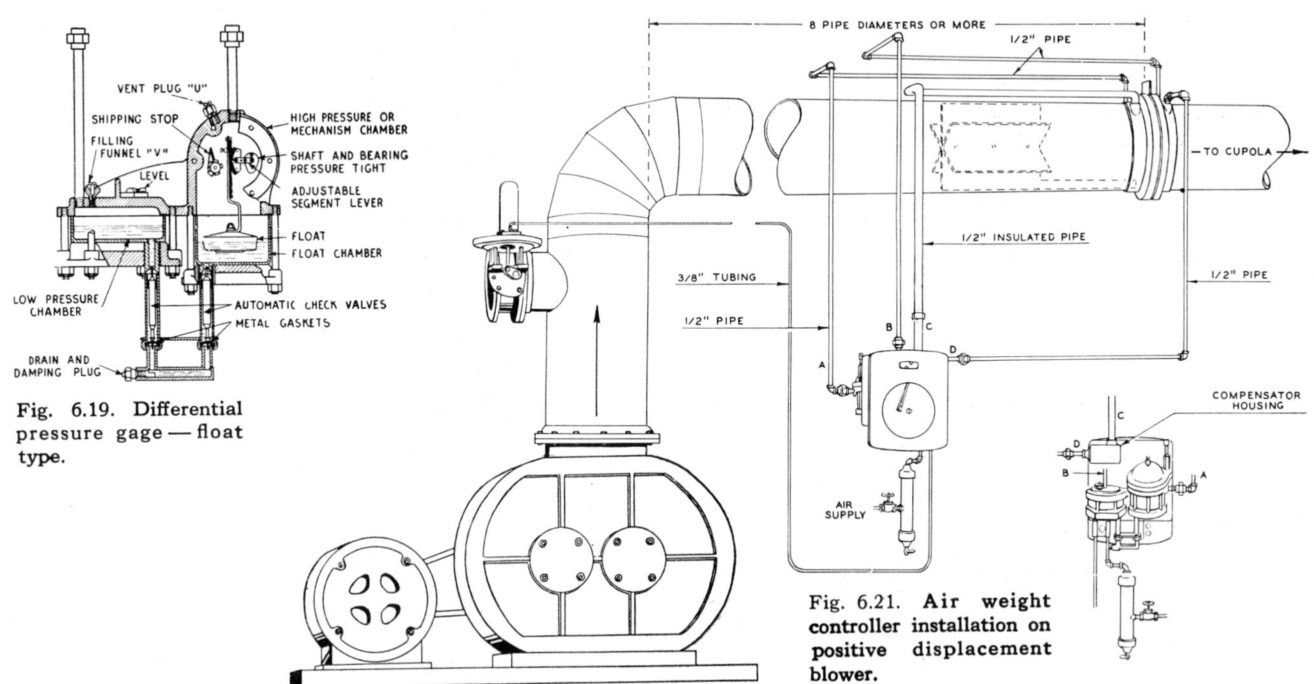

Fig. 6.19. **Differential pressure gage — float type.**

Fig. 6.21. **Air weight controller installation on positive displacement blower.**

the flow measurements at the predetermined flow point. Provisions are made for switching the instrument to manual control, if necessary.

This type of control as used with a centrifugal or fan-type blower is shown in Fig. 6.20. The controller positions the pneumatically-operated control valve in the blast piping system to maintain the flow of predetermined weight of oxygen to the cupola.

This control valve may be the butterfly type; it is mounted in the piping to the blower (Fig. 6.20), or it can be in the piping from the blower.

The vane type valve mounted at the inlet to the blower (Fig. 6.3) may be preferred. This vane type valve will improve the overall efficiency of the blower. Because of its cost, however, it is warranted economical only on larger installations.

When this type control is used with a centrifugal blower, an orifice or Venturi tube is selected that will result in a differential pressure of 2½ in. of water (approx. 1.45 oz) for full scale of the flow chart. Approximately 50 per cent of this drop in pressure is recovered at the cupola windbox when an orifice is used, and appreciably more when a Venturi tube is used.

This kind of control is used with a positive type blower as shown in Fig. 6.21. The controller positions the butterfly valve on the piping from the blower discharge to vent off the proper amount of air from the blower so that only the air containing the predetermined weight of oxygen goes to the cupola.

When this type of control is used with a positive blower, an orifice or Venturi tube is selected that will result in a differential pressure of 10 in. of water (approx. 5.8 oz) for full scale of the flow chart. This higher differential is advisable due to pulsations in the air flow from the positive-type blower. Approximately 50 per cent of this pressure drop is recovered at the cupola windbox when an orifice is used, and appreciably more when a Venturi tube is used.

This type of control instrument is available with a second pen which will record, on the same chart, the windbox pressure necessary to maintain the required flow through the cupola.

CHAPTER 7

Blast Conditioning

PREHEATING AIR FOR CUPOLA COMBUSTION

By preheating the cupola blast both the efficiency and speed of cupola combustion are increased. Increased efficiency results in the use of less coke to produce a given quantity of molten metal at a given temperature. Combustion technology is discussed in detail in Chapter 33.

ADVANTAGES

Actual practice in foundries producing a variety of types of castings has shown that preheating of cupola blast, commonly called "hot blast," results in coke savings of from 20 to 25 per cent when using blast temperatures in the range of 300 to 500 F, as compared to conventional "cold blast" practice producing the same type of iron at the same termperature. In addition, improved cupola operation is obtained with much less tendency to bridge, and with practically no problems due to plugging of tuyere openings with "cold" slag.

Additional advantages include somewhat lower sulfur pick-up, decreased oxidation losses of silicon, manganese and iron (and oxidizable alloys), lower cupola refractory cost and lesser use of fluxes.

If iron at a higher temperature than is obtained with cold blast practice is wanted, it may be obtained by not reducing coke between charges by the amount indicated above, or by not reducing it at all. For example, if a metal temperature of about 2800 F is obtained at the cupola spout with a coke-to-iron ratio between charges of 1 to 7.5 using cold blast, a temperature of 2900 F or more may be obtained using the same coke-to-iron ratio with blast preheated to 350 to 450 F. Such high melting temperatures are accompanied by increased carbon pick-up, thereby permitting the charging of lower carbon materials, and often economies in charge cost.

The principles of the application of hot blast to the cupola, the economies in fuel and improvements in operation that can be accomplished by its use have been discussed in detail by Vial,* and have been substantiated by many others.

The use of hot blast at temperatures of from 350 to 500 F results in the following advantages:

1) Fuel economy of the order of 20 to 25 per cent for a given metal at a given temperature and/or faster melting.
2) Better cupola operation—less tendency to bridge.
3) Better control of metal—more uniform composition.
4) Lower oxidation losses and slightly lower sulfur pick-up.
5) Lower consumption of refractories and fluxes.
6) Less variation in metal temperature when intermittent melting is unavoidable.

Charts showing the results of actual daily operation with cold and hot blasts are shown in Figs. 7.1 and 7.2. A comparison of the results obtained in the manufacture of cast iron pipe during a 6-month period is shown in Table 7.1. It will be noted in the charts that in the hot blast operation with a metal-to-coke ratio of 9½-10:1 the metal temperature averaged more than 50 F higher than that of the cold blast operation with an iron-to-coke ratio of 7½:1.

* Vial, F. K., "Preheating Cupola Blast," *Transactions*, A.I.M.E., Iron & Steel, vol. 51, pp. 21-30 (1929).

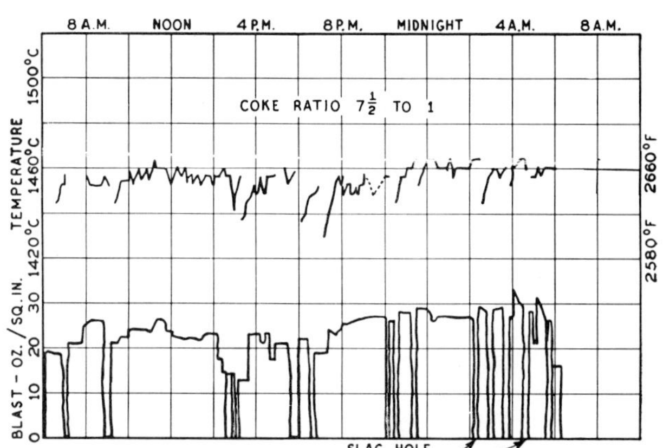

Fig. 7.1. Cold blast cupola operation chart — 24-hr heat — melting rate approx. 18 tons per hr.

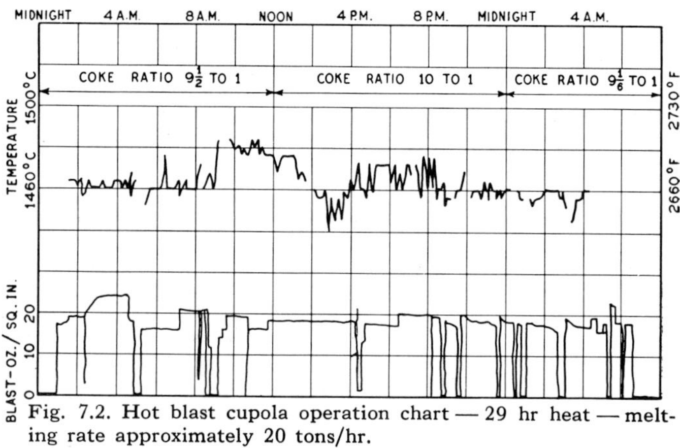

Fig. 7.2. Hot blast cupola operation chart — 29 hr heat — melting rate approximately 20 tons/hr.

Improvements in the melting operation and in the metal, as indicated in Table 7.1, can be equal to or more important than the actual savings in fuel.

METHODS USED FOR PREHEATING BLAST AIR

Two methods which are most widely used in preheating the air for combustion in the cupola are: 1) the recuperative type which uses the sensible and potential heat of the effluent gases; and 2) the externally fired type which does not use any products of combustion in the cupola as fuel, but instead utilizes an independent heater fired by coal, gas or oil.

A third type has been used which is a modified recuperative type in which only the sensible heat of the cupola effluent gases is utilized.

RECUPERATIVE HOT BLAST SYSTEMS (AMERICAN)

Griffin System

The Griffin System, developed by the Griffin Wheel Co., Chicago, is the most widely and generally successful method of using both the sensible and latent heat of the cupola gases. In this system a large portion or all of the gases is drawn from the cupola through outlets or ports in the lining located either below or above the charging door.

In those installations in which the gases are drawn off below the charging door, several ports open into a refractory lined duct built around the cupola, and are connected with the combustion chamber of the preheating equipment. As the hot gases pass into the combustion chamber, they are mixed with air supplied by a by-pass from the main blast pipe. In the installations in which gases are drawn off above the charging door, a single duct connects the cupola to the combustion chamber of the preheating equipment. Air from the charging door is drawn with the gases into the duct.

TABLE 7.1. COMPARISON OF COLD BLAST AND HOT BLAST OPERATION FOR SIX-MONTH PERIOD

	Cold blast	Hot Blast
Ratio of iron to coke	7.1 to 1	10.4 to 1
Average number of pipe cast per shift	386	501
Total delays charged to iron, approximate hr	55.5	4.5
Number times cold iron reported	7	1
Number times iron reported slow with no actual delay	22	3
Average blast pressure, oz per sq in...	20	14
Average melting rate per hr, tons	20	25
Average length of heat, hr	12	18

In both types of installations, the oxygen of the air unites with the carbon monoxide of the effluent cupola gases and burns to carbon dioxide with a liberation of heat. The reaction is $CO + \frac{1}{2}O_2 = CO_2 + 4370$ BTU per lb CO.

A schematic view of a Griffin two-stage hot blast equipment is shown in Fig. 7.3. The temperatures shown in Fig. 7.3 are based on the use of a portion (about 60 per cent) of the cupola effluent gas as fuel. The burning of the hot gases in the combustion chamber causes the products of combustion to attain a temperature of about 1700 F. The temperature of the gases as they pass into the distributing chamber falls somewhat, and is maintained at about 1600 F by admitting excess air to the combustion chamber if necessary.

The bottom of the distributing chamber is formed by a steel plate which supports the upper ends of a bank of cast iron heat-exchanger tubes which extend one inch above the tube sheet. The intervening space

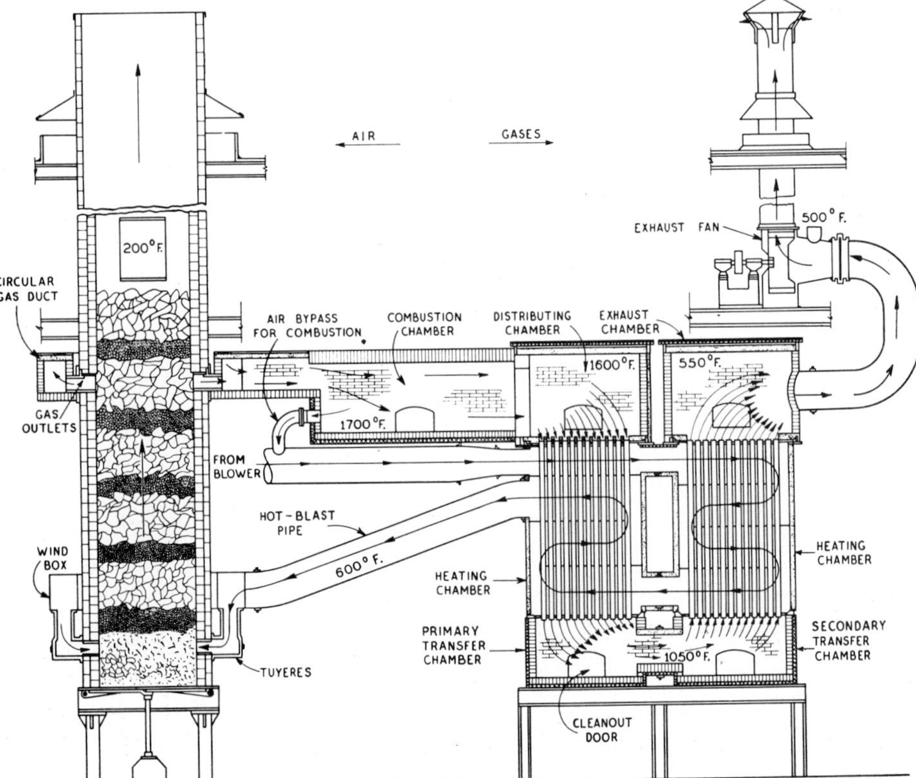

Fig. 7.3. Schematic diagram of two-stage Griffin hot blast equipment.

is filled with plastic fire clay to protect them from attack by the hot gases, to prevent air leakage and to allow for expansion and contraction. The hot gases pass downward through the heat exchanger tubes into the primary transfer chamber, and thence to the secondary transfer chamber. The temperature of the gases at this location is approximately 1050 F, as heat has been given up to the blast air through the exchanger tubes. The gases pass upward through a similar bank of heat exchanger tubes, where additional heat is transferred, to the exhaust fan and into the atmosphere. The temperature of the gases upon reaching the exhaust chamber is approximately 550 F, and is reduced to 500 F when reaching the atmosphere.

A diagrammatic sectional view of the Griffin three-stage recuperator is shown in Fig. 7.4. The efficiency of the exchange of heat in this unit, as compared with that of the two-stage recuperator previously described, is indicated by the relative temperature differential of the hot gases in the distributing chamber and the preheated blast delivered to the tuyeres, 600 and 1,000 F, respectively.

The three-stage unit, because of the longer life of the recuperator, is generally used where sufficient space is available, even when it is desired to preheat the blast to a maximum of only 600 F. Installations of this type have been operated for 8 to 16 hr daily over periods of many years without showing appreciable deterioration.

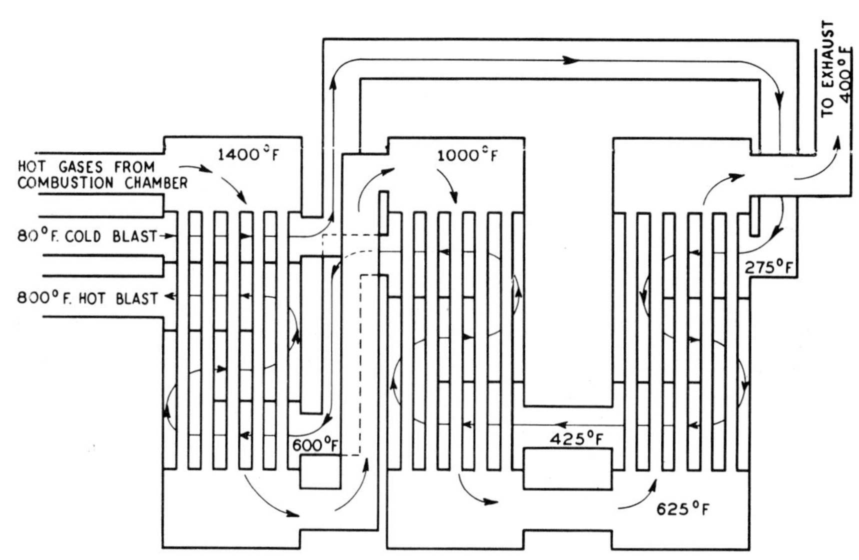

Fig. 7.4. Diagrammatic sectional view of three-stage Griffin recuperator.

The incoming cold blast first passes around the upper sections of the primary heat exchanger, which prevents overheating of the tube ends and tube sheets, and then around the upper sections of the tubes of the secondary heat exchanger. Thereafter, the blast air is deflected by baffle plates so that it flows around the tubes in an opposite direction to the flow of hot combustion gases within the tubes, downward through the secondary exchanger and upward through the primary exchanger, and is thus preheated to a temperature between 350-600 F. The heated blast air passes from the primary exchanger through the hot blast pipe and into the windbox and tuyeres.

When using all of the cupola effluent gases in the Griffin system, somewhat higher temperatures are obtained with the two-stage equipment, the hot blast temperatures being in the range of 600 to 800 F.

Temperatures of all principal and important locations in the systems are continuously recorded. Adequate safety devices are used to assure against overheating and explosions. Principal maintenance problems are cleaning of heat exchanger tubes and tube sheets.

RECUPERATIVE HOT BLAST SYSTEMS (FOREIGN)

Singen Installation

Two makes of recuperative hot blast equipment that are used in Germany and other European countries are the Schack and the "Economizer."

One design of Schack hot blast equipment is similar to the Griffin type. Alloy steel heat exchanger tubes are used, and blast temperatures in the range of 700 to 900 F are obtained. Another, which utilizes about 80 per cent of the cupola effluent gas, results in hot blast temperatures of the order of 800 to 900 F. Still another Schack type uses a spiral radiation type heat exchanger, and has a maximum hot blast temperature capacity of the order of 900 F.

The "Economizer" hot blast system draws off effluent gas above the charging door, uses finned alloy steel heat exchanger tubes, and attains hot blast temperature of the order of 800 F. Blast preheater systems of the recuperative type, using cupola effluent gases for fuel, present the problem of particulate matter removal from the system which, if allowed to build up on the tubes, greatly reduces heat transfer efficiency. Daily brushing of the tubes permits reasonably consistent efficiency; if the tubes are cleaned once a week, the efficiency of the system will be reduced rather noticeably toward the end of the week.

A lag between the time the blast is turned on and the time the blast is preheated to the desired temperature is also inherent in recuperative type systems. Some fluctuation in blast temperature is to be expected as the blast temperature is dependent upon the cupola melting conditions.

To overcome these shortcomings and for economic reasons discussed in the following, externally fired type hot blast systems have been installed in several foundries.

EXTERNALLY FIRED HOT BLAST SYSTEMS

Drying Systems

Externally fired stoves employing natural gas or oil are used in "Drying Systems" externally fired hot blast equipment. The cold blast is passed around unalloyed exchangers and travels on to the cupola at 480 F maximum temperature. Gas combustion (1050 BTU natural gas), will average about 175 cu ft per ton. There is very slight pressure drop across the heat exchanger.

In a typical installation the windbox is hung separately from the cupola and about 5 ft above the tuyeres. Flexible expansion joints connect downcomers to the windbox, and the whole assembly is well insulated.

Todd-Thermo Cupola Hot Blast Heater

Figure 7.5 shows the general arrangement of a 13,000 cfm Todd-Thermo externally fired air heater for temperatures in the range of 150 to 1000 F. The combustion chamber is below the heat exchanger tubes, the design being such that the hot gases leave the combustion chamber at the right, and then pass from right to left up and around the heat exchanger tubes to the exhaust stack. The cold air passes from left to right through the heat exchanger tubes in a counterflow direction, thus improving the efficiency of the equipment. The dimensions of the heater are 12 ft 10 in. in length, 9 ft 4 in. in width, and 19 ft 5 in. high. There are approximately 4,100 sq ft of heating surface and, based on capacity, it is felt that this is a very compact unit.

As an example of the versatility of this type of equipment in one installation, it is operated between 650 and 850 F when melting iron for engineering castings and pipe cast centrifugally in metal molds. Consumption of No. 2 fuel oil is from 60 to 75 gal per hr when melting at a rate of 15 to 20 tons per hr. When melting iron for high-carbon castings (T. C. between 4.0 and 4.2 per cent) or 100 per cent steel charges, the air blast temperature used is 950 F. Under these conditions the consumption of No. 2 fuel oil is 85-100 gph when melting at a rate of 15 to 20 tons per hr.

The principal maintenance expense has been found to be in connection with the block-type refractories at the exhaust end of the combustion chamber, where the highest temperatures prevail. Repairs have been made in this area on five different occasions, but the heater has been out of service only one day in the three years it has been in operation. The cost of these repairs is not excessive as semi-skilled labor can be used.

The heater is fired with a single oil burner, a feature which makes temperature control circuits relatively simple. Oil atomizers of different sizes are used in the burner to take care of the various load requirements imposed on the heater. For example, a single atomizer may be used to heat between 450 and 600 lb of air per min (approximately 5,800 to 7,800 cu ft per min) to temperatures ranging from 500 to 900 F. To heat this same quantity of air to temperatures ranging from 900 to 1000 F a larger atomizer is required.

When necessary, atomizers can be changed during the course of operation. The change can be made in a few minutes, and the resulting drop in temperature is negligible. The blast temperature is held within

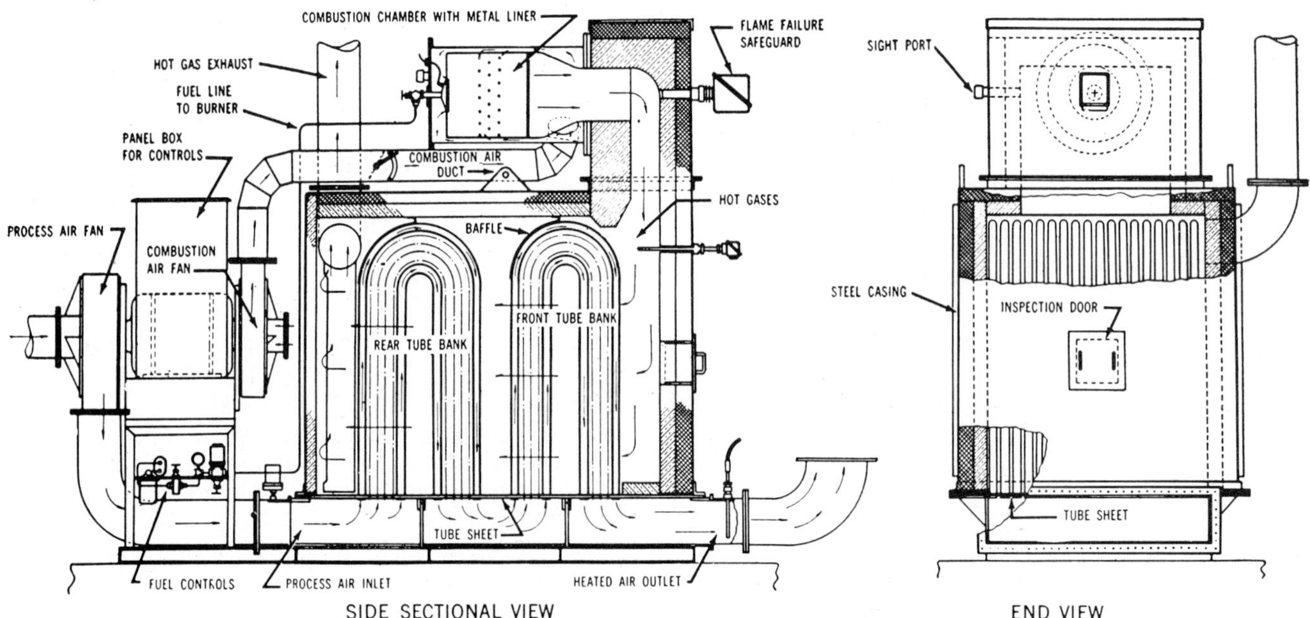

Fig. 7.5. General arrangement of 13,000 cfm Todd-Thermo air heater.

narrow limits by means of automatic control equipment of the modulating type. This results in much closer control than can generally be obtained with the "on-and-off" type control. All control equipment, pressure gages, starting switches and the like are mounted on a control panel located in a clean, well-lighted control room. Thus, the man in charge, when making routine visual inspection of the instruments, can tell at a glance whether or not the desired conditions are being maintained.

From a "cold" start the air heater may be brought up to operating temperature at a maximum rate of 20 F per min. This rate is controlled manually until the air blast is within 50 F of operating temperature, and then the control is turned over to the automatic equipment. After the heater has been in operation for a period of an hour or more and it is desired to change the blast temperature, it can be done by re-setting the automatic controls. During the warm-up period, air going through the heat exchanger is spilled to the atmosphere by opening a specially designed, motorized by-pass valve. As soon as the blast has reached the desired operating temperature, the by-pass valve is closed and melting starts, thus providing hot air at a predetermined temperature from the very beginning of the heat.

If for any reason it is necessary to stop melting temporarily during the course of a heat, the cupola blower is not shut down but the by-pass valve is opened, just as it is, while the heat exchanger is being brought up to operating temperature. Melting is resumed by closing the by-pass valve, and with this procedure the cupola air blast temperature remains the same as it was prior to the shutdown. It is felt that the by-pass feature is a distinct advantage over hot blast systems operated in conjunction with cupola blowers which must be shut down in case it is necessary to stop the melting operation.

In connection with the heater there are a number of built-in safety devices. For example, when the blower stops or the air flow falls below a certain minimum level, the burner in the combustion chamber goes out. If the burner flame goes out, the oil flow to the burner stops for a length of time sufficient to purge the combustion chamber of any explosive air-oil mixture, and if the combustion air blower fails, the flow of oil to the burner is cut off. In case of failure of any of the thermocouples in the system, there is a signal light to indicate that this condition exists.

Whiting-Thermo Hot Blast System

A similar preheater, separately fired by a single gas or oil burner, is the Whiting-Thermo hot blast system (Fig. 7.6).

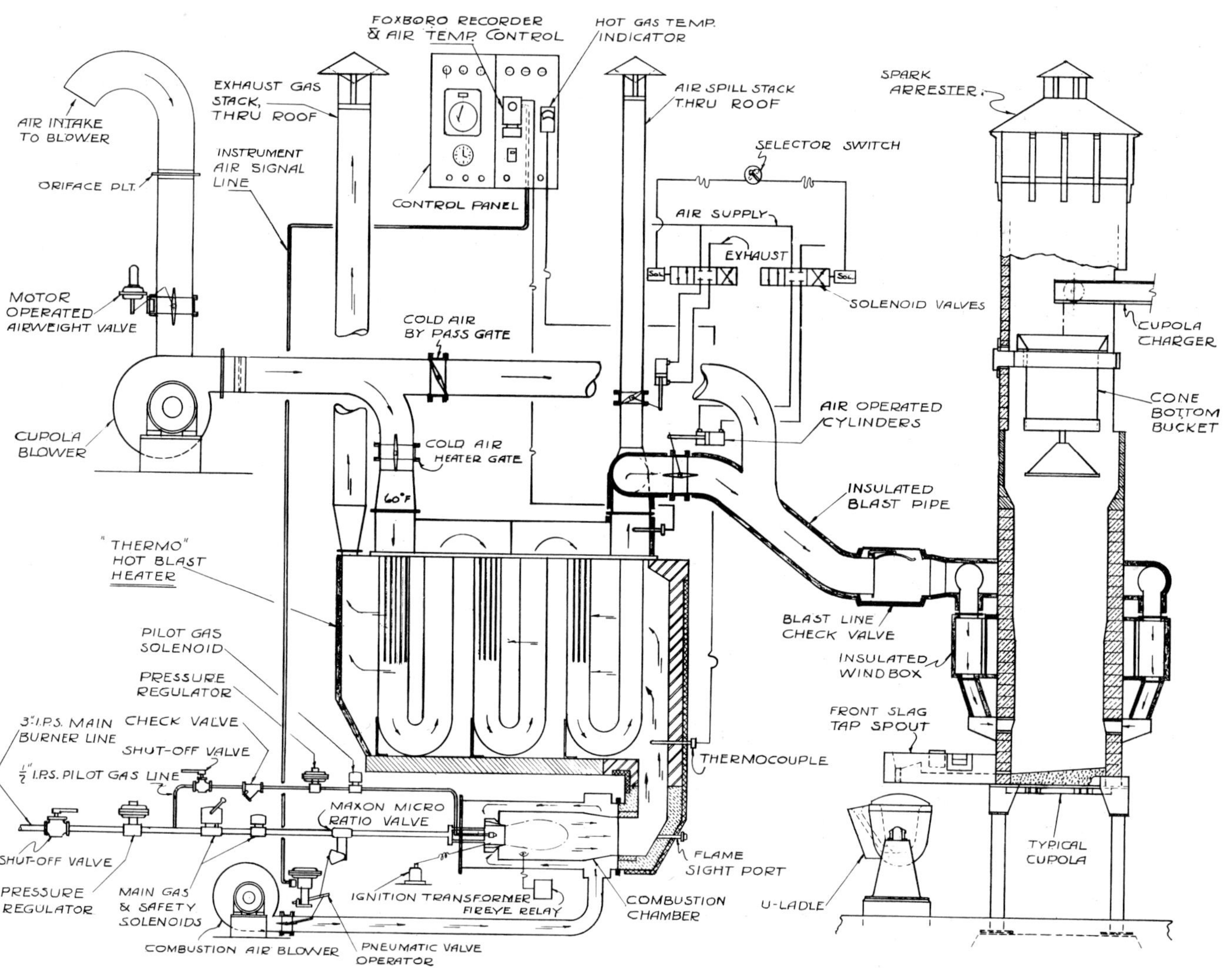

Fig. 7.6. Whiting-Thermo hot blast system fired by single gas or oil burner.

GENERAL CONSIDERATIONS OF HOT BLAST EQUIPMENT

In general, the capital investment required for the recuperative types of hot blast equipment is higher than for the externally fired types. Maintenance costs may be higher for recuperative types, although advances in design and in materials used should reduce such costs. Advantages of the recuperative types include the following:

1) Use of cupola effluent gas for fuel.
2) Their assistance in solving the cupola smoke and particle discharge problem by removing much of the heavier material before it passes through the final smoke and fume removal apparatus.
3) The compatibility with completely closed cupola systems.

In addition to having a lower first cost, the externally fired types in general have lower maintenance costs and are more flexible in operation in that blast temperatures may be controlled at definite levels. The lower maintenance costs are offset in part by the cost of the fuel used to preheat the blast. The operation of externally fired units is independent of the composition of the cupola effluent gas, and thus imposes no restrictions on the coke to iron ratio or on types of metal used in the cupola charges.

HUMIDITY CONTROL

In a number of metallurgical operations where a carbonaceous fuel is in direct contact with material being treated, to which it supplies heat by combustion with air, it has been found that the moisture content of the air is a matter of great importance. This is the case in the cupola melting of both gray and white iron castings for malleablizing. It is a matter of common knowledge that the operation of a foundry cupola is dependent upon the weather. If the day be a dry one, the air entering the cupola will be low in moisture, and this will have a beneficial effect upon the operation. On the other hand, if the moisture content of the air be high, the operation of the cupola is affected adversely.

These facts in themselves are responsible for many of the ups and downs encountered in cupola operation. During the winter season, the moisture content of the air is usually low, and this checks with the common observation that the operation of the cupola is more uniform in winter than in summer. During the summer season, the moisture content of the air varies widely and these fluctuations occur rather suddenly, at times during the course of a single day, with a consequent upsetting of the cupola operation.

This fact is so well recognized that it has become good practice in the operation of cupolas to take periodic moisture readings of the air used in the blast and adjust the coke in the charge. This requires constant attention, and at the best does not accomplish the same results obtained by maintaining a uniform moisture in the cupola air.

If the amount of excess moisture that is blown into a cupola on a high humidity day is calculated, the quantity of water is found to be astounding. For example, for a cupola requiring air at the rate of 10,000 cfm, and assuming that the outside air has a moisture content of 9 grains per cu ft, and further assuming that the optimum moisture content is 3 grains per cu ft, the excess moisture in the blast air amounts to about 4,100 lb, or 500 gal of water in an 8-hr operating day. Thus, approximately 2 tons of excess moisture is blown into the cupola.

Some of the larger companies with proper facilities carried on experimental work to determine just what effect the moisture in the cupola blast had on the cupola operation. The results of these experiments proved that increased moisture content slowed the melting rate, increased the manganese and silicon losses, and decreased the carbon pick-up of the iron. Further, the tensile, transverse and impact strengths of the iron decreased with increased moisture, while the chill depth increased.

A large producer of malleable iron castings, using the cupola-electric melting unit, controls the humidity of the blast by dehumidifying in the summer and humidifying in the winter by holding the moisture around 55 grains per lb of air, or about 4.2 grains per cu ft. This amount of moisture was chosen primarily because the cost of dehumidifying from 4 grains down to dry blast is out of proportion to the benefits derived from it. Rather than vary from 0.6 grains up to 4 grains in the winter, they provide for adding water to the blast during this period to make the operation uniform during the entire year.

In the production of white iron for malleable iron castings, control of the moisture content in the cupola blast improves the carbon control of the iron, reduces the tendency for the iron to shrink and crack, and aids in the annealability in producing an iron which responds more readily to heat treatment. In general controlled humidity is desirable both from the standpoint of metallurgical control and increased casting yield.

A schematic diagram of airflow for cupolas is shown in Fig. 7.7. Fresh air is taken from the outside and passes through the humidity control unit, next through the blower into the hot blast stoves, and then into the cupola.

Having once established the advantages of a relatively dry blast, the next problem was to find a suitable and economical means of controlling the moisture content of the air.

METHODS USED FOR MOISTURE CONTROL

Refrigeration

Since high moisture content was more troublesome than low, means were first sought to remove excessive moisture. The obvious way to accomplish this, with the equipment then available, was to cool the air to a temperature sufficiently low to condense the excess moisture. This procedure involved passing the air either through a chilled water spray or a cold finned coil. With this method a refrigerating medium was necessary, either to chill the water or chill the coil directly.

Systems of this kind were tried, and the results further proved the advisability of using a dry blast. However, the first cost of the equipment required was fairly high, and the operating costs were extremely high since a tremendous capacity was required to cool the large volume of air to a temperature low enough to remove an appreciable amount of moisture. It is wasteful thermo-dynamically to cool the air, blow it into the cupola, and then charge more coke into the cupola to heat the air from the low temperature back up to the original outside air temperature.*

A further disadvantage of this system lies in the fact that when the outside air moisture drops below 3 grains per cu ft, no means are available to add moisture to the air to raise it to 3 grains per cu ft. This can be accomplished, however, by turning live steam into the blast air or by passing the air through hot-water sprays. Both of these methods are effective but very hard to control.

Chemical Methods

Realization of the advantages of dry blast for cupolas led to a search for a more economical means of removing this moisture. The next approach was the use of adsorbent or absorbent chemicals. It may be well to define adsorption and absorption.

a) Adsorption involves removal of water by chemical means, with no change in the chemical composition of the adsorbing agent. Adsorbent materials are usually solids.
b) Absorption involves removal of water by chemical means, accompanied by a chemical change of the absorbing material. Absorbents usually are hygroscopic salts used in a water solution.

Adsorbent Method

The most common adsorbents are silica gel and activated alumina. Since they are similar in action, the use of silica gel only will be described.

In the adsorption process, the air to be treated is passed through a dry bed of the gel material. Here adsorption takes place adiabatically, that is, the latent heat of condensation is changed into sensible heat with a consequent rise in air temperature. In this process no change takes place in the chemical composition of the bed. With commercial equipment of this type available today, it is not possible to reduce air from, say, 9 grains per cu ft to 3 grains per cu ft without first pre-cooling the air with a refrigeration coil to about 7 grains per cu ft.

While the adsorption method is more efficient than the straight cooling system, it has the following disadvantages:

1) The rate of moisture removal from the air is not constant. The rate of moisture adsorption by the gel is highest when the bed is dry, and approaches zero as the bed approaches saturation. Hence, the air leaving the unit does not have a constant moisture content. This major disadvantage has been somewhat alleviated by forming

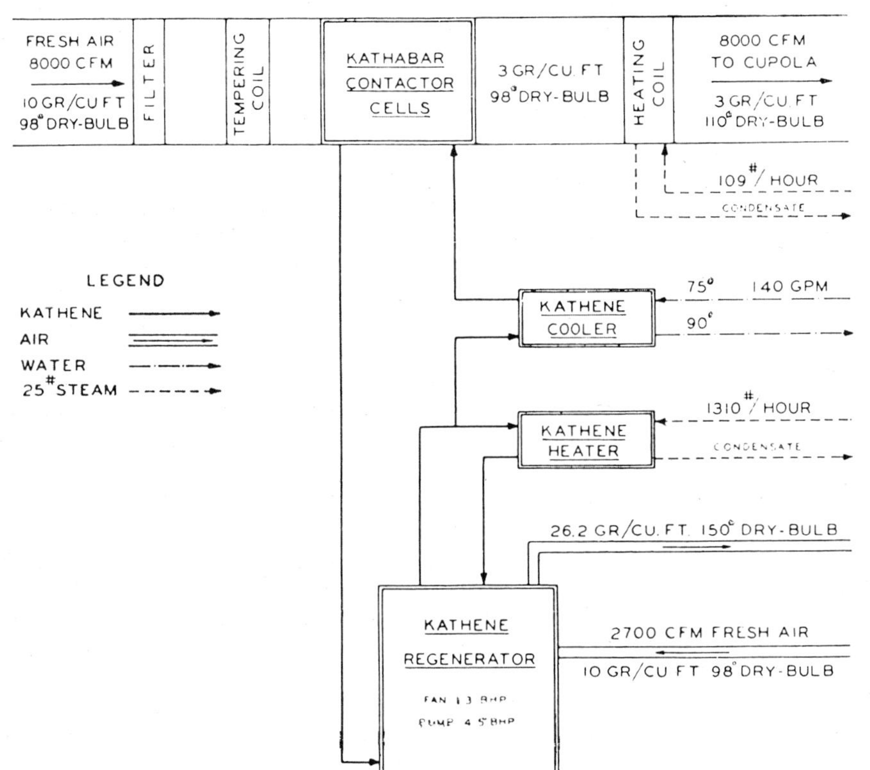

Fig. 7.7. Air flow diagram for a cupola dry blast system.

*To illustrate, for the 10,000 cfm cupola mentioned previously, it is desired that the moisture content of this air be reduced from a maximum summer condition of 9 grains per cu ft to 3 grains per cu ft. To do this with a refrigerated coil would require cooling the air to approximately 43F. Assuming the outside air temperature to be 90F with the maximum moisture condition, the total heat to be removed from the air is 1,084,500 Btu per hr, or the equivalent of about 90 tons of refrigeration. To cool air to 43F will require about a 35F refrigerant temperature.

It is characteristic of refrigerating machines that the lower the refrigerant temperature, the higher the horsepower per ton required. A reciprocating compressor operating at 35F evaporator temperature will require about 0.9 bhp per ton of refrigeration or, for this example, approximately 81 hp. Of this 81 hp expended, only 53 per cent is useful work, the other 47 per cent being used for unnecessary air cooling. Now 0.47 x 1,084,500= 509,700 Btu per hr that must be put back into the air to heat it to the original outside air temperature of 90F. This, added to the unuseful work of cooling, makes a total unproductive energy consumption of 1,019,400 Btu per hr. Since only 53 per cent of the cooling load is employed for useful work, that is, actual moisture removal, 1,594,200 Btu per hr must be supplied to get a useful 574,800 Btu per hr, which is about a 36 per cent efficiency.

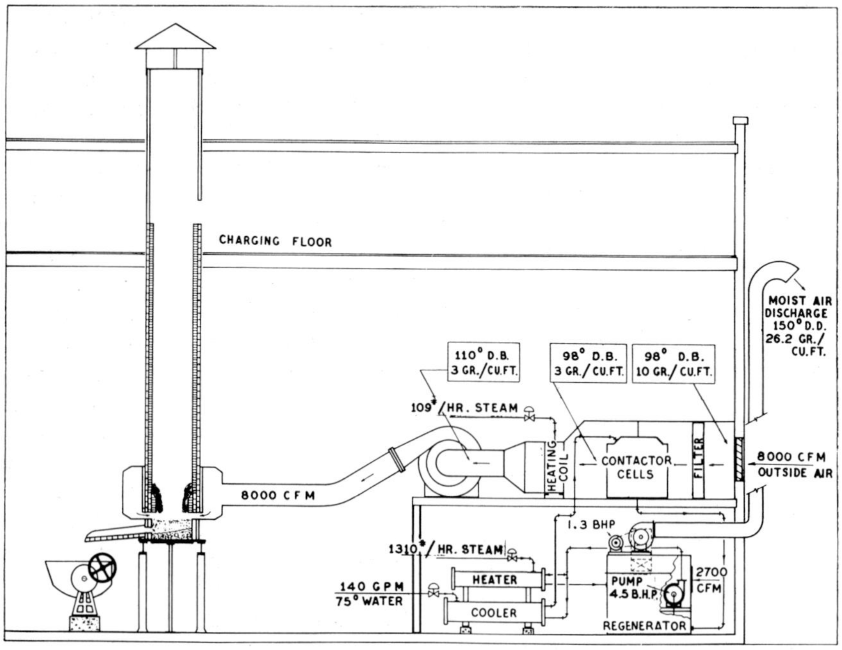

Fig. 7.8. **Installation diagram of absorbent-type humidity control system.**

the gel bed in the shape of a drum, which is rotated periodically to bring a new dry bed into place at short intervals. When one bed of gel approaches saturation, the new dry bed is brought into place and the wet one is heated by gas, or high pressure steam, to remove the moisture. This necessitates the use of essentially duplicate apparatus, and consequently makes the equipment quite bulky. Large quantities of air are difficult to handle due to the number of units required.

2) Dry beds are easily clogged with foundry dust and efficiency is lost.
3) As with the refrigeration method, this system also has no accurate means of humidification.

Absorption Methods

The common absorbent solutions are lithium chloride, calcium chloride, zinc chloride, calcium-lithium-chloride mixtures, calcium bromide and sulphuric acid. All are more or less corrosive. However, an inhibitor has been developed for use with lithium chloride which permits the use of inexpensive materials of construction with no corrosion difficulties. The most widely used of the above solutions is lithium chloride, since it has a relatively low freezing point and high concentration as compared with the other salts, and is non-corrosive. Figure 7.8 illustrates diagrammatically an absorbent-type humidity control unit.

Commercially, the salt is used in solution at concentrations as high as 45 per cent. In this form it is passed through a contact medium to bring the air and solution into intimate contact to facilitate the transfer of moisture from one to the other. The direction of moisture flow depends on which has the higher vapor pressure, the air or the solution. At constant density the vapor pressure is a function of the solution temperature, that is, raising the solution temperature gives a higher solution vapor pressure and vice versa. Hence, by varying the solution temperature moisture can be added to or removed from the air as desired.

As moisture is absorbed from the air the solution is diluted. Since the operation is continuous, the density of the solution decreases. To maintain a constant density of solution it is necessary continually to remove from the solution the water which has been absorbed from the air. This is accomplished by heating a small portion of the solution, usually with steam, and passing this hot solution over another contact surface and, at the same time, forcing a small quantity of outside air through this contact surface. In this case the solution, being at an elevated temperature, has a vapor pressure much higher than the outside air, and consequently the moisture flows from the solution into the air. This small amount of hot moist air is discharged to the outside. This process is known as regeneration.

Cooling Solution

In both the absorption and the regeneration operations, some heat has been added to the solution. The mixture in the sump of the unit is at a higher temperature than was the solution which entered the air-conditioning contactor at the beginning of the cycle. The solution then is cooled to the original starting temperature with well water, city water, cooling tower water, river water or whatever is available in the particular location.

For winter operation the solution going to the air-conditioning contactor is heated slightly, and moisture is readily given up to the air, so that a constant moisture condition can be maintained the year around. The control of the system is simple in that it is necessary only to control the temperature of the solution to obtain the exact conditions desired. Further, straight-line control can be obtained, since the absorption rate is constant. Since the flow of steam for regenerating the solution is automatically controlled by a density control in the unit, both the steam and water consumption are approximately in direct proportion to the amount of water removed from the air, which makes for extremely low operating costs. The power cost is insignificant, since the only electrical energy required is for the lithium-chloride pump and a small regenerator waste-air fan.

This system differs from both the refrigeration and adsorption systems in that there is very little change in the temperature of the air through the absorption contactor. The air leaves at approximately the same temperature as it entered. It is also possible to deliver air at both a constant temperature and a constant humidity throughout the year.

The equipment also is flexible in application. The air-handling portion is made in standard units which can be grouped together to handle almost any air volume. Units are in operation which treat over 80,000 cfm of fresh air.

OXYGEN ENRICHMENT

Occasional lengthy cupola shutdowns occur which result in cold iron. All foundries are faced at times with cold iron problems after unexpected shutdowns or after lunch periods and shift changes. These shutdowns often result in the pigging of a few or several ladles of iron, and at times pouring of iron of questionable temperature into molds.

A useful tool for the correction of such temperature problems is that of oxygen enrichment of the blast, as an immediate response can be obtained when the temperature of the metal drops. This is due to the fact that a faster combustion reaction is brought about by the concentration of oxygen in the blast, and a corresponding decrease in nitrogen volume. The nitrogen does not contribute to combustion but absorbs heat. Oxygen is generally used for about 15 min in starting the cupola, and the enrichment is from 1 to 4 per cent. Greater enrichment has not been found to be practical, either through additional operating benefits or costwise.

The coke ratio does not have to be changed to make intermittent oxygen enrichment effective. If the bed height is correct, metal temperature will increase about 50° after 10 min of enrichment. If the metal temperature drop is due to a low coke bed, oxygen enrichment will not have an immediate effect and adjustments in bed height will have to be made. However, no adjustments in coke splits are necessary to compensate the bed height when added oxygen has been used for relatively short periods.

Bridging in the cupola can be eliminated through the use of oxygen in the blast. If the bridge is caused by an accumulation of slag brought about by lack of fluidity of the slag, corrective measures can be taken by adding fluxes to the charge. However, time is required to bring the fluxes down into the melting zone. During that time additional oxygen in the blast will eliminate the bridging due to increase of temperature.

Oxygen, when used intermittently, will not appreciably affect the chemical analysis of the iron. Recent investigations prove that refractory wear is no greater when oxygen is used intermittently than with ordinary blast air. This is logical inasmuch as the intermittent use of oxygen merely restores the desired melting conditions in the cupola.

Considerable work has been done to evaluate the continuous use of oxygen in the blast. Tests prove that coke consumption can be reduced by the continuous use of oxygen, but that the economies of this practice are not favorable at present due to high cost of oxygen.

CHAPTER 8

Temperature Measuring

The temperature of molten cast iron leaving the cupola is determined by cupola operation – principally by coke ratio and air supply. The resulting pouring temperature determines to a considerable degree the fluidity of the molten metal, the structure of the cast iron, and the physical characteristics of the casting. The importance of control of temperature in cupola operation is therefore obvious.

Exact measurements of molten iron temperatures in the cupola, the spout, the forehearth, the ladle, or the pouring stream are difficult; however, procedures have been established by which temperatures can be measured with acceptable accuracy and reproducibility.

The three types of measuring instruments in general use are the optical pyrometer (Fig. 8.1), radiation pyrometers (Figs. 8.2, 8.3 and 8.4), and the immersion thermocouple.

The use of these instruments for measuring the temperature of molten cast iron is conditioned by:

1) the use of the device under conditions for which it is calibrated,
2) operator's understanding of these requirements,
3) the operator's recognizing limitations of the equipment and of the method being used.

The optical pyrometer is used more extensively in cupola operations than any other method.

FUNDAMENTAL LAWS OF TEMPERATURE MEASUREMENT

The temperature of a heated surface can be determined with precision by measurement of the radiant energy emitted, because the latter increases at a rate many times as great as the rate at which the temperature increases. The total energy radiated varies as the difference between the fourth power of the absolute temperature of the radiant body and the fourth power of the absolute temperature of the surroundings. This is the fundamental law upon which the operation of radiation pyrometers is based.

The spectral energy in the red portion of the spectrum increases at a rate which, at 1832 F (1000 C), is 18 times, and at 3632 F (2000 C), is about 10 times the rate at which the absolute temperature increases. This is the fundamental law upon which the operation of the optical pyrometer is based. Therefore, to attain a precision of 1 per cent of the absolute temperature, the total energy radiated need be measured only to 4 per cent, and the spectral energy within 10 to 18 per cent. The radiant energy emitted per unit area per unit time by all hot bodies depends upon the temperature and the surface characteristics of the body.

Black Body Conditions

To eliminate the varying effects of surface characteristics, both optical and radiation pyrometers are calibrated for use under black body conditions. A black body may be defined as a radiator which, at any specific temperature, emits in each part of the spectrum the maximum energy obtainable per unit time as a result of temperature alone.

Black body conditions are achieved in a space that is completely surrounded by uniformly heated walls. The ratio of the radiant energy per unit time and per unit area emitted by a body to that emitted by a black body at the same temperature, is termed the emissivity. Total emissivity refers to radiation of all wave lengths; monochromatic emissivity refers to radiation of a particular wave length.

OPTICAL PYROMETERS

The operation of an optical pyrometer depends upon the photometric comparison of the intensity of the light radiated from the body under observation with that emitted by the filament of a standard incandescent lamp. The intensity of the radiation from the filament is proportional to the current passing through it. This principle is applied in two ways: 1) the brightness of the filament is varied to match that of the apparent radiation to be measured, and 2) the filament is maintained at constant intensity and the radiation to be measured is varied.

Variable Intensity (Disappearing Filament) Meter

With this instrument, the radiation to be measured is taken from a limited range of the visible red spectrum and compared with that from a standard source; e.g., a black body at the temperature of the melting point of gold (1063 C – 1945.4 F – by international agreement).

The filament of the standard lamp is calibrated under black body conditions, usually by comparison with a pyrometer which has been calibrated by the Bureau of Standards and is used exclusively for this purpose. Since the brightness of the filament is related definitely to the current passing through it, a precise means of measuring the current, resistance or voltage is required. Usually the potentiometric method is employed and adjustments are made with a rheostat.

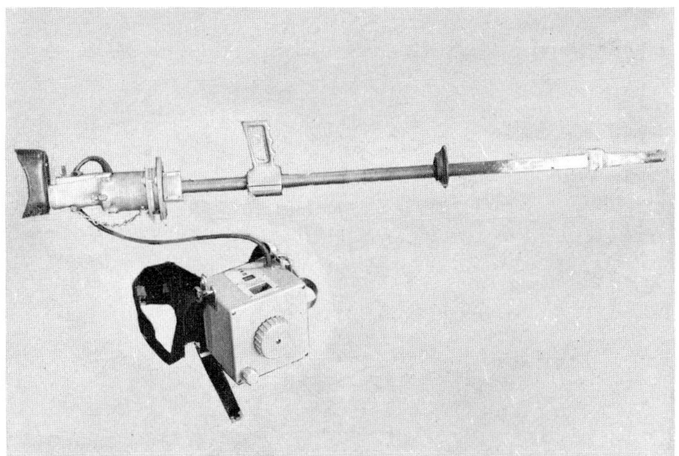

Fig. 8.1. Left — Optical Pyrometer equipped with closed end immersion tube; above — Same pyrometer in use to determine temperature of molten cast iron in ladle.

The telescope, which contains the comparison lamp, is focused so that a sharp image of the filament is seen on that of the hot surface. If the filament appears as a bright line, its temperature is higher, and if it is seen as a dark line, the temperature is lower than that of the body under observation. By manipulation of the rheostat, and therefore the current, the filament can be brought to the same temperature as that of the hot surface, and then becomes invisible.

Thus when the image of the filament disappears, a photometric match has been established, and the temperature can be determined from the potentiometer reading by the use of conversion tables, or directly in degrees when the instrument is equipped with a screen which compensates for a specified emittance. The Bureau of Standards will certify the readings of this type of instrument to plus or minus 5 F for the range 1950 to 3200 F (2-3 C from 1066 to 1760 C).

The brightness or intensity of the light, rather than its color, is compared and, therefore, it is possible for a person who is color blind to make accurate determinations of temperature.

Precautions

The limitations imposed by the laws of radiation must be considered carefully when taking temperatures with an optical pyrometer. The telescope should not be sighted through an atmosphere of incandescent gas, smoke, fume or steam, nor directly toward sunlight or strong artificial light, nor on slag or oxide films, as these conditions introduce errors of considerable magnitude. The telescope objective should be clean. The target energy passes through the objective, while the comparison source energy does not; errors can result if objective is dirty.

The measurement of the temperature of molten cast iron with the optical pyrometer requires close attention to detail. The emissivity of the molten cast iron surface, when free from oxide films, is low (0.4 in comparison with 1.0 for the ideal black body). However, there is a characteristic emissivity for each molten metal which must be known, and the corresponding correction applied to the apparent or brightness temperature to obtain the true temperature. Alloying elements such as manganese may increase the emittance, and consequently lead to errors.

Temperatures at Cupola Spout

The temperatures of iron in the cupola spout are taken by sighting the telescope on the darker background rather than on the brighter streaks in the metal stream. A sighting location should be selected which is as free from fume as possible. It is possible to deflect the cloud of fume by placing a small piece of metal sheet across the top of the spout or by the use of a small volume of low pressure air.

The air should not impinge directly against the stream of metal, which would cause a chilling of the metal surface and lead to errors in the temperature reading. It is not difficult to develop a procedure for taking temperatures in the spout, or on the metal as it leaves the spout, which are sufficiently reliable for foundry purposes.

When this procedure has been worked out and a satisfactory reading is obtained with the optical pyrometer, which is calibrated for black body conditions, the emissivity of 0.4 may be used to obtain the true temperature. The newer optical pryometers used for taking spout temperatures are provided with a compensating screen (emissivity 0.4) which, when used under the conditions described, makes the correction automatically and the true temperatures are read directly on the optical pyrometer scale.

Temperatures in Ladles and Forehearths

The presence of slag, fumes, and oxide films further complicate the measurement of temperature in ladles or forehearths. Several methods may be used to compensate for these factors.

Slag and oxide films can be swept away momentarily with a skimmer to obtain temperatures with a direct reading instrument having the 0.4 emissivity compensating screen.

Since the oxide film changes in emissivity with the metal temperature, corrections can be made to temperatures taken with an optical pyrometer calibrated for black body conditions. Correction factors for these readings have been studied by Wensel and Roeser[1] and appear in the literature.

If an optical pyrometer is sighted into a closed end clay graphite tube immersed in molten metal (Fig. 8.1), these interferences are eliminated and accurate

Fig. 8.2. (left to right) Radiation pyrometer installation measuring temperature of molten cast iron in the spout between the cupola and forehearth. Pyrometer removed from spout to show immersion tube. General view (above) of installation showing temperature recorder at right; white arrow locates pyrometer.

temperature readings are obtained under black body conditions. A stream of air may be forced through the tube to prevent metal from entering. This results in only the apparent metal temperature; the process is consistent from heat to heat so that readings may be correlated with foundry practice.

Advantages of Disappearing Filament Pyrometer

The optical pyrometer is applicable to the measurement of temperatures from 1400 F (760 C) to the highest temperatures encountered in foundry practice. It may be used to measure the temperature in inaccessible places, small surfaces, and moving bodies wherever the pyrometer can be sighted properly at the surface. No part of the pyrometer is exposed to destructive heating effects and, when carefully handled, requires practically no maintenance.

The indicated temperature is related directly to the temperature of the heated body under test, not the temperature of some adjacent body which is assumed to be at the same temperature as the body under test.

Since its corrections for nonblack body conditions are well known and are generally less than those of the total radiation pyrometer (discussed in next section), the optical pyrometer is frequently used to check or calibrate the total radiation pyrometer on the job.

As outlined previously, the principal disadvantage is the possibility of errors due to sighting through fume, smoke, steam, and flame, and the possibility of error due to carelessness in making the photometric match. The accuracy of the temperature measurement depends upon the honesty and accuracy of the operator, as the optical pyrometer is not self-recording.

Constant Intensity Pyrometer

In pyrometers of this type, the comparison lamp filament is maintained at a constant brightness, and the radiation from the hot body is cut down to match it by means of an absorbing device such as a glass wedge or a polarizing prism interposed between the hot body and the comparison source. The latter is usually an electric lamp which requires standardization of the filament current at only one value, so that the use of a long scale ammeter is unnecessary. The instrument is therefore more compact and lighter in weight.

The disadvantages are: 1) that all brightness matches must be made at the relatively low intensity, corresponding to the lowest temperature to be measured with the instrument; and 2) the reading involves the maintenance of the lamp current at the standard value as well as the manipulation of the absorbing device.

RADIATION PYROMETERS

The radiation pyrometer depends upon the heating effect of all or a large part of the radiant energy emitted by a unit area of the heated surface. The energy is concentrated upon the hot junction of a thermocouple or series of thermocouples, thus generating an emf (electromotive force) which is recorded in terms of temperature.

Radiation pyrometers are classified according to the optical system employed in their construction: a) mirror or lens type, depending upon the focusing arrangement, and b) fixed or variable focus, depending upon whether means are provided for changing the distance of the thermocouple from the focusing agent to compensate for changes in the distance of the focusing agent from the hot surface.

Advantages and Limitations

Radiation pyrometers are calibrated to measure temperature under black body conditions. Therefore, the limitations imposed by the laws of radiation must be taken into consideration when using them to measure molten cast iron temperatures. Sighting the receiving tube through an atmosphere of steam, fume, or smoke, introduces errors of greater magnitude in the temperature reading than is the case when optical pyrometer readings are taken under like conditions. This is due to the fact that the radiation pyrometer receives energy from the total spectrum, while the optical pyrometer is calibrated for one wave length of the visible spectrum. The corrections necessary for emissivity conditions also are of greater magnitude for the radiation pyrometer.

In commercial practice, radiation pyrometers are available which measure surface temperatures from 300 F to much higher temperatures than those encountered in foundry practice. In this respect they cover much wider ranges than the optical pyrometer.

The radiation pyrometer is seldom used as a direct sighting instrument to measure the temperature of molten cast iron because of the difficulty of obtaining a sighting field which meets the requirements of the pyrometer, and also because of the difficulty in preventing dust, smoke, and water vapor from depositing upon the lens or other parts of the optical system.

Either special immersion radiation pyrometers or nonimmersion pyrometers may be used to measure the temperature of molten cast iron.

Measuring Temperature of Molten Metal in Spout

Immersion radiation pyrometer[2]

This type radiation pyrometer (Fig. 8.2.) can be a permanent installation to measure the temperature of molten cast iron in the front slagging well, the spout or the forehearth of continuously operated cupolas.

The radiation pyrometer is protected from heat, dust, and damage by being located in the upper water-cooled section, while the lower section consisting of a closed-end clay-graphite tube is immersed approximately 10 in. into the molten cast iron. The energy radiated from the bottom of the tube is directed onto the thermocouple (actually a series of couples called a thermopile) by a quartz lens. The heat absorbed by the thermopile sets up a proportionate electrical potential which, by the use of proper instruments, is converted into a continuous chart record of temperature.

Provision is made for keeping the immersion tube free from smoke, fume, and gases which absorb radiant energy and introduce errors in the temperature measurements. Thus installed, the radiation pyrometer measures temperatures under the black body conditions for which it is calibrated.

The clay-graphite immersion tube can be used until failure occurs without any risk of damage to the radiation pyrometer. The immersion tubes can be replaced easily and, although the useful life of the immersion tube varies considerably with the operating conditions and the amount of iron flowing by it, the replacement cost is exceedingly small in comparison with the value of the continuous temperature record obtained.

To date the clay-graphite immersion tubes have been successfully used in those cupola operations where large volumes of hyper-eutectic irons are produced at moderate melting temperatures. Their life is expected to be shorter when hypoeutectic irons are melted or high melting temperatures are used. The wider use of immersion tubes awaits the development of improved refractory materials to better cope with these limiting conditions.

The radiation pryometer has a decided advantage over other types of immersion thermocouples in that it is not exposed to risk of damage when the immersion tube fails in service. It is sufficiently removed from the molten metal area to be protected from excessive heat. It measures temperatures under black body conditions and its response is rapid, the speed of response being dependent upon the thickness of the protection tube and its thermal conductivity. The temperature may be recorded continuously and filed for future reference.

Nonimmersion radiation pyrometer

Use of the radiation principle has been satisfactorily extended to the nonimmersion radiation pyrometer[3] of the type in Figs. 8.3 and 8.4. Pyrometers of

Fig. 8.3. Nonimmersion radiation pyrometer mounted about 18 in. above molten iron in cupola spout leading to receiving ladle.

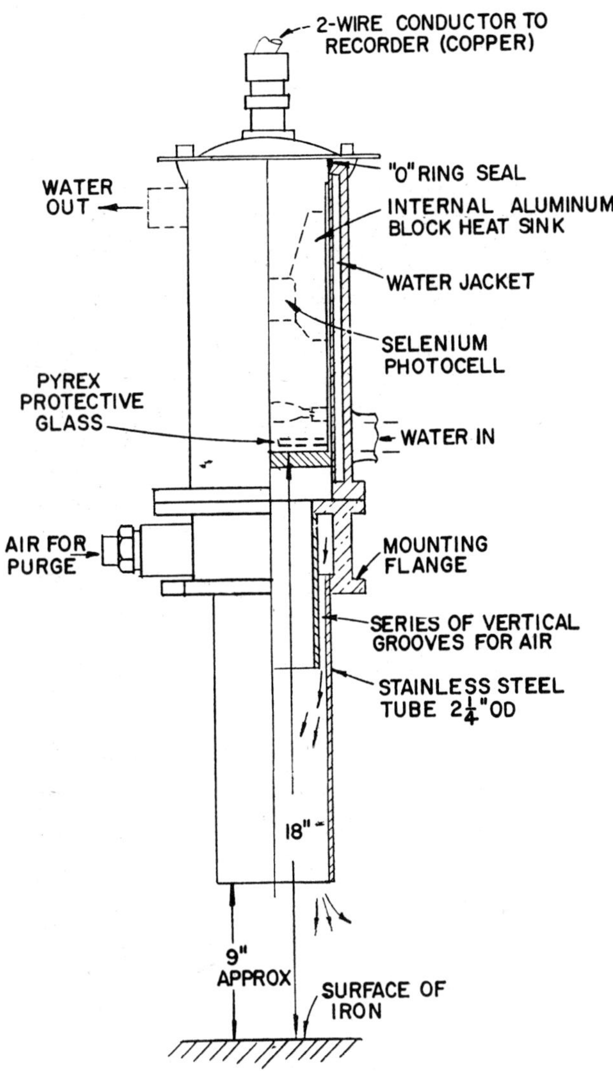

Fig. 8.4. Cross-sectional view of radiation pyrometer showing construction details. Upper half is water cooled to protect heat sensitive photocell. An air purge clears the view to the iron surface.

this type operate in the short wavelength band of visible radiation where the emissivity changes caused by dirt, oxides, fumes, etc., are not as large as those measured by total radiation pyrometers.

The radiation pyrometer is water cooled to protect the photocell used to record the radiation. An air stream is maintained in the stainless steel tube to insure a clear view to the molten iron surface which is kept free of slag, oxide, or changes in surface conditions, and kept smooth (free of turbulence and ripples).

If the precautions stated are adhered to, these units may be used for the accurate and reproducible continuous recording of molten metal temperatures in the cupola spout.

IMMERSION THERMOCOUPLES

When two dissimilar metals are joined in a circuit, a voltage will be generated when the junctions between them are at different temperatures. The practical application of this principle is the measurement of temperatures with thermocouples.

Although some use is made of chromel alumel (type K) thermocouples for intermittent temperature measurement, the most commonly used immersion thermocouples for measuring molten iron temperatures are the platinum platinum, 10 per cent rhodium (type S) and the platinum platinum, 13 per cent rhodium (type R) thermocouples. These alloys differ principally in their millivolt output.

The platinum platinum rhodium thermocouple, installed in a ceramic primary protection tube, which in turn is placed in a graphite or clay-graphite tube, is immersed in the molten metal, the temperature of which is to be determined. The necessity for using double protection tubes introduces considerable lag in the temperature response and tends to blank out small and rapid temperature changes. However, the temperatures may be indicated or recorded on a potentiometer located nearby or in the superintendent's office.

Platinum thermocouples may be used to measure temperatures up to 2900 F for short intervals, but if used at this temperature for long periods the rhodium distills gradually from the alloy wire and the thermocouple drifts off calibration. Platinum thermocouples must be watched carefully for contamination, a condition which causes a change in the calibration of the couple or, in some cases, may destroy it completely.

Fume and smoke around the thermocouple location do not introduce errors in the temperature measurement. However, the assembly has to be handled with care to prevent cracking of the protection tubes. If the outer protection tube breaks, the inner tube usually breaks at the same time, and the platinum couple is destroyed quickly by contact with the molten iron. The high initial cost of platinum thermocouples, replacement cost and maintenance are important considerations in the use of this type of immersion pyrometer.

Other types of immersion thermocouples are discussed in the literature, but are generally of only passing interest in molten iron temperature measurement.

REFERENCES

1. H. T. Wensel and W. F. Roeser, *Temperature Measurements of Molten Cast Iron,* AFA Transactions, vol. 36 (1928) p. 191.
2. R. H. Koch and A. E. Schuh, *Temperature Measurement of Molten Cast Iron with Rayotube and Optical Pyrometers,* AFA Transactions, vol. 50 (1942) p. 1163.
3. J. H. Schaum, *Forest City Uses New Concept in Pyrometry,* Modern Castings, vol. 41, no. 6 (June 1962) p. 44.

Carl F. Joseph, *Measuring and Controlling Pouring Temperature and Fluidity,* AFA Transactions, vol. 44 (1936) p. 103.

Fulton Holtby, *Rapid Temperature Measurements of Cast Iron with Immersion Thermocouples,* AFA Transactions, vol. 47 (1939) p. 854.

G. A. Lillieqvist, *Steel Foundry Control,* AFA Transactions, vol. 54 (1946) p. 553.

G. Vennerholm and L. C. Tate, *Determination of Molten Metal Temperatures,* AFA Transactions, vol. 55 (1947) p. 500.

W. E. Belcher Jr., D. Robertson, W. F. Hickes, *Temperature Measurement,* A.S.M., Metals Park, Ohio (1956).

H. E. Bennett, *Noble Metal Thermocouples,* Johnson, Matthey & Co., Ltd., London (1956).

F. Kreith, *Principles of Heat Transfer,* International, Scranton, Pa. (1958)

Pyrometry, A.S.M. Metals Handbook (1948) p. 174.

CHAPTER 9

Slag and Drop Disposal

After the slag has performed its function in the cupola it becomes a by-product which must be disposed of as efficiently and economically as possible. The amount and rate of slag generated, as well as the location of the cupola, available conveyance, etc., determines the possible methods of slag disposal.

In short heats, where only a small quantity of slag is involved, it may be desirable to run it out on a dry sand bed below the slag trough. After the heat, the solidified slag is carried out with the bottom drop.

However, if sizable amounts of slag are generated, allowing it to collect back of the cupola makes it very hot for men to work in that area. Also, the labor of breaking up and loading the cold slag later becomes uneconomical. Then one of the following methods should be considered.

SLAG CONTAINERS

Some foundries use containers consisting of steel boiler plate rolled and clamped into a cylinder approximately 5 ft in diameter and telescoped on a bottom. The interior is given a clay wash and set under the slag spout either by lift truck or dragging on a skid. When filled with hot slag it is set aside for cooling and another placed in position. When the slag has cooled sufficiently it is hoisted into a truck, either by lift truck or by a hoist and chains. The container is unclamped to release cold slag (Fig. 9.1).

Hot slag can also be run into cast iron slag pots, which may be simply mounted on two wheels with a support and tongue as shown in Fig. 9.3. When the pot is filled it is pulled to a convenient location and dumped as soon as the slag has congealed. The pots are sometimes dumped on skids under the crane so that the skids can be picked up and loaded into a truck. The slag pots are clay-washed on the inside to prevent sticking, and dry sand is placed in the bottom of the pot to protect it from any iron that may run in. Any iron will be collected on the bottom of the slag ball as a button that can easily be removed when loading the cooled slag.

Fig. 9.2. Side dump slag pot on trailer truck.

Slag pots may be mounted on wheels as illustrated in Fig. 9.4. Side dump pots conveyed on trailer trucks also are used (Fig. 9.2).

When the arrangement of the melting department is suitable, slag pots can be suspended on a monorail which will transport the slag to a siding, where it is cooled and then dumped into a truck or gondola. A typical arrangement is shown in Fig. 9.5.

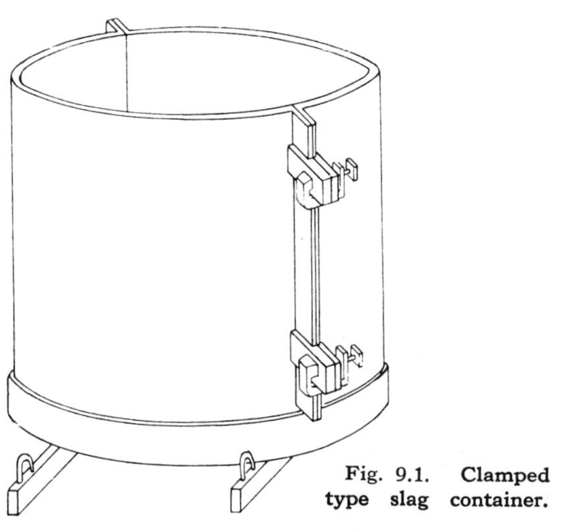

Fig. 9.1. Clamped type slag container.

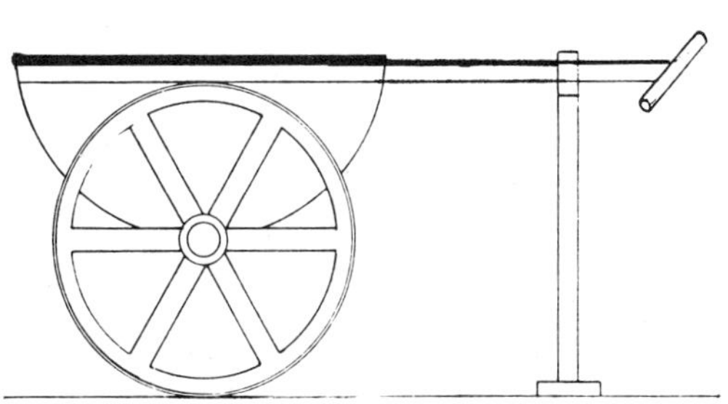

Fig. 9.3. Slag pot mounted on wheels.

METHODS EMPLOYING WATER

In one such method the slag is allowed to flow directly into a sump filled with water, as shown in Fig. 9.8, which cools and granulates the slag. The slag does not become fluffy if enough water is supplied to keep it from heating. A perforated bucket is set in the sump and, when filled, is lifted out and carried to the slag dump. The granulated slag is sometimes used for plant roads or sold for fill. If used on roads, some type of binder is needed. Sometimes the granulated slag is run over a magnetic separator to recover any iron.

A variation on the above method employs a ¾-yard capacity side-dump trailer mounted on a skid or on wheels. The trailer body is placed under the slag spout and kept filled with water from a ½-in. pipe inlet (with a 2-in. outlet near the top). When the trailer is filled with granulated slag, it is shifted from under the slag spout, the water drained out, and conveyed to the slag dump or put over a magnetic separator. Another trailer is connected with the water lines and placed under the slag spout.

A more mechanized version of the method is shown in Fig. 9.6. This is a portable unit consisting of a tank of circulating water into which the slag drops. The granulated slag in the tank is discharged by a bucket conveyor into any available box or truck.

A number of foundries are using a wood-plank-lined slag trough, while others use cast iron pipe split in half lengthwise. The trough or spout should be sloped as steeply as possible. Water from two or more ½-in. pipes (at city pressure) enters at the top of the trough back of the slag, serves to prevent sticking, and flushes the slag down the trough. The granulated slag and water then usually run into a tunnel in the floor (with removable cover) which conveys it to a sump (Fig. 9.10).

Sometimes this sump is a settling tank under a crane, and a perforated clamshell bucket takes the slag out for loading into a car or truck. Other installations use a bucket conveyor system to remove granulated slag from the sump. Usually two or more cupolas can be connected into this system (Fig. 9.7).

In all of these water methods the volume and pressure of the water used cannot be exactly calculated, but must be adjusted on the job. However, there must be enough volume to cool the slag quickly or it will foam instead of granulate. The temperature of the water is relatively unimportant, but should be cold if possible. There must be enough pressure to keep the slag moving. The water can be re-circulated in the system, or water from other cooling devices can often be used economically.

It is important to run as little iron as possible out of the slag hole, as iron clogs up the water system. Also, granulated slag with the minimum of iron is more salable to the producers of cement blocks, insulating materials, etc.

The method of slag disposal to be employed at any particular foundry should be determined by the quantity of slag and the rate at which it is generated, the adaptability of the cupola room layout, means of conveyance, distance from the cupola or cupolas from the slag dump, or end use of the slag, etc.

Fig. 9.4. **Side dump slag pot mounted on wheels.**

Fig. 9.5. **Slag pots suspended from monorail system.**

Fig. 9.6. **Portable unit: slag is dropped into water tank, then discharged by bucket conveyor into disposal unit.**

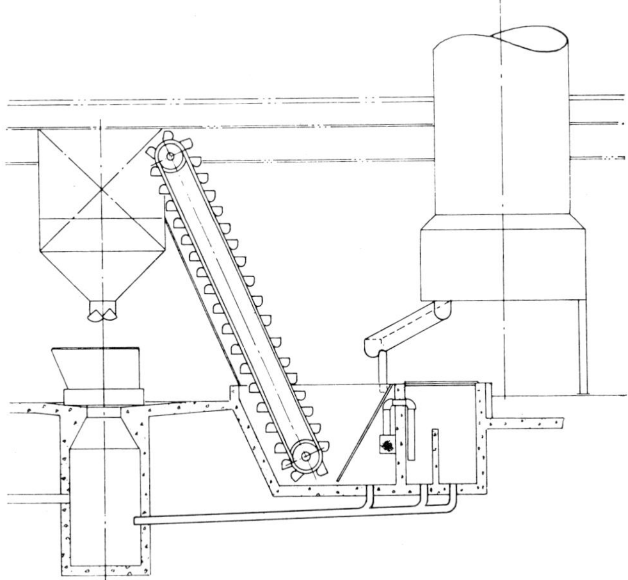

Fig. 9.7. Bucket conveyor takes granulated slag from sump.

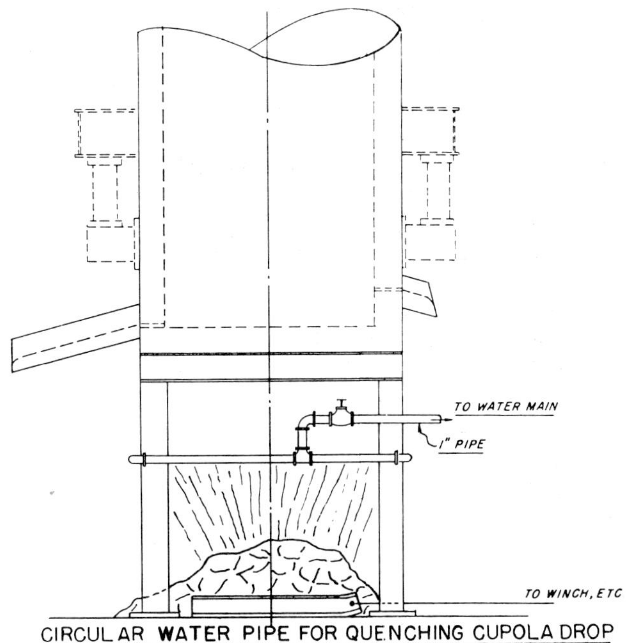

Fig. 9.9. Ring water pipe installation quenches cupola drop.

A water system, while a more expensive installation than containers, is usually less costly to operate. The operating factors to consider are cost of slag men vs. cost of water. The installation cost should be considered with respect to the amount of slag to be handled and the arrangement of the equipment.

CUPOLA DROP DISPOSAL

After the last tap from the cupola the well is completely drained through the tap hole so that the drop will contain no molten iron. It is then important to promptly dislodge the key bottom-door prop, causing the doors to swing open and drop the sand bottom, bed coke, unmelted iron and slag on a dry area beneath the cupola. The burning coke should be promptly drenched with water. This cools off the drop so that it can be handled sooner, and also preserves the coke if it is to be picked out and used again (it should not be used for bed coke).

One method of getting water on the drop promptly is a 1-in. pipe installed in a ring around the bottom of the cupola. This pipe ring has drilled holes on the inner circumference, and a valve connecting it to a water line. As soon as the drop is completed this pipe ring is turned on (Fig. 9.9), and a water hose is also played on the drop. It is important that all connections be kept right so that no water will get under the cupola before it is dropped.

When the drop is cool enough it is broken up, the good coke sorted out and the rest hauled to the dump. A tractor with a front scoop is convenient for loading the drop material.

Fig. 9.8. Slag flowing into water filled sumps at rear of cupolas. Perforated buckets or pans are lifted from sump and removed to dump when filled with granulated slag.

Fig. 9.10. Trough system, in which slag is conveyed by water stream to sump, may serve a battery of cupolas.

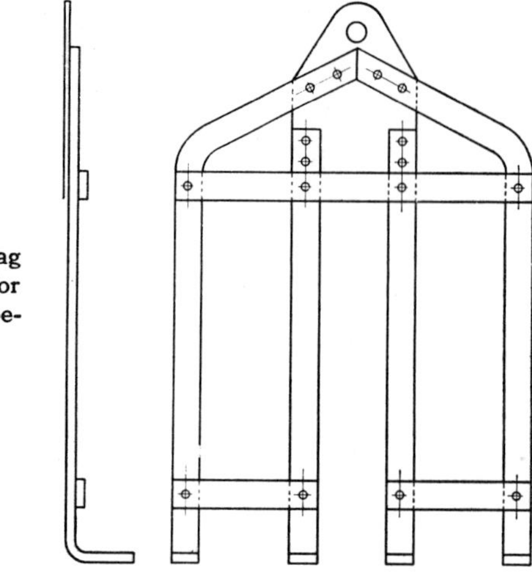

Fig. 9.11. Drag arrangement for removing drop beneath cupola.

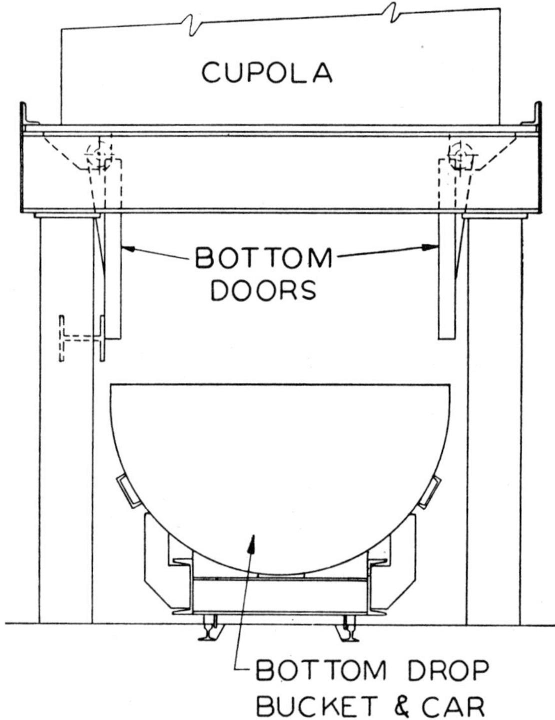

Fig. 9.13. Sketch showing bottom drop container and car for removing cupola drop.

If a winch or similar equipment can be made available, there are definite advantages in dragging the drop from under the cupola. Not only is the amount of labor lessened for removing the drop, but the cupola cools off faster.

A cupola drag (Fig. 9.11), is a convenient way of removing cupola drop. With such a drag, the drop may be taken from under the cupola just after the bottom is dropped.

While Fig. 9.11 shows a typical drag, a simple triangle of railroad rails or a heavy steel plate can be used. The drag is covered with sand to prevent slag from sticking. A chain sling is hooked around the kep prop to the winch, with the slack loop of the chain hooked to the drag so that, as the winch is actuated, tension is first applied to knock out the prop, and then to pull the drag with the drop from under the cupola. The drop is then in position to be cooled rapidly and loaded easily either by hand or, preferably, with a tractor scoop.

Special bottom door locking devices are available in case it is desired to catch the cupola drop in a container on car or skid (Fig. 9.13).

Slag wool is a nuisance in most foundries as it collects on beams, pipes and wires in the area of the cupola, and prevents good housekeeping. Therefore, the problem is either to prevent the formation of slag wool or keep it from getting out into the area back of the cupola.

Air blowing over the top of the slag bath in the cupola and out the slag hole forms the slag wool. If the slag hole is kept about 5 in. below the bottom of the tuyeres, and not allowed to become too enlarged, very little slag is wool generated.

Some foundries have found that an iron cover (sometimes lined with fire clay or brick) keeps the slag wool from flying around the room. This cover is hinged to the cupola shell so that it can be raised if any work is to be done on the spout or slag hole (Fig. 9.12).

Another method of collecting slag wool is to use a suction fan and hood on the slag spout. The wool is collected against a screen in an expansion chamber, which is cleaned after each heat. A more detailed system is illustrated in Fig. 9.14.

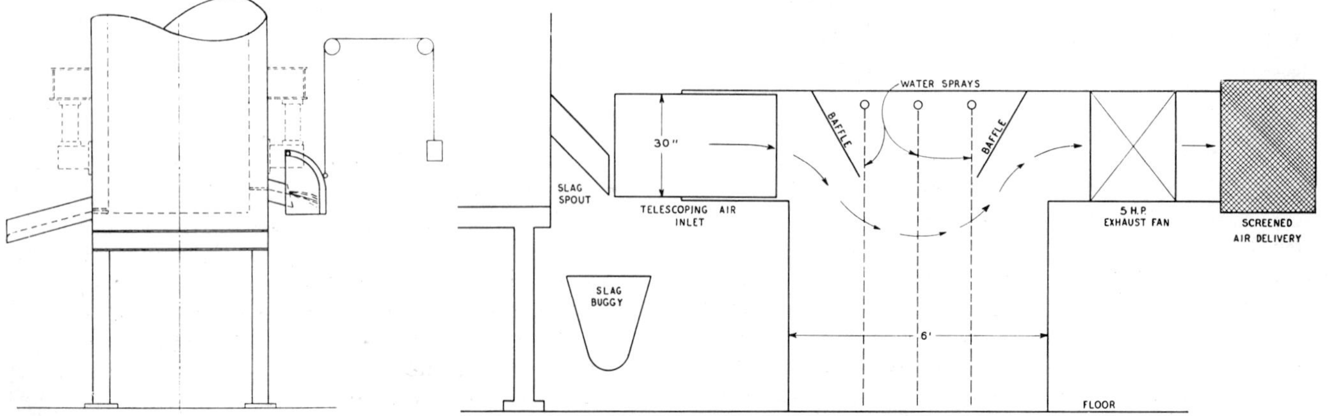

Fig. 9.12. Hinged cover over slag hole to prevent escape of slag wool.

Fig. 9.14. Exhaust washer arrangement to eliminate slag wool in cupola area.

CHAPTER 10

Emissions Control

The cupola is a source of air pollution from the foundry. Special equipment for controlling cupola emissions is available in all ranges of efficiency.

The principal differences between the conventional local exhaust and dust collection equipment used for controlling dust within the foundry and the equipment used for control of air pollution outside the plant are based on:

A) The small particle size of a portion of cupola emissions.

B) Visible color of these emissions which may be classed as a smoke.

C) The high temperature and increased volumes of the entraining gases which the air pollution equipment must handle.

The cupola melting operation presents the foundry industry with a particularly perplexing problem, as this operation exhausts gases at high temperatures and large volumes laden with dust particles and fume. The volumes of gas exhausted and the quantities of coarse and fine materials making up the total emission vary in cupola operations, depending on melting rate, charging methods and cleanliness of materials.

Average Emission Loads

It would be helpful to the average foundryman if an average emission load from the cupola melting operation could be established. This is impossible, however, due to the varied operations from one foundry to another, and due to the complex melting cycle, metal composition and operations of various foundries. The Gray Iron Foundry Smog Committee, a group of foundrymen in the Los Angeles, Calif., area conducted investigations on the emission from cupolas in the Los Angeles area. Their report, issued by the Bureau of Mines, U.S. Department of the Interior, in Information Circular 7627, presents some averages from three cupola sizes. This information will give the foundry operator an indication of the composition of cupola emissions (Table 10.1).

The foundryman's problem of air pollution control, and in particular, controlling the emissions from cupola melting operations, is largely a problem of nuisance since measurable injury to human health by industrial pollutants is rare. When the emissions from the cupola melting operations are analyzed, it will be readily seen that no emissions are given off which could conceivably injure the health of any person.

ATMOSPHERIC POLLUTION

Atmospheric pollution has been defined in air pollution codes as any substance emitted to the atmosphere in concentration sufficient to interfere with the comfort, safety or health of man or with the full use and enjoyment of his property. This narrows the foundryman's problem down to one of nuisance.

What constitutes a nuisance in one area may not be of great concern in another. For a given mass rate of emission from industrial stacks, it is the topography of the surrounding country and the meteorology of the area that determine the ground level concentration of pollutants. For a given concentration of pollutant at ground level, it is the land usage in the area that determines the presence or absence of a nuisance.

SOLIDS IN FURNACE STACK GASES

Dust, fume and smoke are commonly present in gases from melting operations. They may be classified according to particle size and mode of generation.

Dusts are formed from solid, inorganic or organic materials by mechanical force (i.e., crushing, grinding, etc.). Particle size ranges from microscopic to submicroscopic; however, particles of 50 microns settle rapidly and are of lesser significance. The A.S.M.E. in its recommended smoke regulation ordinance, defines dust as gas and airborne particles larger than one micron in mean diameter.

Fumes are formed from solid particles by oxidation, sublimation and condensation. Fumes are usually less than one micron in size, although they may flocculate and form larger particles.

Smokes are formed from the combustion of carbonaceous materials and are generally the product of incomplete combustion. The size of smoke particles is usually less than 0.5 micron.

Generally gases from cupolas contain both dust and fume particles.

Stack emissions from the cupolas that have been studied and analyzed contain varying percentages of carbon, silicon, iron, sodium, iron oxide, manganese, calcium, silicate, sulfur and other metallic and nonmetallic solids. They produce from 64,000 to 182,000 SCF (standard cubic feet) of stack gases containing 10 to 50 lb (but averaging 14 to 29 lb) of solids per ton of material charged. The particle size of these solids varied from submicroscopic to 1,000 microns

TABLE 10.1 TEST CUPOLA OPERATIONS[1]

Operating conditions	Cupola A	Cupola B	Cupola C
Diameter of melting zone	48 in.	37 in.	48 in.
Height - bottom plate to top of stack	41 ft. 5 in.	30 ft. 3-1/4 in.	51 ft. 1 in.
Height - bottom plate to bottom of charging door	20 ft. 8 in.	16 ft. 1/4 in.	16 ft. 6 in.
Size of charging door (height by width)	8 ft. 9 in. x 5 ft. 3 in.	2 ft. 3 in. x 2 ft. 6 in.	3 ft. 7 in. x 3 ft. 6 in.
Charging method	Mechanical	Hand	Hand
Air-weight control	Yes	Yes	No
Type of blower	Positive	Positive	Positive
Type of blast	Regular	Regular	Regular
Height of bed coke	73 in.	56 in.	44 in.
Kind of bed coke	(2/)	(3/)	(4/)
Weight of coke in bed, pounds	3,000	1,400	2,000
Kind of coke charge, cupola A	(5/) (7/)	(3/)	(4/)
Charge:6/			
Scrap iron ... 450 lb.	375 lb.	100 lb.	800 lb.
Scrap steel ... 300 lb.	675 lb.	225 lb.	-
Returns ... 750 lb.	300 lb.	300 lb.	500 lb.
Pig ... -	150 lb.	175 lb.	-
Coke ... 240-300 lb.	240-300 lb.	130 lb.	-
Limestone ... 60 lb.	60 lb.	17 lb.	30 lb.
Ferroglaze ... -	-	5 lb.	3 lb.
Cast iron ... -	-	-	1,200 lb.
Melted-iron temperature, °F.	2,760-2,800	2,700-2,840	-
Tap method	Intermittent	Intermittent	Intermittent
Total tons melted	14.35	5.2	45
Total time of blast	2 hr. 36 min.	1 hr. 20 min.	5 hr. 20 min.
Melting rate, tons iron per hour	5.52	3.9	8.3
Process weight, pounds per hour	13,500	9,282	18,900
Results from sampling and testing emissions			
Light-off period			
Volume of cupola emissions cu. ft./min. (note 1)	16,300	3,000	5,920
Velocity of emissions at stack temp. ... f.p.s.	12.6	5.7	7.6
Orsat analysis of gases ... percent CO_2	0.3-0.8	1.0-10.3	0.8-3.0
O_2	19.3-20.3	10.1-19.2	17.4-20.5
CO	0.0	0.0	0.0
Particulate matter...grain per cu. ft.	0.009	0.0014	0.360
Particulate matter ... lb.	1.260	0.026	18.300
Condensible oils, greases, etc. ... grain per cu. ft.	0.002	0.00002	0.001
Smoke opacity (see note 2)	0	2	52
Melting period			
Volume of emissions ... cu. ft./ min.	20,570	5,020	15,600
Velocity of emissions at stack temp. ... f.p.s.	41.7	31.8	37.5
Orsat analysis of gases ... percent CO_2	2.0-5.4	10.0-13.4	2.2-510
O_2	14.4-18.5	6.5-10.1	14.5-19.2
CO	0.0	0.0	0.0

Results from sampling and testing emissions (Cont.)	Cupola A	Cupola B	Cupola C
Melting period (Cont.)			
Particulate matter..grains per cu. ft.	1.110	1.604	0.798
Particulate matter..lb. per hour, loss	196	69	107
Loss ... percent of process weight	1.45	0.74	0.57
Allowable loss ... lb. per hr.	12.5	9.5	15.5
Condensible oil, greases, etc. ... grain per cu. ft.	0.019	0.008	0.025
Volatiles ... do.	Negligible	Negligible	Negligible
Zinc oxide ... do.	.008	.009	.003
Lead ... do.	.006	.010	.003
Sulfur compounds (SO_2) percent by volume	.002	.012	.013
Proximate analyses of emissions, percent:			
Volatile	6.77	6.70	6.66
Fixed carbon	11.93	3.04	19.17
Ash	81.30	90.26	74.17
Sulfur content of bed coke ... percent by weight	0.630	0.520	0.660
Sulfur content of charge... do.	.550	.520	.660
Sulfur content of cast iron do.	.143	.130	.170
Smoke opacity (see note 2)	90	83	18
Volume of emissions at stack conditions ... c.f.m.	65,000	20,400	37,000
Volume of emissions at standard conditions ... c.f.m.	20,570	5,020	15,600
Maximum stack temperature ... °F.	1,280	1,700	1,200
Average stack temperature ... do.	1,188	1,656	775
Particulate matter ... gr./cu. ft.:			
At stack conditions	0.355	0.655	0.190
At standard conditions	1.110	1.604	0.798
Report of tests: Screen analysis, percent:			
+ 60-mesh	19.8	8/5.91	8/10.90
- 60- + 80-mesh	2.9	4.43	6.26
- 80- +100-mesh	3.0	5.80	6.64
-100- +200-mesh	15.5	18.38	16.88
-200- +325-mesh	45.1	12.46	31.64
-325-mesh	13.7	53.02	27.68
Total	100.0	100.02	100.00
Particle size of the -325-mesh material:	Percent	Percent	Percent
50 to 25 microns	35 4.8	25 13.3	25 6.9
25 to 10 microns	25 3.4	30 15.9	30 8.3
10 to 5 microns	10 1.4	25 13.3	15 4.2
Minus 5 microns	30 4.1	20 10.6	30 8.3
	100 13.7	100 53.1	100 27.7
Condensible oils, grease, etc. at stack conditions ... gr./cu. ft.	0.006	0.002	0.010
Volatiles at stack conditions do.	Negligible	Negligible	Negligible
Volatiles at standard conditions do.	do.	do.	Do.
Water-soluble sulfates in particulate matter, as SO_3 ... percent by weight	1.81	1.47	1.04

1/ Source: Industrial Air-Control Associates, Technical Subcommittee Gray-Iron-Foundry Smog Committee Report, Dec. 16, 1948.
2/ Indianapolis Power & Light - sulfur content, 0.63 percent. 3/ Mixture of 1 and 2 - sulfur content, 0.52 percent.
4/ American Brake Shoe Byproducts - sulfur content, 0.66 percent. 5/ St. Paul Koppers - sulfur content, 0.55 percent. 6/ 8 charges. 7/ 13 charges.
8/ Wet screened "brush-down" sample as received, using distilled water and wetting agent.
Note 1. - Volumes and concentrations are reduced to standard conditions of 60° F. and 14.7 lb. pressure.
Note 2. - Percent of time in period during which opacity equaled or exceeded prescribed limit of 40 percent by Ringlemann chart.

in size. The sizes of the total emissions on a percentage basis were as follows:

> 45 per cent to 75 per cent was greater than 44 microns in particle size; 15 per cent to 25 per cent, 20 to 44 microns in size; and one per cent to 15 percent, under 20 microns in size. The percentage of emissions that are over 44 microns in size could be efficiently removed from the gas stream by many types of dust collectors without difficulty. A portion of the percentages of particles below the 44 microns in size would be collected in the medium efficient type of collector, but the part under five microns would be collected only in the most efficient type of equipment.

The micron is the unit of measurement for the particles making up the emissions from the cupola. A micron is one-millionth of a meter, or 1/25,400 of an inch.

The specific gravity of dust particles from metallurgical and combustion processes varies from 1.30 to 7.50. Dust from cupolas weighs between 0.60 and 0.85 lb per cu ft depending upon the amount of fines collected.

The sulfur dioxide in the escaping gas from the cupola is in the neighborhood of 0.004 per cent by volume, and is considered a nuisance only when there is a temperature inversion causing a concentration of these fumes at ground level or when water is circulated through the gas, in which case sulfuric acid is formed. This nuisance can be reduced by using a neutralizing agent.

DUST AND FUME DISPERSION

In the case of cupolas using dirty scrap materials in the charge, considerable coarse dust is carried up the stack to become a problem in the immediate neighborhood. However, the metallic fumes, oil smoke (from oily scrap) and gaseous impurities may be dispersed by air currents over wide areas, contributing to haze and pollution of the type encountered in Los Angeles County.

Obviously, where land usage permits and topography and meteorology are favorable, it may be sufficient to install dust collection equipment of the type which will prevent settlement of coarse material around the plant, exhausting the fume particles through a tall stack in order to disperse them over a wide area. It must be pointed out that the instances in which this procedure would be acceptable are becoming fewer as public awareness of atmospheric pollution increases. The abatement of atmospheric pollution, as contrasted to a purely local nuisance, requires the elimination of a major portion of the extremely fine particles at the lower end of this particle size spectrum.

The problem of selecting equipment for cleaning cupola gases is intensified by the high temperature usually encountered, as well as the extreme fineness of the offending particles and the difficulty of entrapping them in many conventional types of dust arresters. Pre-cooling or conditioning the hot gases is usually required, depending on the type of equipment installed, and special materials to withstand heat and corrosion must be employed in many cases.

EMISSION CONTROL EQUIPMENT

The Problem

In choosing a cupola dust collecting system, the first decision which must be made is whether to install a medium cost, medium efficiency system which will remove enough of the stack gas solids to eliminate local neighborhood dust nuisances and avoid foundry roof cleaning costs, but which at the same time will not accomplish any striking improvement in stack discharge appearance, or whether to install a high cost, high efficiency system which will remove practically all of the stack gas solids in order to obtain an essentially clear stack gas discharge.

CYCLONES

Cyclones are probably the most widely used of all dust collectors. They consist of a cylindrical or conical chamber with a tangential entry and axial discharge. The inlet gas stream spirals downward along the wall and then upward and out through the center. Suspended particles are projected to the wall by centrifugal force where they fall by gravity toward the bottom of the unit.

Since cyclone diameter is the design factor having the greatest effect on efficiency, recent trends have been toward high efficiency multiple units in which unit diameter is smaller and multiple cyclones are utilized in parallel (Fig. 10.1). Pressure drops for these collectors may be in the range of 2 to 10 in. H_2O, but this type design can extend efficient collection to particles as small as 5 to 10 microns.

Advantages of the multiple cyclone include low initial cost, relatively simple construction, dry and continuous disposal of collected material, low to moderate pressure loss and relatively low maintenance costs where no highly abrasive materials are present. In addition, these units can be used satisfactorily at high temperature or high pressure, as long as appropriate materials of construction are used. Disadvantages are low efficiency for particles below 5 to 10 microns and susceptibility to severe abrasive deterioration in certain cases.

FILTERS

Gas filters may be divided into two basic types, the fabric filter and the deep bed filter. The fabric filter is, at present, by far the more important of the two for industrial dust control. The basic difference between the two types lies in the mechanisms by which particle deposition occurs. In a fabric filter, the fabric serves primarily as a filter support, and particulate collection is accomplished during the passage of the gas stream through the previously collected dust cake. Actual "sieving" is a major collecting mechanism.

A deep bed filter, on the other hand, consists of a loosely packed mat of fibrous materials which is, in reality, an inertial separator in which the collecting elements are the fibers themselves. Deep bed filters are widely used as domestic furnace filters and on air conditioning systems, but they are not common where high grain loadings are encountered.

Fabric filters offer high efficiency collection of particles as small as 0.1 micron or less. The most common type is the shaker baghouse in which mechanical or pneumatic shakers are used periodically to clean the collected dust cake from vertically suspended tubular bags (Fig. 10.2). The dust stream enters the collector near the bottom through a combination inlet plenum-dust hopper and then passes upward and outward through the tubes forming a dust cake over their internal surfaces.

Gas velocities through the fabric are normally between 1 and 4 ft/min and maximum pressure drops are usually held to 4 to 6 in. H_2O. Air flow must be stopped when the filters are cleaned but multi-compartmented, automatically programmed equipment may be used when continuous service is desired. Woven fabrics are the usual filter media in this type of collector, with cotton sateen the cheapest and most commonly used. Materials used for higher temperature service or to resist chemically active gases include wool, nylon, dacron, orlon and glass.

Normal temperature limits for these materials are: cotton, 180 F; wool, 220 F; nylon, 225 F; orlon and dacron, 275 to 300 F and glass, 450 to 500 F. Baghouse inlet temperatures, of course, may be somewhat higher than these limits.

Reverse Jet Collector

In addition to mechanical shaking, other filter cleaning techniques are sometimes used. They include reverse jets, collapse cleaning, air pulsing, sonic cleaning and combinations of these methods. In a reverse jet unit (Fig. 10.7) felts serve as filter media, and cake removal is accomplished by a high velocity jet of compressed air issuing from a narrow slot on a closely fitted or spring-loaded hollow ring which traverses the entire length of the filter. Filter velocities up to 15 or 20 ft/min are sometimes possible. This means that these units can be appreciably smaller than shaker baghouses of the same volumetric capacity.

Cleaning is carried out continously or semicontinuously while air flow continues yielding a relatively constant pressure drop and, therefore, relatively constant flow rate rather than the cyclic fluctuations in flow inherent with periodic cleaning. Disadvantages of reverse jet units are higher purchase and maintenance costs, lower temperature limits ($\sim$300 F), and a tendency towards gradual blinding of the felt media with fine dusts.

In the last several years, cleaning by collapsing tubular filters with a slight reverse pressurization has become popular on high temperature units using glass bags. This "single stroke" cleaning appears to decrease filter wear appreciably, an important matter considering the relatively poor wear-resistance of glass fabrics. The technique, however, may not be satisfactory where "hard to clean" dust-fabric combinations exist.

Several manufacturers are also supplying filters in which cleaning is accomplished by air pulsing, i.e., by directing short bursts of high-pressure air into the filter bags and "popping" them open. With this design, the bags are mounted over wire frames and the gas to be filtered flows from the outside to the inside of the bags. Recently, tubular baghouses, combining collapse cleaning and air pulsing, and sonic filters, using low frequency sonic energy for cleaning, have become available.

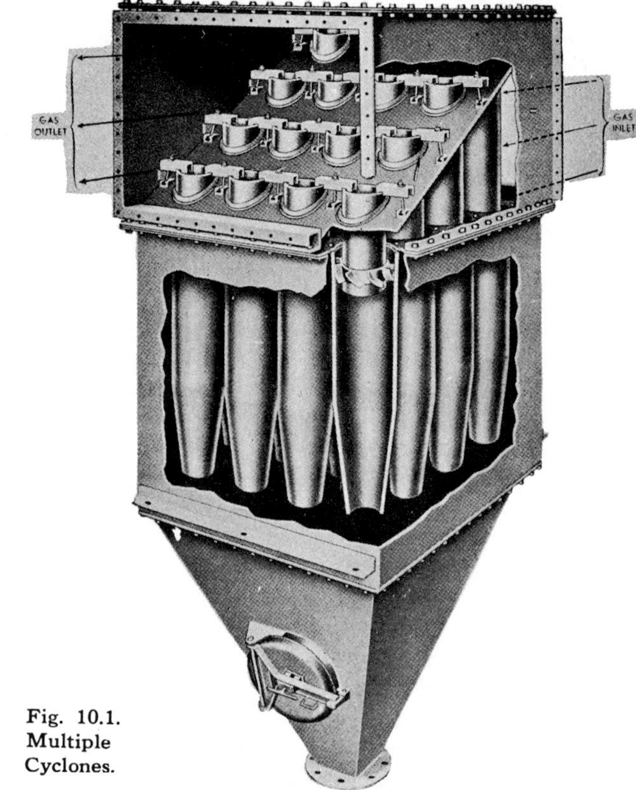

Fig. 10.1. Multiple Cyclones.

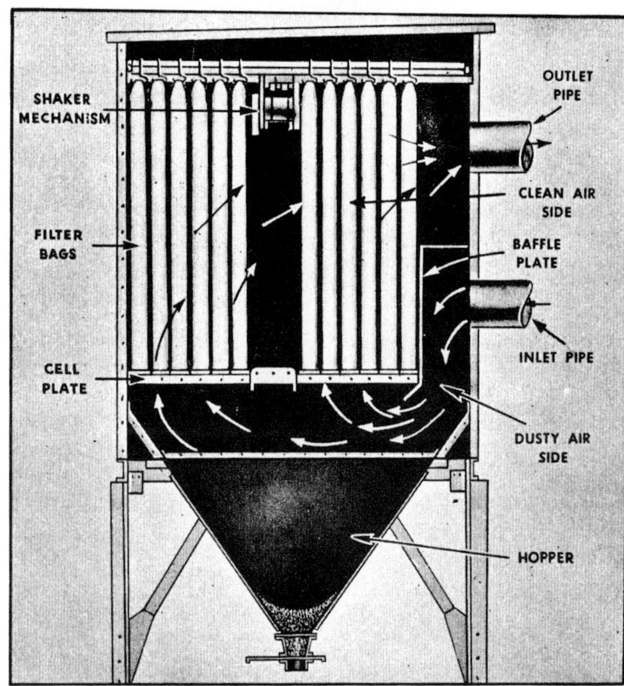

Fig. 10.2. Baghouse filter.

Cloth Envelope Collector

Differing in geometry from the tubular filter is the cloth envelope type (Fig. 10.3). Flat filter bags one to 2 in. thick and roughly 2 x 4 ft are mounted over wire frames from a vertical tube sheet.

The filter cake is formed on the external surface of these bags and is removed by mechanical rap-

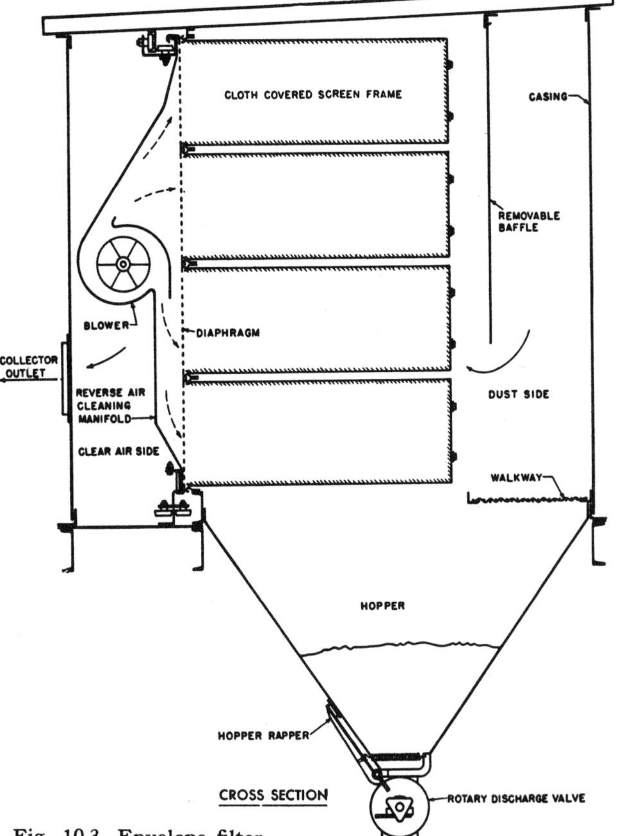

Fig. 10.3. Envelope filter.

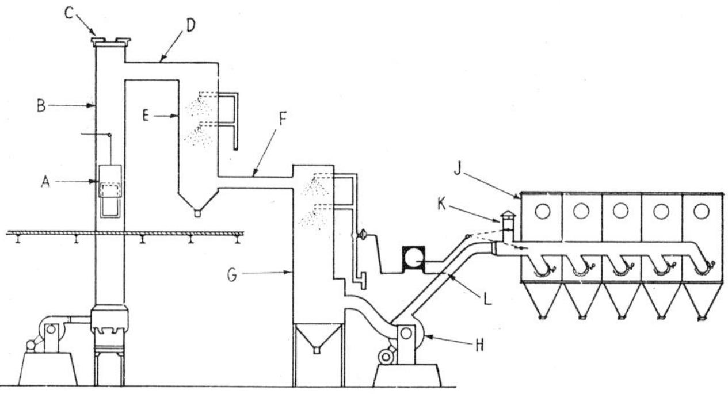

Fig.10.4. Flow sheet of continuous automatic fume collection system shown in Fig. 10.5.

Fig. 10.5. Completely automatic bag filter installation on 54 in. ID cupola at a Los Angeles foundry.

ping. These filters can be cleaned continuously without shutting off the air flow to the unit when specially designed cleaning equipment is employed to supply a slight reverse air flow sequentially to the filter bags during rapping.

Advantages of fabric filters are high collection efficiency for all particle sizes even when variable flow rates and variable inlet concentrations exist, relatively simple construction, moderate cost, dry collection and nominal power consumption. Disadvantages relate to size, temperature and humidity limitations and maintenance costs.

With respect to temperature limitations of this and other types of collectors, it is well to discuss gas cooling briefly. Three methods can be used:

1) Cooling by radiation and convection.
2) Cooling by evaporation.
3) Cooling by dilution with ambient air.

The dilution method increases the volume of gas to be filtered, and is normally used only in conjunction with one of the first two methods. Radiation and convection cooling generally requires a greater initial capital outlay than evaporative cooling, but operation is less costly. Evaporative coolers, on the other hand, are usually cheaper to install but require a continuous supply of cooling water and have higher maintenance costs due to wet corrosion. Evaporative cooling is the most popular technique in the foundries of the Los Angeles area where fabric filters have found wide usage. When using evaporative cooling, the biggest concern is with overhumidification and resultant condensation problems.

Bag Filters

Figure 10.4 is a flow sheet and Fig. 10.5 a photograph describing a completely automatic bag filter installation on a 54 in. ID cupola at a Los Angeles foundry. A refractory lined, counterweighted baffle (A, Fig. 10.4), restricts air infiltration through the charge door to reduce filtration volume and permit secondary combustion in the raised stack B). Cupola lids C) are counterweighted and power operated from the charge floor. Hot gases pass through a stainless steel stub pipe D) to a spray quencher E) where they are cooled to 450 F before passing through a carbon steel duct F) to the secondary cooler G) where the temperature is further reduced to 275 F. An exhauster H) blows the gases through a five compartment, continuous automatic bag filter J) equipped with orlon filter bags and electrically operated shaker mechanisms. A thermocouple, located in the inlet duct L), actuates a controller which, in turn, regulates cooler sprays and provides for bypassing at K) in the event of water or power failure. Performance of this system is shown in Table 10.2.

ELECTRICAL PRECIPITATORS

High-efficiency collection of particles 0.1 micron in diameter and even smaller under severe operating conditions is offered by the electrical precipitator (Fig. 10.6). Particle deposition is achieved by passing the gas stream between electrodes across which a high voltage is impressed. The discharge electrode has a much smaller radius of curvature than the collecting electrode and, as a result, corona discharge. A powerful ionizing field is established near the discharge electrode; potentials as high as 100,000 volts are used.

Particles passing through the ionizing field become charged and subsequently migrate to the collecting electrode. Once deposited, they lose their charge and are removed either by mechanical vibration or by washing.

Both single-stage and two-stage precipitators are in use as particulate collectors. In the two-stage unit, ionization is achieved in the first stage and particle collection in the second. This kind of precipitator is rarely used for industrial dust collection, but is employed most often in air conditioning installations.

With the single-stage precipitators, ionization and particle collection occur simultaneously at the same set of electrodes. In plate-type precipitators, the collecting electrodes consist of parallel plates either of solid or expanded metal closely spaced rows of rods, chains or wire or specially formed shapes. In the pipe-type precipitator, the collecting electrodes are formed by a nest of parallel tubes which may be square, round or octagonal. In each case, discharge electrodes are wires or small, twisted rods suspended vertically either midway between the parallel collecting electrodes of the plate-type unit or axially along the length of the pipes of the pipe-type unit.

Electrode cleaning is normally carried out while gas flow continues, and is accomplished by periodic or continuous mechanical rapping or by a flowing liquid film. Electrodes may range from 5 to 20 ft in length, and electrode spacing is usually 3 to 8 in.

Potential Efficiency

The potential collection efficiency is greatly affected by the electrical resistivity of the particulate matter. Relatively small changes in resistivity can cause appreciable differences in operating characteristics of the precipitator. High-resistivity material results in a reduced potential gradient across the gas space and in back ionization at the collecting electrode. Both of these factors contribute to reduced efficiency.

The induced lowering of resistivity of the particulate matter being collected is called conditioning. This may be accomplished by humidification, temperature control or by the addition of chemical agents, notably ammonia, sulfuric acid or SO_3.

Gas velocities average 3 to 10 ft/sec but, obviously, as velocity increases retention time decreases and this leads to reduced efficiency. A common design deficiency is unequal flow distribution. This matter is so important that baffles, guide vanes or distributor plates are often used to improve the flow pattern.

The chief advantages of the precipitator are its high efficiency collection under varying and quite severe conditions, high-temperature applicability, low maintenance and operating costs and low pressure drop. Disadvantages include high initial cost, large size and possible explosion hazards with flammable materials. Of great importance is the logarithmic relationship of outlet concentration to the size of the equipment. That is, a precipitator giving 90 per cent efficiency must be doubled in size to give 99 per cent efficiency and tripled to give 99.9 per cent.

SCRUBBERS

In a general sense, "scrubbers" includes gas absorption equipment as well as particulate collectors. However, in current air pollution control usage the term generally applies to devices which utilize a liquid to achieve or assist in the removal of solid or liquid dispersoids from a carrier gas. Water is by far the most common liquid employed, but in certain special cases other liquids have been used.

Scrubbers are constructed in such a wide variety of designs that no single type can be considered as representative. Some scrubbers are simply previously

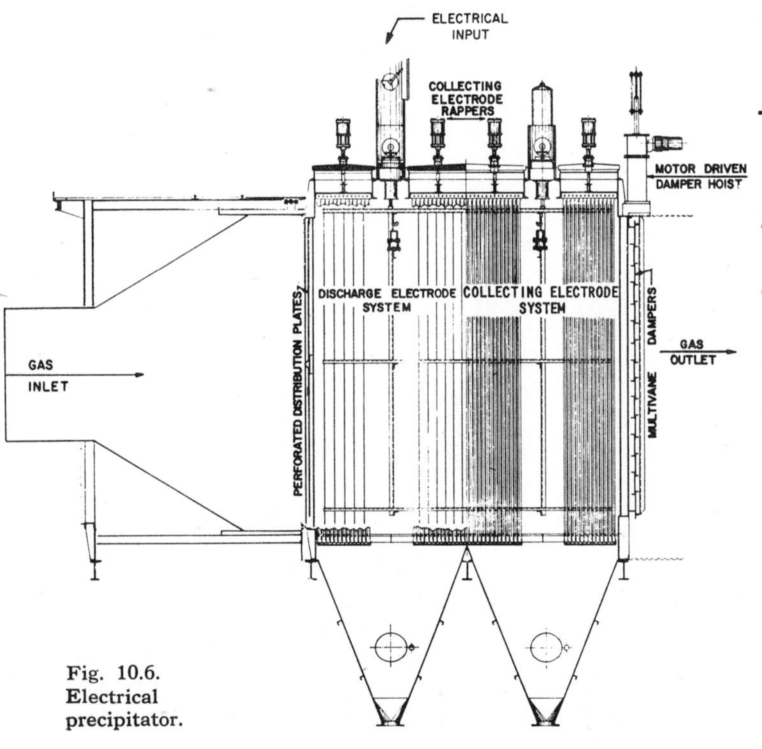

Fig. 10.6. Electrical precipitator.

TABLE 10.2. PERFORMANCE OF FUME COLLECTION SYSTEM

	Measured 10-8-52
Gas volume entering filter @ 275 F, cfm	16,900
Square feet of cloth	
with 5 compartments filtering	7,320
with 4 compartments filtering	5,856
Gas-to-cloth ratio	
with 5 compartments filtering	2.3
with 4 compartments filtering	2.9
Shaking cycle, minutes between shaking periods, each compartment	15
Shaking duration, minutes per cycle	1
Gas temperature, degrees F	268
Calculated dew point, degrees F	167
Pressure loss through bags, inches water	
with 5 compartments filtering	5.9
with 4 compartments filtering	6.7
Exhauster motor hp rating	40
Average weight dust caught, lb per hr	
in quencher	31.2
in secondary cooler	6.4
in dust collector	47.3
Total	84.9
Average dust loss in collector exhaust (thimble test), lb per hour	0

existing dry-type collectors which have been modified to allow the introduction of a liquid phase; other units are specifically designed as wet collectors.

Particle collection is generally achieved by one of four mechanisms:

1) Particles may be made to impinge on a liquid surface.
2) Particles may be allowed to diffuse to a liquid surface.
3) Liquid may condense directly on individual particles, increasing their size and thereby their ease of collection.
4) Carrier gas may be partitioned into a number of small individual elements within which particles are collected by Brownian* diffusion and gravity settling.

According to theory, collection by the impingement mechanism should increase in efficiency as collecting droplet size decreases. This is true to a point, but as spray droplet size falls below 30-50 microns impingement efficiencies decrease rapidly, since smaller droplets are accelerated almost instantaneously to the carrier gas velocity and then no relative velocity exists between the droplets and the particles to be collected. Impingement is most effective for particles larger than 5 microns. For finer particles, the diffusional mechanism becomes of increasing importance.

Condensation Nuclei

Condensation occurs when the carrier gas is cooled through its dew point. Submicron particles serve as condensation nuclei. As a result effective particle size is increased, thereby enhancing inertial collection. This mechanism, however, is generally effective only where hot gases containing relatively low loadings are concerned. Gas partitioning is achieved by dispersing the carrier gas into small volumetric increments, i.e., small bubbles or foam. Here, efficiency of collection increases as the size of the incremental gas volumes decreases.

In most practical applications, the particles to be collected cover a range of sizes and more than one mechanism plays a part. Regardless of the mechanism, however, high efficiencies are favored by large interfacial areas, and, therefore, small droplet size is advantageous. Also, current thinking is that properly designed scrubbers will be highly efficient collectors for any particle size if the power input to the scrubber is high enough.

Power may be consumed by high pressure atomization of the liquid phase, by high velocity jetting of the liquid, by high carrier gas velocities or by mechanical energy input to rotating elements. Available commercial scrubbers offer high efficiency collection of particles larger than about 5 microns at relatively low power input, of particles in the 2- to 5-micron range at moderate power input and of particles down to 1 micron or below with high power consumption.

Scrubbers may be grouped roughly in seven design types. The first, and most common, is the spray tower. These units are simply chambers in which the carrier gas passes through banks of sprays positioned either parallel or normal to the gas stream. The sprays are followed by some type of inertial collector which serves as a mist entrainment separator. A common example of this type collector is the cupola wet cap (Fig. 10.8). For such units water consumption runs about ½ to 2 gallons/1000 cu ft of gas. Pressure drops are usually in the range of 0.1 to 0.5 in. H_2O.

Jet Scrubber

In the jet scrubber (Fig. 10.9) a high velocity water jet is directed axially into the throat of a venturi section. This is followed by an entrainment separator,

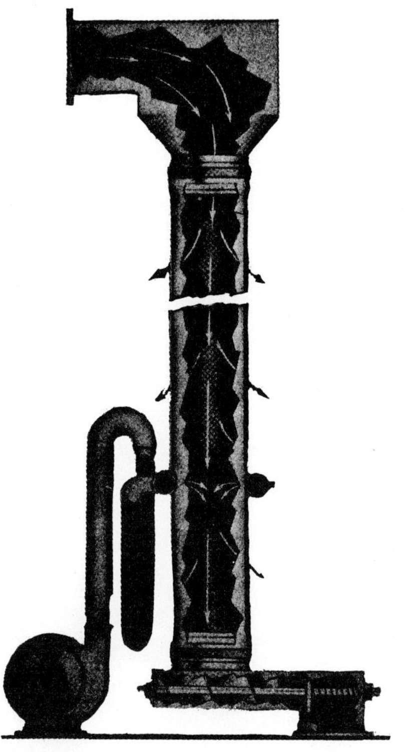

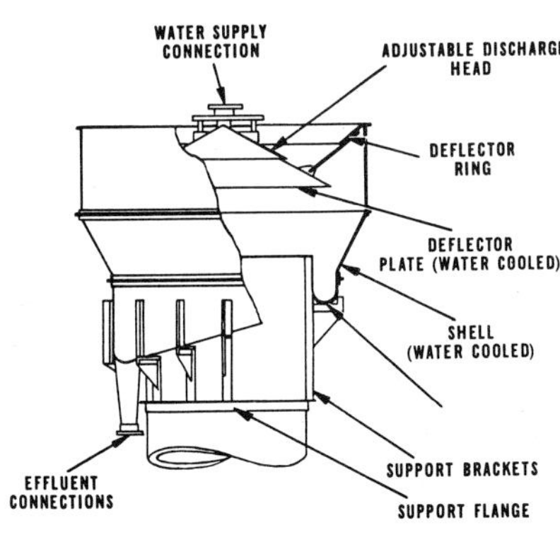

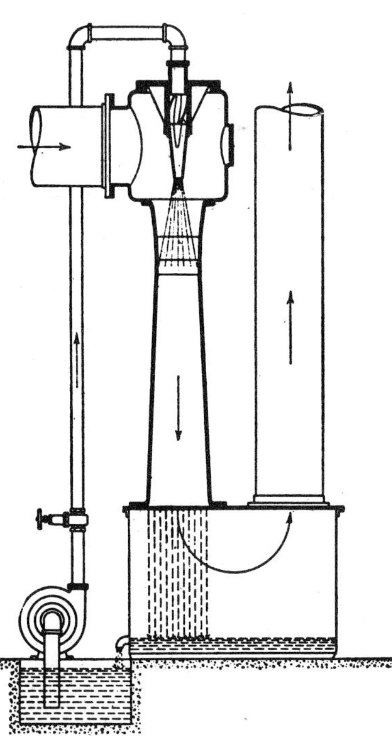

Fig. 10.8. (above) Cupola wet cap.

(left) Fig. 10.7. Reverse jet filter.

(right) Fig. 10.9. Jet scrubber.

*Dr. Robert Brown first demonstrated the rapid vibratory movement exhibited by microscopic particles in about 1827.

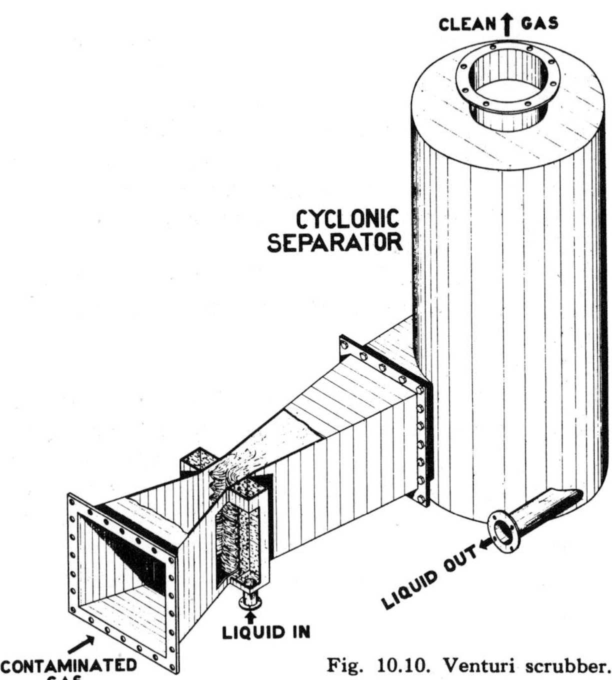

Fig. 10.10. Venturi scrubber.

usually a simple gas-reversal chamber. These units serve as collectors and also may act as aspirating-type air movers. Pressure gains up to as much as 7 or 8 in. H_2O may be developed. Water consumption is high, often in the range of 50 to 100 gallons/1000 cu ft. Of somewhat similar design is the venturi scrubber (Fig. 10.10).

In this scrubber, it is the gas phase which is passed through the venturi throat at high velocity (200-300 ft/sec). Water sprays are injected just preceding the throat, and the entrained droplets are subsequently removed by a cyclonic separator. For these units, water consumption is normally 3 to 10 gallons/1000 cu ft, and pressure drops range from 10 to 15 H_2O. For collection of fine fume, for example, pressure losses of 30-35 in. H_2O may be required.

Cyclonic Scrubber

In cyclonic scrubbers, radial sprays are introduced into typical dry type cyclones. The liquid phase assists in collection and also serves to decrease re-entrainment. Pressure drops are usually 2 to 8 in. H_2O, and water consumption is roughly the same as for the venturi scrubber.

When particle-liquid contact is obtained as the result of the carrier gas velocity itself, the scrubbers are classified as inertial scrubbers. They are of two types. One is the impaction scrubber, in which the liquid and gas phases are intimately mixed and then impacted onto a baffle plate; the second is the deflection type scrubber, in which the gas stream impinges on liquid-film covered baffles. In the former type, impaction velocities are from 30 to 150 ft/sec, and pressure drops may be as high as 30 in. H_2O. In the latter, pressure drops are appreciably lower, ranging up to about 6 in. H_2O.

Packed scrubbers are conventional, packed tower liquid-gas contactors. Packing may be composed of Raschig rings, Berl saddles, fiberglass, etc., and gas and liquid flows are normally countercurrent. The separating mechanism is believed to be primarily impingement of the particles on the packing with the liquid medium serving merely to clean the packing surface. Excessive velocities through these units produce channeling with resultant loss of efficiency. Pressure drops range from ½ to as high as 10 in. H_2O.

CHARACTERISTICS OF COLLECTION EQUIPMENT

Table 10.3 is a summary of performance specifications for the various types of dust collection equipment and approximate cost of each collector.

It is important to remember that from a technological standpoint all particulate emissions can be controlled to better than 99+ per cent efficiency through use of appropriate collection equipment. It is equally important to remember that cost of collection increases with collection efficiency, with the severity of the collection conditions and with decreases in particle-size of the material to be collected.

If required collection efficiency is based on local air pollution control legislation, the criterion for sat-

TABLE 10.3. APPROXIMATE CHARACTERISTICS OF DUST AND MIST COLLECTION EQUIPMENT

Equipment Type	Purchase Cost* ($/cfm)	Smallest Particle Collected (microns)**	Pressure Drop (in. H_2O)	Power Used† $\left(\frac{kw}{1000\ cfm}\right)$	Remarks
A. *Settling Chambers*					
1. Simple	0.1	40	0.1-0.5	0.1	Large, low pressure drop, precleaner
2. Multiple tray	0.2-0.6	10	0.1-0.5	0.1	Difficult to clean, warpage problem
B. *Inertial Separators*					
1. Baffle chamber	0.1	20	0.5-1.5	0.1-0.5	Power plants, rotary kilns, acid mists
2. Orifice impaction	0.1-0.3	2	1-3	0.2-0.6	Acid mists
3. Louver type	0.1-0.3	10	0.3-1	0.1-0.2	Fly ash, abrasion problem
4. Gas reversal	0.1	40	0.1-0.4	0.1	Precleaner
C. *Cyclones*					
1. Single	0.1-0.2	15	0.5-3	0.1-0.6	Simple, inexpensive, most widely used
2. Multiple	0.3-0.6	5	2-10	0.5-2	Abrasion & plugging problems
3. Mechanical	0.2-0.6	5	—	0.5-2	Compact
D. *Filters*					
1. Tubular	0.3-2	<0.1	2-6	0.5-1.5	High efficiency, temp. and humidity limits
2. Reverse jet	0.7-1.2	<0.1	2-6	0.7-1.5	More compact, constant flow
3. Envelope	0.3-2	<0.1	2-6	0.5-1.5	Limited capacity, constant flow possible
E. *Electrical Precipitators*					
1. One-stage	0.6-3	<0.1	0.1-0.5	0.2-0.6	High efficiency, heavy duty, expensive
2. Two-stage	0.2-0.6	<0.1	0.1-0.3	0.2-0.4	Compact, air conditioning service
F. *Scrubbers*					
1. Spray tower	0.1-0.2	10	0.1-0.5	0.1-0.2	Common, low water use
2. Jet	0.4-1	2	—	2-10	Pressure gain, high velocity liquid jet
3. Venturi	0.4-1.2	1	10-15	2-10	High velocity gas stream
4. Cyclonic	0.3-1	5	2-8	0.6-2	Modified dry collector
5. Inertial	0.4-1	2	2-15	0.8-8	Abrasion problem
6. Packed	0.3-0.6	5	0.5-10	0.6-2	Channeling problem
7. Mechanical	0.4-1.2	2	—	2-10	Abrasion problem

*Steel construction, not installed, includes necessary auxiliaries, 1960 prices.
**With ~90-95% efficiency by weight.
†Includes pressure loss, water pumping, electrical energy.

isfactory control normally is based on either effluent loading (grains/ft^3) or upon plume opacity (Ringelmann number). If the requirement is in terms of effluent grain loading for the process concerned, then collection equipment may be selected on the basis of an overall collection efficiency by weight. However, if plume opacity is of concern, then even high weight collection efficiencies, e.g., 98+ per cent, may be unsatisfactory, since the small particles contribute little to weight but by far the most to light scatter because of their high surface-to-weight ratio.

The selection of a dust collector for a given application, therefore, requires consideration of the various possible types in terms of all the selection criteria outlined earlier, but the most important of these must inevitably be collection efficiency. In short, the collector must do the job it is supposed to do.

ADDITIONAL METHODS OF CONTROL

Some helpful operational hints that will eliminate some of the emissions from the cupola melting operation are as follows:

1) Analyze contaminants to ascertain the cause and source of dust. Determine total solids concentration or mass emission rate and separate into the various size ranges to indicate their distribution.
2) Close control over melting in order to minimize metallic oxides (Fe, Si, Mn) in the stack gas.
3) Prevent carbonaceous smoke such as is caused by incomplete combustion of oily or tarry substances in the charge. Remove cutting oils from scrap before charging. Reduce excessive smoke during light-up period by use of gas burner, oil torch or an electric igniter. In most cases the cost of lighting the coke bed is less than with purchased wood. In addition, the first iron tapped is hotter than when wood is employed due to the fact that there is no arching of the coke above the wood; this permits heating the cupola bottom to nearer the desired molten metal temperature before melting starts.
4) Avoid rough handling of coke. Reduce the distance the intermediate coke charges fall by adding charge when the melting stock is one charge down in the furnace. Eliminate fines. Screen or have holes in chute bottom plates. If no screening arrangement is used, fork over the coke.
5) Compactly briquett fine steel chips.
6) Prevent weathering of limestone.
7) Remove loose sand from remelt. Remove dirt and corrosion products from scrap. Separate sand magnetically or by dropping returns onto a set of inclined bars.
8) Dilute stack gases. Open charging door. This often makes it possible for a unit to comply with a local ordinance without installing a suppressor. Dilution functions in the following ways:
   A) Cools hot gases, especially when used in conjunction with a wet suppressor. Cooler gas evaporates less water.
   B) Reduces both gaseous and solid matter concentrations.
   C) Supplies fresh oxygen to burn the CO, coke breeze, cutting oil vapors and carbonaceous smoke.
   D) Ventilates the charging door.

   However, if heat is to be recovered, dilution may not be desirable since it 1) lowers the latent heat in the CO which is necessary for combustion, and 2) increases the volume of gas which the system must handle.
9) Extend the stack height. This gives better draft, and "puff-backs" at the charging door are eliminated.
10) Install a cap deflector.
11) Add pilot burners or igniter lamps at quadrants inside the stack to ignite the effluent gases (charging door open). On installation records, 284.1 grains collected from the stack gases before adding the burners; 17.1 grains after (over the same time interval).
12) Install a dust suppressor.

Air Pollutants

With increasing interest in air pollution, foundrymen should understand the effects of it on man, animals, vegetation and property; know the types of air pollution ordinances presently enacted, and be aware of the characteristics of available control equipment.

EFFECT : MAN

In only a few isolated cases has air pollution been blamed for sickness. Many victims already were afflicted with a respiratory disease or other physiological complications. Rare indeed is the combination of topographical and meteorological conditions which permit the accumulation of sufficient pollution to produce an acute effect.

The systemic effect on man of more normally encountered types of air pollution from foundries has not been demonstrated. There may be instances where stack emissions contain toxic materials, such as beryllium, that must be evaluated with the same procedure used in inplant industrial hygiene.

Results of surveys in polluted areas have been inconclusive insofar as health effects are concerned. Most courts refuse to consider health injury in litigation involving air pollution. In these cases, the tendency has been to evaluate the pollution on the basis of nuisance and damage to property.

EFFECT : ANIMALS

Cupola emissions, in most cases, contain no known contaminants in concentrations which affect the well-being of domestic animals.

Cattle grazing on fluoride-containing pasture in Utah have had fluorosis which causes embrittlement of bones and loss of milk. The source of the fluorspar emission probably was in greater measure due to a steel mill rather than to a cupola installation.

However, when fluorspar is charged into the cupola as a desulfurizer, foundrymen should be aware of this potential. Where it is charged into the forehearth, atmospheric contamination by fluorides is usually an inplant problem.

EFFECT : VEGETATION

Instances of crop damage traceable to cupola operation (except by fluorides) has not been substantial.

Characteristics of the gladiolus plant and the tulip — of being particularly susceptible to fluorides — and Spanish needles — easily killed by sulfur dioxide but resistant to fluorides — can be used in differential diagnoses to determine the causative agent of damage.

As a district becomes industrialized, the surrounding agricultural land becomes less desirable for its original purpose. In some cases the value of the land due to nearby industrialization becomes so great, that it is uneconomical to continue to raise crops.

EFFECT : PROPERTY

The estimated annual cost of corrosion in large industrial areas is tremendous. Such corrosion comes from sulfur dioxide and other acid gases emitted to atmosphere by industrial plants and from all other types of buildings using heating equipment which burns sulfur bearing fuel. Industry alone cannot be held responsible for corrosion due to air pollution.

With respect to particular contaminants, it is necessary to differentiate between the emission of coarse solid particles which may create a nuisance in the immediate vicinity of the plant, and the emission of extremely fine particles or fumes which are ordinarily carried for miles by prevailing winds without settling.

Local nuisances resulting from the settling of coarse material discharged to atmosphere are the source of most neighborhood air pollution complaints and are the ones most easily corrected.

The effect of the fine material which is distributed over large areas is debatable, and may be aesthetic rather than economic in significance. Very fine material, because of its visibility in the air, may create more complaints from an area than does coarse material that settles quickly.

Where widely dispersed solid and liquid particles create problems, unfavorable topographical and meteorological conditions play important parts in creating these problems.

Fortunately, pollution problems of the magnitude encountered in Los Angeles are rare.

Since in coping with an air pollution problem the psychology of public reaction to it is important, it may be desirable to eliminate completely visible discharged material whenever practical from an initial and maintenance cost standpoint.

Factors Exaggerating Problem

If the foundry industry's air pollution problem was confined to collection of solid contaminants from shakeout and cleaning room operations, the physical difficulties involved would be minor and the financial hardship minimized.

However, cupola effluents are hot and must be cooled before collection. If recirculated water is used for cooling, corrosion problems may be introduced. If fresh water is used, water cost may be high.

Much of the metallic effluent from cupolas contains particles of 0.5 micron size requiring efficient equipment for satisfactory collection.

After collection, there is often a serious problem of disposing of the collected materials.

EFFLUENTS

The complex problem of air pollution from cupolas has been given more attention during the past few years than the problem of emissions from any other foundry operation.

It is difficult to determine the nature and amount of emissions. Equipment suitable to remove the mixture of cinders, dust, and extremely fine fume from the effluent gases is of moderate to high cost. It is doubtful that the sampling procedures employed to date give an accurate or reproducible picture of such variables as gas flow, weight of solids discharged, and particle size of discharged solids.

Information has been published however, regarding tests conducted in certain foundries in the Los Angeles area and elsewhere.

Up to 24 per cent by weight of the solids emitted by three cupolas in Los Angeles County were below 10 microns in particle diameter.

In order to comply with the provisions of the Los Angeles County air pollution code, it would be necessary to install gas cleaning equipment capable of removing most of this extremely fine material.

On the other end of the scale, these tests showed a maximum of 74 per cent of the total weight of solid effluents which was coarser than 325 mesh. This is the material which normally settles on the foundry roof and adjoining property creating a nuisance and a costly cleanup job.

The selection of gas cleaning equipment for cupolas depends on the degree of cleaning efficiency required by neighborhood occupancy, existing pollution codes and topographical and meteorological conditions in the surrounding area.

For example, to prevent the deposition of cinders and coarse dust on the foundry roof, an installed cupola stack washer will trap the offending material but permit the intermediate and fine solids to pass through to atmosphere.

Where a local nuisance or air pollution problem exists, it is essential to trap not only the coarse material but all of the remaining particles which could be expected to settle over the area.

The removal of solid particles in the range of plus 2 microns can be effectively accomplished in high efficiency scrubbers (Figs. 10.9 and 10.10) or centrifugal collectors (Fig. 10.1). These devices will permit extremely fine fume to escape in a visible plume which may, under certain circumstances, contribute to general air pollution of relatively large areas.

It has been stated that only electrostatic precipitators, fabric filters and venturi jet collectors can remove extremely fine particles from cupola gases at least to the degree required by a very stringent code, or to the extent that all visible solids in the effluent gases are removed.

In order to successfully apply electrostatic precipitation (Fig. 10.6) to foundry cupola fume, it is necessary to determine the temperature at which the peak resistivity of the fume occurs and to design the gas conditioning system to maintain a gas temperature well above or below that in which the resistivity reaches its highest point.

Fabric type collectors require manual or mechanical shaking devices (Figs. 10.2, 10.3, 10.4-.5 and 10.7). There are several installations with completely automatic tubular filters. All fabric type collectors require cooling of hot gases prior to filtration. Venturi scrubbers (Fig. 10.10) require high volumes of water and high horsepower for efficient operation.

In any of the three types of collectors, it is necessary to maintain efficient secondary combustion in the cupola stacks. Where secondary combustion is not practiced, the operation of the gas cleaning equipment is adversely affected.

A reducing atmosphere in the cupola stack will allow carryover, to the gas cleaning equipment, unburned oil vapor and tarry matter as well as coke fines and other combustibles.

It is management's responsibility to determine its requirements with respect to low, medium or high efficiency gas cleaning equipment. In many areas it is doubtful that stringent air pollution codes will be required. In others it is inevitable that, from year to year, more rigid restrictions on industrial plant effluents will be put into effect.

In the latter areas, a decision must be made based on the economics of installation of control equipment designed to meet only present requirements, or equipment which not only meets present requirements but which will satisfy any reasonable future restrictions on cupola emissions.

Gas Cooling

Gas temperature is one of the principal problems confronting the foundry operator who must install air pollution control equipment. Stack temperatures as high as 2000 F are encountered in cupolas where secondary combustion occurs; and, some degree of gas cooling is often required.

Cooling by radiation and convection is ordinarily accomplished with U-tube coolers or heat exchangers such as waste heat boilers or forced draft tubular condensers.

U-tube coolers require a large amount of ground space and require considerable lengths of heavy steel ductwork from which heat is radiated at a low rate. U-tube coolers lack flexibility in final temperature adjustment. Their use often results in inadequate cooling in hot weather and overcooling in the winter.

Tubular heat exchangers, using outside air supplied under forced draft around the outside of the hot gas carrying tubes, have been successfully used. Because of the use of forced draft for secondary cooling air, tubular heat exchangers are relatively economical insofar as space requirements are concerned and offer more flexibility in final temperature adjustment than do either U-tube condensers or waste heat boilers.

The use of both kinds of cooling devices is more attractive if they are supplemented either by spray cooling or the use of tempering air for final temperature adjustment.

The cooling of gases already high in water vapor content is frequently accomplished by the admission of outdoor air through full modulating bleed-in dampers. However, since the outside air admitted for cooling purposes must also pass through the dust collector, it is obvious that the size of the collector itself must be considerably larger for temper air cooling than for the two methods previously mentioned.

Since a gas cleaning system installed for air pollution abatement is usually a nonproductive expenditure, equipment cost must be kept to a minimum. For this reason, spray cooling of hot gases is the most attractive of the available methods since it is reasonable in first cost, easily maintained, and results in only a nominal increase in the volume of gas to be filtered.

Economics

The material collected from cupola stack emissions is worthless and often requires additional expenditure for disposal. Thus no financial return is realized on the investment in control equipment.

First cost is not always the criterion of the most economical pollution control installation. The capital investment should be as low as is commensurate with existing and anticipated operating and maintenance costs.

Preferably the overall installation, operation, and maintenance costs should be estimated for the expected life of the equipment, and the selection made on the basis of the apparatus which meets present and anticipated code requirements and shows the lowest overall costs.

LEGAL LIMITATIONS : CUPOLA EMISSIONS

A single set of limitations on industrial atmospheric emissions applied on a national basis is not practical because of local differences in meteorology, topography, population and the type of pollution problem existing.

A significant pollution problem arises from sawdust burning in the Portland-Seattle area. The prime offender has been smoke from soft coal used as a fuel in Pittsburgh. Organic vapors and oxides of nitrogen in southern California are thought to be of major significance.

Just as the pollution type varies from place to place, so the contribution of foundry operations also varies as does the degree to which these emissions should be controlled.

An air pollution ordinance relating to foundries which would be adequate in Los Angeles, for example, would work an unnecessary hardship in Sioux City, Iowa; and, one satisfactory elsewhere would be unacceptable in Los Angeles. Thus air pollution control, where required, should be dealt with as local, not as a national problem.

While it is impossible to establish universally applicable limits for emissions from the various foundry operations, it is nevertheless reasonable, and in fact desirable, to outline certain ordinance provisions which are compatible with cupola operations, as well as some which are not properly applicable.

Ordinances Applicable

Limitations on emissions in terms of pounds of emission/1000 lb of process weight/hr are acceptable as a type of limitation reasonably applied to cupola emissions. *Process weight is the total weight of all materials* (except air) *introduced into a specific process, which process may cause discharge to the atmosphere.*

Codes of this type have been criticized in the past as being too strict. It seems, however, that the critics confuse the philosophy with the severity. This method of fixing limits can be severe, moderate or lenient, depending entirely upon the needs of the community. It also eliminates the need for defining words and the need, in this instance, for mathematical formulas.

Equipment of the most expensive type is available for collecting 99+ per cent of cupola emissions. However, local conditions may be such that collection of emissions to this degree is unnecessary and unduly onerous.

THIS INFORMATION MAY BE HELPFUL IN DETERMINING A PERMISSIBLE LIMIT OF EMISSIONS —

Effluents from a cupola in normal operation will range from 3 to 15 lb/1000 lb process weight/hr. A fair average is 8 lb/1000 lb.

It is estimated that the average cupola in the United States melts in the range of one-half ton to 30 tons/hr with an average of 5 tons/hr. These values yield an average emission rate of 80 lb/hr and a range of 1½ to 900 lb/hr.

With these facts, it should be easier to fix a reasonable limit of emissions according to the needs of a particular locality. For example, an emissions limit curve of cupola operations based on process weight/hr can be made to suit local needs.

Inapplicable Ordinances

Certain ordinances have been passed throughout the country by legislative bodies who failed to recognize the difference between melting processes and combustion processes.

Consequently ordinance provisions have been enacted and are being enforced which were designed specifically for application to combustion effluents and which cannot logically be applied to metal melting operations. Among these are —

ORDINANCES WHICH RESTRICT STACK DISCHARGES BY COMPARING THEIR OPACITY WITH THE RINGELMANN CHART OR OTHER VISUAL SMOKE INSPECTION GUIDES

The Ringelmann chart as defined by A.S.T.M. is a *chart used in air pollution evaluation for assigning an arbitrary number — referred to as smoke density — to smoke emanating from any source.*

This chart originally was designed to measure only black smoke emissions from the coal burning equipment. Such guides can have definite utility for this purpose since the opacity of a plume from a carbonaceous fuel-burning operation is related to the degree of combustion of the fuel.

Their use may be proper for the evaluation of emissions from fuel burning equipment since adjustments in firing practice to achieve proper combustion will bring about concurrent reductions in plume opacity. Their use to measure nonblack emissions such as iron oxide fumes from cupolas was never intended nor foreseen.

Stack emissions from cupolas are normally not black, basically are not smoke, and cannot usually be reduced in opacity by process adjustment.

Metal melting operations generate quantities of fumes of metallic oxides which have light scattering power because of the extremely fine size of the particulate matter emitted.

These metallic oxide fumes vary from white to dark brown in color depending on the metal being melted and their average particle size is of the order of one micron.

A Ringelmann number, however, when applied to these emissions is meaningless from a technical standpoint.

. . . CONTAINING PROVISIONS FOR ADJUSTMENT OF EMISSIONS RATES TO 12 PER CENT CO_2

These ordinances, from the A.S.M.E.'s *"Sample Sections of a Smoke Regulation Ordinance,"* are not properly applicable to cupola operations because the percentage of carbon dioxide in cupola stack gases has no relationship whatsoever to efficient operation of the cupola. The title . . . *Smoke* Regulation Ordinance clearly indicates that its extension to metal melting operations was never visualized nor intended by A.S.M.E.

The percentage of CO_2 in cupola stack gases may properly range from zero upwards depending upon many factors.

As further evidence of the inapplicability of such adjustment to cupola stack gases, it may be pointed out that limestone ($CaCO_3$) normally charged into a cupola, decomposes on calcining to lime (CaO) and carbon dioxide (CO_2).

One mole of limestone will yield one mole of lime and one mole of carbon dioxide. Thus by charging for more limestone than is necessary, the CO_2 content of the stack gas could be increased without in any way lowering the particulate emission.

The 12 per cent CO_2 requirement is undoubtedly applicable to boiler installations.

To illustrate the effect of corrections on cupola emissions consider that —

a boiler stack and a foundry cupola stack each discharge 0.60 lb of particulate matter/1000 lb of stack gases, and each discharges the same weight of stack gas/hr. The weight of emissions in then clearly equivalent.

If the CO_2 content of the boiler emission is 10 per cent, the adjusted rate for control purposes would be —

$$\frac{12 \times 0.60}{10} = 0.72 \text{ lb of particulates/1000 lb stack gas}$$

In a cupola melting operation, combustible fuel is a small fraction of the charge (iron to coke ratios are as high as 11:1) and the CO_2 content of the gases may be, and often is, of the order of 5 per cent even with complete combustion of the coke.

Hence at 5 per cent CO_2 content, the adjusted rate for the cupola stack would be —

$$\frac{12 \times 0.60}{5} = 1.44 \text{ lb/1000 lb of stack gas}$$

Such a regulation, therefore, burdens metal melting operations with much more stringent control requirements than fuel burning operations, even though the cupola may contribute no more and perhaps much less to air pollution on an absolute basis.

. . . CONTAINING PROVISIONS FOR ADJUSTMENT TO 50 PER CENT EXCESS AIR

This is merely another way of expressing adjustment to a stated percentage of CO_2 and the same objections to it apply as stated.

This type ordinance refers to complete combustion where approximately 21 per cent of the oxygen in air is used up and converted to 21 per cent CO_2.

Then an excess of 50 per cent of unused air is allowed to produce a total of —

$$\frac{100\%}{150\%} \times 21\%\ CO_2 \text{ or } 14\%\ CO_2$$

. . . WHICH ADJUST A STACK DISCHARGE RATE TO THAT AT A SPECIFIED TEMPERATURE

As in the case of corrections to CO_2 content, volume corrections to a given temperature (usually 500 F) were originally proposed for application to boiler equipment. For this purpose such an adjustment has merit since a stack temperature in excess of 500 F normally indicates an incorrectly operated or inefficient boiler.

In contrast to a boiler stack, however, a cupola stack gas temperature may reach 1700 F or higher under efficient operating conditions.

An ordinance of this type imposes stricter control requirements on cupolas than other stacks. For example, consider both a cupola stack and a boiler stack which are discharging the same rate of gas/hr. Each contains 0.60 lb/1000 lb of stack gas.

If the boiler emission is at 600 F and the local ordinance requires correction to 500 F, the adjusted stack loading would be —

$$\frac{460 + 600}{460 + 500} \times 0.60 = 0.66 \text{ lb/1000 lb of gas}$$

A cupola stack discharging at 1500 F would have an adjusted loading for control purposes of —

$$\frac{460 + 1500}{460 + 500} \times 0.60 = 1.25 \text{ lb/1000 lb gas}$$

Again a foundry operator is severely handicapped by an ordinance provision never intended for application to his emissions.

. . . WHICH CALL FOR SOURCE CONTROL ON THE BASIS OF GROUND LEVEL CONCENTRATIONS OF POLLUTANTS

Some areas have enacted air pollution codes which have as their criterion for control, the measurements of pollutant concentrations at ground level rather than at the source. The concept is sound because there is no need to limit stack emissions if atmospheric dispersion is good and no nuisance or damage occurs.

In one such code (Oregon) control is required only when dust fall rate exceeds 45 tons/sq mile/month above normal background or when suspended particulate concentration exceeds 250 micrograms/cu m above normal background.

It would be desirable if this type of ordinance could be applied and enforced since it automatically adjusts control requirements for the differences in meteorology and topography from place to place.

However it is doubtful if such an ordinance can be practically applied in industrial areas because:

1. No feasible method is available for determining normal background values for a given area.
2. No correlation exists between dust fall rates and emissions from specific stacks. (Theoretically a correlation does exist.) In other words it is practically impossible to determine which sources should be controlled and how efficient the controls should be.
3. Control equipment suppliers cannot give guarantees of ordinance compliance since efficient control of any one source would not decrease the area dust fall rate by any easily predictable amount.

. . . WHICH HAVE EMISSION LIMITATIONS BASED ON PLANT PROPERTY AREA

Codes of this type relate allowable source concentrations to the area of the property upon which the source is located. The theory is that the larger the property area, the less contamination will be transported onto adjacent land.

Such an ordinance is unrealistic in most cases since the theory on which it is based holds only if the source is near the geometric center of the plant property; only if all discharges are emitted at the same elevation; only if all the contaminant particulates are large enough to settle out since the contribution to pollution by any source is determined by both the *type* and *quantity* of contamination involved.

There is no consistent relationship between plant area and pollution contributions of plants and different processes.

ORDINANCES WHICH MAY BE CALLED RETROACTIVE

These ordinances usually allow a six-month period for compliance after enactment. They are applied to all existing installations regardless of financial or technical ability to comply in that period.

It is preferable to exempt all existing installations and those in process of construction but then require all new installations to control atmospheric pollutions to a point of no visible discharge.

Then as melting equipment is replaced or new plants considered, the collection equipment can be budgeted as a part of the new installation.

This type of ordinance would eventually result in complete control of cupola emissions without the financial impact of enforced compliance for existing equipment.

Pig Iron

Pig iron is the metallic product obtained by the reduction of iron ores in the blast furnace. The name is derived from the characteristic shapes in which this primary metal is cast and used in the processing of commercial iron and steel products. The term "pig" is also applied to small ingots of trapezoidal cross section, of the ferroalloys, copper and other metals.

Practically all blast furnace iron produced in present-day practice is cast on a pig machine, which consists of an endless chain of cast iron or pressed steel pig molds that pass continuously in front of the pouring ladle. The filled molds are cooled by a water spray, or by submersion in water, as they pass on up the machine.

At the end of the chain, the mold turns over and the solid pig falls into a waiting railroad car or other receiver. The small and uniform dimensions of machine-cast pig have the universal approval of foundrymen. The present-day pig weighs under 60 lb and is more easily handled than the old sand-cast pig, which often weighed as much as 100 or 125 lb.

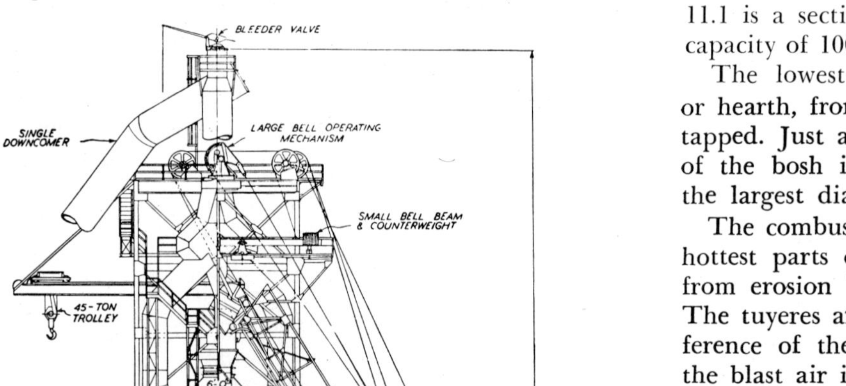

Fig. 11.1. Diagrammatic sketch of blast furnace section. Furnace has capacity 1000 tons/24 hr.

BLAST FURNACE

A blast furnace, like a cupola, is fundamentally a steel stack lined with highly refractory lining. Figure 11.1 is a sectional view of a blast furnace having a capacity of 1000 tons/24 hr.

The lowest part of the furnace is the crucible or hearth, from which the molten iron and slag are tapped. Just above the hearth is the bosh. The top of the bosh is the part of the furnace which has the largest diameter.

The combustion zones are in the bosh and are the hottest parts of the furnace. To protect the lining from erosion by the slag, the bosh is water cooled The tuyeres are spaced regularly around the circumference of the lower part of the bosh and convey the blast air into the furnace below the combustion. zone from the firebrick lined bustle pipe which encircles the exterior of the furnace.

The cinder notch, from which the slag is tapped, is located 30-40 in. below the tuyeres, and the tapping hole, or iron notch, from which the molten metal is tapped, is placed slightly above the bottom of the hearth.

At the top of the furnace are the charging hopper and bells. The charge is conveyed from ground level by a skip hoist and dumped into the hopper. The upper bell is lowered and the charge drops onto the lower bell. The upper bell then is raised to prevent the escape of gases and the charge is dropped from the lower bell into the furnace.

At pressure of 15-30 psi, air for the smelting process is forced into the furnace through the bustle pipe and tuyeres by large blowing engines. The name *blast furnace* derives from this part of the process. Prior to its entering the furnace, the air is heated to 1200-1600 F by hot blast stoves, cylindrical firebrick lined steel structures about 100 ft high and 20 ft in diameter. Three or more stoves serve each furnace (Fig. 11.2).

The approximate normal blast furnace charge consists of 3100 lb of beneficiated iron ore* (chiefly iron oxide), 1800 lb of coke, and a half ton of limestone. About 4½ tons of air are required for the production of one ton of pig iron. A given charge passes through the furnace in about 9 hr. The iron is tapped and pigged every 4 to 8 hr. The slag (calcium aluminum silicate), formed by the reaction of the limestone with the siliceous gangue of the ore, is tapped about two times for every tap of iron.

The chemical reactions which take place in the blast furnace are very complex and their discussion is beyond the scope of this book. Principally, however, carbon dioxide, which results from the combustion of the coke, is reduced to carbon monoxide (as in the cupola) and the latter reduces the iron oxide of the ore to metal. The reduction proceeds as the charge descends through the stack and is substantially complete when the melting zone is reached.

Phosphorus, silicon, and manganese compounds in the charge also are reduced to the elementary forms, and these are dissolved by the iron along with some carbon from the coke. Sulfur contained in the ore and in the coke is largely dissolved in the slag. The silicon content of the iron is controlled by the amount of silica (SiO_2) in the charge and by the temperature at which the furnace is operated. The temperature of the iron in the melting zone is 2800-3000 F, and it is tapped from the hearth at about 2750 F.

For further study of this subject, the reader is referred to *Blast Furnace Practice* by R. H. Sweetser, McGraw-Hill Book Co., New York (1938).

CONTROL OF ELEMENTS IN BLAST FURNACE

In addition to elemental iron, normally present in amounts of over 90 per cent, blast furnace metal for the production of pig iron contains phosphorus, manganese, silicon, sulfur, and carbon.

Phosphorus. No commercial method has been developed whereby iron is dephosphorized in the blast furnace operation. In the charge, virtually all of the phosphates — metallic or otherwise — are reduced to phosphorus dissolved in the liquid metal. Hence the phosphorus content of the pig iron is determined by the phosphorus content of the ores, and this varies widely depending on geographic location.

Standard domestic grades of pig iron ranging in phosphorus content from a few hundredths to 0.9 per cent are commercially available. Although the phosphorus content of a given burden cannot be reduced in the blast furnace, phosphate rock can be added to the charge to increase the phosphorus content in the pig iron.

* The iron ore from a single mine may vary greatly in analysis. This variation is corrected by the ore producers by the employment of a system of blending and grading the ores by which each cargo approximates a certain average analysis. Equipment is available at every blast furnace plant whereby further mixing of the ores during unloading and stocking is effected, and a still higher degree of uniformity is attained. The result of this process is not ideal, but the technique has been developed to the point that the product meets the requirements of both the steel mill and foundry.

Manganese. As in the case of phosphorus, the manganese content of the pig iron is largely determined by the manganese content of the burden charged into the blast furnace. All iron ores carry some manganese and the amount varies considerably, permitting a manganese content in the pig iron of up to 1.50 per cent in the standard grades, excepting the silvery pig irons where manganese contents up to 2.0 per cent are obtainable.

In contrast to phosphorus, the blast furnace operation can be manipulated to offset the manganese content. High operating temperatures coupled with basic slags favor the reduction of manganese oxide in the ore to manganese, whereas lower hearth temperatures and less basic slags favor the absorption of manganese in the slag. However, the temperature at which a blast furnace is operated is not normally dictated by the desired manganese content or recovery, but instead by the desired silicon content in the pig iron.

Sulfur, normally viewed as a contamination in pig iron, originates primarily from the coke burned in the blast furnace. The maximum allowable sulfur content in the standard grades of pig irons is 0.05 per cent, and the actual values supplied are normally under 0.04 per cent. The following combination of operating conditions keeps the sulfur level in line: selection of suitable coke; high slag volumes; basic slags; and high operating temperatures in the blast furnace. Ores with relatively high manganese contents usually have lower sulfur contents in the pig iron, and higher silicon irons are usually accompanied by lower sulfur contents, owing to the higher operating temperatures required.

Silicon. The silicon found in pig iron results from the reduction of silica occurring as gangue in iron ores and in the ash of the coke. Most ores have sufficient silica present to provide the silicon desired in the resulting iron, and also to yield a volume of slag great enough to remove the sulfur liberated by the combustion of the fuel (coke).

The reduction of silica to silicon is effected by carbon or carbon monoxide, and the amount of silicon reduced is in direct proportion to the heat available to drive the equation to completion, i.e., the greater the available heat, the greater the amount of silicon reduced.

The chemistry of this process is shown in the following equations:

1) $SiO_2 + 2\,CO = 2\,Si + 2\,CO_2$ — 119,700 Btu

2) $2\,CO_2 + 2\,C = 4\,CO$ — 140,400 Btu

Adding

3) $SiO_2 + 2\,C = Si + 2\,CO$ — 260,100 Btu or — 9,289 Btu/lb silicon

Silica may be reduced to carbon monoxide to form metallic silicon and carbon dioxide according to Equation 1). However, the carbon dioxide thus formed reacts immediately with the carbon present to form carbon monoxide, according to Equation 2). The net chemical and thermal effect is indicated in Equation 3).

Carbon. Next to iron this is the most important element found in pig iron. It is also the one element which is almost primarily dependent on the manner in which the blast furnace is operated.

Fig. 11.2. View of blast furnaces, hot-blast stoves, and material storage and handling facilities. Each furnace has capacity of approx. 1200 tons per 24 hr. (Inland Steel Co., Chicago.)

Under normal blast furnace operation sufficient coke and temperature are available, even under the dynamic conditions which prevail, to saturate the iron with carbon. Hence practically all pig iron is on the hypereutectic side, making due compensation for the associated silicon and phosphorus contents according to the well known and accepted carbon equivalence concept –

$$CE = \%\,TC + \frac{1}{3}(\%\,Si + \%\,P)$$

This more or less automatic control of carbon content does not, however, detract from the desirability of knowing more about the actual carbon content of any particular shipment of pig iron. With time and continued interest this situation will probably be clarified to the mutual satisfaction of both supplier and consumer.

The foundryman must realize that it is not an easy technical matter to produce pig iron to chemical specification. The raw materials available to the blast furnace operator are highly variant, and hence careful selection and blending of all the materials entering the charge must be continually exercised.

In addition, the many operating factors, such as air-blast volume and temperature, coke to air ratio, slag volume and chemistry, and the physical state of the various raw materials must be closely regulated in order to obtain the requisite silicon control, which from an operating standpoint is the primary objective with a given combination of raw materials.

The use of large mixing ladles to receive the metal helps considerably toward homogenizing and regulating the composition of any tap. It is at this point where the sorting of pig irons into their respective subgrades takes place. It is quite probable that once a given lot of pig iron has been properly graded as to chemical composition, many of the complaints by the consumer regarding the quality of the pig iron may be erroneous, and the difficulty he encounters may more properly be attributable to the operation of his cupola.

USE OF PIG IRON

Pig iron is used in some degree in the production of virtually all ferrous castings. In the production of gray iron and ductile iron castings made by the acid cupola melting process, pig iron is used to provide control of carbon, sulfur, phosphorus, silicon, and manganese content. Pig iron is also used for the control of these elements in production of malleable iron castings. In the production of steel castings by acid melting processes, pig iron is used as a basic portion of the charge and is also frequently added near the end of the heat for adjustment of chemical analysis.

Various investigators have noted that cupola melted gray irons containing pig iron in the charge show lower chill tendency in thin sections. Pig iron is also valuable to the foundry operator as a means of controlling and diluting the effects of various alloys and tramp elements. To the foundryman, pig iron is virtually the only material available having both controlled chemical analysis and shape. The regular and consistent shape of pig iron contributes to better flow of charge materials down the cupola stack during the melting operation.

CLASSIFICATION OF PIG IRON

Merchant pig iron is classified into several standard grades based primarily upon the phosphorus content of the material.

The following grades are presently recognized within the trade and are generally referred to by grade name rather than designation number.

LOW PHOSPHORUS PIG IRON. This grade is standardized as having a phosphorus content of .075 per cent maximum.

BESSEMER PIG IRON. This grade is standardized as having a phosphorus content within a range of .076 to .100 per cent.

MALLEABLE PIG IRON. This grade is standardized as having a phosphorus content within a range of .101 to .30 per cent. Commercial practice generally has limited the acceptable phosphorus content within the range of .101 to .15 per cent, except for specialized requirements.

FOUNDRY PIG IRON. This grade is standardized as having a phosphorus content in excess of .30 per cent. A wide range of phosphorus content is produced commercially to satisfy the requirements of certain industrial applications for Foundry Pig Iron. Some of these applications are soil pipe, ornamental cast iron, stove and burner castings, and other types of thin section gray iron castings.

For a detailed discussion of standard grades and classifications of merchant pig iron, the reader is referred to: *1) A.S.T.M. Tentative Specification, Designation A43-55T. 2) Steel Products Manual, Pig Iron and Blast Furnace Ferroalloys, Section 1 (May 1951),* American Iron and Steel Institute, 350 Fifth Ave., New York 1.

SAMPLING AND CHEMICAL ANALYSIS OF PIG IRON

For methods of sampling carload lots of pig iron, the reader is referred to Section 3 of the *Standard Method of Sampling Steel, Cast Iron, Open-Hearth Iron, and Wrought Iron* (ASTM Designation: E-59); and for methods of chemical analysis to the same source (ASTM Designation: E-30).

CHAPTER 12

Scrap

Both iron scrap and steel scrap are very important components of most metal mixtures melted in the cupola. There are many reasons, metallurgical and economic, for this widespread use of scrap materials.

Scrap used in cupola melting can be placed in three broad classifications.

1) *Return Scrap or Home Scrap*

In this classification are the sprue, gates and risers involved in the foundries' production, as well as defective castings which may be produced. Depending on the type of castings made and gating employed, the yield of good castings in a given foundry may vary from less than 50 per cent to as high as 90 per cent of the metal melted. The balance of the melt is returned to the cupola as scrap for use as a portion of the charge.

Return scrap, being of known and uniform analysis, forms a desirable grade of melting material. In most cases, all the scrap produced in a given foundry is remelted and the amount of returns available for the melting department will vary with the yield of good castings obtained. Under some conditions, the returns available may be augmented by machine shop scrap and rejections from a foundry's customers or by briquetted borings from the same source.

2) *Purchased Cast Scrap*

Purchased cast scrap consists of iron castings which have served their useful life as parts of machinery, vehicles, heating equipment, municipal water systems or the many other structures in which such castings are or have been used. Purchased scrap may vary widely in geographic origin and the use to which the original castings may have been put. For these reasons, purchased scrap is likely to be of variable chemical analysis and size compared to the foundry's returns. Purchased scrap also is likely to be contaminated with other materials which may have formed part of the original structure, such as steel shafting, bearing metals, non-ferrous materials including copper and aluminum base alloys, and many other miscellaneous materials.

Fortunately, iron castings for given applications are often made to a fairly standard analysis range, either because the service demands adherance to a rather strict standard or because production of certain items is fairly well limited to a geographical area having given melting materials available. Thus, automotive castings are almost invariably of low phosphorus content under 0.20 per cent and in the range of 3.00 to 3.50 per cent carbon and 2.00 to 2.50 per cent silicon. Railroad car wheels likewise can be assumed to analyze 3.50 per cent carbon, 0.55 per cent silicon and 0.30 per cent phosphorus.

Certain types of scrap such as sanitary ware, stove plate and most other thin castings, on the other hand, can be assumed to be relatively high in both silicon and phosphorus. The function of the dealer in scrap materials is to collect worn-out articles, broken down machinery, etc., which can, by intelligent sorting, breaking to size where necessary, and removal of contaminants, be resold to foundry or steel mill as suitable melting material.

3) *Steel Scrap*

Steel scrap is widely used in foundry and steel mill as melting material. Like cast iron, steel is produced in many grades varying in chemistry according to the use to which it is to be put.

Steel scrap is often new material of known analysis, the by-product of some fabricating process. Such scrap is available in large quantities in industrial centers. Flashings from forge plants and new steel bundles are typical of this class of scrap. Scrap of this type usually commands a premium price because of its known analysis and cleanliness. In addition to new process scrap, a great deal of steel scrap comes on the market as the result of dismantling obsolete or worn-out structures and machines.

Like cast scrap, such old steel scrap is of variable composition and size. It may contain unwanted tramp alloys, or nonferrous attachments. Again it can be sorted according to the use to which the article was put and it is the function of the dealer to cut such scrap to usable size and to sort it according to probable analysis. In this manner, he converts worn-out equipment into a salable product which can be used with confidence in the cupola charge.

REASONS FOR USING SCRAP

Scrap iron and steel are used in the cupola charge for many reasons. These may be metallurgical or may be based on availability and economics.

Practically all foundries find their own returns desirable melting material, and returns are used as a matter of course in the quantities available.

Cast scrap may be used for a variety of reasons. Pig iron is usually the most expensive material charged in large quantities, and where suitable scrap is available, it can often form a fairly large percentage of the charge at a considerable saving in cost. In addition, the high carbon content of pig iron in the range of 3.50 per cent to over 4.00 per cent can be a problem if excessive amounts are used in the production of higher strength irons in which carbon must be controlled at a fairly low level.

An excessive amount of pig may cause a coarse graphitic structure and open grain; replacement of a portion with suitable scrap may result in a more desirable structure. Many foundries in isolated localities find scrap more readily available than any other melting material and, in such cases, the cupola charge is often entirely made up of suitably selected scrap with briquetted alloys or other sources of manganese and silicon to provide for melting losses.

While some foundries producing soft iron for small castings may operate on a pig iron and return scrap basis, the average iron foundry, for one or more of the foregoing reasons, uses rather large amounts of iron scrap varying from 10 or 20 per cent to almost 100 per cent of the metal charged.

Steel scrap, like iron scrap, is used for many reasons. Steel, being low in carbon content, is almost universally used as a source of low carbon material in the cupola charge. While steel in melting in the cupola absorbs considerable carbon, the use of this material in appreciable amounts almost invariably results in production of lower carbon content in the iron melted.

For this reason, some steel is generally used in all but the softest grades of gray iron, and charges for high duty irons of low carbon content often contain from 40 to above 80 per cent of steel scrap. For the same reason, large percentages of steel scrap are used in melting cupola malleable or duplex malleable iron, which must of necessity be well below 3 per cent in carbon content.

In addition to its function in helping control the carbon level of the product, there is often an economic advantage to be gained by using as much steel as is practicable. Steel scrap is usually the most reasonably priced material charged. While allowance must be made for its low silicon content, there are many conditions under which substantial savings can be made by using steel scrap up to the limit allowed by the melting process and the product being made.

Technological changes in the wrought steel industry during recent years have resulted in greater proportions of molten pig iron and a decline in the amount of scrap used in the steel mill melt shop. This trend has in turn made increased quantities of scrap readily available for foundry use. Developments in basic and water cooled cupolas have permitted increased use of steel scrap. Removal of the limitations imposed by the traditional acid refractories allows such cupolas to be operated with neutral or basic slags. More basic cupola slags tend to produce metal of high carbon content and under these conditions high percentages of steel can be used to produce cast irons of normal analysis.

Use of high temperature preheated blast is also becoming more common and again influences the percentage of steel scrap which can be used in the cupola. Due to the use of carbon steel in construction of earlier blast preheaters, blast temperature was usually limited to about 400 to 500 F. Recent installations of hot blast equipment usually use stainless steel heat exchangers permitting blast temperatures up to 1400 F. Higher temperature blast can be used to promote increased metal temperature and increased carbon absorption from the coke.

It is reported that an increase of 100 F in the temperature of the blast yields approximately 0.10 per cent higher carbon in the metal. More foundries now use rapid methods of chemical analysis such as direct reading spectrographs or solidification temperature techniques to obtain frequent checks of product chemistry. Combining such rapid quality checks with use of high temperature blast allows the cupola operator to make prompt adjustment of melting conditions and to rely on carbon absorption by steel scrap to a greater extent than formerly.

HOW TO SELECT SCRAP FOR CUPOLA USE

Many of the charge materials used in the cupola are made for that purpose to rather strict specifications covering chemistry, size and shape. This applies to pig irons, addition agents such as silvery pig or alloy briquets, and to a certain extent to the foundryman's own return scrap. Purchased scrap iron or steel scrap, on the other hand, may vary widely in both analysis and physical shape and size unless carefully prepared by conscientious sorting, removal of contaminants and breaking or cutting to predetermined size.

The foundryman has a wide selection of grades of pig iron and can purchase this material containing various percentages of carbon, silicon, manganese and phosphorus to best meet his needs. Scrap, if properly prepared, can also be purchased to fairly narrow analysis ranges to fit the needs of the individual foundry.

The first requisite of a satisfactory melting material is knowledge of its analysis within fairly narrow limits. There are many indications as to the chemistry of a given piece of iron or steel scrap which the foundryman can use as a guide to proper selection and use. It must, of course, be recognized that the following rules are approximations and will not apply to every piece of scrap but, taken as a whole, they will indicate rather closely the average analysis of a given lot of material.

Cast Scrap

For cast scrap the following indicators are of value:

1) Pieces of iron scrap which show evidence of machining operations (machinery cast) will be high enough in carbon and silicon to yield a gray fracture in the sections involved. Thus, light castings which have been machined will probably contain a minimum of 3.40 per cent carbon and 2.00 per cent silicon. Castings of medium section from 1 to

2 in. in thickness will probably contain a minimum of 3.10 per cent carbon and 1.50 per cent silicon. Very heavy castings may be even lower in silicon content down to 1.25 per cent.

2) Automotive castings, cylinder blocks, heads, manifolds, housings, etc., are almost invariably of low phosphorus content, under 0.25 per cent, and probably average closer to 0.15 per cent in this element. This also applies to truck and tractor castings. Such automative castings will usually be fairly uniform in silicon content in the neighborhood of 2.00-2.25 per cent for cylinders and 2.25 to 2.50 per cent for lighter parts.
Light castings can be assumed to be free of alloys. Passenger car blocks normally contain 0.10 to 0.35 per cent chromium, and some may contain up to 0.35 per cent nickel. Molybdenum is seldom used in passenger car cylinders. Heavy duty truck cylinders often contain greater amounts of alloy up to 2 per cent nickel, 0.75 per cent chromium, or 0.50 per cent molybdenum. Scrap containing a high percentage of such heavy blocks may, on this account, be dangerous for use in production of light-section parts cast in soft iron. Purchase of automotive cast is probably the surest way of controlling the phosphorus content of cast scrap at a low level.

3) Farm machinery castings will usually be substantially free of alloys, somewhat higher in phosphorus in the 0.25 to 0.40 per cent range, and somewhat higher in carbon and silicon, averaging 3.40 per cent carbon and 2.25 to 2.50 per cent silicon.

4) Chilled castings or castings showing white fracture are almost invariably of low silicon content. Thus, chilled car wheels are uniformly about 3.50 per cent carbon, 0.55 per cent silicon and 0.30 per cent phosphorus. Car wheels, incidentally, are an excellent and uniform type of scrap if their low silicon content is recognized and corrected for. Other chilled castings are of variable analysis and the foundryman will do well to look with suspicion on any lot of cast scrap containing an appreciable amount of such material.

5) Very light section castings such as hollow-ware, sanitary ware, radiation, very light machinery, stove plate, etc., are almost invariably high in both silicon and phosphorus content. This can be either an advantage or disadvantage, depending on the foundry's product.

6) Burnt and heavily oxidized scrap such as fire pots, burnt stove plate, annealing boxes etc., is always dangerous. It is low in carbon and silicon, high in sulfur, and introduces variable quantities of unwanted oxide into the cupola. The result of using such material will be deep and erratic chilling, poor machining qualities, excessive shrinkage, and the possibility of cracked castings.

7) Some types of iron castings such as railroad brake shoes, sash weights, mill stars and many white iron parts are traditionally melted from the poorest grades of scrap. Such products are not included in properly sorted cupola scrap. They should never be used in producing castings to specification and their presence in selected iron scrap is usually cause for rejection.

8) Malleable iron analyzes about 2.00 per cent carbon and 1.00 to 1.50 per cent silicon. It is excellent melting material for certain uses, but an admixture in gray iron scrap can be dangerous because of its low carbon and silicon content.

9) Ductile iron is similar in analysis to soft gray iron, running about 3.50 per cent min. carbon and approximately 2.50 per cent silicon. Sulfur is very low at 0.02 per cent max. and phosphorus under 0.10 per cent. With the exception of nickel, ductile iron scrap can be assumed to be alloy-free and low in other residuals. When nickel base magnesium alloys are used in production the nickel can run up to 1.50 per cent.

10) Cast scrap should not contain appreciable amounts of steel. In dismantling machinery, it is common practice to cut off steel shafting at the edges of a wheel hub, removal of the entire shaft often being impractical. Cylinder blocks may contain steel camshafts, but the heavier crankshaft should be removed. Excessive and unpredictable amounts of steel can constitute a serious hazard. On the other hand, the dealer is faced with problems in removal of every piece of steel, and contamination with steel scrap to a limit of possibly 5 per cent should not be objectionable.

11) Ductility is a quality of wrought, ductile and malleable irons and steel. A large quantity of any of these materials presents a serious hazard due to their wide variation in analysis from that of gray iron. So called "farm scrap" containing a mixture of cast iron, malleable and steel should never be used in appreciable quantities in any but cupola charges designed to produce metal for applications not requiring metal of controlled quality.

12) Pieces which do not rust or are not lifted by the electro-magnet are high in alloy content. They may be stainless steel of up to 20 per cent chromium and 10 per cent nickel, 13 per cent manganese steel, or high alloy irons. While seldom found in properly sorted scrap, these pieces can be dangerous and most cupola operators have encountered them.

13) Nonferrous attachments such as aluminum, copper alloys, bearing metals, etc., are dangerous and should not be present in properly prepared scrap. The same is true of galvanized or tinned parts. Other contaminents sometimes found are rubber, plaster of paris, and cement or concrete. These materials, in the first two cases, introduce large amounts of sulfur. In any case, they upset the cupola charge and, as they are paid for as metal, represent poor value to the purchaser.

STEEL SCRAP

Steel, like cast iron, is made in a variety of analyses to meet varying requirements. Also, like iron, the analysis of an individual piece can usually be predicted rather accurately by observing the following rules.

1) Structural steel (angles, beams, etc.) usually is unalloyed and contains relatively low carbon,

approximately 0.20 per cent, with manganese at about 0.50 per cent. Silicon usually is very low with sulfur and phosphorus 0.05 per cent max.

2) Ship plate, boiler plate, tanks and other commonly used plate will analyze 0.25 per cent max. carbon, 0.75 per cent manganese, 0.35 per cent max. silicon, 0.04 per cent max. phosphorus, and 0.05 per cent max. sulfur.
3) Sheet and strip scrap often purchased bundled usually analyzes 0.10 per cent carbon, 0.40 per cent manganese and is low in silicon, sulfur and phosphorus.
4) Railroad rails are made of unalloyed high carbon steel analyzing 0.70 per cent carbon, 0.75 per cent manganese, and 0.10 to 0.23 per cent silicon.
5) Railroad joint bars and tie plates are made of unalloyed low or medium carbon steel. These parts are sometimes made from bessemer steel containing up to 0.11 per cent phosphorus.
6) Automotive frames, rims and wheels are made from low carbon unalloyed steel. Bumper stock in some cases is one of the low alloy-high strength steels containing appreciable amounts of silicon up to 0.80 per cent and chromium of about 0.60 per cent.
7) Automotive crankshafts are usually made from 0.45 per cent carbon unalloyed steel. Some heavy duty crankshafts are heavily alloyed. A few manufacturers now use ductile iron or pearlitic malleable iron crankshafts; use of these materials is expanding.
8) Railroad coil springs are unalloyed high carbon steel.
9) Automotive leaf springs and similar springs may be high carbon unalloyed steel, but often contain appreciable amounts of chromium, nickel, molybdenum and vanadium.
10) Forgings may be unalloyed carbon steel, but for heavy duty applications alloy steels of various types are often used.
11) Forge flashings will, of course, vary in analysis, depending on the part being made.
12) Small steel parts which involve considerable machining are often made from free-machining steels containing from 0.08 to 0.30 per cent sulfur. Such steels are usually high in manganese, often running up to 1.50 per cent. Use of leaded grades containing about 0.25 per cent lead now accounts for about 25 per cent of the production of free machining steels. A large percentage of such parts in steel scrap is questionable.

SAMPLING FOR CHEMICAL ANALYSIS

It is a difficult matter to select a sample from a car of miscellaneous scrap which is representative enough to use for chemical analysis. This is particularly true of cast scrap, and it is probably safer to rely on estimation of the analysis of a given lot of scrap by following the foregoing guide than to rely on chemical analysis of an unrepresentative sample. Of course, chemical analysis should be used to check doubtful material.

The case of steel scrap is a somewhat different matter. Steel is often available in carload lots of uniform material as the result of dismantling some structure. This is particularly true of new industrial scrap such as plate trimmings, forge flashings and new bundles. In such cases, it is a simple matter to determine the suitability of a given type of scrap by taking a sample for laboratory checking.

In checking cast scrap, the silicon and phosphorus contents are of prime importance, as well as the presence or absence of alloys. In steel scrap, the presence of alloyed grades in large amounts can be troublesome. High-sulfur free-machining steels should also be guarded against. Presence of alloys in known amounts can be a definite advantage in some types of work, providing a low-cost source of alloying elements. Uncontrolled alloy in variable amounts is likely to be troublesome.

SIZE AND PREPARATION

Control over the size and thickness of individual pieces of scrap is at least as important as close control of its chemistry. The size of individual pieces which can be used depends largely on the size cupola being operated, the use of mixing ladles and other peculiarities of a given foundry's operations. As a general rule, individual pieces of iron or steel scrap should be sized so that no single dimension exceeds ⅓ of the cupola diameter. Thus, scrap for use in a 72 in. cupola should be controlled to a maximum dimension of about 24 in.

Very small pieces of scrap are also objectionable, particularly in steel scrap. Such material in large amounts tends to make an excessively tight charge, preventing proper penetration of the cupola blast. Very small pieces also may migrate from charge to charge as the cupola settles, thus arriving at the melting zone ahead of the balance of the charge. This condition is particularly dangerous in the case of steel scrap, and a large and variable amount of punchings or other small pieces in steel scrap may result in rather wide fluctuation in the analysis of the iron produced.

As far as thickness is concerned, the rate at which individual pieces absorb heat and melt in the cupola is largely governed by the ratio of surface area to weight. Thick pieces of either iron or steel thus absorb heat slowly and tend to melt low in the cupola. The reverse is true of very thin stock. A variable mixture of very heavy and thin scrap can, in this way, cause fluctuation in the chemistry of the iron.

A large amount of heavy melting stock can also adversely affect metal temperature and degree of oxidation of the metal. For this reason, many foundries specify maximum thickness of 1½ in. or a maximum diameter of 2½ in. in individual pieces. This limitation is more important for steel scrap than for cast iron, and most specifications for iron scrap merely limit the weight of individual pieces to 125 or 150 lb maximum.

Bundled deep drawing sheet clippings have a particularly desirable chemistry for melting in the cupola. Unfortunately, the cost of making small bundles for cupola use is considered prohibitive by many dealers, in view of the fact mill purchasers are glad to accept bundles of 1000 lb. and more in weight.

Small new bundles weighing not over 125 lb are

very desirable cupola steel. For some foundries, operating large cupolas, the advantages of desirable chemistry may outweigh the disadvantages of large bundles, and such foundries sometimes use steel bundles which are much larger than desirable, weighing several hundred pounds each. Use of large mixing ladles or some other means of blending the iron is a necessity in such cases.

Number 2 bundles or so-called dealers bundles are made from old steel scrap such as automobile fenders, body steel, steel wire, clippings, etc. Such material is likely to be contaminated with galvanized stock, tin plate, terne plate, etc. It is also usually rather heavily rusted, and unless of unusually good quality, No. 2 bundles are not considered desirable for cupola use.

Very thin pieces are also objectionable. Thin steel plate carries an excessive percentage of rust and much oxide is formed on its surface during descent in the cupola, resulting in excessive melting loss of silicon and manganese. Use of such stock also results in excessive sulfur pickup during melting. The same is true of very light steel flashings.

An excessive amount of flat plate stock in steel scrap is objectionable in that flat plates tend to overlap and force the blast up the cupola walls.

Obviously, the maximum sizes of scrap usable will depend on the cupola size and charging equipment in use. It costs money to cut steel scrap to short lengths and the operator of a small cupola may have difficulty in obtaining such material properly sized for his operation. A compromise on this point can be made, but it will be reflected in poor operating conditions and erratic control of metal quality.

Caution: closed vessels of iron or steel are occasionally found in scrap. Such parts should be open at one end or should be broken or punctured to prevent a possible explosion.

BORINGS AND TURNINGS

Cast iron borings and steel turnings have, for many years, offered a challenge to the foundryman in that these materials normally have a market value a great deal less than that of other types of scrap. While many schemes have been developed for the usage of borings and turnings as melting stock in the cupola, the most satisfactory method of using these materials has been to charge them in the form of briquets.

Briquetted borings are made by compressing the material under high pressure without the use of binders. The process of making them affords an economical means for disposition of borings, with a resultant saving over the use of purchased scrap of the usual kinds. The same press may be used for making cast iron or steel briquets by changing the forming dies.

Cast iron briquets are normally approximately 4 in. in diameter, 3¾ in. in height, and weigh about 11 lb. They are reported to have a density of about 80 per cent that of cast iron.

Steel briquets may be about 7 in. in diameter, 3½ in. in height, and weigh approximately 22½ lb, with a density of 60 to 65 per cent of the density of steel.

Briquetting machines are available in various sizes, capacities and costs. The type or size of equipment to be considered for a given foundry will depend, of course, upon the tonnage of material to be briquetted.

Briquetting of borings, as a rule, is undertaken by captive foundries attached to plants which produce a large quantity of borings. This material is of known analysis. Normally, it has a low market value, and by briquetting it can be converted into a usable material for return to the foundry melting department.

Borings to be briquetted should be clean and free of mineral oil, excessively fine material and foreign materials such as shop refuse, nonferrous turnings, etc. They should be drained of water soluble cutting oil and be relatively free of moisture.

Briquetting Cost

The cost of briquetting cast iron borings is in the range of $4.50 to $7/ton.

In using briquets as a portion of the cupola charge, it has been common experience that the silicon oxidation losses are slightly increased and that carbon content of the iron produced may tend to be a little lower than when using an equivalent amount of cast scrap. Briquets form a dense charge which may affect penetration of the cupola blast if an excessive amount is used. In most operations utilizing briquetted borings a maximum of 20 to 25 per cent is considered practical. There are individual operations which, however, use considerably greater percentages of borings regularly.

Briquetted borings are used most advantageously by companies which produce their own borings. Purchase of large amounts of borings of high quality for briquetting may often be impractical due to easy contamination of this material and difficulty in controlling its analysis. Borings are occasionally briquetted by dealers and resold to the foundry trade. However, briquets are a little fragile at best and rehandling results in abrasion of corners and the production of a rather large amount of loose borings. For this reason, handling of borings after briquetting should be held to a minimum whether the briquets are purchased or produced in the foundry itself.

The Crofts process, which employed equipment for mechanically forcing loose borings into the cupola at the melting zone level, was used in Europe but found little application in the United States. A newer development along this line is the Roxy injector. This equipment uses compressed air to inject a quantity of borings into the melting zone at predetermined intervals. A cupola can be fitted with one or more injectors depending on the quantity of borings used. The Roxy injector has been installed by a number of American foundries and is reported to perform satisfactorily.

SPECIFICATIONS FOR PURCHASING SCRAP

While fairly definite classifications of the various types of iron and steel scrap have been established, the process of preparation and careful sorting requires a great deal of judgment and no small degree of integrity on the part of the dealer. The small foundry purchasing from a limited number of sources may find it most satisfactory to settle the matter of what is usable and desirable for its operation by discussing the matter in detail with its suppliers, inasmuch as the requirements will vary widely from plant to plant, depending on product and the available equipment. Careful inspection of incoming scrap is important, and any deviation from standards which have been agreed upon should be called to the attention of the supplier.

Foundries which regularly purchase large quantities of scrap through brokers will find a written specification describing their requirements desirable, inasmuch as individual shipments are often prepared in scrap yards which may be at a great distance, and the broker with whom orders are placed seldom sees individual shipments. Usually, scrap purchased by iron foundries is in relatively few classifications, and the following excerpts from existing specifications will cover most of them.

MATERIAL SPECIFICATION—IRON AND STEEL SCRAP

Number One Machinery Cast Scrap shall consist only of first quality cast scrap which possesses evidence of having been machined, i.e., planed or turned surfaces or bored or drilled holes. Pieces must be of cupola size and must not weigh more than 150 lb nor exceed 24 in. in length or 18 in. in width.

Non-Acceptable

Car wheels, brake shoes, stove plate or any burnt, chilled, malleable hard iron or steel. Aluminum or other nonferrous parts.

The following must not be shipped under this classification without special permission of the buyer:

Locomotive wheels and cylinders, broken machinery and similar high grade cast scrap, broken to cupola size, which may not show evidence of machining.

Number One Machinery Breakable Scrap. Machinery breakable cast scrap shall consist of cast iron scrap weighing more than 150 lb which can be broken under a drop ball. It must be free from chilled iron and steel scrap. In other respects than size, breakable scrap shall conform to the specification for No. 1 machinery cast scrap.

Auto Cast Scrap shall consist of auto cylinder blocks, heads, manifolds, crankcases and flywheels, clean and reasonably free from grease and dirt.

Non-Acceptable

Steel or pearlitic malleable crankshafts, connecting rods, magnetos, transmission gears, loose piston rings, aluminum or other nonferrous parts, and all steel and malleable attachments, except camshafts, valves, studs and nuts.

Number One Agricultural Cast Scrap shall consist of cast gray iron parts of agricultural machinery. Pieces must not weigh more than 150 lb nor exceed 24 in. in length or 18 in. in width.

Non-Acceptable

Steel, malleable and chilled iron, such as plow points, car wheels, brake shoes, stove plates, and white or burnt iron of every description.

Number One Railroad Cast Scrap shall consist of railroad cast scrap, no piece to weigh more than 150 lb nor to exceed 24 in. in length or 18 in. in width.

Non-Acceptable

Stove plate; grate bars, car wheels, steel; malleable, chilled, white or mottled iron.

Car Wheels shall consist of clean cast iron freight car wheels.

Stove Plate Scrap shall consist of clean stove plate.

Non-Acceptable

Malleable iron and steel parts, grates, burnt iron and other miscellaneous scrap usually collected with this material.

Malleable Scrap shall consist of all kinds of malleable castings from railroad equipment; also, from automotive and agricultural machinery. No piece is to weigh more than 150 lb, nor to exceed 24 in. in length or width.

Non-Acceptable

Gray iron or steel parts.

Brake Shoe Scrap. Driving and railroad car brake shoes of all types except composition-filled shoes.

Foundry Melting Steel Scrap shall consist of steel or wrought iron from 1/4 in. in thickness up to 1 1/2 in. in thickness for flat pieces, and from 1/2-in. diameter to 2 1/2 in. diameter for round pieces. No piece shall weigh over 50 lb. No piece shall be over 24 in. in length or 18 in. in width, nor be less than the equivalent of 1/2 in. square and 10 in. long. Individual pieces must be trimmed of attachments and cut into shapes that will not tangle with other material in the charging buckets or in the cupolas. All material must be clean and free from dirt, refuse and burnt material.

Non-Acceptable

Cut pipe, punchings, turnings, curly materials, alloys.

Alloy Free Automobile Shoveling and Heavy Melting Steel shall consist of chassis, rims, drums and rear axle housings. Housings to be cut into three pieces and shall be free from gears and shafts. Chassis and rims to be cut into shoveling size 12 in. or under.

Non-Acceptable

All alloy material.
All non-ferrous metals or foreign material.
Sheet steel such as fenders and bodies.
Excessive rust, scale, or dirt-covered parts.

Cut Rails shall consist of 50 lb or over standard section rails cut to lengths of 2 ft or under, free from concrete and other foreign material.

Structural and Plate. This classification consists of clean open hearth steel (containing not over 0.04 per cent phosphorus or 0.04 per cent sulfur) such as plates, structural shapes, shearings, punchings and crop ends. Maximum size shall be 2 ft long x 12 in. wide (18 in. in diameter in instances of circular material) having a maximum weight of 100 lb to determine maximum thickness. Minimum size shall be ¼-in. section with minimum weight of ½ lb to determine minimum length and width. To further qualify minimum size and weight, not more than 5 per cent (by weight) of material less than 1-lb unit weight will be acceptable in any one shipment. Individual pieces must be free of all attachments, dirt and excessive rust or scale.

Heavy Flashings consist of trimmings from steel forging operations, ¼-in. and over in thickness and not over 8 in. in width or over 18 in. in length.

Non-Acceptable

Flashings coated with excessive rust, scale, lime, dirt or enamel.

Light Flashings consist of trimmings from steel forging operations, 1⁄16 to ¼-in. in thickness and not over 8 in. in width or over 18 in. in length.

Non-Acceptable

Flashings coated with excessive rust, scale, lime, dirt, paint or enamel.

Tin or terne plate and galvanized stock.

Hydraulically Compressed Bales for Foundry Use shall consist of new, pickled or cold rolled, deep drawing stock, compressed tightly, weighing 120 lb max., the dimensions of which shall not exceed 8 x 8 x 14 in. The material shall be a low carbon, low phosphorus, low silicon scrap for foundry use.

Non-Acceptable

Loosely compressed bales.

Steel with silicon over 1.00 per cent.

Steel with sulfur or phosphorus over 0.05 per cent.

Bales coated with excessive rust, scale, lime, dirt, paint or enamel.

Bales containing tin, terne plate, galvanized or alloy steel scrap.

PRECAUTIONS IN USE OF SCRAP

Inasmuch as scrap is likely to vary from piece to piece in both analysis and weight or section thickness, certain precautions are desirable if satisfactory metal is to be obtained. Many of these have been mentioned earlier in Chapter 12. Others are:

1) When large quantities of scrap are purchased from several sources it is often desirable to spread each incoming shipment over the pile to obtain as much mixing as possible rather than to use right from the car as received. In this way, the effect of peculiarities which may apply to a given shipment such as a large amount of low silicon or alloyed material can often be minimized.
2) If large percentages of scrap are used, it is wise to provide for a liberal well capacity and use of an adequate mixing ladle or receiver in order to minimize the possibility of a large individual piece in the charge unduly affecting the metal analysis.
3) It should be unnecessary to suggest that changes in the type of scrap in use may require adjustment of the balance of the charge to compensate for variation in chemistry. Thus, many types of steel have manganese of around 0.30 per cent and silicon under 0.01 per cent, while other types may be considerably higher in both elements.
4) Railroad car wheels and other heavy iron scrap should always be broken before use.
5) When charges are made up manually, the charging crew can do much to promote uniformity by mixing heavy and light scrap or scrap of different types rather than using all of one type on individual charges. The same thing can often be done to a lesser extent using magnet make-up. Likewise, heavy iron scrap may sometimes contain pieces of steel shafting or steel attachments, and with care it is possible to prevent use of more than one such piece per charge.
6) Charging crews can watch for nonferrous attachments and other contamination. Incidentally, a small bonus for such material removed will sometimes uncover astonishing quantities of these materials and substantially reduce the possibility of serious difficulty.
7) Yard personnel and charging crews should be instructed to promptly report any unusual or suspicious material encountered in the course of their work.

TRAMP ELEMENTS IN SCRAP

A pile of iron scrap may contain many of the chemical elements because the pieces may be painted, plated, welded, brazed or coated in various manners. It may also contain attachments of various kinds, spark plugs, bearings, grease cups, wood, cement, plaster, etc. Fortunately, most of these materials are present in small amounts and do little or no harm. However, cast iron has a low tolerance for some of the materials encountered and constant vigilance is needed to prevent their introduction into the metal in harmful amounts.

This is particularly true for ductile iron. In this case small amounts of several tramp elements prevent formation of spheroidal graphite when the iron is alloyed with magnesium. In order to avoid presence of such subversives and to keep phosphorus low, cast scrap is seldom used in ductile iron charges and steel scrap must be of known and reliable composition.

Among the tramp elements which usually are not harmful in small amounts are the alloys nickel, chromium, cobalt, copper, molybdenum, titanium, vanadium, etc. It will be recognized that most of these elements are often added to molten iron to improve the properties of the castings. However, excessive and erratic amounts of alloys introduced in the scrap may be harmful in the production of soft iron castings where machinability is a major requirement. Naturally, constant vigilance against the introduction of materials containing large amounts of alloys such as stainless steel, etc., should be maintained.

Difficulties can be the result of contamination with relatively small quantities of the nonferrous metals, including the following 10.

Aluminum

Aluminum at levels in the order of 0.05 per cent or even less may contribute to pinholes in light section castings poured in soft iron. In larger amounts, it renders the metal sluggish in pouring and causes the formation of dross, resulting in surface defects in the castings. Aluminum may be introduced by poorly stripped scrap and on occasion by high aluminum steel scrap. A very small amount is an important ingredient in most inoculants.

Antimony

Antimony is a constituent in enameled scrap and in many bearing metals. Whether present as metal or reduced from enamel, it is harmful to the static and impact properties of cast iron. Antimony has been reported to interfere with satisfactory enameling of sanitary ware. It has also been reported to cause a reduction in strength and impact when present in relatively small quantities under 0.25 per cent.

Bismuth

Bismuth is one of the elements occurring in bearing metal and can get into the cupola from scrap so contaminated. The strength of cast iron is seriously decreased by minute amounts of bismuth.

Boron

The principal source of boron is enameled scrap. The amounts which might be introduced in this form are unlikely to cause difficulties in cast iron.

Cadmium

Cadmium derived from cadmium plated metals and nonferrous alloys is volatile, and is probably eliminated during the melting operation.

Lead

Small amounts of lead or lead-bearing metal may find its way into the cupola. Although only traces can be retained in cast iron it exerts a detrimental influence on the properties of the iron. A trace of lead in very heavy section castings is reported to cause abnormal types of graphite and to drastically lower the strength of the iron. Lead has also been reported to cause extreme gas porosity in iron castings. It is also subversive in ductile iron. When present in large amounts lead collects in the bottom of the cupola well and may penetrate the bottom sand or refractories.

Sulfur

Sulfur in excessive amounts may be derived from sulfur cements, rubber, plaster of paris or free-machining steels.

Tellurium

Tellurium may be derived from nonferrous attachments. It is a potent chill producing element, as little as 0.001 per cent having a marked effect.

Tin

Tin may be present in the form of tin plate, bearing metals or in the steel and cast iron scrap used. All tin introduced is found in the iron melted. Tin in small amounts under 0.10 per cent stabilizes pearlite in the structure and increases Brinell hardness. Although it has little effect on tensile strength tin has an embrittling influence and adversely affects transverse properties.

Zinc

Zinc is introduced largely in the form of galvanized coatings on scrap. No appreciable amount is likely to be retained in the iron, as it volatizes and oxidizes readily. It may, however, be carried into cast iron with copper, and it has been reported that zinc added as a constituent in brass scrap had a markedly detrimental effect on both impact and tensile strength.

HIGH SCRAP CHARGES

Certain foundries make a practice of utilizing very high proportions of scrap in cupola mixtures, either because of ready availability or for economic reasons. In developing a suitable melting practice for use of a preponderance of purchased scrap, certain peculiarities of this type of charge should be borne in mind. The usual charge for production of a medium soft grade of gray iron by conventional acid melting probably contains 25 to 30 per cent of pig iron and another 35 to 40 per cent of foundry returns. Thus, such a charge can contain only 30 to 40 per cent of purchased iron and steel scrap.

Compared to the usual iron scrap, pig iron contains considerably more carbon and less sulfur. Substitution of iron scrap for this high carbon, low sulfur material may upset the chemistry of the charge unless there is full understanding of the principles involved.

While some foundrymen believe a certain proportion of virgin pig iron is highly desirable in preventing foundry difficulties such as excessive shrinkage, warping and cracking of castings, etc., it has probably not been definitely established whether the foundry difficulties sometimes encountered in using metal melted from high scrap charges are not actually due to variation in the chemistry of the iron.

Satisfactory use of high proportions of scrap no doubt requires more skill in formulating the charge and better control of the melting process than a more conservative practice. That it can be done is proved by the successful foundries that have for years melted iron of good quality using charges containing little or no pig iron.

The following suggestions may prove helpful in developing a practice built around the use of high proportions of scrap.

1) Control of Carbon

This may be a problem, particularly when producing rather soft grades of iron. Carbon content is no doubt the most important factor involved in controlling the properties of iron and its founding qualities, such as shrinkage, depth of chill, etc. As scrap is almost invariably lower in this important element than the pig iron it replaces, unusual measures may have to be employed in order to obtain metal of the desired carbon level.

The carbon level of cast iron is fixed not only by the metal charge but, also, by melting conditions; a high bed and liberal coke splits tending to produce hot metal of higher carbon content than when less fuel is used. A soft blast will also tend to produce higher carbon metal than when the cupola is blown at a higher rate.

Cokes will vary considerably in structure; the carbon in some of the cokes is in a form more readily soluble in cast iron. A coke which is low in ash and reactive in nature will produce metal of higher carbon content than coke which is higher in ash or of a very dense structure. Large sized coke will produce higher carbon in the metal than fuel of the smaller sizes. Special fuels of very low ash content, such as pitch coke or special high carbon coke, can be used as a portion of the fuel to increase the carbon level.

Several materials have been used as carbon raisers in cupola melting. These include various forms of carbon, such as scrap graphite electric furnace electrodes, briquets made of Mexican graphite, chunk natural graphite, etc.

The efficiency of these materials varies inversely with their ash content. Calcium carbide added in quantities up to 2 per cent of the charge has proved efficient in increasing the carbon content and temperature of acid melted iron. Silicon briquets con- [illegible] thetic graphite

808.1 B22a
6859g
H221L
THE CHICAGO PUBLIC LIBRARY

[illegible] n into the mol-
[illegible] carrier is being
[illegible] nt. In this prac-
[illegible] nulated without
[illegible] oduct, sufficient
[illegible] iron in receiver

[illegible] gh temperature
[illegible] n and permit in-
[illegible] been treated in

[illegible] s important. As
[illegible] obtaining maxi-
[illegible] cent coke and
[illegible] bed, sufficient
[illegible] be used to pro-
[illegible] ich will readily
[illegible] liceous material
[illegible] age amounts of
[illegible] dition and pro-

[illegible] ffects carbon ab-
[illegible] between silicon
[illegible] ith carbon solu-
[illegible] silicon.
[illegible] blem, it may be
[illegible] on than desired
[illegible] el of carbon in
[illegible] experience that
[illegible] con charged will
[illegible] t 0.08 per cent
in the carbon level of the metal. The deficiency in silicon can be easily made up by ladle addition of ferrosilicon at the cupola spout.

2) *Control of Contaminants*

An increase in the amount of scrap used from relatively small amounts to a major constituent in the charge means that it is even more necessary to avoid contamination by aluminum, tin and such other unwanted metals. Scrap which would not introduce these elements in dangerous amounts in the former case, can be responsible for serious foundry losses when a greater amount is used. It is essential that scrap used in high scrap charges be clean and free of such nonferrous attachments, aluminum pistons, bearing metals, etc.

3) *Control of Chemistry*

Individual pieces of scrap may vary rather widely in analysis. For this reason, it is important to provide a cupola well holding two or three charges to provide mixing capacity. In addition, where practical, a mixing ladle or forehearth of ample capacity should be provided. This unit should be kept as full of molten metal as possible in order to provide for ample blending and to minimize the influence of individual pieces of scrap in the charge which may be of abnormal chemistry.

It is also important in melting high proportions of scrap that the material be carefully graded for size in order to avoid adverse melting conditions. This matter becomes more important as the proportion of scrap used is increased.

Sulfur content of metal from high scrap charges is normally on the high side. It is important to compensate for this condition by charging sufficient manganese in the form of manganese briquets or ferromanganese to provide a manganese level five times that of sulfur. Thus, for 0.15 per cent sulfur, manganese should be about 0.75 per cent. Manganese loss of 15 per cent of that charged can be anticipated.

Where specifications or the use to which the castings are put require metal of lower sulfur than can be melted in the cupola, some form of desulfurization of molten metal in the ladle must be employed. The most commonly used desulfurizer is soda ash or sodium carbonate in the form of fused cakes or soda briquets. New developments in desulfurization of cast iron have involved injection of powdered calcium carbide, suspended in nitrogen gas, into molten metal in the ladle. Use of calcium carbide for lowering the sulfur content of iron will probably find wider use in the near future.

4) *Selecting a Suitable Charge*

As a starting point, the foundryman should select an appropriate type of scrap for use in the castings he is producing. In doing this, he will bear in mind phosphorus content, the effects of alloys, silicon content, etc. as reviewed in the earlier portion of this chapter. He may or may not decide to use some steel in the mixture, depending on desired carbon content and the type of metal required. He will have melting losses of silicon and manganese to provide for and will require a stock of silicon briquets, silvery iron or lump ferrosilicon, as well as manganese briquets, ferromanganese, or spiegeleisen as sources of these elements. Using the average estimated analysis of the available scrap, he is in a position to formulate a cupola charge which will produce metal having the desired level of silicon, manganese, phosphorus and carbon. Calculation of the cupola charge is covered in detail in Chapter 19.

It should again be stressed that as the proportion of scrap in the charge is increased, it becomes more and more important that this material be clean, properly sorted and sized, and free of foreign materials if satisfactory results are to be obtained.

CHAPTER 13

Alloys

Alloys or ferro alloys are used, not only in the grades of cast iron commonly considered alloy irons, but probably to even greater extent in the grades which are classified as unalloyed or plain cast iron. Their use has increased considerably during the past ten years, characterized as they have been by scarcity and erratic supply of many melting materials. Alloys are used in practically all the grades of metal commonly melted in the cupola—gray iron, high strength gray iron, white and chilled irons, malleable iron and nodular iron.

Alloy cast irons are usually defined as cast irons containing a sufficient amount of some element not usually present in cast iron to alter the properties of the iron. Thus, nickel-chromium cast irons contain sufficient nickel and chromium to have a discernable effect on the hardness, strength and other properties of the metal. However, even plain cast irons contain substantial amounts of elements such as silicon and manganese. These elements may be introduced partially or entirely as constituents in pig irons and scrap, or they may be partially introduced in alloy form.

For the purpose of this chapter, any material which is used primarily for the introduction of an element other than iron will be considered an alloy. Thus, the blast furnace silvery irons containing 6 to 14 per cent of silicon are used primarily for the introduction of silicon and control of the silicon level, and thus will be considered as alloys rather than pig irons in spite of the fact that they are blast furnace products, as are the more common grades of pig iron.

Alloys may be added to cast iron:

1. By inclusion in the cupola charge, so that the material is blended with the balance of the charge during melting.
2. By ladle addition.
3. By addition to an electric furnace or fuel fired furnace used with the cupola in a duplexing operation.

Sources of commonly used alloying elements, their limitations and suggested use, and the effects of adding the alloying elements will be given here. No attempt will be made to provide complete and detailed information on the properties conferred by the various alloys and their applications for specific purposes; this is covered in the AFS Cast Metals Handbook. Chapter 13 is a practical guide to the selection of charge materials or suitable materials for ladle addition.

The elements commonly used in cast iron include silicon, manganese, nickel, chromium, molybdenum, copper, titanium, boron, vanadium, zirconium, tin and magnesium.

In addition to alloys used primarily for altering the chemical composition of the iron there is a class of ladle additions known as inoculants. These materials have a physical action in improving the structure and properties of gray iron which cannot be explained by the change in chemical composition which they effect. Inoculants will be fully covered in this chapter.

ALLOYS FOR MELTING IN THE CUPOLA

Alloys or ferro alloys may be used as a portion of the cupola charge for regulation of the silicon and manganese levels in the product, as well as for introduction of such elements as nickel, chromium, molybdenum, copper, etc., which are used to modify the properties of the iron.

Concentration

Alloys used for addition to the charge may vary from relatively dilute ferro alloys such as the silvery irons containing 6 to 22 per cent silicon and spiegeleisens with manganese at the 16 to 30 per cent range to highly concentrated materials such as 75 per cent ferromanganese, electrolytic nickel, or copper scrap.

Concentration of the addition agent is not considered important as long as care is taken in weighing and distribution of material in the charge to insure arrival at the melting zone of a predetermined amount of addition agent at regular intervals.

It is necessary to have accurate low capacity scales. High capacity scales normally used for charge preparation are usually not sufficiently sensitive to accurately weigh small amounts of materials.

Physical Form

Alloys for addition to the cupola charge come in many different forms. The silvery irons are usually cast in pigs of 30 to 60 lb which can be broken to permit accurate weight adjustment. These materials can also be purchased in 10 or 12½-lb piglets which contain 1 and 2 lb of silicon and can be counted into the charge.

The more concentrated ferro alloys, ferrosilicon, ferromanganese, etc., are usually cast in large slabs and broken into random size lumps. They are sold in different size ranges depending on application. Lump ferro alloy for cupola additions must be sized small enough to permit accurate weighing, large enough to minimize migration as the charge settles.

Alloy briquets provide a convenient and accurate method of using ferro alloys. Briquets contain unit weights of the addition agent to be added by count, eliminating weighing small quantities of material.

Such alloy briquets are available for addition of silicon, manganese, chromium and zirconium, and may be obtained from several manufacturers. The various types are made in differing shapes to identify the alloy being added. Common shapes are cylindrical or brick shaped for silicon, rectangular for manganese, and hexagonal for chromium briquets.

Alloy briquets are made of suitably sized crushed ferro alloy, bonded with a refractory binder which is commonly Portland cement. Types available are:

Ferrosilicon	weighing 2½ lb and containing 1 lb silicon.
Ferrosilicon	weighing 5 lb and containing 2 lb silicon.
Ferromanganese	weighing 3 lb and containing 2 lb manganese.
Silicomanganese	weighing 3½ lb and containing 2 lb manganese and ½ lb silicon.
Chromium	weighing 3⅜ lb and containing 2 lb chromium.
Zirconium	weighing 5 lb and containing 0.55 lb zirconium and 1.90 lb silicon.

Briquets may be purchased notched to permit breaking in half to yield small additions.

Melting losses vary with the element added, but are approximately the same as when the element is added as part of the pig iron or scrap.

Other alloy briquets include several brands of silicon carbide briquets, which are used as silicon additions to the cupola.

Molybdenum is furnished in briquet form as molybdenum oxide briquets. These briquets weigh approximately 5 lb and contain 2.5 lb of molybdenum per briquet.

Sequence of Charging

Preferred location of any of the addition alloys in the cupola charge is on top of the coke split and evenly spread over the coke, keeping about a foot away from the walls. Such precise control of location in the furnace is practical only with hand charging. Almost universal use of mechanical charging has made impractical such exact location of materials. Random distribution through the charge has not seriously affected the results obtained.

In mechanical charging, any of the alloy addition agents are usually added to the charge immediately following the coke split. Actual place in the charge is probably not nearly as important as consistency in making up the charge in exactly the same sequence every time.

ALLOYS FOR LADLE ADDITION

Alloy ladle additions are made to cast iron for many reasons. Most foundries make a variety of work requiring irons of varying analyses to meet customers' requirements or to control the effect of section size and cooling rate on the structure of the iron.

It is impractical to make many changes in the base cupola charge during one heat. Ladle addition of alloys may make practical the production of several grades of iron from a single base iron.

Corrective additions of alloys may be used when chill tests or other tests indicate the metal as melted is not entirely as desired. Ladle additions can be used to either harden or soften the metal and thus facilitate closer control than is otherwise practical. Ladle additions of inoculants are an integral part of the melting process in producing most high strength and processed irons. Closely related to inoculation is the use of graphitizing alloy for the purpose of controlling chill depth and preventing machining difficulties due to chilled corners, etc., in light castings.

Ladle additions of alloys are used in the production of a high percentage of alloyed irons for several reasons. Special alloy compositions are apt to comprise a relatively small portion of a foundry's output. For the lower alloy grades containing up to about 3 per cent total alloy content, ladle addition often proves a convenient and flexible method of making a variety of alloyed compositions.

Alloy Types Used for Ladle Additions

A wide variety of ferro alloys is used for ladle addition including ferrosilicon of the 50 to 90 per cent grades, ferromanganese, several grades of ferrochromium, ferromolybdenum, ferrovanadium, silicon titanium, silicon zirconium, metallic nickel and copper and many other alloys. Ferro alloys usually are more or less brittle and readily crushed to the fine sizes suitable for making ladle additions. Ductile metals such as nickel or copper may be added in the form of shot or light section nickel or copper scrap.

In view of the high carbon content of cast iron, there is usually little advantage in using the relatively more expensive low carbon grades of ferro alloy. In most cases, the lower cost high carbon grades are suitable. There are exceptions to this rule, however.

Modifications of standard alloys containing increased silicon or manganese for improved solubility in molten iron are available.

Such high solubility alloys of chromium, vanadium or nickel find wide use. The solubility of different ferro alloys in cast iron varies widely, and many specialized compositions have been developed for ladle addition by the various producers.

The foundryman considering use of ladle addition alloys should consult his supplier concerning advantages and limitations of the various materials offered.

Exothermic alloys of chromium, manganese or silicon are sometimes used. When such alloys are added to iron in the ladle the molten iron triggers a heat producing chemical reaction causing rapid solution. These addition agents consist of finely ground ferro alloy blended with a readily oxidized metal (usually silicon) and an oxidizing chemical (usually sodium nitrate). The silicon is consumed by reaction with the oxidizing agent. Exothermic alloys are available in briquet or as a blend of crushed material.

Conditions for Successful Ladle Treatment

The first requisite for consistent and uniform recovery of alloy from ladle addition is iron at high temperature. If possible, alloys should be added at the cupola spout where temperature is highest, rather than during transfer at some other point in the foundry. When practical, additions should be made to ladles of at least 1000 lb capacity, although successful alloying in ladles down to 200 lb is practiced occasionally. Addition of alloy to hand ladles on the foundry floor should be avoided. It is difficult to obtain consistent results due to the small volume of metal involved and relatively lower temperature existing under these conditions.

Alloy for ladle addition should be crushed to suitable size. Addition at the cupola spout should be made gradually to the metal as it flows down the furnace trough. It can be advantageously added through a funnel or vibratory feeder to insure slow and consistent addition. If added directly to the ladle, the alloy should be slowly poured into the ladle in such a way as to fall at the base of the stream after an inch or two of metal has been accumulated in the ladle.

Recovery from Ladle Additions

Under well controlled conditions involving hot metal and careful addition, recovery of alloy from ladle additions should be consistently high. Actual recovery will vary for different alloys, and will be covered later in more detail for individual alloys.

It is probably unnecessary to mention that alloy used for ladle addition should be carefully weighed, and the weight of metal to which it is added accurately estimated. Scales having the desired degree of accuracy should be furnished the melting department for weighing alloy. They should be kept in a location where they are secure from accidental damage, and must be maintained in working order. Cleanliness and frequent checking are important. The cheap spring scales sometimes used are not entirely reliable, and more accurate weighing equipment should be provided.

Accurately estimating the volume of metal to which an alloying addition is to be made can present serious problems. In some foundries, ladle scales are provided, either in a section of monorail directly above the cupola trough, or a suitably protected scale may be located in front of the cupola on which the ladle can be placed for filling. Such ladle scales may invove a substantial investment, but will return their cost many times over by reducing the amount of over iron taken and making possible more accurate alloying.

When estimating metal volume, it is not uncommon for an error of 10 per cent or more to be encountered and, in such cases, it is usual to make a "liberal" alloy addition to make sure specifications are met. The accuracy made possible by weighing molten metal can be a source of real savings when a large amount of alloy iron is produced by ladle addition methods.

Most foundries are not provided with ladle scales, and it is necessary to estimate by volume the amount of metal to which an alloy addition is being made. Molten cast iron can be considered as weighing 400 lb per cu ft, or 0.23 lb per cu in. If ladles are carefully lined to predetermined dimensions and the linings maintained to these dimensions, it is possible with experience to estimate quite accurately the volume of metal tapped.

A steel rod bent and hung over the edge of the ladle can serve as a gage and may prove helpful. Where alloy iron is regularly used in the same castings, pouring weights of individual molds should be known and can be used as a check on the amount of metal tapped. Obviously, wear of ladle linings will introduce some inaccuracy and, under the best of conditions, estimation of metal volume falls far short compared to actually weighing the metal as it is tapped from the cupola.

Sizing for Ladle Addition

Preferable size for ladle addition will vary with the alloy being added. Heavy alloys such as those of molybdenum and chromium are usually added in fine sizes such as 8 mesh x down, or 20 mesh x down. Alloys which are less dense or are subject to oxidation may be preferred in somewhat coarser sizing such as ½ in. x down, ⅜ in. x 12 mesh, ¼ in. x down, etc. Such alloys include the ferrosilicons and some of the proprietary inoculants. A minimum of fines which may tend to sinter and float on the surface of the metal is an advantage in alloys which are low in density or subject to oxidation.

As a general rule, foundries alloying very hot iron or relatively large quantities of iron at a time will use alloys of larger size. Thus, ferrosilicons of ½-in. × down or ⅜-in. × 12 mesh might be preferred for ladles of one ton or larger while the ¼-in. × down or 8 mesh × down sizes might work better for addition to ladles of 200 to 500 pounds.

SILICON

As cast iron is essentially an alloy of iron and carbon, with the properties controlled by regulation of the silicon content, this element is present in considerable amount in all cast irons. Next to carbon, the silicon content of an iron is the most important factor controlling its properties. The amount of this element present largely determines whether the iron will freeze with the hard white fracture of white iron or as the softer gray iron containing most of the carbon in the form of graphite.

The low silicon gray irons tend to be relatively hard and strong. As the silicon content is increased within the normal range the iron tends to become progressively softer, weaker, and more graphitic in nature. Silicon level thus has a major effect on machinability and strength. Silicon is obtained from the pig irons used in making up the cupola charge, most pig containing some 2 per cent or so of this element. It is also obtained from scrap used in the mixture.

Any silicon over and above that provided by these constituents may be included in the cupola charge as a silicon-rich alloy such as one of the silvery irons, silicon briquets, or lump ferrosilicon. Silicon may also be introduced to the molten iron as a ladle addition of ferrosilicon. Ferrosilicon is available in many different grades varying in silicon content from 50 to as high as 95 per cent.

ALLOYING IN THE CUPOLA

Available Alloys

Silicon is available for cupola addition in several forms. Suitable alloys of iron and silicon for this application include blast furnace silvery irons containing 6 to 14 per cent silicon. Electric furnace products of 16 to 22 per cent silvery, 50 per cent lump ferrosilicon and silicon briquets (Table 13.1).

These materials are largely interchangeable, their choice depends on availability, price, and applicability to conditions in each foundry. They vary chiefly in physical form and silicon content. The next six paragraphs tell of these materials.

Silicon carbide briquets are made of finely divided silicon carbide suitably bonded. They weigh about 5 lb each. Recoveries of silicon are reported as 20 to 40 per cent of the weight of briquets charged. It is claimed that silicon carbide briquets exert a deoxidizing influence on the metal. Briquets of this type are furnished by several producers. Crushed silicon carbide packed in steel cans of unit weight is also used as a source of silicon in the cupola.

TABLE 13.1. GRADES OF SILICON ALLOY FOR CUPOLA ADDITION

	Blast Furnace Silvery	Electric Furnace Silvery	Silicon Briquets	50% Ferro-Silicon	Silicon Carbide
Method of Manufacture	Blast Furnace	Electric Furnace	Electric Furnace	Electric Furnace	Electric Furnace
Silicon Content, %	6-14%	15-22 %	40%	47-51%	—
Carbon Content, %	2.75-1.50%	1.00-0.50%	0.06% max	0.06% max	—
Available as	30 lb pigs 10 lb piglets	30 lb pigs 12½-lb piglet containing 2 lb Si	2½- & 5-lb briquets containing 1 and 2 lb Si each	Suitably sized lump	5 lb briquets Also as crushed silicon carbide in steel cans of unit weight

Blast furnace silvery iron is a product of specialized blast furnace operation so regulated as to yield pig iron of high silicon content varying between 6 and 14 per cent silicon. Carbon content will vary inversely with the silicon level in the range of 2.75 to 1.25 per cent. It is most often used in the range of 8 to 10 per cent silicon content. Silvery iron is available in the form of 30 lb pigs and 10 lb piglets. Silvery iron is magnetic, and can be handled by electromagnet.

Electric furnace silvery iron is a product of electric furnace smelting of steel scrap and a suitable source of silica with a reducing agent. It normally is produced in the range of 16 to 22 per cent silicon. Carbon content is low, being under one per cent. It is furnished in 30 lb pigs, as well as 12½-lb piglets containing 2 lb of silicon each. Electric furnace silvery is magnetic, and can be handled by electromagnet.

Fifty per cent ferrosilicon is an electric furnace product made from steel scrap, a suitable source of silica and suitable reducing agent. It is usually produced to an analysis range of 47 to 51 per cent silicon content. The ferro alloy is cast in large slabs which are broken to random size lumps. It can be furnished in various size gradations to suit given melting operations. Due to its concentration, 50 per cent ferrosilicon must be carefully weighed if it is to give good results. Fifty per cent ferrosilicon is not magnetic. It may be shipped in bulk or in container cars.

Silicon briquets are made of suitably crushed 50 per cent ferrosilicon bonded with Portland cement. They are available in two sizes — a 2½-lb briquet containing one lb silicon and a 5 lb briquet containing 2 lb silicon. Silicon briquets are either cylindrical in shape or in a brick shape suitable for palletizing.

Briquets are not magnetic, cannot be handled by electromagnet. They can be purchased packed, in bulk and palletized. Briquets will not deteriorate from exposure to the weather and can be stored outside. They are added to the charge by count.

Recovery

There is some oxidation of silicon in cupola melting and, therefore, some melting loss will occur. A normal recovery of 90 per cent of the silicon contained in the cupola charge is anticipated for average cold blast acid operation. This figure will vary somewhat, depending on the melting technique and degree of oxidation encountered. Liberal coke ratio and mild blast result in a lower silicon loss. Use of less coke or high blast volume results in greater oxidation and higher loss of silicon. The figure of 90 per cent silicon recovery applies to the total silicon charged, and will not materially change when a portion is introduced as any of the preceding materials.

ALLOYING IN THE LADLE

Available Alloys

While silicon is not usually considered an alloying element in cast iron, ferrosilicons are often used as ladle additions. Silicon added to the ladle has an inoculating or late addition effect on cast iron which will be covered under inoculation.

In addition to its inoculating effect, ferrosilicon can be used for alteration of the silicon content of iron, thus making it practical to produce a metal of increased silicon content from a standard base charge. This practice gives flexibility and often avoids the necessity of melting several base mixtures in a given cupola heat.

Ferrosilicons come in several grades, varying in silicon content from 50 to 95 per cent. The grades normally used in cast iron as ladle additions are:

50% FERROSILICON, *foundry grade,* 47% to 51% SILICON
75% FERROSILICON, *foundry grade,* 73% to 78% SILICON
85% FERROSILICON, *foundry grade,* 83% to 88% SILICON
90% FERROSILICON, *foundry grade,* 92% to 95% SILICON

These ferrosilicons usually contain one to 2 per cent aluminum. Low aluminum grades of ferrosilicon, containing 0.50 per cent max., also are available.

A small but controlled amount of aluminum and calcium in ferrosilicon used for ladle addition increases the graphitizing and inoculating value of the alloy and is generally beneficial. Very soft irons melted under reducing conditions have a low tolerance for aluminum, and in such cases, low aluminum grades of alloy may be indicated. Foundrymen will find it to their advantage to discuss with the supplier the matter of aluminum content of ferrosilicon used for ladle additions.

Size

Silicon alloy is manufactured in sizes varying from coarse lumps to smaller than 20 mesh. While some operators prefer fine size for ladle additions, in recent years somewhat coarser sizes have been given preference. The most commonly used sizes are ⅜-in. through 12 mesh and 8 mesh x down. The coarser grade is considered preferable for addition to large ladles and where heavy additions are made. The 8 mesh x down size is preferred by some operators and probably is preferable for addition to small quantities of metal.

Recovery

Ladle additions of silicon do not materially reduce the temperature of the molten metal if added as ferro-alloys containing 65 per cent or more silicon, but the usual precautions should be observed. Whenever possible, ferrosilicon should be added to the metal at the cupola spout, preferably through a funnel suspended above the metal stream.

The recovery of silicon from ladle additions depends largely on the care with which the ferrosilicon is introduced. When carefully added to high temperature metal, recoveries should be in the order of 90 per cent.

Although high and consistent recovery of silicon is indicative of accurate control of ladle addition practice, ferrosilicon additions are usually used for nucleation of graphite formation and control of chill. These are largely dependent on the amounts of certain reactive elements contained in the alloy and actual recovery of added silicon may not be as important as the inoculating or nucleating effect resulting from the addition.

MANGANESE

The major influence of manganese in the amounts usually present in cast iron is to neutralize the harmful effects of sulfur. Manganese to the extent of five times the sulfur level is usually provided for. Thus, at a sulfur content of 0.10 per cent manganese should be controlled at 0.50 per cent or higher. At 0.15 per cent sulfur the minimum manganese content should be about 0.75 per cent.

In quantities approaching one per cent or higher manganese exerts a true alloying effect. In this range it has a pearlite stabilizing and strengthening effect somewhat similar to that of chromium, although milder in degree. In high strength engineering irons manganese is generally controlled at a level above 0.80 per cent in order to take advantage of this effect. In addition to neutralizing sulfur, manganese in the higher ranges will limit the sulfur pickup encountered during cupola melting.

Manganese is introduced by the pig irons used in the cupola charge, as well as the scrap used in the mixture. Any manganese over and above that provided by these constituents may be included in the cupola charge as ferromanganese briquets, silicomanganese briquets, lump ferromanganese or silicomanganese, spiegeleisen, or as high manganese silvery iron. Manganese may also be introduced to the molten iron as a ladle addition of ferromanganese or silicomanganese.

ALLOYING IN THE CUPOLA

Available Alloys

Manganese for cupola addition is available in these several forms. Standard ferromanganese, an electric furnace product in two grades of either 74 to 76 or 78 to 82 per cent manganese, is approximately 7 per cent carbon, under one per cent silicon with the balance mostly iron. It is available in several lump sizes as well as crushed sizes varying from 2 in. × down to 20 mesh × down.

Silicomanganese contains 65 to 68 per cent manganese with silicon varying from approximately 14 to 20 per cent depending on the grade. Carbon varies from about 1.25 per cent for the 20 per cent silicon grade to about 2.5 per cent at 14 per cent silicon. A low carbon grade containing approximately 51 per cent manganese, 25 per cent silicon and 0.50 per cent carbon also is available.

When suitably sized, either standard ferromanganese or silicomanganese are suitable for use in the cupola charge. Neither of these materials is magnetic. They are usually shipped in bulk or in pallet boxes to simplify handling and storage.

Spiegeleisen is a blast furnace product. It is available in various grades containing from 16 to 25 per cent manganese and silicon up to 3 per cent. It is in piglet form. Spiegeleisen is not magnetic and cannot be handled by electromagnet.

Ferromanganese briquets weigh 3 lb and contain 2 lb manganese each. Ferromanganese briquets are made of suitably crushed standard ferromanganese bonded with Portland cement. They are oblong.

Silicomanganese briquets are made of suitably crushed silicomanganese alloy bonded with Portland cement. They weigh 3.5 lb each and contain ½-lb silicon and 2 lb manganese. They are square.

Manganese briquets of either type are not magnetic and cannot be handled by electromagnet. They will not deteriorate from exposure to weathering and can be stored outside. They can be purchased in bulk, palletized and packed. They are added by count.

Special briquets containing various amounts of silicon and manganese are furnished to meet the needs of large foundries whose requirements are great enough to justify manufacture of a special product. Such materials are nonstandard and are not usually carried in stock by ferro alloy producers.

Manganese can be purchased in the form of high manganese silvery iron, containing from one to 7 per cent manganese. It is magnetic and can be handled by electromagnet.

In addition to standard ferromanganese, there are various low carbon grades of ferromanganese available. Such low carbon alloys offer no advantages as cupola charge materials and are not generally used for this purpose.

Scrap intermediate manganese steel containing approximately 1.50 per cent manganese is sometimes used as a cupola charge material. Hadfield's steel containing 11-14 per cent manganese is generally available only in heavy pieces and usually finds its way back to producers of this alloy.

Recovery

A portion of the manganese charged is lost during cupola melting by oxidation and by combination with sulfur to form manganese sulfide, part of which finds its way to the slag. Manganese losses will vary depending on the melting technique and degree of oxidation. Liberal coke ratio and mild blast result in low manganese loss. Use of less coke or high blast volume results in greater oxidation and higher loss. Use of high sulfur melting stock or high sulfur coke will result in an excessive manganese loss, the manganese tending to limit the sulfur level in the product.

A greater percentage of charged manganese is lost when melting high manganese grades of iron. Normal recovery of 85 per cent of the manganese charged is anticipated for average cold blast operation, producing metal in 0.65 to 0.85 per cent range. Recovery will, of course, vary from the 85 per cent figure.

ALLOYING IN THE LADLE

Available Alloys

Standard ferromanganese of 74 to 82 per cent manganese and 7 per cent carbon is suitable for ladle addition of manganese to cast iron. Medium carbon ferromanganese containing 1.25 to 1.50 per cent carbon, and several low carbon grades varying in carbon from 0.07 to 0.75 per cent, also are available. Silicomanganese containing 65 to 68 per cent manganese and approximately 17.50 per cent silicon can be used for simultaneous addition of manganese and silicon.

These alloys are available in a variety of size gradings from ½-in. x down to 20 mesh x down suitable for ladle additions.

Precautions

All of the manganese alloys are readily soluble in molten iron but the usual precautions should be observed in making ladle additions. Whenever possible, manganese alloys should be added to the iron at the cupola spout, preferably through a funnel suspended above the metal stream.

Under certain conditions, heavy ladle additions of high-carbon ferromanganese to cast iron result in a type of gas porosity in the castings. This condition appears to be dependent on the composition of the base iron. In such isolated cases, the use of low-carbon or medium-carbon ferromanganese is advisable.

Foundrymen making heavy ladle additions of manganese to malleable iron have encountered similar difficulties using high-carbon alloy. Foundrymen who are doubtful as to which grade of ferromanganese should be added may find it to their advantage to discuss the matter with the supplier. In general, high-carbon standard ferromanganese is used. In certain isolated instances involving heavy ladle additions, the use of lower carbon alloy may be indicated.

Recovery

The recovery of manganese from ladle additions depends on the care with which the ferromanganese is introduced. When carefully added to high-temperature metal, recovery should exceed 90 per cent.

NICKEL

Nickel, when added to cast iron in the usual quantities, acts as a graphitizer to reduce the chilling tendency of the iron. It has a further mild strengthening and hardening influence due to solid solution in the matrix. As a graphitizer it is approximately one-third as potent as silicon. In the range up to one per cent it acts to improve the strength of gray iron and to improve machinability.

An addition of 3 per cent or more of nickel renders the grain very fine, increases strength and hardness and produces an iron having a desirable combination of moderately high hardness combined with low chill and excellent machinability. Nickel is often used with chromium in proportions of two or three times the chromium content. Such nickel and chromium additions increase the hardness, strength and resistance to wear and heat, largely due to the chromium content.

The function of nickel in such instances is one of controlling the carbide stabilizing influence of chromium and conferring machinability. Such nickel-chromium irons generally contain from one to three per cent nickel and up to one per cent chromium. Nickel is often used in combination with molybdenum in the production of irons having an excellent combination of strength and machinability. The so-called acicular irons containing one to 2 per cent nickel and approximately one per cent molybdenum exhibit a particularly fine combination of high tensile and impact strength, high hardness and relatively good machining qualities.

Nickel in larger amounts is used in austenitic corrosion and heat resistant irons. A typical composition of 14 per cent nickel, 4 per cent chromium and 6 per cent copper, called ni-resist, is widely used. A copper-free variety also is produced for special applications.

Nickel and chromium often are added to white iron to produce a martensitic structure of increased hardness and wear resistance. A typical composition commonly known as ni-hard has about 4.5 per cent nickel and 1.5 per cent chromium.

ALLOYING IN THE CUPOLA

Available Alloys

When nickel is added to the cupola charge, the alloy is usually in the form of pure nickel squares 4 x 4 in., nickel pig, or pigs containing either nickel-copper-chromium or nickel-chromium in proportions needed to produce ni-resist or ni-hard compositions. Compositions of these materials are shown in Table 13.2.

Silvery iron containing nickel, usually in combination with other alloys, is sometimes used as a source

TABLE 13.2. NICKEL FOR CUPOLA CHARGES

	4 in. Sq.	*F* Nickel Pig	*NCC* Pig	*NH* Pig
Nickel, %	99.9+	92.00	56.0 - 59.0	44.0 - 47.0
Chromium, %	—	—	7.5 - 8.5	15.0 - 17.0
Copper, %	—	—	23.0 - 25.0	—
Carbon, %	—	0.20 - 1.00	1.0 - 1.5	1.5 - 2.0
Silicon, %	—	5.0 - 6.0	1.0 - 1.5	0.60 max.

of nickel in the cupola charge. Made to the foundry's specification, such materials generally are used in irons of relatively low nickel content.

Recovery

Nickel is not oxidized in cupola melting. As there are no losses due to oxidation, a yield of 100 per cent of the nickel charged is recovered in the iron. In charging nickel pig, the precautions given under "Sequence of Charging" should be observed, and care must be taken to ensure even distribution of the alloy in the molten iron. With suitable mixing of two or more cupola charges in the receiver or ladle, the analyses of nickel irons can be maintained at uniform levels.

ALLOYING IN THE LADLE

Available Alloys

Nickel is usually added to the ladle when producing alloy irons containing less than 2 per cent of this element. This practice has the advantage of flexibility in that alloyed and unalloyed iron can be produced at will from the same cupola charge. "F" nickel shot containing 92 per cent nickel and 5.0 - 6.0 per cent silicon is the most commonly used ladle addition, although pure nickel shot is occasionally used.

The silicon content of the "F" shot lowers the melting point from 2650 F (1454 C) for pure nickel to approximately 2300 F (1260 C), with a resultant improvement in ease of solution.

Nisiloy, a graphitizing inoculant containing 60 per cent nickel and 30 per cent silicon, is used for simultaneous addition of nickel and silicon. See INOCULANTS later in Chapter 13 for other reference to this product.

Ladle addition agents containing nickel, combined with chromium or copper in the desired ratio, are occasionally used as ladle additions of these elements.

Size

Most materials used for the ladle addition of nickel are furnished in the form of shot having an average size of ½-in. x down.

Recovery

The alloys commonly used for ladle addition of nickel are readily soluble in cast iron. However, to ensure uniform recovery and satisfactory control of composition, the usual precautions should be observed in making ladle additions. Whenever possible, nickel should be added to the iron at the cupola spout, preferably through a funnel suspended above the metal stream.

There is no loss of nickel by oxidation and, provided it is carefully added to high temperature metal, recovery should be uniformly high, approximately 100 per cent of the amount added.

CHROMIUM

Chromium is a strong carbide stabilizer in cast iron. Used alone in amounts up to 0.5 per cent and in the presence of the usual 2 per cent silicon, chromium acts to increase strength and hardness, resistance to wear, abrasion and heat. These benefits are conferred by the fact: chromium inhibits decomposition of the combined carbon and forms stable double carbides of chromium and iron. Chromium increases chill depth and, when used in excess or when the composition of the base iron is not properly balanced, may for this reason adversely affect machinability.

Chromium is generally used in gray iron in relatively small amounts well under one per cent. In heat resistant gray irons, chromium improves strength at high temperature, minimizes scaling and oxidation and inhibits growth. In such applications, chromium is often added in amounts up to 2 per cent.

Chromium is often used in combination with nickel, molybdenum, copper or vanadium in both gray and white irons. It is also used in the more highly alloyed austenitic types used for resistance to corrosion and heat.

High chromium irons containing 15 to 30 per cent chromium have excellent resistance to abrasive wear, as well as to heat and oxidation. Although these irons are usually electric furnace products, the lower chromium grades are sometimes cupola melted.

ALLOYING IN THE CUPOLA

Available Alloys

Chromium is available in grades of ferro alloy varying 0.01 to 7 per cent in carbon content. In cast iron, higher carbon grades are generally used.

High carbon ferrochrome is an electric furnace product available in a variety of grades of 55 to 70 per cent chromium. Depending on the ores used such ferrochromes may have from one to approximately 10 per cent silicon. They are available in sizes suitable for cupola use.

Ferrochrome briquets weigh 3⅜-lb. Each contains 2 lb chromium. Ferrochrome briquets are made of suitably crushed high carbon ferrochrome bonded with Portland cement. They are usually hexagonal. Briquets are not magnetic and cannot be handled by electromagnet. They can be purchased in bulk, palletized and packed. Briquets will not deteriorate by weathering and can be stored outside. They are added by count, and generally are considered more satisfactory as a chromium addition to the cupola charge than lump ferrochrome.

Chromium may be added to the cupola in the form of nickel-chromium-copper (NCC) pigs, and nickel-chromium (NH) pigs just described under NICKEL.

Special briquets of various proportions of chromium with silicon and manganese are made for large foundries with requirements great enough to justify manufacture of a special product. Such briquets are non-standard and available only by special order for large quantities.

Silvery iron, with chromium usually in combination with other alloys, is sometimes used as a source of chromium. Such irons, made to the foundry's specification, generally are used to introduce chromium in relatively small amounts.

Recovery

Chromium is subject to oxidation in cupola melting. Chromium losses will vary, depending on the melting technique and degree of oxidation encountered. Liberal coke ratio and mild blast result in low chromium loss. Use of less coke or high blast volume results in greater oxidation and higher loss. A normal recovery of 90 per cent of the chromium charged is anticipated when good melting conditions exist.

Recovery will, of course, vary from this figure, as indicated above. The usual precautions should be observed in order to ensure a consistent level of chromium in the iron as it is tapped from the cupola.

ALLOYING IN THE LADLE

Available Alloys

Inasmuch as relatively small amounts usually are added, chromium often is introduced as a ladle addition. Several ferro alloys are suitable for the addition of chromium to cast iron.

Any of the high carbon ferrochromes are satisfactory for ladle addition when added to high temperature metal and when care is taken in making the addition. Presence of several per cent silicon improves the solubility of ferrochrome in cast iron. One of the high silicon grades variously known as charge chrome or blocking chrome may be preferable to alloy of low silicon content for this reason.

High carbon foundry ferrochrome of 55-63 per cent chromium, 4-7 per cent carbon and 8-12 per cent silicon is widely used as a ladle addition.

The silicon content improves solubility and, due to its greater affinity for oxygen, it acts to protect the chromium from oxidation. The result is improved consistency of recovery at a somewhat higher level. This is particularly true under adverse conditions of metal temperature.

"SM" ferrochrome has 60-65 per cent chromium, 4-6 per cent carbon, 4-6 per cent silicon and 4-6 per cent manganese. This is a high solubility grade for ladle addition to cast iron. The manganese and silicon contents improve both solubility and recovery, particularly under adverse conditions.

Exothermic ferrochromes are used as ladle additions in cast iron, particularly when making relatively large additions about 2 to 3 per cent chromium.

Exothermic alloys are compounded so that a heat producing chemical reaction preheats the alloy to its melting point when added to molten iron, resulting in excellent recovery.

Stabilizing Inoculants

There are several alloys containing chromium combined with silicon or other graphitizing elements. In using these alloys, the increase in chilling tendency induced by the chromium addition is balanced by the inoculating effect of the graphitizers present. Alloys in this group include materials containing about 50 per cent chromium and 30 per cent silicon, variously identified by different producers as foundry ferrosilicon chrome, ferrochrome-silicon and low carbon foundry ferrochrome; "V-5" alloy of 38-42 per cent chromium, 17-19 per cent silicon and 8-11 per cent manganese. Alloys of this type are covered in more detail under INOCULANTS.

Size

Chromium alloys are used for ladle additions in the 8 or 20 mesh × down sizes.

Recovery

The chromium alloys generally used as ladle additions have satisfactory solubility in cast iron. Whenever possible, chromium alloys should be added to the iron at the cupola spout where metal temperature is highest, preferably through a funnel suspended above the metal stream.

Recovery of 85 per cent or more of the chromium added to the ladle as ferrochrome can be anticipated, provided care is taken in making the addition. Presence of silicon and manganese in the addition alloy results in improved solubility and consequently higher recovery. Recovery from the higher silicon alloys listed in the foregoing should be noticeably better than in the case of the straight high carbon ferrochrome.

MOLYBDENUM

Molybdenum often is used in cast iron in amounts up to about one per cent. It is a mild carbide stabilizer, small additions in the range of 0.20 to 0.50 per cent slightly increasing Brinnell hardness without decreasing machinability. Such additions improve tensile strength and, particularly, toughness or resistance to impact, also resistance to wear and abrasion.

Molybdenum is used in combination with chromium, nickel, copper and vanadium. Chromium-molybdenum irons have an excellent combination of strength and resistance to wear, and are often used in heavy duty automotive or similar applications.

Irons containing enough molybdenum to produce acicular structure in the section size cast, exhibit unusually high tensile strength and resistance to impact, when properly balanced with other alloys such as nickel, copper, etc.

For large increases in the tensile strength of a given iron, molybdenum is among the most effective of the more common alloys. Used alone, a moderate addition effects a decided improvement, while its influence on chill is slight enough to permit relatively heavy additions. Used with other alloys, it has the faculty of working well with combinations of either graphitizing or carbide stabilizing alloys, depending on the application.

ALLOYING IN THE CUPOLA

Available Alloys

Molybdenum is usually added to the cupola charge in the form of briquets composed of molybdic oxide held together by a pitch binder. Each briquet weighs 5 lb and introduces 2½-lb contained molybdenum.

Ferromolybdenum can also be used as cupola charge material. This alloy contains 58 to 64 per cent molybdenum. It is available in lump size approximately 3 x 1 in. suitable for addition to the charge.

Recovery

Since molybdenum oxide is reduced by molten iron, the recovery from briquets is high, in the range of 90 to 95 per cent. An average recovery of 95 per cent can be anticipated when using ferromolybdenum in the charge.

As small additions of molybdenum exert a strong effect on the properties of the iron, it is important in making cupola addition to observe the precautions mentioned under "Sequence of Charging."

ALLOYING IN THE LADLE

Available Alloys

Molybdenum alloys used for ladle additions to cast iron include: ferromolybdenum containing 58-64 per cent molybdenum, 0.10 per cent max. carbon, 1.00 per cent max. silicon.

Size

Ferromolybdenum is furnished in sizes suitable for ladle addition to cast iron, approximately ⅕-in. x 8 mesh and 8 mesh x down.

Recovery

The molybdenum alloys used for ladle addition are readily soluble in cast iron. However, to ensure uniform recovery and satisfactory control of composition, the usual precautions should be observed in making ladle additions. Whenever possible, molybdenum alloys should be added to the iron at the cupola spout, preferably through a funnel suspended above the metal stream.

Recovery of molybdenum from ladle additions to cast iron is high, averaging 95 per cent.

VANADIUM

In cast iron, vanadium acts as a strong carbide stabilizer, producing more uniform graphite distribution, fine grain, increased chill depth, increased strength and resistance to wear. Vanadium finds its greatest application in heavy gray iron and chilled castings such as steel mill rolls, dies, etc., in which it is used to control density of structure in heavy sections. It is usually added in small amounts under 0.25 per cent.

ALLOYING IN THE CUPOLA

Available Alloys

Vanadium is available as the ferro alloy in several different grades. As this element is partially oxidized in cupola melting, the small amounts of alloy required are usually added to cast iron as ladle additions made to the molten iron.

Vanadium is found in small amounts up to about 0.75 per cent in certain "special" pig irons and is probably largely responsible for the excellent reputation of certain of these irons.

Recovery

Vanadium containing pig irons generally contain an appreciable amount of titanium also, an element which tends to protect the vanadium content from loss by oxidation during cupola melting. Recovery of approximately 80 per cent has been reported from the use of these vanadium containing irons.

ALLOYING IN THE LADLE

Available Alloys

Ferrovanadium is available in several grades varying in carbon and silicon content. The foundry grade generally used in cast iron contains appreciable silicon to improve solubility. Vanadium content of the alloy will vary with the producer. Typical analyses of foundry grade ferrovanadium are:

A. 38-42 per cent vanadium, 7-11 per cent silicon, 1 per cent carbon.

B. 50-55 per cent vanadium, 10 per cent silicon, 3 per cent max. carbon.

Size

Ferrovanadium is usually purchased for use as a ladle addition to cast iron in the 8 mesh x down or 20 mesh x down sizes.

Recovery

Foundry grade ferrovanadium is readily soluble in cast iron.

The recovery of vanadium from ladle additions depends on the care with which the alloy is added. If the addition is carefully made, recovery of 85 to 90 per cent can be anticipated.

COPPER

Copper, when added to cast iron in small amounts exerts a mild graphitizing and solution hardening effect. In low-silicon irons the graphitizing effect is much more pronounced than when this alloy is added to iron containing 2 per cent silicon or above. Copper has limited solubility in cast iron, the maximum amount that can be readily put into solution being approximately 1.50 per cent. Copper added in excess of this amount may appear as a layer of metallic copper. Copper is often added to cast iron in combination with nickel, chromium, molybdenum or vanadium.

ALLOYING IN THE CUPOLA

Available Alloys

Copper can be introduced into the cupola charge as ingot copper, either refined secondary metal or virgin metal. It may also be introduced as solid copper scrap such as cut trolley wire, bus bar, commutator segments, etc. Such cut electrical copper is electrolytically refined and practically 100 per cent pure copper. Fine copper clippings, stampings, fine wire, etc., is normally baled. Such material can be used in the cupola if of known purity.

While electrical scrap is of high purity, it should be free of solder, tin and other contamination. Miscellaneous copper scrap often contains variable amounts of tin and zinc bearing alloys, tellurium and other contaminants. Clean copper scrap of known purity forms excellent charge material.

Recovery

Copper is not oxidized in cupola melting and recovery will approach 100 per cent of the amount charged. The normal precautions should be followed to ensure a uniform level of the alloy in the metal tapped from the cupola. The contaminants often present in the poorer grades of scrap may seriously affect the quality of cast iron, and such contamination should be guarded against.

ALLOYING IN THE LADLE

Available Alloys

Metallic copper has a low melting point of 1980 F, and is readily alloyed with cast iron in the ladle.

Copper may be added in the form of scrap such as clipped trolley wire, clipped cable, punchings, clippings, etc. Such scrap should be electrical copper of high purity. It is also added in the form of copper shot. Such shot is usually refined secondary metal of known purity and possesses the advantages of ease in handling and weighing.

Alloy shot containing both nickel and copper is used as a ladle addition material.

Precautions

Copper in the range of 1.5 per cent and less is readily soluble in cast iron.

Only copper of known purity should be used. Addition of miscellaneous scrap can readily result in serious contamination of the iron.

Recovery

As there is no loss of copper by oxidation and it is easily soluble in cast iron, recovery of 100 per cent should be obtained by ladle addition of this alloy.

TITANIUM

Titanium in small amounts is a potent graphitizer, scavenger and grain refiner in cast iron. In amounts greater than 0.05 per cent it acts to promote the formation of very fine graphite flakes in a matrix of fine pearlite or ferrite, depending on the composition of the base iron and the titanium level. Titanium additions promote a fine velvety fracture, a mild increase in strength and improved machinability. The maximum graphitizing effect is obtained by addition of 0.10 per cent titanium as a ladle addition. Amounts greater than this which promote a ferritic matrix may greatly increase deflection in the transverse test.

ALLOYING IN THE CUPOLA

Available Alloys

Concentrated alloys of titanium are seldom added to the cupola, as this element is readily oxidized by the cupola blast and recovery would be low and erratic.

Many pig irons contain small amounts of titanium and at low levels this element may pass through the cupola and appear in the castings without serious loss, so that most cast iron contains this element in the range of 0.02 to 0.06 per cent.

Special pig irons containing titanium in the range of 0.10 to 0.50 per cent are available. Such irons introduce sufficient titanium to exert a noticeable effect on graphite flake size, and promote a fine, dense, velvety fracture. Certain of these titanium bearing pig irons may contain vanadium and other alloying elements in significant amounts.

ALLOYING IN THE LADLE

Available Alloys

The 70 per cent ferrotitanium containing 0.10 per cent max. carbon is a low melting eutectic composition which unlike some other grades is readily soluble in cast iron.

Other titanium alloys generally used to add to cast iron contain large amounts of silicon, an element which confers improved solubility. Grades commonly used are:

Foundry ferrotitanium containing 27-31 per cent titanium, 20-24 per cent silicon.

Silicon-titanium containing 40-50 per cent titanium, 42-50 per cent silicon.

Size

Titanium alloys used for ladle additions to cast iron are generally sized to approximately 8 mesh to promote rapid solution and satisfactory recovery.

Precautions

Alloys of titanium readily combine with the oxygen and nitrogen of the air at high temperature. If satisfactory recovery is to be obtained, it is essential that the usual precautions be observed. Whenever possible, titanium alloys should be added to the iron at the cupola spout, where metal temperature is highest, preferably through a funnel suspended above the metal stream. Care should be taken to prevent caking and floating of the alloy on the surface of the metal, a condition which promotes oxidation of the titanium content and results in low and erratic recovery.

Recovery

With good practice, recovery of titanium should be from 50-60 per cent of the alloy added.

BORON

Boron is a powerful carbide stabilizer in cast iron, increasing chill depth and promoting a white fracture if appreciable quantities are added. In white or chilled irons it increases hardness and refines the columnar structure of the chill. Boron (0.05 per cent) is used in both chilled iron and grain rolls to improve hardness and refine the structure. It has been reported that 0.01 per cent boron effectively suppresses eutectiform graphite structure in rapidly cooled sections of gray iron.

A martensitic abrasion resistant white iron containing approximately 4.5 per cent nickel with one per cent boron replacing the usual chromium content is reported to be harder and more abrasion resistant than ni-hard, although more brittle.

Boron is used in malleable iron in small amounts (0.0005 to 0.003 per cent) to nucleate temper carbon during annealing and to shorten the time required for the anneal. It often is introduced in the cupola charge as a boron containing 50 per cent ferrosilicon with boron in the range of 0.05 to 0.10 per cent. Boron containing silvery irons also is put to this use.

Boron also counteracts the adverse effect of residual chromium on the carbide stability in malleable iron, promoting rapid annealing. About 0.001 per cent is usually added for each 0.03 per cent chromium above 0.03 per cent when used for this purpose.

Boron acts as a deoxidizer in cast iron.

CUPOLA ADDITION

Available Alloys

When added to the cupola charge, boron is usually introduced alloyed with ferrosilicon or silvery iron.

Recovery

Boron introduced in the cupola charge in ferrosilicon or return scrap, etc., is reported to yield approximately 50 per cent recovery.

ALLOYING IN THE LADLE

Available Alloys

Ferroboron is available for ladle addition to cast iron in grades containing boron in the 12 to 18 per cent range.

Size

Ferroboron for ladle addition to cast iron is usually the 20 mesh × down size.

Precautions

Ferroboron is readily soluble in cast iron. Boron exerts a great effect on cast iron. The small additions used must be accurately weighed and the metal volume to which they are made measured accurately.

In duplex melting of malleable iron, boron may be added to the metal as it is tapped for distribution to the foundry, or the alloy may be added to the cupola metal as it is introduced to the air or electric furnace.

Recovery

Due to difficulties involved in analyzing for the small amounts of boron used, average recovery figures are difficult to quote.

ZIRCONIUM

Zirconium in small amounts acts as a graphitizer, deoxidizer and grain refiner in cast iron. In amounts greater than 0.05 per cent it promotes formation of very fine graphite flakes. As the zirconium level is increased, this element promotes formation of a ferritic matrix which, together with fine graphite distribution, results in increased strength and improved machinability. This effect is particularly noticeable in irons of low sulfur content.

Zirconium combines with sulfur in cast iron to form sulfides in a manner somewhat similar to manganese, and can be used in low manganese irons to counteract the effect of sulfur.

Zirconium is an important constituent in certain of the complex alloys used as inoculants.

ALLOYING IN THE CUPOLA

Available Alloys

Zirconium is available for cupola addition in the form of briquets composed of suitably sized crushed zirconium alloy bonded with Portland cement. The alloy used in these briquets contains 12-15 per cent zirconium, 39-43 per cent silicon, 0.20 per cent max. carbon. Zirconium briquets weigh 5 lb, and contain 0.55 lb zirconium and 1.9 lb silicon each. They are used for simultaneous addition of zirconium and silicon to the cupola charge.

Recovery

Zirconium readily combines with the oxygen and nitrogen of the cupola blast so that a substantial melting loss will occur. Recovery will depend largely on the melting technique and degree of oxidation encountered. A liberal coke ratio and mild blast result in minimum loss. Use of less coke or high blast volume results in greater oxidation and higher loss of zirconium.

Recovery of this element from cupola additions will average 20 per cent under normal conditions. The effect of zirconium is largely as a scavenger and deoxidizer, and the benefits derived are more definitely related to this effect than the zirconium level retained in the metal.

ALLOYING IN THE LADLE

Available Alloys

Zirconium alloys used for ladle additions to cast iron contain considerable silicon, an element which promotes solubility. They include:

12-15% zirconium alloy containing 12-15% zirconium, 39-43% silicon, 0.20% max. carbon.

35-40% zirconium alloy containing 35-40% zirconium, 47-52% silicon, 0.50% max. carbon.

Due to the high silicon content of these zirconium alloys, they exert an inoculating effect on cast iron.

Size

Zirconium alloys are available in the 8 mesh x down size suitable for ladle addition to cast iron.

Precautions

In making ladle additions of zirconium, it should be remembered that this element is a potent deoxidizer and that it is readily oxidized at elevated temperatures. If satisfactory recovery is to be obtained, it is essential that the usual precautions be observed. Whenever possible, zirconium alloys should be added at the cupola spout, where metal temperature is highest, preferably through a funnel suspended above the metal stream. Care should be taken to minimize caking and flotation on the surface of the metal in the ladle.

Recovery

Zirconium recovery from ladle addition to cast iron should average 50 per cent, provided care is taken in making the addition. The effect of zirconium in cast iron is largely that of a deoxidizer and scavenger. For this reason, the benefits derived are not necessarily directly related to the residual analysis.

TIN

Although foundrymen have regarded residual amounts of tin with suspicion for many years, this metal is finding some use as an alloying agent in both gray and ductile iron. Tin up to 0.10 per cent stabilizes the pearlite preventing its decomposition to ferrite and graphite. Thus, it increases hardness and improves both strength and resistance to wear.

ALLOYING IN THE CUPOLA

Tin is used in small amounts. Due to its low melting point and good solubility, tin is usually added in the ladle. Tin additions are seldom if ever made to the cupola charge.

ALLOYING IN THE LADLE

Available Alloys

Tin is usually added as pure tin shot. Solubility is excellent and recovery high.

MAGNESIUM

Retained magnesium of approximately 0.05 per cent in cast iron of suitable carbon, silicon and sulfur content develops a spheroidal or nodular graphite structure resulting in high strength and appreciable ductility in the as-cast condition.

Lower levels of magnesium may yield a partially spheroidal structure or a modified type of flake graphite. Such iron, while inferior in properties to metal having well developed spheroidal graphite, may exhibit considerable toughness and improved properties compared to conventional gray iron.

ALLOYING IN THE CUPOLA

Magnesium is readily oxidized and is never added to the cupola charge.

ALLOYING IN THE LADLE

Available Alloys

Magnesium may be added to cast iron in several forms including metallic magnesium, or alloyed with other metals which serve as carriers. In the latter classification are alloys of magnesium with nickel, copper, silicon, and combinations of these elements.

Due to the low boiling point of magnesium metal (2030 F – 1110 C), its low solubility in molten cast iron and the violent reactions which take place when it is added to cast iron, the use of metallic magnesium involves serious difficulties. For these reasons dilute alloys of magnesium are generally used in metals, such as nickel or silicon, with which it is readily alloyed.

Typical analyses of common alloys of this type—

TYPE 1. Nickel Base
 NMA no. 1:
  15% Mg, 82% Ni, 2% C, bal. Fe
 NMSA no. 2:
  15% Mg, 30% Si, 50% Ni, bal. Fe
TYPE 2. Magnesium Ferrosilicon Type
  9% Mg, 45% Si, 1.5% Ca, bal. Fe
 Cerium-Bearing Magnesium Ferrosilicon
  9% Mg, 45% Si, 1.5% Ca, 0.5% Ce, bal. Fe
TYPE 3. Magnesium Rich Silicon Base Alloys
  18% Mg, 65% Si, 2.0% Ca, 0.60% Ce, bal. Fe

Methods of Addition

Magnesium is usually added by the bulk addition method. The alloy is placed in the bottom of a preheated ladle and the metal rapidly poured over the alloy.

The plunging method gives higher recovery and is being adopted by many foundries. The alloy is placed in a refractory bell and plunged beneath the surface of the molten iron.

Size

Magnesium addition agents are in various sizes suitable for ladle addition. As the rate and resulting violence of the reaction is somewhat dependent on the particle size of the alloy, a larger size alloy is generally preferred as the quantity of iron treated increases. Thus, a ½-in. x 32 mesh material might be selected when treating quantities of iron up to 1000 pounds, one in. x 32 mesh from 1000 to 4000 pounds and a 2 x one in. size for ladles above 4000 pounds.

Large amounts of fines are undesirable due to the tendency of fine materials to oxidize when added to molten iron.

Precautions

Preferred technique for making additions of magnesium varies for the types of alloy used and conditions in the individual foundry. Personnel (see Safe Practices : Chapter 18, last section) should be protected from splashed metal and slag, which might result from the violence of the reaction, by use of suitable protective clothing. The brilliant white glare of burning magnesium vapor may constitute a hazard. Foundry personnel should wear protective, dark eyeglasses or should be required to avoid looking at the ladle while the magnesium addition is being made.

Magnesium is an effective desulfurizer in cast iron, any magnesium added being used to reduce the sulfur content of the metal to approximately 0.02 per cent before a residual level can be retained in the metal. Magnesium-sulfur compounds formed as the result of this reaction rise to the surface of the metal in the ladle in the form of dross. Sulfur content of metal to be treated must be taken into account in deciding on the size of the addition. Base metal of low sulfur content is preferred.

Recovery

Recovery of magnesium from ladle additions will depend on the type of alloy used, sulfur content of the metal, technique employed in making the addition, temperature of the metal to which the alloy is added, and other factors. Generally, recovery will improve as metal temperature is lowered. A recovery of 15 to 50 per cent can be anticipated, depending on the above conditions.

MAGNESIUM METAL

Treatment techniques using magnesium metal have been developed and find limited use. These involve plunging of magnesium billets in covered pressure tight ladles or lance injection of magnesium shot.

Briquets composed of magnesium chips and steel turnings or cast iron borings are also available and find limited use in the plunging process.

CERIUM—RARE EARTHS

Cerium, one of the rare earth metals, when added to cast iron having high carbon and silicon content combined with low sulfur promotes spheroidal graphite, resulting in improved strength, together with considerable toughness and ductility. The cerium process of producing spheroidal (or nodular) cast iron is in many respects similar to magnesium treatment for the same purpose. In the United States, at least, the magnesium process has been more widely used.

Cerium also finds use in magnesium treated ductile iron. Small quantities of several elements such as tin, antimony, lead, titanium and others appear to supress the formation of fully nodular graphite. Addition of a small amount of cerium, either in the form of mischmetal or as a constituent of the magnesium alloy used, minimizes the harmful effect of such contaminents and improves the certainty with which the desired nodular structure is obtained.

Use of the rare earth metals in cast iron is relatively new, and greater experience with these elements may develop wider application.

Alloys of the rare earths are never added in the cupola charge.

LADLE ADDITION

Available Alloys

Cerium is available combined with other of the rare earth metals in the form of mischmetal. The most commonly used grades contain approximately 50 per cent cerium, the balance being composed of other metals of this group. A typical analysis of mischmetal might be 45-55 per cent cerium, 22-30 per cent lanthanum, 15-18 per cent neodymium, 5 per cent max. praseodymium, 2 per cent other rare earth metals. Grades containing a higher percentage of lanthanum are also available.

Precautions

Mischmetal is readily soluble in cast iron. The usual precautions should be taken to ensure satisfactory recovery and uniform results from use of the alloy.

Cerium is an active desulfurizer in cast iron, the metal reacting with any sulfur present to form sulfides which are removed by flotation. For this reason, it is impossible to build up a retained level of cerium until the sulfur is reduced to approximately 0.02 per cent. In view of the relatively high cost of cerium alloys, prior desulfurization of the iron to which they are to be added is indicated.

Size

Mischmetal is available in the form of

Pellets weighing approximately 0.05 lb each.
Wafers weighing approximately ¾-lb each.
Ingots weighing 1½-to 2 lb and 3 to 4 lb each.

Recovery

In view of the high affinity of the rare earths for oxygen and sulfur, recovery of the ladle addition elements will depend on many factors. These include sulfur content of the metal, presence of other deoxidizing elements, technique used in making the additions, etc. Addition to high sulfur metal will result in very low recovery. In iron of low sulfur content, ladle addition of cerium should result in a recovery of 25 to 75 per cent, depending on these factors.

INOCULANTS

Of the ferro alloys used as ladle additions to cast iron, the inoculants are among the most important.

Inoculation might be defined as the addition of a material which has an effect on the properties of the metal to which it is added which cannot be explained by the change in chemistry produced. In gray iron, inoculation is employed largely to promote random graphite distribution and the pearlitic matrix which usually accompanies it, rather than the supercooled types of graphite having preferred orientation which are often associated with variable amounts of primary ferrite.*

Effective control of microstructure, particularly as regards graphite distribution, results in better uniformity of mechanical properties at a higher level. This is true for tensile and transverse strength, resistance to impact, resistance to wear, uniformity of hardness and sensitivity to freezing and cooling rate as affected by section thickness.

The usually objectionable supercooled structures often found in cast iron are promoted by low carbon equivalent, excessive superheating (especially when the metal is held at high temperature for any considerable period), high steel charges, rapid solidification caused by thin sections in the casting, abnormal oxidation during melting, use of burnt and oxidized scrap such as grates in the charge, etc. They may also be promoted by the presence of considerable amounts of titanium and zirconium.

Supercooled structures are not always objectionable as they promote density of fracture, good machinability, fine machine finish, freedom from leaks in hydrostatic testing, etc. Indeed, the two alloys mentioned above are often intentionally added to obtain these advantages. However, a random graphite distribution in a pearlitic matrix usually is desired for applications requiring high strength, resistance to impact, or resistance to wear (either lubricated or dry) combined with satisfactory machinability.

Low carbon equivalent irons melted from high steel charges are likely to solidify with supercooled structure. This means that iron, which should by virtue of its analysis yield superior properties, is likely to have disappointingly low properties due to abnormal structure.

The addition of a suitable inoculant to the metal at tap will overcome this tendency. Indeed, most of the high duty gray iron melted, whether of the trade named processed varieties or not, is produced using some sort of inoculation as an important part of the melting process.

Inoculants can be divided into two groups:

A. GRAPHITIZING INOCULANTS represented by ferrosilicon, calcium silicon (or silicide) and proprietary alloys graphidox and S.M.Z.

Ladle additions of ferrosilicon exert greater graphitizing effect or are more potent than an equal amount of silicon introduced through the cupola.

Such ladle additions of ferrosilicon, usually of higher silicon such as the 75, 85 and 90 per cent grades, are characteristic of the graphitizing inoculants.

The more complex types of proprietary inoculants in this group have been developed to combine special advantages beyond those obtainable by simple ferrosilicon ladle additions. These include improved solubility and increased chill reduction compared to most ferrosilicons.

Graphitizing inoculants are most effective when added to irons of low carbon equivalent which, as melted, exhibit deep chilling properties and are usually so used in making high strength grades of iron.

Graphitizing inoculants are often used for simple chill control rather than as a means of improving mechanical properties. In such cases, small quantities are added to reduce section sensitivity and to prevent chilled structure in light-section castings, light flanges in heavier castings, etc.

Use of an inoculant may make for increased flexibility in the melting department. By regula-

*Refer to photomicrographs in Chapter 35, and to the AFS GRAPHITE CLASSIFICATION CHART.

tion of the ladle addition, a single base cupola metal can often be made suitable for use in castings of widely varying section thickness and weight.

Post inoculation of ductile iron represents another application of a graphitizing inoculant. Addition of 0.25 to 1 per cent silicon as ferrosilicon, following magnesium treatment, causes nucleation of an increased number of graphite nodules. Such post inoculation eliminates carbidic structure in light section, reduces hardness, and improves ductility.

The quantity of the addition needed varies with the inoculant used and results desired. Generally, the addition will vary between 0.10 and 0.50 per cent silicon. For purposes of chill control, the smaller quantities may be satisfactory. When added to low carbon equivalent high strength irons, greater amounts may be necessary to secure effective inoculation. Also, there is considerable variation in the effectiveness of alloys. The complex proprietary inoculants and ferrosilicons of relatively high aluminum and calcium content are most effective.

B. STABILIZING INOCULANTS combine chromium with suitable graphitizing elements, usually so proportioned that the graphitizers present will balance the increase in chill depth which would be anticipated by a given chromium addition.

Use of these balanced compositions allows the foundryman to benefit from increased hardness, stability of structure, resistance to wear and abrasion and resistance to high temperature conferred by chromium (see CHROMIUM) without suffering from the limitations imposed by the tendency of this element to increase chill depth.

This tendency may limit the field of usefulness of chromium, particularly in light castings, unless it is controlled by simultaneous addition of some suitable graphitizer.

Use of one of the stabilizing inoculants, such as one of the silicon-chromium alloys or V-5 alloy, accomplishes this by the use of a single easily controlled ladle addition.

The quantity used is dictated by the chromium level desired. Most stabilizing inoculants are so balanced in composition that there is little effect on chill depth with variation of chromium level in the range normally used in cast iron.

CUPOLA ADDITION

Inoculation involves ladle addition of a suitable ferro alloy to cast iron. Thus, alloys are never added to the cupola charge for the purpose of inoculation. While some alloys which are effective inoculants may be added to the cupola, they are used in such cases for alteration of the chemistry of the iron and the inoculating effect is lost.

This applies to the various grades of ferrosilicon as well as silicon or zirconium briquets. These materials have little or no inoculating effect when included in the cupola charge, whereas a similar amount of the same alloy added to the ladle may exert an effect on the structure and properties of the metal far out of proportion to the change in chemistry involved.

LADLE ADDITION

Graphitizing Inoculants

50% ferrosilicon, foundry grade, of 47-51% silicon.
75% ferrosilicon, foundry grade, of 73-78% silicon.
85% ferrosilicon, foundry grade, of 83-88% silicon.
90% ferrosilicon, foundry grade, of 92-95% silicon.

The foregoing ferrosilicons contain aluminum in the range of 1.00 to 2.00 per cent. Low aluminum grades of ferrosilicon containing 0.50 per cent max. are also available. A small but controlled amount of aluminum increases the inoculating value of the alloy and is generally beneficial. Very soft irons melted under reducing conditions may have a low tolerance for this element and, in such cases, use of low-aluminum ferrosilicon may be indicated.

The presence of calcium also increases the effectiveness of ferrosilicon as an inoculant and ferrosilicons having calcium controlled at various levels are available. Foundrymen will find it an advantage to discuss with the supplier the aluminum and calcium content of ferrosilicon used as an inoculant.

Calcium-silicon containing 30-33 per cent calcium and 60-65 per cent silicon.

Graphidox No. 4 of 5-7 per cent calcium, 9-11 per cent titanium, 48-52 per cent silicon.

S.M.Z. alloy of 5-7 per cent manganese, 5-7 per cent zirconium, 60-65 per cent silicon, 3-4 per cent calcium.

12-15 per cent zirconium alloy containing 12-15 per cent zirconium and 39-43 per cent silicon.

Nisiloy of 60 per cent nickel and 30 per cent silicon. This product is used for simultaneous addition of nickel and silicon. It combines the function of a graphitizing inoculant with the alloying effect of the nickel addition.

Note: Ladle addition of carbon as either synthetic or natural graphite should probably be classified as inoculation. Such ladle additions reduce chill and exert a graphitizing influence. The effect appears to be largely mechanical. Such additions of graphite do not as a rule increase the carbon content of the metal.

BB graphite—synthetic graphite containing 98 per cent carbon.

Mexican Graphite—natural graphite. Product is mined and crushed to size. Contains about 85 per cent carbon; balance is largely ash.

Stabilizing Inoculants

Ferrosilicon-chrome and ferrochrome-silicon alloys containing approximately 50 per cent chromium and 30 per cent silicon.

V-5 alloy of 38-42 per cent chromium, 17-19 per cent silicon, 8-11 per cent manganese.

Size

Both the graphitizing and stabilizing types of inoculants are furnished in sizes suitable for ladle addition. Typical sizes of inoculants are ½-in. x 12 mesh, ⅜-in. x 12 mesh, ¼-in. x 32 mesh, ¼-in. x down, 8 mesh x down, etc.

Precautions

Most of the alloys used as inoculants are readily soluble in cast iron. Many of these alloys contain substantial amounts of elements which are easily oxidized at high temperatures, and if consistently satisfactory recovery is to be obtained, it is essential that the usual precautions be observed. When possible, inoculants should be added at the cupola spout where metal temperature is highest, preferably through a funnel suspended above the metal stream. Use of a vibratory feeder is another very satisfactory way of adding the inoculant.

Recovery

In use of an inoculant, recovery depends largely on the care with which the addition is made. When carefully added to high temperature metal, recovery should exceed 90 per cent of the silicon added.

Fig. 14.1. Typical battery of coke ovens used in producing byproduct coke.

CHAPTER 14

Fuels

In the United States the cast iron industry began in 1642. Charcoal then was used universally as the fuel for melting iron. About 1833 anthracite displaced charcoal in most foundries, and beehive coke, first produced in 1841, finally replaced both charcoal and anthracite as the principal foundry fuel. Byproduct coke first was produced in this country during 1893, and its use gradually has increased so that today beehive coke is used as cupola fuel in comparatively few foundries.

FOUNDRY COKE

Coke is the solid, cellular mass obtained when selected bituminous coals are heated, out of contact with air, above the temperatures at which active thermal decomposition occurs. During the process, the volatile matter in the coals is driven off as gases. Coke having somewhat different characteristics is formed when other raw materials, such as petroleum residues and coal tar pitch, are similarly heated.

When coking coal is heated in the absence of air, after the moisture is driven off, its decomposition is accompanied by a softening process, beginning between 660-750 F, in which the individual particles fuse into a more or less fluid mass. As the temperature rises to about 930 F, gases are evolved, and the charge solidifies to form a hard cellular mass.

Continued heating results in further gas evolution and some contraction of structure. Coke made at temperatures up to about 1112 F is classed as low-temperature coke, and the product formed by continued heating above 1652 F is called high-temperature coke. Low temperature coke is not used in foundry cupolas.

Byproduct Coke

Most high grade foundry coke is produced today in slot type byproduct ovens under carefully controlled conditions of heat application. The ovens are so called because, during the coking operation, the gases evolved are drawn off and treated for the recovery of chemicals as byproducts such as benzene, toluene, coal tar and others. The cokes are made from carefully selected blends of high, low, and/or medium volatile bituminous coals, ranging from 16 to 38 per cent volatile content; to which varying amounts up to 13 per cent anthracite fines, finely pulverized coke or petroleum coke or pitch, are usually added to improve blend in order to obtain the desired physical and chemical properties in the coke. As many as five to six coals are used in the blend.

Coking and chemical properties of bituminous coals vary widely and are characteristics of the particular seam from which each bituminous coal was mined. The individual coal used in a blend is selected on the basis of carbonizing and chemical properties contributed by it to the resultant coke. For example, a ton of coal of 30 per cent volatile matter content and 7 per cent ash content would theoretically yield 0.7 tons of coke by the loss of the volatile matter during coking. The ash content of the coke would be 10 per cent, as all of it originally in the coal remains in the coke. Sulfur is present in coals in varying amounts; chemical forms and is partly eliminated in the gases during coking, following the equation of Lowry—

$$\underset{\text{COKE}}{\text{Sulfur}} = .759\ \underset{\text{COAL}}{\text{Sulfur}} + .084$$

The individual coals used in the blends are selected on the basis of carbonizing properties as well as ash and sulfur content. Because the former change slowly in storage, however, frequent checks are made of coking properties and the blend adjusted accordingly.[1,2,3]

In addition to control of the quality and coking properties of individual coals, considerable attention must also be given to the degree of pulverization of the charge, to adequate proportioning and mixing of the blend, and to bulk density of the blend charged to the oven. Current practice at most ovens calls for pulverization to at least minus ¼-in. size to insure against introduction of coarse size slate or high ash particles that might cause points of weakness in the coke.

The recent trend is toward finer pulverization, 85 to 95 per cent through a ⅛-in. screen which, in general, facilitates more uniform blending. Proportioning of the individual coals is best obtained with continuous automatic weighing equipment, but any method that insures uniform control of the mix is satisfactory. Bulk density control is attained by adjustment of moisture content and/or oil treatment.

For any given size consist of the charge, adjustments in moisture content and/or the use of up to 2 quarts of oil per ton of charge will give adequate control and permit the high degree of uniformity of charge density necessary to the production of a uniform quality of product.

Coke is made in batteries of individual ovens (Fig. 14.1). Each oven is a gas tight, externally heated chamber 37 to 45 ft long, 9 to 15 ft high, and 14 to 24 in.

average width which holds a coal charge of 16 to 20 tons and is equipped with individual doors at each end which are sealed prior to charging. The ovens are charged through 4 holes in the top provided with gas tight covers and the coal charged into the oven is leveled by a traveling bar introduced through a small door on one side of the oven. The desired operating temperature is maintained by the combustion of fuel gas in the flues between adjacent walls; the operation is continuous and the oven is recharged immediately after removal of coke at the end of the coking cycle.

After an oven is charged and the doors and charging holes sealed, carbonization begins immediately and progresses inward through the charge from both heated walls. The volatile products of carbonization are removed by an offtake on each oven and processed for the recovery of coal chemicals and fuel gas. Generally 45 per cent of the processed gas is required for maintaining oven temperatures by burning in the flues where it is mixed with air heated in regenerators by the waste flue gases.

The time required to produce high grade foundry coke varies with the width of the oven and the characteristics of the blend carbonized but usually ranges from 20 to 36 hr and coking rates of 0.5 to 1.0 in. of oven width/hr (usually 0.5 to 0.7) are employed. Faster coking rates tend to produce foundry coke of smaller size and of less strength due to the more rapid penetration of heat and evolution of gases in the coal charge whereas longer coking cycles have little or no effect on coke quality. The physical requirements of blast furnace coke being different from foundry coke, permit faster coking rates even as low as 14 hr. Because carbonization occurs simultaneously from both walls, there is always a line of demarkation down the center of the coke charge where the two plastic layers meet and contract away from each other in the final phases of carbonization (Fig. 14.2).

The coke surface adjacent to the walls will have a cauliflower-like appearance, and that in the center where the plastic layers meet will have a coarser cell structure. The shrinkage cracks will radiate inward from wall to center, and the maximum length of the individual coke pieces will be one half the oven width. The average diameter of the coke may be from less than 2 in. to over 6 in. Careful control of coal blend, bulk density, rate of heating and coking temperature will minimize cross fractures and produce structurally strong coke of uniform quality.

When carbonization of the charge is complete, the hot coke is pushed from the oven mechanically into a quench car, which carries it to a quenching station where it is sprayed with a large volume of water to cool it below combustion temperature. The quenched coke then is discharged onto the coke wharf where most of the moisture on the coke surface is evaporated by the heat within the individual coke lumps.

Beehive Coke

Beehive coke is usually produced in hemispherical ovens (Fig. 14.3) built in long rows at or near the mines. The hot ovens, which average about 12 ft inside diameter, are charged through an opening in the top with 5 to 7.5 tons of coal. After leveling this forms a layer 18 to 24 in. deep.

New beehive ovens built during the past ten years or more are larger and equipped with mechanical coal charging and coke pushing devices. Coking periods for beehive coke are much longer than in by-product oven cokes and the only control of heat is by air admitted to ovens to burn gases evolved as no gas or coal chemicals are recovered.

Fig. 14.2. Side view (left) of coke oven charge being pushed. End view (above) of same coke oven charge shows how coal has coked toward center, leaving cleavage plane.

The charge is usually a strongly coking high or medium volatile bituminous coal, and no extensive crushing or mixing is normally employed. After leveling the charge, air is admitted through openings in the top of the door and burns the volatile matter released by the coal and, during the later stages of carbonization, some 5 to 8 per cent of the coke. The heat for coking is thus supplied principally from above the charge, and fissuring tends to run from the top down. Expansion of the charge during carbonization is unrestricted in the beehive type oven.

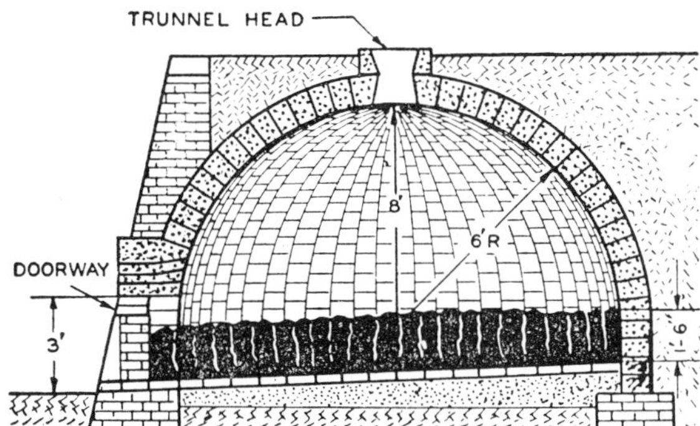

Fig. 14.3. Cross-section hemispherical beehive coke oven.

Crude temperature regulation is exercised by control of air admission. Coking time ranges from 48 to 96 hr, although 72 hr is normal for foundry quality coke. The coke is quenched "in situ" with a spray of water and raked or pushed out of the ovens. The coke pieces may range in length up to about 36 in., the full thickness of the expanded coke mass. In diameter the coke ranges from small fingery pieces up to lumps 12 in. or more. Beehive coke is characterized by its silvery gray luster and slick, knobby surfaces; chemically, it is highly graphitic.

PREPARATION AND HANDLING

Sizing

Byproduct coke as it comes from the ovens is known as run-of-oven coke and consists of a mixture of sizes due to shrinkage of the charge during coking and some breakage in pushing and handling.

Normal practice is to pass the run-of-oven coke over a series of screens to remove successively the largest size marketed and then subsequent size fractions. No definite standards of sizing have been adopted due to the varying requirements of the foundry industry and size is generally designated by agreement between the coke producer and consumer.

The designation 6 x 5 in. means that the pieces have passed through a screen with 6 in. by 6 in. square mesh openings but have been retained on a screen with 5 in. by 5 in. square mesh openings. The screening units are so arranged that each size or any desired combination of sizes can be loaded readily into railroad cars (Fig. 14.4) or trucks. Hand picking to remove poorly coked material is usually employed. Coke seldom is held in storage by the producer.

Coke Handling

In general coke leaving the producers plant has been carefully sized to meet the size limit specifications designated. In all too many instances, however, the care taken by the producer in accurately sizing the product is negated by the user through careless handling. The use of clamshell unloaders or other handling systems where the fuel is subjected to severe mechanical shocks can result only in size degradation for which the foundry pays heavily in decreased efficiency and control. (Chapter 4, page 40, has information on coke handling equipment; Table 14.1 shows significance of size degradation.)

Storage

It is common practice at many foundries to store coke in the open where it is subjected to the action of the elements. No appreciable deterioration of the coke results from this practice during mild weather, but when exposed to alternate freezing and thawing wet coke can and does degrade seriously in size due to water freezing in coke fissures. Then covered storage is best. In using coke from open storage, subjected to increased moisture, allowance should be made.

Fig. 14.4. Coke from sizing screens being handpicked before direct loading into railroad cars.

TABLE 14.1. COKE SIZE vs SURFACE AREA AND VOIDS[12]

Size	Solid Wt. per Cu Ft, lb	Actual Wt. per Cu Ft, lb	Coke %	Voids %	Avg. Size, in.	Surface Exposed (Assuming Cubes) Sq Ft per 100 Cu Ft of Coke	Sq Ft per 100 lb of Coke
No. 68 (+ 6 in.)	57.5	24.8	43.1	56.9	6.54	473	19.1
No. 56 (5 in. x 6 in.)	56.5	24.9	44.0	56.0	5.545	570	22.9
Spec. 56 (No. 56 + Nut)	56.5	32.2	57.0	43.0	4.54	903	28.0
No. 45 (4 in. x 5 in.)	59.0	26.5	44.9	55.1	4.555	705	26.6
No. 34 (3 in. x 4 in.)	55.2	25.4	46.0	54.0	3.57	929	36.6
No. 253 (2⅝ in. x 3 in.)	56.7	26.9	47.4	52.6	2.772	1232	45.8
Egg (1⅝ in. x 2⅝ in.)	56.4	27.4	48.6	51.4	1.973	1777	64.6
Nut (⅞ in. x 1⅝ in.)	56.4	28.8	51.1	48.9	1.09	3070	106.6
Pea (⅜ in. x ⅞ in.)	54.5	28.4	52.1	47.9	0.51	7350	259.0

OTHER FUELS

Although byproduct coke, supplemented in some cases with beehive coke, is the principal fuel in the foundry industry, other fuels are being used to a limited extent. It is probable that as the supplies of quality coking coals diminish, some of these other fuels will be even more extensively used, especially if the current research and development work along these lines result in the expected improvements in quality.

Anthracite

Considerable tonnage of anthracite is used in areas where it has a marked price advantage over byproduct foundry coke. Anthracite is a dense, hard, natural product[5,6,15] with a typical proximate analysis on a dry basis: volatile matter 6 per cent, fixed carbon 84 per cent, ash 10 per cent.

Agglomerate Fuels

In recent years several attempts have been made to produce specialty foundry fuels by agglomeration. The raw materials may be anthracite, bituminous coking or non-coking coals, petroleum coke or mixtures of two or more of these with or without the addition of pitch or tar binders. In some instances the material is formed into shapes by briquetting or extrusion prior to carbonizing, in others the mixture is carbonized directly.

Various types of ovens and furnaces are used for the carbonization step, but in all cases the material must be subjected to temperatures in the vicinity of 1832 to 2192 F to drive off volatile matter and develop satisfactory strength and reactivity properties.

SIGNIFICANCE COKE TESTING AND PROPERTIES

The original criterion of the value of foundry coke was doubtless its performance in the cupola, and that is still the final test. However, numerous tests have been devised and specifications have been set up to distinguish between good and poor foundry cokes by laboratory methods. The physical and chemical properties of the fuel are determined and correlated with the thermal and metallurgical performance in the cupola. These properties and their effects on the utility of coke are hereinafter discussed in detail.

The methods of the American Society for Testing Materials[4] widely used in the examination of engineering materials, are referred to wherever applicable in the following brief description of the tests commonly used for determining the physical and chemical properties of foundry cokes.

Also useful for reference and guidance in testing coke are the methods published by the U.S. Steel Corporation,[7] the U.S. Bureau of Mines[8] and the American Gas Association.[9] The standard test methods employed currently in England may also be of practical interest.[10] Individual references are made to uncollected methods of certain special tests.

Sampling

The value of laboratory tests and any conclusions reached as a result of interpreting these results are only as good as the sampling procedure employed. The need for utmost care in sampling, therefore, cannot be too strongly emphasized.

Coke may be expected to vary in both its physical and chemical properties, not alone with different lots of coke from different sources of manufacture or from different periods of operation, but also because of the nature of its processing and the equipment used. It may vary also with various portions of the individual lots produced by single units of less modern equipment.

Modern oven design and construction have advanced to the point where oven-heating control produces practically uniform carbonization from end to end and from top to bottom of the coke oven. However, the nature of heat flow with its variable rates and gradients from oven walls into the carbonizing coal charge is such that some variations in the mechanism and extent of carbonization may still occur despite prolonged maintenance of the coke at the final coking temperatures.

This results in gradations in the properties of the coke obtained at various points from wall to center of oven. It is for this reason that the sampling procedures for different tests will vary both with the nature of the tests and for the various stages in the subsequent handling of the coke.

The use of standard procedures, based upon statistical control, has made the uniformly accurate sampling of coke by both producer and consumer somewhat less difficult. It has reduced the number of possible sources of common variations in test results which are so much dependent on the technique of sampling.

For obtaining statistically sound sampling results, there are definite relationships between maximum size of pieces, number and size of increments or groups of pieces taken, quantity to be sampled, and size of sample before subsequent division or reduction is attempted, which have been established for various materials. Equally important relationships also exist for broken or sized coke and its mixtures.

For sampling run-of-oven coke for certain physical tests, it is still necessary to select, by careful inspection, a fair minimum number of pieces of full length, each comprising portions of both the cauliflower or oven-wall end, and the inner or oven-center end.

With run-of-oven coke and mixtures of broken coke, as well as with screened sizes of coke, representative sample increments for ordinary testing may be obtained in accordance with statistical principles by the periodic removal of a complete cross section of the coke traveling on a conveyor.

It must be borne in mind that larger increments are required with the larger sizes, and that a minimum number of such increments, proportional in amount to the maximum-sized pieces present, must be obtained to represent the entire lot.

For general analytical purposes, where small laboratory samples are required as in chemical analysis, the sample preparation procedure given as part of A.S.T.M. Standard Method D 271 should be used for further handling of the sample obtained by the sampling procedure of D 346. The latter should be used for sampling various sizes and mixtures of coke.

Special provision also is made for the much less desirable method of sampling of coke in railroad cars when sampling cannot be done during the loading or unloading operations. Also, modifications are cited for the special handling required for moisture samples.

Special selective sampling procedures for the drop shatter and the tumbler tests have been specified under A.S.T.M. Standard Method D 141 for the former, and under A.S.T.M. Standard Method D 294 for the latter test. Likewise, for determination of cell space volume in A.S.T.M. Standard Method D 167, selective sampling is specified. Special sampling procedures for coke, differing for by-product and beehive, for certain sizes and tests also are required in U.S. Navy specifications.[11]

Physical Tests

The tests for physical properties comprising size, strength, hardness, weight per cu ft, specific gravity, and volume of cell space or porosity are now covered by A.S.T.M. procedures.[4]

Size

Method. As specified under Standard Method D 293, square-hole sieves conforming to A.S.T.M. Standard Specification E 11 for "Sieves for Testing Purposes" are employed. Sampling procedure should preferably be that of D 346, except that sampling for this test should never be attempted from railroad cars or from storage piles. It is as important as the test itself that the sample increment be a complete cross section taken while the coke is being loaded or unloaded from a moving stream, which is halted periodically. This will tend to present the entire lot for sampling and to eliminate the effects of size segregation.

The method consists essentially of screening or sizing, with the aid of a series of the sieves mentioned, a weighed sample (which may be as much as 500 lb with the larger sizes of coke) into fractions of sized pieces ranging down to approximately 1-in. minimum dimension. In foundry coke practice, the series of sieves employed consists of the 4-in., 3-in., 1.50-in., and 1.06-in. openings.

The larger pieces of this range are sized by hand (up-ending) to determine passage by the smallest dimension of each piece of coke. Coke smaller than 2 in. is screened by shaking. The fractions are weighed and their percentages calculated with provisions for the weight losses entailed in the operation. Several samples of each lot should be tested.

Significance. The size and distribution of sizes of the coke entering the cupola is one of the major factors in efficient control of cupola operation. Pressure drop through the bed and the chemical reactions occurring in the various zones are dependent upon void volume and surface exposed. As may be seen from Table 14.1 these factors are directly related to both size and size distribution.

The proper size of fuel for cupola operation is still a somewhat debatable question as different foundries have different requirements. In general, however, an average lump size between $\frac{1}{12}$ and $\frac{1}{10}$ the inside diameter of the cupola seems most satisfactory. Under no circumstances should coke smaller than 1-in. size be introduced with the charge.

Strength

Method. A.S.T.M. Standard Method D 141 for the drop shatter test is employed for the determination of strength and describes the special sampling procedure, the apparatus, and the method of test. Briefly, it consists of dropping about 50 lb of the sample (carefully sized to remain on the 2-in. screen) four times upon a heavy steel plate from a height of 6 ft.

Breakage then is determined by sieve tests of the coke with a series of standard square-hole sieves of 2, $1\frac{1}{2}$, 1 and $\frac{1}{2}$-in. nominal openings. The weights of the fractions are calculated to percentage of the total, and the total percentage on 2 in. is used as an index of strength.

As practically all cokes today average 95 per cent or higher, the 2 in. shatter index has little value in evaluating foundry coke. A modification is sizing the dropped coke to plus 3 in. and 4 in. and reporting these indexes as well as the 2 in. index.[13,14]

The crushing strength of a one in. coke cube has been proposed and tried but the procedure is not official. To prevent breakage of the test piece during preparation, the cubes are cut from one piece of coke without internal cracks or flaws. Since only perfect cubes can be used, they would not be representative of the coke as a whole. Moreover, the test appears to be relatively insensitive to variations in coke performance. Research work also has been done on the compressive strength of coke at temperatures found in the cupola melting zone; the same difficulties were found.

Significance. The ability of the coke to reach its final destination in the cupola in its original specified size is the practical criterion of strength. Shatter-test data from many investigations appear to be most closely indicative of coke strength as compared with actual tests made in the cupola. It shows what may be expected of the coke when it is dropped into the cupola and subjected to the impact of the metal charges.

The strength of a coke from a given coal blend can be raised by finer grinding and more thorough distribution of the ash content. Excessive carbonization temperatures and faster coking rates often cause fissuring of the coke structure, reduction of blockiness and loss of strength in the larger pieces.

The 2 in. shatter index for foundry coke generally will average 95 per cent or higher. The 3 in. and 4 in. indexes for the modified test generally will average, respectively, 85 per cent and 60 per cent or better.

Hardness

Method. This property is measured mechanically in a drum or tumbler test, A.S.T.M. Standard Method D 294, in which relative resistance to abrasion is determined by the amount of degradation products. Some impact effects also are involved in this test. This standard specification describes the apparatus, the selective sampling, sample preparation, and the test procedure.

Approximately 22 lb of dried coke (carefully sized to pass the 3-in. square-hole sieve and to be retained on the 2-in.) are tumbled at 24 rpm for 1400 revolutions in a steel drum 18 in. wide and 36 in. inside diameter, made of ¼-in. steel plate and turning on its horizontal axis. The product is screened into fractions on 2-in., 1.50-in., 1.06-in., 0.56-in. and 0.265-in. standard sieves and the weight percentages determined. The cumulative percentage remaining on the 1.06-in. sieve is termed the stability factor, and that retained on the 0.265-in. the hardness factor.

Specifications for hardness on the mineralogical scale, where the diamond is rated as 10, have also been suggested but have not been used extensively.

Significance. The tumbler test is essentially a combination of abrasion and impact and has not proved as satisfactory as the drop-shatter test in correlating coke behavior in the cupola. The significance of the results are, therefore, open to considerable question.

Bulk Density

Method. This measurement is made by A.S.T.M. Standard Method D 292 in which coke of less than 5-in. maximum dimension is weighed in a 24 x 24 x 24-in. measuring box. The sampling equipment and box-filling procedure, which gives the "struck" measurement, are described in this method. For proper interpretation, this datum usually is accompanied by the sieve analysis and moisture content of the coke. Coke in railroad cars often has been leveled, and the cu ft weight calculated from the coke weight and car volume.

Significance. The weight per cubic foot or bulk density is an important relationship, especially in estimating storage capacity, and where charge additions are made by volume. It varies with apparent specific gravity, size, size consist, shape and moisture content of the coke. For closely sized foundry size coke it varies from about 24 to 27 lb per cu ft.

However, the same coke with a wide range of sizes admixed can have bulk densities up to 30 per cent higher due to the smaller pieces filling in the voids between the large ones. For the same size, moisture content and ash content, higher bulk densities are believed desirable as indicative of a denser and less reactive coke. In practice, however, higher values are usually indicative of poorer sizing or higher moisture content.

Porosity and Specific Gravity

Method. Porosity or cell space is determined as the ratio between the apparent and true specific gravities in the "Method for Volume of Cell Space," Standard Method D 167, in which two test procedures are involved. In these are described the sampling procedures, the apparatus for the two methods, and the calculation.

In the determination of apparent specific gravity, a 25 lb selected sample of dried coke, of greater than 1-in. size, is immersed in an apparatus which permits measurement of the water displaced by the coke after a 15-min immersion. The wet coke is permitted to drain 1 min after removal from the water and is then weighed. The apparent specific gravity is:

$$\frac{\text{Weight Dry Coke}}{\text{Weight Water Displaced} + (\text{Weight Wet Coke} - \text{Weight Dry Coke})}$$

For true specific gravity, it is necessary that the dried coke sample be properly reduced to pass a 200 mesh standard sieve so that each particle of coke contains no closed cells to cause error in determination. In the procedure, using a glass Hogarth specific gravity bottle with side tube for final water level adjustment, a 10 gram sample of this coke is carefully boiled in water for 1 hr, the bottle with contents is cooled, then filled with water to the leveling mark, and weighed on an accurate balance. The true specific gravity is:

$$\frac{\text{Weight Dry Coke}}{\text{Weight Dry Coke} - [(\text{Weight Bottle} + \text{Dry Coke} + \text{Water}) - (\text{Weight Bottle} + \text{Water})]}$$

For the calculation of the percentage cell space or porosity, the following is used:

$$100 - 100\left(\frac{\text{Apparent Specific Gravity}}{\text{True Specific Gravity}}\right)$$

Significance. Porosity with proper interpretation is considered by the foundryman to bear an important relation to combustion characteristics. The preceding method of determination gives the per cent of closed cell space in the coke but gives no indication of the size of the cells or cell wall thickness so that, of two cokes having the same porosity, one might have many small cells and the other fewer but larger cells. Since combustion in the cupola takes place on the exposed surface of each piece of coke, this difference in comparative cell size could readily affect the combustion characteristics. The extent of the communication of the interior pores with the surface, or lump permeability, may also be a factor in the relation between porosity and reactivity with carbon dioxide. Preferably a coke should not be less than 50 per cent porosity and conform with the requirements of dense, small celled coke.

The apparent specific gravity of foundry cokes range from about 0.80 to 1.30. In general, it decreases with increase in the percentage of low volatile coal used in the blend, and increases with carbonizing temperature and degree of pulverization of the charge in the coke oven.

True specific gravity is a measure of the cell-wall material and will normally range from 1.9 to 2.0 for foundry cokes. The value will increase with ash content, carbonizing time and graphite content.

Because so many diverse factors can influence porosity, and apparent and true specific gravity, arbitrary interpretation of results can be misleading. For this reason, their significance in cupola operation or specification is open to some doubt.

Cell Structure

Method. For visual examination or measurements of cell size, openness of cell structure, cell-wall thickness, etc., special procedures have been developed[16] which involve sectioning the coke pieces and polishing the plane of exposed cell-wall edges either with or without plaster of paris filler for reinforcing material. Scales of cell sizes also have been proposed.[17]

Significance. Other factors being equal, a denser cell structure appears to be desirable in foundry coke. The method of test has not been standardized, however, and is not generally used.

Chemical Tests

Chemical determinations generally include the items of moisture, volatile matter, fixed carbon, ash, sulfur and phosphorus. The analytical procedures followed are the well-known standard chemical laboratory methods for solid fuels[4] and are described in detail in A.S.T.M. Standard Method D 271.

This method also includes procedures for preparation of the laboratory samples and the special handling required for coke samples. Details of special apparatus used, materials required, and manipulative procedure for the determination of moisture, volatile matter, ash, fixed carbon and sulfur, together with methods of calculation, are presented.

Although not normally determined on foundry coke, the aforementioned standard also describes the method for the ultimate analysis for elemental carbon, hydrogen, nitrogen and oxygen. When available, data for hydrogen content are useful as a measure of the maximum temperature to which a particular sample of coke has been subjected. The relationship is expressed by the equation[18]

$$T_F = 1510 - 1040 \log (\% \text{ Hydrogen})$$

where T_F is maximum temperature of coking in °F, and per cent hydrogen is on ash moisture-free basis.

Moisture

Method. The determination may include total moisture, air-drying loss, and moisture in the analytical sample. Analytical data then may be corrected to the dry basis or to the as-received moisture content. The use of dried samples for the analytical work obviates these calculations.

Separate total-moisture samples are obtained from the original material by a special procedure which insures against the moisture losses incurred in preparing the regular sample. The drying operations are carried out at 105C (221 F) for specified periods of time. Controlled atmospheres are now used for drying the analytical samples.

Significance. Moisture is a physical contaminant of foundry coke which reduces the heating value of the fuel in proportion to the amount present. For this reason, allowance should be made for moisture in figuring coke charges, although it has little or no metallurgical effect because it is quickly driven off by the heat in the cupola. The moisture content depends principally upon the size of the coke and, to a very much smaller extent, upon the cell structure because generally the cells are not continuous.

Large-sized coke, because of the smaller surface area exposed per unit weight, usually contains less moisture than the smaller sizes under similar conditions. In quenching, the surface of large lumps of coke cools rapidly and the residual heat evaporates the superficial moisture. On the other hand, the small lumps cool completely and moisture can accumulate on the surface and in the fissures.

Moisture in coke is present principally because of exposure to rain or snow, either in cars or in storage. The amount of moisture absorbed is generally of the order of 2 to 3 per cent, unless the rain is unduly prolonged or the coke is badly degraded by handling or freezing.

Brown or iridescent spots, sometimes seen on coke which has been exposed to humid conditions, result from superficial oxidation or ferrous compounds, and should not be considered an indication of inferior quality.

Volatile Matter

Method. The volatile combustible matter is determined in a covered platinum crucible, preferably in an electrically heated muffle furnace, at a controlled temperature of 950 C, ±20 C (1742 F, ±36 F). In this arbitrary test, a 1-gram sample of dried 60-mesh coke is heated for 7 min with precautions to prevent mechanical oxidation losses, and the resulting weight-loss is termed the volatile matter.

Significance. Some doubt exists as to the significance of the volatile matter results obtained by the foregoing procedure, as it is difficult to understand how a coke held for several hours at temperatures in excess of 1852 F (1000 C) can release additional volatile matter on heating for 7 min at 1742 F (950 C). Values up to about one per cent are probably more indicative of adsorbed gas and surface complexes with oxygen than of true volatile matter.

Repeated determinations on the same coke sample, with the test conducted in an atmosphere of nitrogen to prevent possible oxidation, continued to show losses in weight which tend to confirm the preceding. Volatile matter above 1.50 per cent indicates undercoked or 'green' coke.

The A.S.T.M. Committee on Analyses of Coal and Coke is currently re-examining this procedure. Tests[19] on a number of satisfactory foundry cokes showed values of 0.73 to 1.25 per cent volatile.

The average volatile matter in a number of commercial foundry cokes[20] was found to be 0.9 per cent. Values significantly higher than these are probably indicative of undercoking. The average volatile content of a large sample is not always a reliable criterion of possible trouble from green coke, however, as the charge may be well coked at the wall but undercoked in the center if the oven charge is pushed too soon.

Significant variations in volatile content in a single lump of coke from the cauliflower or wall end to the punky end or oven center are indicative of too fast a pushing schedule. Undercoked or "green" coke is more reactive than normal coke and is detrimental to satisfactory cupola operation and control, especially if admixed in varible amounts with normal coke.

Ash

Method. Ash content is defined as the residue from a 1-gram sample of coke after ignition, with precautions against mechanical losses, in a ventilated muffle-furnace at a temperature not over 950 C (1742 F). The previous reference also gives details of the method for determining the softening temperature of coke ash. Analysis of the ash may be carried out using the standard analytical methods employed in mineral analysis.

Significance. The ash content is the non-combustible portion of the coke resulting from the mineral matter present in the coal from which the coke was made. It varies in both amount and composition, and is believed to influence the combustibility of the coke, its melting efficiency and, consequently, the operation of the cupola. The fuel value of the coke is reduced as the ash content increases. Coke ash is one of the sources of cupola slag and, therefore, has a bearing on the amount of fluxing compounds that must be added to the cupola charge.

Coke manufacturers make every effort to keep the ash content of their product as low as practicable. If it is necessary to use coals of high ash content, a cleaning process generally precedes carbonization. The ash content of commercial grades of foundry coke normally ranges from about 8 to 12 per cent.

Fixed Carbon

Method. With dry coke, the fixed carbon content, by definition, is the difference between 100 per cent and the sum of the ash and volatile-matter contents.

$$\% \text{ Fixed Carbon} = 100 - (\% \text{ Volatile Matter} + \% \text{ Ash})$$

Any errors in the other determinations, therefore, are included in its calculation.

Significance. The fixed carbon content of coke usually is interpreted as an index of its fuel value because the fixed carbon is the only portion of the fuel that actually contributes useful heat to the melting operation. It must be pointed out, however, that a high fixed-carbon content, indicating good fuel value, can be mitigated by poor structure, high reactivity, and small size.

Phosphorus

Method. This element is determined by chemical analysis of the ash of the coke. Ordinarily this is part of the ash analysis, but when it is to be performed separately, the procedures cited permit its separate determination.

Significance. Phosphorus is present in the ash in varying amounts up to about 0.01 per cent of the coke weight. Like sulfur, it is absorbed by the iron during melting. With ordinary gray-iron mixtures carrying 0.15 per cent and higher phosphorus contents, the pick-up in cupola melting is relatively unimportant. However, in the production of low-phosphorus metal, such as in converter-steel practice, the phosphorus pick-up from the coke can be a determining factor in meeting specifications.

Sulfur

Method. This element may be determined in the bomb washings obtained in the calorimetric determination, or separately by the Eschka method.

Significance. The sulfur picked up in the cupola by molten iron varies almost directly with the sulfur content of the coke. In this respect, sulfur behaves somewhat like carbon, except for the fact that carbon absorption is higher at high temperatures, whereas the sulfur pick-up usually is higher at low temperatures. The sulfur content of foundry coke should be as low as practical and ranges from .55 per cent to 1.00 per cent. With .06 per cent sulfur in the coke, the sulfur pickup by the metal will be about 0.03 per cent for normal operations. Excess coke will tend to increase the ratio.

Tests have indicated a greater sulfur pickup with smaller coke sizes,[44] and pickup usually is greater in deep cupolas. Both results can be attributed to lower temperatures in the upper portions of the shaft. Sulfur pick-up also is usually greater with soft cokes or cokes made with shorter than normal coking times. The form in which sulfur occurs in coke also appears to be important, since a coke having an ash which retains more sulfur seems to produce iron of lower sulfur content.

Graphite

Method. The methods currently in use for the estimation of the graphitic carbon content of coke include x-ray spectrography,[21] wet oxidation in chromic-phosphoric acid[22] and electrical conductivity.[23] No one of these procedures has gained complete acceptance as a standard procedure, due in part to the fact that graphitization of carbon is a measure of degree rather than of kind. X-ray methods appear to be the most reliable at the present time.

Significance. The graphitic carbon found on the surfaces of coke results from the thermal cracking of volatile decomposition products by the hot coke surfaces. This form of carbon is less reactive to carbon dioxide and is considered to be a highly desirable constituent of foundry coke. Such cokes have been found experimentally to produce higher metal temperatures than normal cokes.

Thermal Properties

The primary property of foundry coke is its ability to unite with the oxygen of the blast air (combustion) to generate heat with which the metal is melted and brought to the desired tapping temperature. The relative importance of the effects of each physical and chemical property upon the combustion of coke should be thoroughly understood because upon them depends the thermal efficiency of cupola operation.

Many exhaustive investigations have been carried out in this field,[24,25,26,27,28,29] but the results in many respects appear to be contradictory, principally because of the diverse operating conditions under which the tests were made. The reader is referred to Chapter 33 on Combustion for a detailed discussion of principles involved. The tests commonly employed to measure thermal properties are calorific value, ignitibility, combustibility and reactivity.

Calorific Value

Method. The calorific value of coke is determined by the oxygen bomb calorimeter method according to A.S.T.M. Standard Method D 271.

Significance. The calorific or heating value of foundry coke is a measure of the heat delivered to the cupola, but is not an accurate measure of useful heat available for melting metal. The volatile matter contributes its proportionate share to the total heating value, but contributes little if any to the melting operation because it is released in the cupola above the melting zone where no excess air is available to liberate the heat through combustion reactions.

Highly reactive cokes will deliver less useful heat to the melting operation than less reactive cokes of comparable ash and moisture content, because a larger portion of the heat is lost in the form of carbon monoxide in the stack gases.

Ignition Temperature

Method. This property may be determined empirically by one of several methods[30,31,32] which differ primarily in details of manipulation or complexity of equipment. Basically, the procedure consists of observing with sensitive thermocouples the temperature behavior of closely sized coke, heated at precisely controlled temperature rates, in which air or oxygen is passed through the coke bed at a specified rate.

Significance. The determination of the ignition temperature of coke yields little information of probable practical value other than the ease of ignition.

Combustibility

Method. This term has been applied to the rate of reaction with oxygen in beds of coke. Laboratory tests,[30,33,34,35] as well as weight-loss curves in natural-draft brazier tests,[36] or temperature-rise data in forced-draft shaft tests have been employed in such determinations. The U.S. Bureau of Mines[33,34] has adopted as a definition of combustibility the ratio of carbon contained in the effluent gases to the maximum carbon that the gases might contain. This is indicated in the following equation as:

$$\text{Combustibility (\%)} = \frac{CO_2 + CO}{CO_2 + CO + O_2} \times 100$$

Significance. As can be seen from the foregoing equation, "combustibility" is an over-all measure of the two basic reactions occurring in the cupola:

$$C + O_2 \rightarrow CO_2$$
$$C + CO_2 \rightarrow 2\,CO$$

Combustibility factors are interrelated functions of lump size, size consist, surface area, temperature of operation, rate of air supply and reactivity to carbon dioxide. Also marked differences in the strength or abrasion resistance of cokes may lead to inaccurate predictions when based on the correlation of operating results with combustibility.

Reactivity

Method. The reactivity of coke toward carbon dioxide is determined generally from the analysis of the combustion gases for CO_2, CO and O_2, obtained by burning a sample of coke in apparatus similar to that used for ignition tests. Calculation of the ratio of carbon monoxide to the total carbon in the gas gives a numerical value for reactivity.[35,37]

$$\text{Reactivity (\%)} = \left(\frac{CO}{CO + 2\,CO_2}\right) \times 100$$

Significance. The term *reactivity* has often been confused as synonymous with combustibility and burning rate. As understood by the fuel technologist reactivity is a measure of the reduction of carbon dioxide to carbon monoxide by contact with coke (carbon) at elevated temperatures according to the reaction:

CO_2 + C(coke)→ 2 CO *minus* 5,820 Btu per lb carbon

The carbon consumed in this reaction is a heat loss, and the stack gases which heat the charges above the melting zone are reduced in temperature due to this endothermic reaction. Thus, reactivity is of importance as a measure of the usable heating value of the coke and as an indication of actual operating condition in the cupola. The principles involved are shown in detail under CHEMICAL REACTIONS of Combustion, Chapter 33. A coke of low reactivity is to be preferred.

Carbon Pickup

Method. The carbon pickup characteristic of a coke relates to its ability to be dissolved in the iron during melting. It is determined by subtracting the total carbon content of the charge from the total carbon content of the iron tapped at the spout. Since it must be determined by actual melting it will vary for each set of cupola conditions and will vary in significance value.

Significance. This value is particularly important to malleable iron foundrymen who wish to balance the increase in carbon content of the iron tapped from the cupola with the tapping temperature for iron that is duplexed through electric furnaces. High carbon pickup cokes necessitate reducing the amount of the after charge coke with a corresponding decrease in tap temperature. Such knowledge may be applicable in nodular iron operations.

General Summary of Foundry Fuel Properties

Many articles have been written concerning the factors influencing the quality of foundry fuel and the properties desired. Although complete agreement has not yet been reached on all points, certain generalizations can be made to assist those faced with the problem of selecting the most desirable fuel. It must be emphasized, however, that the following points are not absolute rules applicable to all the manifold conditions under which foundry fuel may be used.

1) The size of the individual pieces should be as nearly uniform as possible and should average about $\frac{1}{10}$ to $\frac{1}{12}$ the I.D. of the cupola.
2) The strength, hardness, carbon content, graphite content and calorific value should be high.
3) The reactivity, ash, moisture, volatile matter, sulfur and phosphorus should be low.
4) Effective sulfur removal is dependent upon slag basicity, fluidity, adequate slag volume and a reducing atmosphere.

The complexity of the factors involved in the evaluation of the properties of foundry coke has been influenced greatly by local conditions and operational features such as cupola size, charging and tapping schedules, blast pressure, fuel ratio, mèlting rate, tapping temperature, length of heat, and type of metal to be produced.

These considerations make the formulation of a specification for foundry coke difficult. In general, coke should be strong, properly sized, fully coked, uniform from day to day in physical and chemical properties, and as low in ash and sulfur as practical.

No formula or small laboratory scale test has been developed which would directly correlate with actual cupola operations. Spout temperatures and gains in the carbon content of the iron cannot be predicted by inspection, chemical or physical specifications. The ultimate test is use of the coke in actual operation. Table 14.2 shows the proximate analyses of cokes presently in use.

Attempts have been made, especially in connection with cokes for blast furnace use, to weigh the relative importance of the various properties in terms of a mathematical formula and arrive at the physical fuel value. One such formula for blast furnace coke is [38]

$$[0.1 \times \% \text{ on 2-in.} \times (100 - \% \text{ on 4-in.})] + (0.1 \times \% \text{ porosity}) + (0.2 \times \% \text{ shatter on 2-in.}) + (0.6 \times \% \text{ tumbler on 1-in.})$$

Although not directly applicable for foundry coke, a formula of this general type, weighing the factors of greatest importance in cupola operation, would be of advantage in comparing results obtainable with different fuels.

SPECIFICATIONS FOR FOUNDRY COKE

Outward appearance and manual inspection were originally the sole criteria for comparing foundry cokes. The gradual development of physical and chemical tests indicating differences in thermal and metallurgical behavior in the cupola has led to the establishment of published specifications intended for the guidance of foundry coke manufacturers and users. From opinions as to color, lustre, musical resonance when struck, and the mechanical results of throwing a lump of coke against a wall, detailed specifications have been developed for size, density, porosity, strength and hardness among the physical properties.

In addition, the chemical composition, including moisture, volatile matter, fixed carbon and ash content, together with sulfur, reactivity and other chemical or physiochemical properties, have been used in various forms. and combinations. The discussion which follows deals with the best known of the recent specifications.

In 1915, after 10 years of committee activity, the American Society for Testing Materials, in collaboration with the American Foundrymen's Association,

TABLE 14.2. TEST DATA ON SHIPMENTS OF FOUNDRY COKE FROM VARIOUS PRODUCERS (1962)

Coke Plant	Analysis on Dry Basis				Shatter on			Porosity	Apparent Specif. Gr.
	Volatile	Fixed C	Ash	Sulfur	2 in.	3 in.	4 in.		
A	.57	93.93	5.50	.57	97	90	70	49.0	
B	.81	94.48	4.71	.67	—	—	—	38.1	
C	.56	93.63	5.81	.59	95	89	73	51.0	
D	.97	92.36	6.67	.61	97	89	73	50.8	
E	.55	88.39	11.06	.80	96	89	69	48.0	
F	.85	93.05	6.10	.59	97	90	71	53.5	
G	.53	92.98	6.49	.61	97	89	71	48.5	
H	.70	94.49	4.81	.60	95	88	72	52.8	
I	.70	92.70	6.60	.56	97.8	94.8	—	.943	
J	.50	93.80	5.70	.54	96.4	90.4	78.0	.983	
K	.40	92.84	6.76	.54	96.2	94.6	80.2	.916	
L	.60	93.10	6.30	.57	96.6	93.8	76.8	.933	
M	.42	93.42	6.16	.56	97.9	94.6	83.6	.984	
N	.40	96.45	3.15	.68	96.5	—	—	—	1.3
O	.40	95.05	4.55	.63	97.5	—	—	—	1.1

published tentative specifications for foundry coke which were finally adopted in 1916 as Standard Specification D 17-16.[39] The specifications were discontinued in June, 1941, when the need for more comprehensive specifications became apparent. At present no specification on foundry coke is listed by A.S.T.M.

Other American and foreign specifications are found in References 11, 40, 41, 42, 43.

It has been suggested[13] that in addition to those items listed in A.S.T.M. Specification D 17-16, ash analysis, ash fusion temperature, bulk density and combustibility data should be included. Also proposed are definite tolerance limits on under- and oversize, and the use of the modified drop-shatter test employing large size material.

Shatter: not under 95 per cent on 2 in.; not under 89 per cent 3 in.; not under 80 per cent 4 in.

Apparent specific gravity: 0.88-1.30 generally found to be 0.95-1.02.

REFERENCES

1. Davis, J. D., *Selection of Coals for Coke Making,* RI 3601, U.S. Bureau of Mines (1942).
2. Rose, H. J., *Selection of Coals for the Manufacture of Coke,* Published by Koppers Co., Pittsburgh, Pa.
3. Roberts, I. M., "Increasing Percentage Production of Large-Size Coke at Fast Coking Rates," *Transactions,* A.I.M.E., vol. •157, p. 306 (1944).
4. A.S.T.M. *Standards,* 1949, Part 5, American Society for Testing Materials.
5. Wright, C. C., "Selection and Use of Anthracite for Cupola Fuel," *Foundry,* pp. 96 and 210, March, 1951.
6. Wright, C. C., and Reagan, W. J., "Cupola Operations with Anthracite," *Transactions,* 6th Anthracite Conference, vol. 6, p. 119 (1948).
7. *Methods of the Chemists of the United States Steel Corporation for the Sampling and Analysis of Coal, Coke and By-Products,* 3rd Edition, pp. 20-143, 1929, Carnegie Steel Co., Pittsburgh, Pa.
8. Stanton, F. M., Fieldner, A. C. and Selvig, W. A., *Methods of Analyzing Coal and Coke,* U. S. Bureau of Mines, Technical Paper 8 (1938 ed.).
9. *Gas Chemists' Handbook,* 3rd ed., pp. 1-58, 1929, American Gas Association, New York.
10. *British Standard Methods for the Analysis and Testing of Coal and Coke,* British Standards Institution, no. 1016, 1942, London.
11. U. S. Navy Specifications on Coke Q-C-571B.
12. Snyder, F. R., "Effects of Coke Sizing on Control of Cupola Melting Operations," A.C.C.C.I., April (1952).
13. Mulcahy, B P., "Foundry Coke Specifications," AMERICAN FOUNDRYMAN, vol. 2, no. 9, Sept. 1940, pp. 5-9.
14. Lowry, H. H., and Mayers, M. A., "Properties of Blast Furnace Cokes. Their Measurement, Significance and Control," *Iron & Steel Engineer,* Feb. 1943.
15. Wright, C. C., "Some Metallurgical Uses of Anthracite," *Transactions,* 9th Annual Anthracite Conference, p. 155 (1951).
16. Rose, H. J., "The Study of Coke Macrostructure," *Industrial and Engineering Chemistry,"* vol. 17, pp. 895-901 (1925).
17. Ramsburg, C. J., and Sperr, F. W., Jr., "By-product Coke and Coking Operations," *Journal,* Franklin Institute, vol. 183, no. 391-431 (1917).
18. Lowry, H. H., Landau, H. G., and Naugle, L. L., "Correlation of BM-AGA Carbonization Assay Tests with Coal Analyses," *Transactions,* A.I.M.E. vol. 149, p. 297 (1942).
19. Clendenin, J. D., and Kohlberg, J., "The Blending of Anthrafines in Coke Production," *Transactions,* 6th Annual Anthracite Conference, vol. 6, p. 217 (1948).
20. Private communication from G. Vennerholm to C. C. Wright.
21. Franklin, E F., "The Structure of Graphite Carbons," *Acta. Crystallographica,* vol. 4, p. 253 (1951).
22. Blayden, H. E., and Riley, H. L., "Wet Oxidation Test," *Journal, Society of the Chemical Industry,* vol. 54, p. 159T (1935).
23. Davis, J. D., and Auvil, H. S., "Electric Conductivity of Coke," *Industrial and Engineering Chemistry,* vol. 27, pp. 1196-1200 (1935).
24. Powell, A. R., "Physical and Chemical Properties of Coke in Relation to Its Manufacture and Use," *Recent Progress in Science in Relation to the Gas Industry,* Chapter II, Published by the American Gas Association, New York (1926).
25. Blayden, H. E., Noble, W., and Riley, H. L., "Experiments in a Small-scale Cupola," *Foundry Trade Journal,* vol. 57, pp. 261-266 (1937).
26. Schmid, L., *"Der Bau und der Betrieb der Kupoloefen,"* vol. II, pp. 54-77 (1937). Published by W. Knapp, Halle, Germany.
27. Braunholtz, W. T. K., Nave, G. M., and Briscoe, H. V. A., "Correlation of the Physical and Chemical Properties of Cokes with Their Value in Metallurgical Processes," *Fuel,* vol. 8, pp. 411-437 (1929).
28. Koppers, H., "Foundry and Furnace Coke Compared," (Abstract R. Moldenke), *Iron Age,* vol. 111, p. 825 (1925).
29. Piwowarsky, E., and Krämer, K., "Fundamental Studies on an Experimental Small Cupola," *Die Neue Giesserei,* Techn.-Wissensch. Beihefte, vol. 1, p. 3 (1949).
30. Russell, C. C., and Shaffer, C. E., "The Combustion Properties of Coke," Unpublished method of the Koppers Co. (1932).
31. Reynolds, D. A., and Davis, J. D., "Reactivity of Coke," *Industrial and Engineering Chemistry,* Analytical Edition, vol. 8, pp. 33-6 (1936).
32. Sebastian, J. J. S., and Mayers, M. A., "Coke Reactivity—Determination by a Modified Ignition Point Method," *Industrial and Engineering Chemistry,* vol. 29, pp. 1118-24 (1937).
33. Nichols, P., Brewer, G. S., and Taylor, E., "Properties of Cokes Made from Pittsburgh Coal," *Proceedings,* American Gas Assn., pp. 1129-1143 (1926).
34. Davis, J. D. and Greene, J. W., "Reactivity of Pulverized Cokes in Air, Carbon Dioxide and Water Vapor." *Proceedings,* American Gas Assn., pp. 1160-1164 (1926).
35. Boegehold, A. L., "Quality of Pig Iron and Castings as Affected by Blast Furnace Practice," TRANSACTIONS, American Foundrymen's Assn., vol. 37, pp. 91-152 (1929).
36. Rhead, T. F. E., and Jefferson, R. E., "Determination of Relative Ignitabilities and Combustibilities of Domestic Coke," *Journal,* Society of the Chemical Industry, vol. 46, pp. 166-72T (1927).
37. Mayers, M. A., "Methods of Determining the Reactivity of Cokes," Carnegie Institute of Technology, Coal Research Lab., Contribution No. 36 (1936); *Chemistry of Coal Utilization,* vol. I, pp. 863-920 (1945).
38. Campbell, R. W., "Physical Testing of Coke and Correlation with Furnace Operation," Presented before Blast Furnace and Coke Association of the Chicago District, 1936.
39. 1939 Book of A.S.T.M. *Standards,* Part III, Non-Metallic Materials—General, American Society for Testing Materials, pp. 59-61.
40. Federal Specifications Q-C-571B.
41. Dyer, Y. A., "Characteristics of Foundry Cokes and Slags," *Iron Age,* vol. 108, pp. 407-9 (1921).
42. Gluud, W., and Jacobson, D. L., *International Handbook of the By-product Coke Industry,* New York, 1932.
43. Colomer, Felix, and Lordier, Charles, *Combustibles Industriels,* 3rd Edition, pp. 190-1, Paris, 1919.
44. Bowers, J. A., and MacKenzie, J. T., *"Cast Iron as Affected by Coke Size in Cupola Melting,"* TRANSACTIONS, American Foundrymen's Association, vol. 45, pp. 293-324 (1937).

CHAPTER 15

Fluxes

Additions of fluxes or fluxing agents are necessary for continuous efficient cupola performance. As explained in Chapter 29, a flux is a substance which lowers the fusion point and improves the fluidity of the slag naturally produced in the melting operation. The condition of the slag influences the physical cleanliness, the various reactions, and the combustion efficiency of the cupolas. The principles of slag control and analyses of constituents are described in Chapter 29 PART 2, along with factors that determine the proper amount of flux.

The basic constituents useful as fluxes are listed along with their sources:

Primary Fluxes

Lime (calcium oxide, CaO) from limestone (calcium carbonate, $CaCO_3$)
 Calcite (calcium carbonate, $CaCO_3$)
 Oyster shells

Magnesia (magnesium oxide, MgO) from
 Dolomite ($MgCO_3$ and $CaCO_3$)

Secondary or Supplementary Fluxes

Sodium carbonate (Na_2CO_3) from
 Fused soda ash (Na_2CO_3)
 Mineral trona (sodium sesquicarbonate)

Calcium fluoride (CaF_2) from mineral Fluorspar or "Spar."

Calcium carbide (CaC_2) from commercially produced "carbide."

Proprietary combinations of above.

Most cupolas can be slagged properly with primary fluxes added in amounts equivalent to 2 per cent to 7 per cent of the metal charge. On larger cupolas, with clean charges and favorable conditions, 2 per cent might be sufficient, while on smaller cupolas with dirty charges and poor conditions as much as 7 per cent flux might be required. Under poor conditions 0.2 to 2 per cent of one of the supplementary fluxes may be justified.

Many of the fluxes are naturally occurring materials and relatively inexpensive. Satisfactory results may be obtained with any of several fluxes or combinations, but certain precautions are necessary to insure consistent performance. Freedom from undesirable impurities and proper sizing are two of the most important considerations.

LIMESTONE

Limestone is a natural basic rock containing chiefly calcium carbonate. In the preheating zones of the cupola CO_2 gas is driven off and calcium oxide (CaO) or lime is left as the active fluxing constituent. Because of the CO_2 present the purest limestone contains theoretically only 56 per cent calcium oxide.

Most limestones contain small quantities of silica, iron oxide, alumina, magnesia, and possible traces of other oxides. Magnesia and alumina are not detrimental since they also improve slag fluidity. Any silica present as impurity sharply reduces the effectiveness of the flux. Since lime is necessary to flux an excess of silica, a good limestone should contain less than 2 per cent silica.

A potentially good limestone may be contaminated with mud or sand, or may contain occasional lumps of shale, all of which are high in silica. Sometimes a good limestone is contaminated within the foundry in handling or storage. Such physical contamination should be avoided. The more careful foundries have each car of limestone inspected, sampled and analyzed for impurities, especially silica.

Oyster shells, marl and chalk are sources of calcium oxide that may be used if more readily available than limestone.

Calcite is a pure mineral form of calcium carbonate and may be used, although normally more costly and worth little more from a practical standpoint than a good grade of limestone or dolomite. Aragonite is also a pure mineral but breaks up into very small pieces under heat, and is not suitable for cupola use. Particles below ¼-in. tend to blow out of the cupola stack.

DOLOMITE

Dolomite is a natural rock very similar to limestone. It contains a combination of magnesium carbonate and calcium carbonate. For most practical purposes magnesium oxide is comparable to calcium oxide as a flux, and under some conditions the combination seems more effective. Some acid cupola operators prefer dolomite to limestone. In some of the highly basic slags limestone is preferred because sufficient magnesia is available from the refractories.

Dolomitic limestones are stones containing some magnesium carbonate, but are predominantly calcium carbonate.

Action of Limestone and Dolomite

When limestone or dolomite is heated to a temperature of about 1470 F (799 C), it begins to dissociate or calcine to calcium and/or magnesium oxide (CaO-MgO), giving off carbon dioxide gas (CO_2), according to the reaction

$$CaCO_3 = CaO + CO_2$$

The reaction is endothermic, absorbing 788 Btu/lb of $CaCO_3$. The fluxing reaction of lime with silica to form calcium silicate

$$CaO + SiO_2 = CaOSiO_2$$

starts only after decomposition of the stone into the oxide, its reactive form, and after contact with silica.

Decomposition Rates

Calcination begins at the surface of the piece of stone and proceeds toward the center in a very narrow zone, the phase boundary between $CaCO_3$ and

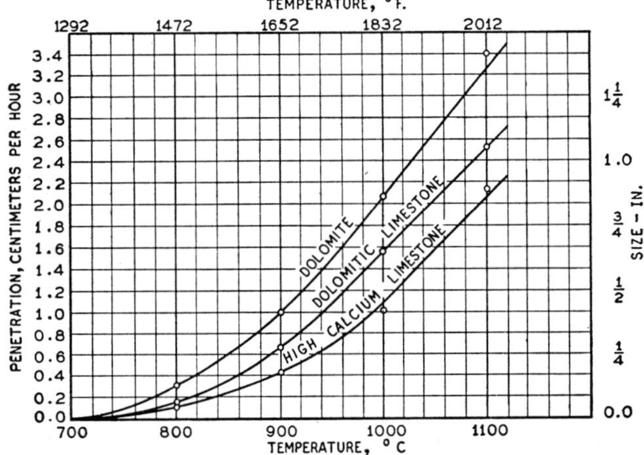

Fig. 15.1. **Effect of temperature on calcination rate of fluxing stones.**[1]

CaO, at a constant rate, which depends upon the temperature. The rate of calcination increases with each degree of temperature above 1472 F (800 C), but it varies widely among stones of similar analysis, in general being fastest with the more porous stones and slowest with the denser stones.

Dolomite, which contains about 45.5 per cent magnesium carbonate, begins to decompose at 662 F (350 C). In the lower temperature ranges, the reaction proceeds at a faster rate than it does in the case of calcite or high calcium stone, the rate for dolomitic stones generally falling in between. The difference in the rate of calcination of these classes of stone is illustrated by the curves in Fig. 15.1, which also show the effect of temperature upon the rate of calcination.

It will be recognized from the foregoing that the time required for complete calcination of fluxing stones, irrespective of density or composition, varies directly with the screen size of the stone. In other words, at the same temperature, a ½-in. mesh stone will be decomposed into its reactive form (CaO) in one-fourth the time required for a 2-in. mesh stone. This relationship between the time required for complete calcination of limestones of varying sizes up to 3 in. at temperatures from 1472 F to 2102 F (800 C to 1150 C) is shown in Fig. 15.2.

1. Joseph, T. L., Beatty, H. M., and Bitseanes, G., "Calcination Rates and Sizing of Blast Furnace Flux," *Metals Technology*, vol. 9, no. 8, Dec. 1942, A.I.M.E. Technical Publ. 1522.

Behavior in the Cupola

In general, lighter weight, or porous dolomitic or high calcium stones not only decompose into the oxide more rapidly than the denser types, but the calcined form is softer and more friable and is broken up or crushed by the movement of the coke and iron charge in settling down through the cupola. Thus, with the more porous stone and with smaller screen sized stone, because of the greater surface area and more rapid decomposition, fluxing occurs higher up in the stack and the reactions proceed at a faster rate. On the other hand, more or less flux always is lost as lime dust blown out of the stack, and this loss will be proportionately higher with soft, porous stone or very small sized stone.

From the foregoing, it will be seen how both the size and kind of stone may affect its fluxing action in the cupola, and thereby influence melting conditions and cupola operations generally. Therefore, it is evident that, for best results, the screen size of the fluxing stone should be controlled in accordance with its calcining characteristics, depth of the cupola charge, rate of travel through the stack, and the temperatures existing at different levels in the stack down to the melting zone.

Limestone Sizes

Generally, stones screened to minus 2 in. and plus ¾-in. are considered to be most satisfactory for cupola use. On some very large cupolas, stone up to 3 in. has proved satisfactory, although there is increased danger of calcining too low in the cupola to be fully effective. On some of the smaller cupolas (below 36 in.) stone ¼ to 1 in. is preferred. The danger of blowing out of the stack increases as the size approaches and goes below ¼-in.

SODIUM CARBONATE

Sodium carbonate (Na_2CO_3) or soda ash is a strongly basic flux and an effective slag liquefier. Slags with high concentrations of sodium have potential desulfurizing capacity, but the volatility of sodium compounds and attack on acid refractories makes it difficult to retain such concentrations in the final slag of an acid cupola. Desulfurizing and dephosphorizing reactions are possible in a basic cupola, and sodium carbonate is an effective reactant.

Sodium carbonate is used in the cupola largely as a secondary flux to supplement the effect of the limestone. Since pure soda ash melts at 1564 F (851 C) its fluxing action starts much higher in the cupola stack. This low melting point makes soda fluxes more effective in fusing away bridges and congested areas of the cupola. Many operators use some soda fluxes on the bed and/or the first few charges to make sure that the first slag is fluid enough to overcome lower temperatures and neutralize the additional source of slag.

Sodium Carbonate Sources

The composition and physical properties of the

different soda fluxes available for use in foundries are generally established by their trade names.

Fused soda ash is available in 2-lb pigs and 2-oz tablets, and is normally recognized by the trade name "purite." Since soda ash as manufactured for the chemical industry is a powdery product unsuitable for use in the cupola charge, some compacting is necessary. This fused soda ash contains over 98 per cent sodium carbonate (Na_2CO_3) or 58 per cent

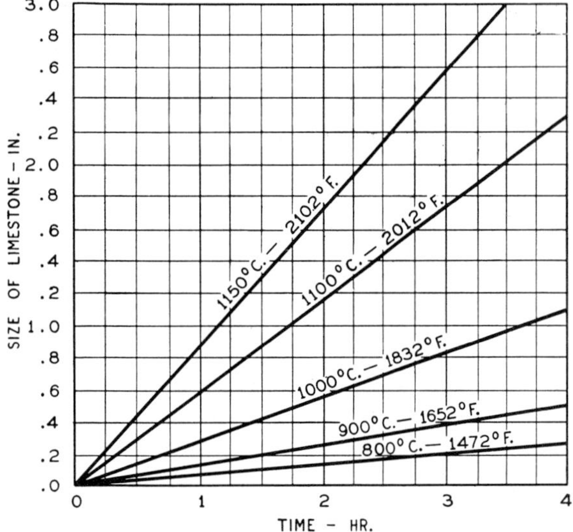

Fig. 15.2. Time-temperature relationship for complete calcination of limestones.[2]

sodium oxide (Na_2O), which is the effective fluxing ingredient. Soda briquets have been marketed for cupola use that were bonded with water and a bonding agent. These chemically bonded briquets contain 88 per cent Na_2CO_3.

Another source of sodium oxide is the natural mineral trona which consists essentially of sodium sesquicarbonate and combined water of crystallization. The rock as mined is crushed to lumps ¾ to 2½ in. and sold by the more familiar trade name "sultron." Sodium oxide content is reported to be 40 per cent compared to 58 per cent Na_2O in pure soda ash.. The fusion point is reportedly lower than pure soda ash and the mineral does not absorb moisture. More favorable physical condition, fusion point, and dispersion are claimed to compensate for the lower Na_2O content.

The several sources of sodium oxide have all been found effective to essentially the same degree when equivalent amounts of sodium oxide (Na_2O) are used. Some physical properties seem advantageous on some applications while other properties may be more important under different methods of application.

FLUORSPAR

Fluorspar or "spar" is the mineral calcium fluoride (CaF_2), and may be purchased in lump or pea size. Calcium fluoride content should be over 85 per cent. Fluorspar tailings, containing 12 to 20 per cent CaF_2 are sold in bonded bricks under various trade names. The fluxing value is based on the fluorspar content.

Fluorspar is a strong basic flux and slag liquefier. It melts at 2426 F (1330 C), which is a temperature prevailing in a zone above the normal cupola melting zone. Some fluorine gas is evolved, which is very reactive toward both silica and lime. The reactions of fluorspar are highly complex and have never been completely explained.

The presence of small amounts of fluorspar seems to accelerate all the fluxing reactions, cleaning the coke and making the slag more fluid by the time it reaches the critical tuyere areas. Like soda ash its high solvent power makes spar useful to overcome temporarily bridged or congested conditions. Excessive amounts of fluorspar can be very destructive to normal acid refractories. Its use must be carefully supervised. Proper sizing and even charging are even more important on the more reactive fluxes.

Certain geologic deposits of fluorspar occur with high levels of stress. When this is the case, the spar may disintegrate in the preheat zone of the cupola and be blown out. Some foundries test incoming spar in a laboratory furnace, heating the material to the range of 800 F (420 C) and observing that only a minimum of fines is produced.

In basic operation fluorspar additions of ½ to 3 per cent are often very useful in improving the fluidity of the highly basic slags which are inclined to be sluggish without some such supplementary flux.

Heavy fumes from fluorspar should not be breathed for long periods since they contain some fluorine gas. Draft from the cupola stack and good ventilation in the cupola area are normally adequate to eliminate the fumes. The presence of excessive fluorspar fumes can be readily detected by the irritation to the nostrils.

CALCIUM CARBIDE

Calcium carbide is produced from lime and coke in electric furnaces operated near 4000 F. Molten carbide is cast into pigs, cooled and crushed to size. Two grades are available suitable for cupola use: the regular grade and a special foundry grade, with lower fusion and combustion temperatures.

Certain precautions are necessary in handling and storing carbide, and persons handling this material should be thoroughly familiar with safe practices regarding its use. Carbide reacts with water to form acetylene, which will be explosive if confined and ignited. No hazards have been encountered in using this material in the open cupola—the only hazards are in storage.

Regular carbide has been used effectively in some basic cupola operations. Carbide with limestone and fluorspar makes possible low sulfur thoroughly deoxidized iron, which is suitable for nodular treatment. Reduction in amounts of nodulizing alloys may justify the cost of carbide. Increased metal temperature, increased carbon pickup, and improved desulfurization from carbide sometimes make it easier to use lower cost charge materials where the savings more than justify the cost of special fluxes.

In the acid cupola small percentages of carbide have been used effectively to overcome periods of

2. Furnas, C. C., "Rate of Calcination of Limestone," *Industrial and Engineering Chemistry,* vol. 23, no. 5, May 1931, p. 535.

low carbons or low temperature. Some desulfurization can be accomplished, but efficiency is reduced by reaction with the acid slag. Since carbide increases the basicity of the slag, some reductions in limestone may be advisable if large amounts are used and increased refractory attack is indicated.

Unlike the other secondary fluxes, carbide does not react high in the stack but becomes reactive only after it has worked below the melting zone and into the coke bed. Since carbide does not melt, its reactivity depends upon surface contact with descending droplets of metal and slag. For this reason either additional time must be allowed for carbide to become reactive, or carbide must be added several charges ahead of the charges to be treated.

Foundry carbide melts in the upper part of the bed and drips through the combustion zone. Combustion then occurs and the material burns vigorously as it passes the tuyeres. Carbon dioxide and lime, which enter the slag, are formed.

The reactions of carbide go beyond those of a flux; its function is more nearly that of a special flux. Descending slag droplets are deoxidized and made more basic.

CHAPTER 16

Desulfurization

DESULFURIZERS first were used on a commercial scale in American foundry practice during the early 1920s. Some benefits derived from desulfurizing are:

1) Reduction of sulfur in the iron, thereby making it possible to use more scrap iron in the cupola charge.
2) Improvement in fluidity and soundness of the iron resulting from the removal (or reduction) of entrained silicates and dissolved gases.
3) Reduction in chilling tendency of the iron resulting from an improper manganese to sulfur ratio.
4) Need for less manganese in the iron as a result of maintaining the sulfur content at a lower level than could be maintained without the desulfurizing treatment.

DESULFURIZING REAGENTS

The alkalis available for use in commercial desulfurizing practice in iron foundries include caustic soda or sodium hydroxide (NaOH) and soda ash or sodium carbonate (Na_2CO_3). The active desulfurizing agent in both compounds is sodium oxide (Na_2O), of which caustic soda contains 76 per cent and soda ash 58 per cent.

Caustic Soda

Caustic soda will absorb moisture from the air and must be shipped in airtight containers. As the name implies, it is highly corrosive and must be handled with gloves. It is available as "granular" or "flake" caustic, packed in 100 and 400 lb steel drums with replaceable covers, and also as "solid" caustic in 200 and 700 lb drums. In addition to handling difficulties, caustic produces a large volume of fumes which are injurious to the skin and throat membranes, and for these reasons its use is limited to special applications requiring very low sulfur, and then only where provision can be made for carrying off the fumes.

Sodium Carbonate

Sodium carbonate (soda ash) is used for desulfurizing and refining molten iron in foundries and in converter steel operations. It is available commercially in various forms, some of which are:

1) Granular soda ash, containing 58 per cent Na_2O, carrying 1 to 20 per cent dusty grade.
2) Soda briquets, with 58 per cent soda ash and bonded with water and still distillate. Pressed into ⅓-oz pellets containing about 52 per cent Na_2O.
3) Henning's purifier, 58 per cent soda ash mixed with other ingredients, bonded with glutrin water, and pressed into 1-oz pellets containing about 45 per cent Na_2O.
4) Purite, commercially pure soda ash fused and cast into pigs weighing approximately 2 lb, containing 58 per cent Na_2O.
5) Purite tablets, commercially pure soda ash fused and cast into conical tablets weighing approximately 2 oz, containing 58 per cent Na_2O.
6) Fused soda ash containing other slag-forming materials.

DESULFURIZING REACTIONS

The reactions between the metal and soda slag, and within the slag itself, are both varied and complex, but from the standpoint of the end results and for the purpose of discussion, they are described as follows:

In contact with molten iron, caustic soda breaks down to the oxide, liberating steam

$$2NaOH = Na_2O + H_2O$$

Under similar conditions soda ash breaks down to sodium oxide, liberating carbon dioxide gas.

$$Na_2CO_3 = Na_2O + CO_2.$$

The sodium oxide, thus set free, is the active agent entering into the desulfurizing reactions. The gases set free, steam (H_2O) and carbon dioxide (CO_2), cause turbulence in the slag and metal bath which, by increasing the slag-metal surface contact, promotes the desulfurizing reactions.

Types of Reactions

The initial effect of soda slags is best described as "refining" or the washing out of entrained slag (silicates) and manganese sulfides, which are absorbed by the soda slag. The chemical reactions between sodium oxide and components of the iron and slag bath may be classified as 1) primary, namely, those in which the sodium oxide reacts directly with entrained silicates, manganese sulfide, iron sulfide and iron silicide in the order named; 2) secondary, those in which the compounds originally formed react with sulfides, oxides and silicates in the iron and slag bath; and 3) a sulfur reversion reaction by which sulfur is returned from the soda slag bath to the iron.

These reactions are:

Primary Reaction

1) $Na_2O + FeO.SiO_2 + C = Na_2SiO_3 + CO + Fe$

2) $2Na_2O + 2MnS = 2Na_2S + 2MnO$
$2Na_2O + 2FeS = 2Na_2S + 2FeO$

Secondary Reaction

3) $Na_2S + FeO.SiO_2 + 2MnO = Na_2SiO_3 + Fe + 2Mn + SO_2$

Sulfur Reversion Reaction

4) $Na_2S + FeO.SiO_2 = Na_2SiO_3 + FeS$

The primary reactions continue so long as any free alkali remains in the soda slag bath. The secondary reaction begins with the initial formation of the primary compounds and continues with gradually diminishing intensity as the temperature of the slag is lowered. The speed of the sulfur reversion reaction increases as the temperature falls, and the free alkali content of the slag is reduced by reaction with siliceous compounds.

It will be understood that all of the reactions go on in the slag and between the slag and metal bath at the same time. The foregoing discussion is intended simply to illustrate the combined effect of all reactions upon the sulfur content of the metal bath, at various stages of the process of desulfurization.

Shop Practice

In actual practice the following procedure for sulfur reduction with soda ash may be used, with or without some modifications to suit particular conditions. Before metal is tapped from any cupola, the teapot ladle or forehearth used in conjunction with it must be thoroughly preheated. The temperature of the refractory walls should not be less than 2400 F, and the time required to attain this temperature is usually 3 to 4 hr. After the cupola has been tapped and molten iron has reached a sufficient depth to seal or cover the hole at the bottom of the teapot spout, blocks of soda ash are added in quantities prescribed by experience, type of cupola charge being used, the grade of iron being produced, type and quality of melting coke (particularly its sulfur content), and specified maximum sulfur content of the iron in the finished castings.

When the forehearth is full, the iron is either tapped out or poured into a thoroughly dried and well preheated transfer ladle and taken to the pouring floor. Immediately after iron is poured into the transfer ladle, sufficient soda ash is added to the forehearth to treat an amount of iron equal to that which was removed. This is important, as any delay at this point reduces the time that the iron running into forehearth is in contact with the purifying slag. When conditions are such that the ratio of the capacity of the forehearth to the cupola melting rate is small, any delay will mean that a relatively large percentage of the available contact time has been lost and, consequently, the efficiency of the desulfurizing equipment reduced.

After several ladles have been taken out and a like number of additions of fused soda ash have been made to the forehearth, a layer of slag will have formed on the surface of the metal. This spent slag should be skimmed off by allowing the level of the iron in the forehearth to rise to a point just below the slag spout so that the slag can flow out. It has been noted that more efficient desulfurizing is obtained when a thin layer of slag is allowed to remain on the surface of the iron.

This cycle of adding soda ash to the forehearth, allowing the forehearth to become completely filled, skimming off the slag and then pouring iron into the transfer ladle is continued throughout the duration of the day's cast. However, it is not necessary to add soda ash for the last ladle or two, as the layer of refining slag already present will continue to desulfurize for at least 10 to 15 min.

To obtain the greatest desulfurizing efficiency two things should be borne in mind when forehearth and teapot ladle equipment is designed and placed. First, the soda ash should be added to the molten bath at the point where the stream of molten iron from the cupola enters the ladle or forehearth. Second, the spent slag and refined iron should be drawn off (separately, of course) at the opposite end of the ladle or forehearth, or at a point as far from the entering stream of molten iron as practicable.

When stored in unheated buildings, fused soda ash will pick up some moisture from the atmosphere. Should this damp material be added to the bath of molten iron, it will result in excessive splashing and generation of sparks. This difficulty can be eliminated in several ways. Where the operation requires a relatively small quantity of soda ash, a day's supply can sometimes be conveniently dried out by placing it in a core oven. When this is not convenient, or when daily requirements are large, several hours' supply can be quickly dried with a torch flame.

In other instances, a number of blocks of soda ash may be placed over the cupola trough and dried by the heat radiated from the molten iron flowing beneath the blocks. With this arrangement, dried blocks are pushed off from the end of the cupola trough into the molten iron and are immediately replaced with damp blocks which dry out before the next addition is made. Where a covered stationary forehearth is used, blocks of soda ash can be dried conveniently by placing a number of them on the cover. These are replaced with damp blocks as the dried ones are used.

Factors Influencing Desulfurization

The amount of sulfur that will be present in a cupola melted iron after treatment with fused soda ash is the result of many factors, some of which are listed in the following:

1) Type of desulfurizing reservoir used.
2) "Contact time" between desulfurizing agent and molten iron. "Contact time" in minutes is defined as the ratio of the forehearth capacity to the hourly melting rate of the cupola multiplied by sixty.
3) Amount of sulfur present in the iron at the cupola spout (base metal) before desulfurizing. This, in turn, is proportional to the amount of sulfur present in both the coke and metals charged.
4) Cupola melting rate.

TABLE 16.1. SOME FACTORS AFFECTING DESULFURIZATION USING FUSED SODA ASH IN BLOCK FORM

Case	No. 1	No. 2	No. 3	No. 4
Type Forehearth	Box	U-Shaped	Elliptical	U-Shaped
Capacity, lb	3200	4,000	20,000	20,000
Melting Rate, tons/hr	7.5	7.0	16	16
Contact Time, min	12.8	17.0	37.5	37.5
S before Treatment, %	0.136	0.138	0.137	0.133
S after Treatment, %	0.091	0.095	0.086	0.075
Soda Ash per Ton, lb	11.6	8.0	6.4	5.8
lb. S Removed/lb Soda Ash	0.0776	0.1075	0.159	0.200

TABLE 16.2. DESULFURIZATION WITH GRANULAR SODA ASH

Soda Ash *added by*	Weighed Batches			Cont. Feed
Case	No. 5	No. 6	No. 7	No. 8
Type Forehearth	U-Shaped	U-Shaped	U-Shaped	U-Shaped
Capacity, lb	16,000	16,000	16,000	1,400
Melt Rate, tons/hr	40	30	35	5.2
Contact Time, min	12	16	13.7	8.0
S Before Treatment, %	0.110	0.110	0.075	0.093
S After Treatment, %	0.080	0.055	0.045	0.055
Soda Ash lb/ton	4	12	12	12
lb S Removed/lb Soda Ash	0.150	0.0917	0.050	0.0633

5) Coke ratio used for melting.
6) Amount of desulfurizing agent used per ton of molten iron.
7) Completeness of the separation of the cupola slag from the molten iron before desulfurizing.

Table 16.1 covers results obtained in production foundries with front slagging cupolas using four different desulfurizing reservoirs and shows the effect on sulfur removal of some of these factors.

The box type reservoir used in case No. 1 (Table 16.1) is least efficient from the standpoint of sulfur removed per lb of soda ash, due partly to the shape and partly to a relatively short contact time.

The 4000 lb capacity U-shaped reservoir in case No. 2 is considerably more efficient than that in case No. 1, partly because of the shape and partly because of longer contact time. The greater efficiency of the elongated U-shaped type forehearth is due to the fact that the boiling action of the soda ash is limited to the end where the iron enters, and that the refined metal is tapped out at the opposite end. While the iron travels from one end of the ladle to the other, the soda ash slag rises to the surface and removes sulfur and entrained impurities.

Still better efficiency is obtained in case No. 3 because of the relatively long contact time. However, in case No. 4 the efficiency is even greater, and this added efficiency is accounted for by the shape of the reservoir.

Some foundries now are using soda ash in granular form instead of fused blocks. The granular material can be added in weighed batches, or continuously by means of feeding devices. The factors affecting sulfur removal are the same as those previously mentioned. Table 16.2 covers results obtained in production foundries using *extra coarse dense* soda ash (granular).

In Table 16.2, data in Cases no. 5-7 inclusive were obtained in one plant using the same forehearth. A comparison of Cases 5 and 6 indicates that the sulfur removed per lb soda ash decreases quite rapidly (from 0.150 lb to 0.0917 lb) as attempts are made to drive down the per cent of sulfur after treatment to levels not ordinarily associated with this type of desulfurizing agent. This is further emphasized in Case 7 where the treatment reduced the sulfur by only 0.03 per cent to a final level of 0.045 per cent. In this case the efficiency of the soda ash was only 33.3 per cent of that in Case 5 and in Case 6 the efficiency was only 61 per cent of that in Case 5.

In Cases no. 5, 6 and 7 the soda ash was added in weighed batches while in Case no. 8, the addition was made through a continuous feeder with the soda ash striking the metal stream between the end of the cupola spout and the T-pot ladle. This apparently leads to better desulfurizing efficiency as practically all of the soda ash comes into contact with *bare* metal while, with other methods of addition, a part of the soda ash is frequently trapped (and rendered useless) in some of the spent soda ash on top of the iron in the forehearth. In Case no. 8, attention is called to the fact that *contact time* is only 8.0 min.

DESULFURIZING AND REFINING IN THE CUPOLA

Sulfur Reduction. In average cupola practice 4 lb of soda ash per ton of metal, added with the limestone charge, usually will lower the sulfur in the iron at the spout by about 12 - 15 per cent, or from 0.110 to 0.095 per cent. The effect in the cupola is more to retard sulfur pickup than actual desulfurization. In the case of steel mixtures, which tend to pick up excess sulfur during melting, this effect is normally more pronounced, while with heavy cast scrap and pig iron charges, the effect upon suppressing sulfur pick-up is somewhat less.

When desulfurizing and refining iron in lip ladles, the soda ash should be added in the ladle before the first tap to allow maximum time for completion of the refining with a minimum loss of temperature. The time required for completion of the reaction, which is indicated by a quieting down of the slag, will vary from about 10 min after the tap in one ton ladles to upward of 25 min in larger capacity ladles. The slag must be thoroughly skimmed off when the soda ash reaction has ceased, before the metal is poured into castings. Soda ash slags are very fluid; it is difficult to skim off all of the slag from the surface of the iron. Consequently, the practice of desulfurization in lip ladles should be avoided whenever possible.

At one time it was felt by many cupola operators that teapot ladles and forehearths could be used in foundries producing large heavy castings where high pouring temperatures were not essential. This notion need no longer be the reason for failure to take advantage of the benefits of sulfur reduction. With a little careful thought in the selection and design of equipment and judicious use of insulating refractories, the operation can be made to succeed, even when pouring relatively light castings.

Soda slags are particularly reactive with ordinary clays and air-setting plastic cements used in laying up ladle brick, and tend to attack the joints and loosen the brick. Although soda slag is highly basic, it is somewhat reactive with basic refractories such as chrome and magnesia brick. When ganister or plastic refractories of the high-silica type are used, as recommended for the lining of smaller ladles, they should be mixed with as little water as possible to about the temper of loam molding sand, and should be hard rammed to insure maximum density.

For best results when brick are used, they should be dense, hard burned, true to form and of a type that expands upon being heated. The brick should be laid up with tight joints, either dry or with a milk-thin grout of high-grade fire clay. Such a lining, by expanding on being heated, seals the joints and makes an almost monolithic lining that resists the action of alkali slags quite effectively.

CALCIUM CARBIDE IN THE CUPOLA. Sulfur reduction with soda ash outside the cupola has generally made it possible to lower the sulfur content of the iron to a level satisfactory for a wide variety of gray iron castings. With this method, the attack on refractories in the ladle where desulfurizing takes place is rather severe and the low limit of sulfur is above that desired for some specific applications particularly ductile iron.

Injection of calcium carbide with inert gas has made it possible to reduce the sulfur to lower levels than with conventional desulfurizing agents, but with this method there is generally a sizeable loss in metal temperature and the inconvenience of skimming off the *dry* slag formed. The use of calcium carbide inside the cupola, first reported by Carter,[1] has made it possible to tap iron directly from the furnace at relatively low sulfur levels, thus making it unnecessary to resort to the foregoing methods.

When loose carbide is added to the cupola charge it should be in *lump* form. One size which has been used with good results is the 3½ in. x 2 in. lump. Some beneficial effects are:

1. Reduction of sulfur within the cupola.
2. Increased metal temperature.
3. Development of a condition within the cupola resulting in relatively low percentages of iron oxide (FeO) in the slag and in the metal. This, of course, has a bearing on sulfur reduction.
4. Increased carbon pickup making it possible to use more steel or cast scrap for a given carbon level in the final product along with some reduction in pig iron.
5. Reduction in coke between charges, resulting in an increase in melting rate.
6. Making possible the use of high sulfur coke and/or high sulfur metal in the cupola charge.
7. Some reduction in silicon loss due to a stronger reducing condition than is normally encountered within the cupola. There is also less manganese loss.

Carbide generally is used in amounts from about 1 per cent to 4 per cent by weight of the metal charge. The benefits just described are pronounced in basic or neutral lined cupolas. With hot blast and basic lining the effects are more extreme. Carter[2] reports (Table 16.3) in connection with the operation of a 36 in. ID, basic lined, cold blast cupola.

Regarding Table 16.3, note that the addition of 1 per cent carbide to the previously used flux charge of 4 per cent limestone and ½-per cent spar has:

1. Made it necessary or possible to increase the steel in the charge from 60 per cent to 80 per cent to maintain the same final total carbon.
2. Maintained silicon loss at 30 per cent.
3. Increased carbon pickup from 1.60 per cent to 2.40 per cent.
4. Reduced sulfur from 0.050 per cent to 0.030 per cent, final.

Calcium carbide in the cupola charge can be effective in offsetting the results of poor cupola design. Data in Tables 16.4 and 16.5 were obtained in connection with an internally water cooled 66 in. ID cupola. The well was lined with basic brick, the internal cooling tubes were originally covered with 4½-in. of basic brick and hot blast up to 1000 F was available. The cupola design was such that a pronounced secondary melting zone developed making it practically impossible to produce the desired low sulfur, high carbon iron with the desired raw material unless carbide was used.

TABLE 16.3.
BASIC MIXES WITH VARYING SLAG BASICITY

(Producing Same Final Chemistry — Si 2.00%, C 3.40%, P 0.20%)

Flux Charge	Proportion Steel, %	Silicon Loss, %	Carbon Pickup, %	Sulfur Final, %
ACID				
4% Limestone	30	15	0.45	0.090
BASIC				
None	35	20	0.65	0.075
1% Limestone	40	24	0.85	0.070
2% Limestone	50	27	1.25	0.060
4% Limestone, ½% Fluorspar	60	30	1.60	0.050
1% CaC_2, 4% Limestone, 1% Fluorspar	80	30	2.40	0.030

TABLE 16.4. USING 25% STEEL

Cupola Charge *Materials*	lb	%	Flux Charge	
Steel Scrap	500	25	Dolomite	100 lb
Pig Iron (So.)	700	35	Limestone	150 lb
Cast Scrap	600	30	Spar	50 lb
Silvery (8% Si)	200	10	Total	300 lb
Total	2000	100		

RESULTS OF ANALYSIS, Average

Iron, per cent Si	S	T.C.	Temp. F	Cupola Slag, per cent FeO	CaO	MgO	SiO_2	Al_2O_3
0.83	0.104	2.98	2757	3.7	41.6	7.6	34.4	8.6

Silicon in Charge, %	2.16	Carbon in Charge, %	2.63
Silicon Loss, %	61.5	Carbon Pickup, %	0.35
Air Blast Temp.	900 F	Coke Ratio	6.7:1

Table 16.4 includes operating data and average results obtained with a mixture containing only 25 per cent steel. The results in Table 16.4 are considered unsatisfactory and are attributed largely to cupola design. Analysis of the slag indicates the presence of 3.7 per cent FeO which is considered too high for this operation. Another significant item is the amount of silicon lost or oxidized during melting. The difference between the silicon in the charge and the silicon in the iron at the cupola spout is 1.33 per cent (2.16 per cent *minus* 0.83 per cent). This is equivalent to 26.6 lb of silicon/ton of iron which in turn forms 56.9 lb of silica (SiO_2) for each ton of iron melted. The SiO_2 formed is absorbed by the slag and materially affects the composition or basicity when large quantities are involved. The ratio of basic oxides to acid oxides (basicity) present in the slag is 1.14 to 1. Such a slag is considered only mildly basic.

After some preliminary tests a number of heats were run with 2½-per cent calcium carbide (3½-in. x 2 in. lump), 50 per cent steel in the charge and some modifications in the flux charge and air blast temperature. Results obtained are given in Table 16.5.

From the standpoint of producing low sulfur, high carbon iron, the results given in Table 16.5 are considered satisfactory. The slag contained only 0.5 per cent of FeO and the ratio of basic oxides to acid oxides was 1.8. A comparison of these results with those in Table 16.4 indicates clearly that conditions inside the cupola were vastly different when the carbide was used. Another example of the use of carbide in the cupola is given in connection with Table 16.6 where the charge consisted of 100 per cent steel with 0.65 per cent carbide.

A eutectic carbide is now available for cupola use. This material containing about 72 per cent CaC_2 begins to melt at 2966 F (1620 C) compared to a temperature of about 3326 F (1830 C) for ordinary carbide. It is claimed that the eutectic grade has some advantages over the regular grade due to the relatively low melting temperature.

A good deal of work has been done with this new material particularly in West Germany in acid cupola practice, where the temperature of the iron for a variety of applications is reported to be in the range of 2530 F to 2710 F (1388-1488 C). This is lower than temperatures generally sought in U.S. practice. Some of the results obtained indicate that:

1. Coke between charges can be reduced resulting in increased melting rate and somewhat lower sulfur in the metal at the cupola spout.
2. Using 1 per cent carbide and no change in coke ratio there will be a temperature increase of up to 50-60 F (10-16 C). With 2 per cent carbide the temperature increase will be as much as 100 F (38 C).
3. With 4 per cent carbide on the coke bed and on the first charge or two a rapid temperature rise of as much as 140-180 F is obtained at the start of the heat.
4. When carbide is used on all charges during the heat, metal temperature picks up rapidly after shutdowns.
5. The carbide is a powerful reducing agent and in some instances this helps reduce silicon and manganese losses and the resultant high temperature may increase the carbon pickup.

There appears to be no reason why the eutectic carbide cannot be used in basic or neutral lined cupolas with good success. Ralph Clark, reporting on the use of this material, points out that several in the U.S. have experimented with it but it is a little too early to predict acceptance. One large automotive foundry has an interest in it. Another has used it and has been able to reduce coke from 550 lb to 385 lb. The amount used was 1½-per cent. A 6000 lb charge was being melted and the stone was reduced in the ratio of three lb of stone to one lb of carbide. This installation was using 700 F (370 C) hot blast and needed more tonnage from the cupola.

The material is 2 in. by ½-in. in 250 lb drums and 10 lb cans. It is felt one per cent will give a 50 F temperature rise. It permits reduction of coke, less oxidation, better silicon recovery, more carbon, more economical charge due to less pig and more steel used.

Continuous Sulfur Reduction With Soda Ash. Attempts have been made to reduce sulfur by continuous injection of granular dense soda ash using graphite tubes and nitrogen as the carrier gas, with the discharge ends of the tubes beneath the surface of the molten metal in the treating basin. At one plant this was done in connection with a front slagging cupola melting at rates of 12 and 15 tons/hr, respectively, in

TABLE 16.5. USING 50% STEEL WITH 2.5% LUMP CALCIUM CARBIDE IN CHARGE

Cupola Charge			Flux Charge	
Materials	*lb*	%		
Steel Scrap	1000	50.0	Dolomite	100 lb
Pig Iron	400	20.0	Carbide	50 lb
Cast Scrap	450	22.5	Fluorspar	20 lb
Silvery (8% Si)	150	7.5	Soda Ash	4 lb
Si in Briquets	2	—		174 lb
	2002	100.0		

RESULTS OF ANALYSIS, Average

Iron, per cent				Cupola Slag, per cent					
Si	S	T.C.	Temp. F	FeO	CaO	MgO	SiO_2	Al_2O_3	S
1.61	0.016	4.09	2941	0.5	50.9	8.7	27.6	5.6	1.35

Silicon in Charge, %	1.70	Carbon in Charge, %	1.88
Silicon Loss, %	5.3	Carbon Pickup, %	2.21
Air Blast Temp.	850 F	Coke Ratio	6.7:1

TABLE 16.6.

Steel	2000 lb	Carbide	13 lb
Dolomite	160 lb	Spar	13 lb

RESULTS OF ANALYSIS, Average

Iron, per cent			Analysis Cupola Slag, per cent					
Si	S	T.C.	FeO	CaO	SiO_2	MgO	Al_2O_3	S
0.16	0.033	4.04	0.65	44.8	24.2	12.2	10.3	1.19

Si in Charge, %	0.2	Carbon in Charge, %	0.30
Si Loss, %	20.0	Carbon Pickup, %	3.74
Air Blast Temp.	950 F	Coke Ratio	5.7:1

TABLE 16.7.
CONTINUOUS INJECTION OF GRANULAR SODA ASH

Melt Rate, tons/hr.	12	15
Injection Tubes Used	3	2
S Before Injection, avg.	0.100%	0.092%
S After Injection, avg.	0.025%	0.037%
S Removed, avg.	0.075%	0.055%
Soda Ash/lb S Removed	33.3 lb	36.4 lb
Soda Ash/ton of Iron	50.0 lb	40.0 lb

TABLE 16.8. EFFECT OF TREATMENT ON SULFUR, SILICON and TEMPERATURE

Sodium Carbonate, %	1.07	1.66	3.05
S Before Treatment, %	0.119	0.119	0.119
S After Treatment, %	0.047	0.036	0.023
Si Before Treatment, %	1.26	1.26	1.26
Si After Treatment, %	1.19	1.08	0.92
Si Loss, %	5.6	14.3	27.0
Temperature Drop, F	36	54	108

a treating basin of about 4000 lb capacity. When melting at a rate of 12 tons/hr, three tubes were used simultaneously and soda ash was injected at a rate of 3.33 lb/min/tube. When melting at 15 tons/hr, two tubes were used simultaneously and the injection rate was 5 lb/min/tube. Data obtained are in Table 16.7.

At both melting rates (12 and 15 tons/hr respectively in Table 16.7), soda ash was injected at a rate of 10 lb/min, total. At the lower melting rate, the final sulfur level was lower and less soda ash was required to remove a pound of sulfur from the iron. This is due to the fact that the iron was flowing through the treating basin at a lower rate, the injection rate per tube was lower and the use of three injection tubes (instead of two) results in better distribution of the soda ash in the treating basin.

These observations were made in connection with this process:

1. A large volume of dense fumes is generated which must be removed by an exhaust fan.
2. Refractories in the treating basin were severely attacked. Tests were made with basic brick, carbon blocks and high alumina brick. None of these was satisfactory under the existing conditions.
3. There were no objectionable odors.
4. Soda slag *ran off continuously* without difficulty.
5. Silicon loss was between 25 and 30 per cent.
6. Metal temperature loss was 50 F with 2 tubes (2760-2710 F; 1515-1488 C). Temperature loss was 70 F with 3 tubes (2770-2700 F; 1521-1482 C).

Another method of continuous sulfur reduction has been described by Coates and Leyshon.[3] This process consists of blowing granular sodium carbonate against the metal stream through a ½-in. ID steel pipe using as the carrier gas compressed air at 2 to 9.5 psi.

A specially designed slag separation box which holds about 400 lb of iron was used in connection with a cupola melting at an average rate of 3.9 tons/hr. The slag separation box was lined with a tarred dolomite ramming mixture and the cupola spout was lined with tarred dolomite bricks covered with a layer of the tarred dolomite ramming mix. About 20 tons of iron at 1490 C (2714 F) were treated and there were no difficulties due to refractory failure. However, the report states, "that tarred dolomite may not be entirely satisfactory under production conditions and further trials are at present being carried out to find a more suitable material." Some of the data reported are given in Table 16.8.

Continuous Sulfur Reduction With Injected Calcium Carbide. The calcium carbide injection process consists of injecting finely sized particles of calcium carbide into a bath of molten cast iron by use of dry nitrogen as a carrying gas.

The primary effect is a reduction in sulfur to any level desired. It must be realized that an addition of cold calcium carbide and nitrogen will lower the temperature of the molten metal, so that a sufficiently high iron temperature is necessary in order that a satisfactory pouring temperature will be available after treatment. The process is dividable into four fields:

1) Desulfurizing from 0.10-0.20 per cent sulfur to 0.07-0.08 per cent sulfur. In this range of conventional desulfurization, calcium carbide injection offers a means of control within narrow limits and a reduction in refractory costs. Under normal conditions 10 lb of calcium carbide injected will remove one lb of sulfur.
2) Desulfurizing from 0.10-0.20 per cent sulfur to less than 0.02 per cent sulfur. Calcium carbide injection makes possible reduction of sulphur to lower levels than conventional desulfurizing agents and permits use of relatively inexpensive alloys for high strength cast irons because of the reduction in chill accompanying the calcium carbide treatment. An example of this would be the substitution of chromium for the more expensive molybdenum, nickel, copper, and vanadium used in the manufacture of class 40 or class 45 cast iron.
3) Desulfurizing to less than 0.02 per cent sulfur as a base metal for conversion to spheroidal graphite cast iron. By using a base iron of very low sulfur, there is a saving in spheroidizing alloy since it is not consumed in removing the sulfur. There is evidence that less residual magnesium is required. to obtain satisfactory spheroidal graphite structures in irons previously treated with calcium carbide, as well as a reduction in carbide-forming tendency.
4) To upgrade and spheroidize by injecting calcium carbide or a mixture of calcium carbide and other spheroidizing impelling agents. It is possible under some conditions to upgrade irons of low tensile strengths to as high as 92,000 psi, having fully spheroidized graphite by injecting calcium carbide and rare earth oxides. It is also possible to manufacture irons of 40,000, 50,000, 60,000 and 70,000 psi tensile strength, containing different percentages of spheroidized graphite, by varia-

tions in the spheroidizing agents. These agents consist of calcium carbide, magnesium oxide, rare earth oxides, magnesium alloys, etc.

Apparently the most important commercial application of the process is in connection with the production of spheroidal graphite irons where it is highly desirable to use a base iron of very low sulfur content. It is also known that high pouring temperatures are required in order to eliminate pinholes (a type of cope defect) in thin section castings. The calcium carbide injection process makes it possible to reduce the sulfur content of the iron to less than 0.02 per cent before treatment with the spheroidizing alloys; melting temperatures can be maintained at sufficiently high levels and total carbon can be held within the desired range.

In basic cupola melting it is possible to produce irons with less than 0.02 per cent sulfur in the metal at the spout and also to melt at relatively high temperatures. However, under these conditions, the total carbon is frequently well in excess of 4.0 per cent and this is highly undesirable in that it results in carbon segregation or flotation to the cope side. Henderson* has discussed this process in detail.[4] Particular attention is called to the frequency chart (Fig. 12, p. 665, vol. 67 AFS TRANSACTIONS) which includes 647 determinations for sulfur after carbide injection. It is pointed out that 86 per cent of these sulfurs are in the range of 0.010 to 0.016 per cent and 98 per cent are in the range of 0.008-0.018 per cent.

In another article[5] Henderson gives further details regarding the carbide injection process as practiced by his company. Some of the items reported are:

1. Iron is melted at a rate of 15 tons/hr and the temperature at the cupola spout is between 2950 F and 3000 F (1621-1649 C).
2. The treating basin which holds about 9000 lb of iron is 51 in. long, 28½-in. wide at the top, 16½-in. wide at the bottom and 33 in. deep.
3. Calcium carbide is injected through three graphite tubes (simultaneously) at a rate of 2½ to 3 lb/min/tube. This is equivalent to a total of between 30 and 36 lb/ton of iron. Immersion of the graphite tubes is maintained between 25 and 30 in.
4. Nitrogen is used at a rate of about 50 cu ft/ton of iron and the graphite injection tubes (108 in. long by 2 in. OD by ½-in. ID) are consumed at a rate of one tube for every 3 tons treated.
5. Sulfur in the iron at the cupola spout (base metal) is about 0.085 per cent. This is reduced to an average of about 0.015 per cent which is equivalent to removal of 1.4 lb of sulfur/ton of iron. Based on figures in items 1 and 3 it can be stated that between 21.4 and 25.7 lb of carbide are used to remove 1 lb of sulfur.

Metal temperature loss in the treating basin is about 150 F. The refractory lining in the treating basin consists of high density, high alumina brick. There is virtually no chemical attack on these brick by the carbide slag but the lining has to be replaced after treating from 1200-1500 tons due to mechanical failure resulting from agitation of the metal.

---

*Technical Director, Lynchburg Foundry Co.

REFERENCES

1. S. F. Carter, *Basic Lined Cupola For Iron Melting,* AFS TRANSACTIONS, 1950.
2. S. F. Carter, *Production Experiences With a Basic Cupola,* AFS TRANSACTIONS, 1952.
3. R. B. Coates, H. J. Leyshon, *Continuous Desulphurization of Cupola Melted Iron With Sodium Carbonate,* B.C.I.R.A. Journal, November 1961, p. 848.
4. H. E. Henderson, *Acid Cupola Melting for Ductile Iron,* AFS TRANSACTIONS, vol. 67 (1959), p. 661.
5. H. E. Henderson, *Improvements in the Production of Ductile Iron at LFC's Lynchburg Plant,* The Iron Worker, winter 1961-1962 issue.

CHAPTER 17

Refractories

In order that the cupola may become a furnace, useful for melting iron and other metals, the shell must be properly lined with an adequate thickness of refractory material. While the primary function of these refractory materials is resistance to high temperature in the cupola, they are called upon to resist one or more of the following destructive influences: abrasion, pressure, chemical attack and rapid change in temperature. The selection and installation of these refractories is, therefore, an important consideration.

OPERATING CONDITIONS : REQUIREMENTS

Refractory requirements in the cupola are among the most severe encountered in metallurgical practice since, even under the best controlled conditions, it is usually necessary to repair the lining or replace portions of it after each melting operation has been completed. This daily repair of the refractory is the result of chemical action, mechanical strain and abrasion, and temperature or heat input.

Of the three major causes of failure — chemical, mechanical, and thermal — chemical is the most important in cupola operation. The refractory and the slag in the cupola are often only different proportions of the same ingredients. In fact, very rapidly after the beginning of the heat, a slag forms on the refractory wall. This slag formation then becomes the actual refractory or melting surface. The chemistry of this material is related to the chemistry of the original lining and the fluxing and melting practice. Reactions take place between these two portions of the operation and the resultant slag or refractory essentially controls the rate of loss. For this reason, the metallurgical practice within the cupola is going to have a far reaching effect on the refractory life. Particularly there should be the proper balance between the refractory composition and the metallurgical practice so that the resultant refractory wall slag is of a proper composition.

The flux, coke ash, adhering sand, iron oxide, and all the various components which make up the final slag produced by the cupola operation, reach the hot zone of the cupola in an uncombined form. It is inescapable that some or all of these ingredients will come in contact with the lining and react with it to change its chemistry and its refractoriness. Of particular importance in this regard is the powerful fluxing effect of FeO. High amounts of this ingredient create a very fluid and penetrating slag on the refractory surface. Most of this FeO occurring on the lining is the result of the reaction

$$2\,Fe + O_2 = 2\,FeO$$

Therefore, a major control over the refractory loss is the rate of oxygen travel across the refractory in zones of high temperature and the subsequent reaction and rate of FeO formation. For this reason, one of the vital controls over refractory loss incorporates all those factors which effect the rate of oxidation of iron in the vicinity of the cupola wall. These factors include tuyere design, charge distribution, charge size, coke ratio, coke size, and any other factor which permits or assists the rapid movement of free oxygen past the cupola wall in the melting zone. Every effort should be made to keep the maximum amount of air travel through the center of the cupola, and away from the walls, to minimize this FeO formation.

The solution to low refractory loss lies in a practice which will permit an adequate compromise between a slag on the refractory wall which is so viscous that it remains essentially dormant, and the opposite extreme of a slag more fluid than necessary and therefore more corrosive than necessary.

A slag so viscous that it remains on — and hence protects — the wall gives difficulty in that it does not readily remove itself, through either the slag hole or the taphole, creating mechanical operating problems. A slag more fluid than necessary, in order to make its removal through the slag hole or taphole easy, is also one that will rapidly leave the refractory wall unprotected for further chemical attack which will rapidly remove the refractory by chemical solution. It is quite common in the industry to run slags which are more fluid and more corrosive than necessary since this simplifies the mechanical handling of the slags and minimizes the attention required by the operator to his slag hole or to taphole handling.

The mechanical losses which result from the solid charge materials sliding past the lining, or from the scouring action of the blast air, also are related to the chemical action. In a similar way they relate to thermal or heat factors. The fluid refractory wall slag described is also more apt to suffer abrasion from either solid materials or from the scouring action of the blast. At any given temperature these fluid slags are more easily removed by mechanical abrasion. Heat also is effected in this regard since the higher temperatures soften the refractory wall or refractory wall slag at temperatures even below the theoretical melting point of the refractory. This permits the scouring action to proceed at a more rapid rate.

Heat may soften the refractory sufficiently to allow it to sag or even drip and run. However, the effect of heat is more accurately related to its effect on the chemical reaction and the mechanical action. As described, higher temperatures permit a softer lining and a softer refractory wall slag and therefore permit greater mechanical loss. Of greater importance is the fact that all chemical reactions take place more rapidly at elevated temperatures. The higher the temperature within the cupola, the more rapidly the chemical attack will take place.

IN SUMMARY, the refractory loss is related to the chemical, mechanical, and thermal factors within the cupola. Of these, the *chemical action is* the most *important,* although the rate of such a reaction is directly related to the temperature and the high losses by chemical action are further exaggerated by mechanical abrasion on the softened surface.

The cupola operator has considerable control over his refractory losses, by controlling those factors which would permit or accentuate the formation of FeO on the cupola refractory wall through the presence of iron and oxygen under conditions which permit the reaction to take place. The FeO formations on the wall, and the FeO content of the refractory wall slag, are largely in control of the fluidity of that slag and its ability to penetrate and corrode the refractory lining.

SERVICE CONDITIONS

From the standpoint of service conditions, the cupola is divided into four zones which, arranged in the order of decreasing severity, are: 1) the melting zone; 2) the crucible or well; 3) the charging zone; and 4) the zone above the charging door.

Melting Zone

The melting zone lining extends from the tuyeres upward for a distance depending upon the height of the coke bed, velocity of the blast air, type of charging stock, and other variables. Although this entire zone is subjected to higher temperatures than the other zones of the cupola, the most severe conditions exist in the lower part of this zone where oxidation of iron and other elements takes place and the oxides react with slag which already has been formed by the fluxing action of the limestone of the charge on coke ash, sand and, to a great extent, on the refractory lining itself. Therefore, in the high-temperature zone, the conditions are favorable for further chemical action and mechanical erosion.

Spalling (breaking or cracking of refractories to such an extent that fragments are separated and new surfaces of the mass are exposed) is not likely to take place during the melting operation, but when the bottom is dropped, the cold air rushing past the extremely hot refractory establishes a condition of severe thermal shock.

In some cupolas thermal shock becomes even more severe by the introduction of streams of water to cool the furnace wall more quickly. Such a practice should be considered carefully since the saving in time may be very heavily overbalanced by the cost of refractories destroyed. Spalling of the refractories in the melting zone may result if the lining is not installed in a manner to allow for the extreme pressure which will be created by confined expansion of the refractory.

Some scouring action will take place in the melting zone due to shifting of the charge materials and concentration of the blast air.

Crucible or Well

In the crucible or well of the cupola the temperature is lower than that of the melting zone, and the lining is in contact only with molten metal, slag, and relatively static coke, so that the effects of temperature and abrasion by the air blast and charge materials are not as serious as in the melting zone.

Chemical action with the lining will not be severe unless the melting procedure is out of control, but some attack must be expected in the area exposed to slag, under the best operating conditions. Spalling may occur due to thermal shock or confined expansion, but probably to a lesser degree than in the melting zone because the thermal shock is less severe.

Charging Zone

The lining of the cupola in the charging zone is not subjected to very high temperatures nor to slag attack, but abrasion is very severe both from the impacts of the charging operation and the friction of the downward-moving charge. This condition is influenced by the method of charging. It is at its worst with certain types of mechanical charging, and perhaps scarcely noticeable in careful hand charging. Some foundries have gone to the use of cast iron cupola blocks or flat steel bars in the charging zone to counteract the high degree of abrasion. Figures 17.1 and 17.2 show the applications of these methods.

Above Charging Door

Above the charging door the conditions are not severe, the function of the lining being merely to protect the shell from the heat of the effluent stack gases. A certain amount of weathering takes place in this area, which will be affected by the type of protection on the stack opening and also by the climatic conditions in which the cupola is operating.

Disintegration of the refractories caused by gradual depositation of carbon in the pores of the refractories is seldom encountered in any of the zones of the cupola. This type of failure is encountered in blast furnace operation as a result of catalytic decomposition of carbon monoxide in the presence of iron. The reaction is

$$2\ CO = CO_2 + C$$

The service life of the refractory materials used in lining a cupola depends upon the severity of the conditions just described. These conditions are influenced greatly by the technique used and the skill with which the actual melting operation is conducted, as indicated by the extent to which the lining of the melting zone is affected. No refractory has yet been developed which will withstand the high temperature and the corrosive action of the slag indefinitely and, therefore, it is customary to repair the lining of the melting zone after every heat. Since the conditions in other parts of the cupola are much less severe, it is seldom necessary to reline them as frequently.

CUPOLA OPERATION EFFECT ON REFRACTORY LINING

While the service life of a cupola lining depends upon the quality of the refractory materials used and the care with which they are constructed and dried, it is no less dependent upon the character of the actual cupola operation. Unless the latter is properly conducted, no lining will last very long. It has been pointed out that the lining in the region of the melting zone is most vulnerable because of the very severe conditions there prevailing, and it is generally necessary to repair this part of the lining after every heat. Care can be taken, however, to control the cupola operation so that the extent of these repairs is not excessive.

Fig. 17.2. Diagrams of installation of flat steel bars in charging zone of No. 3½ cupola.

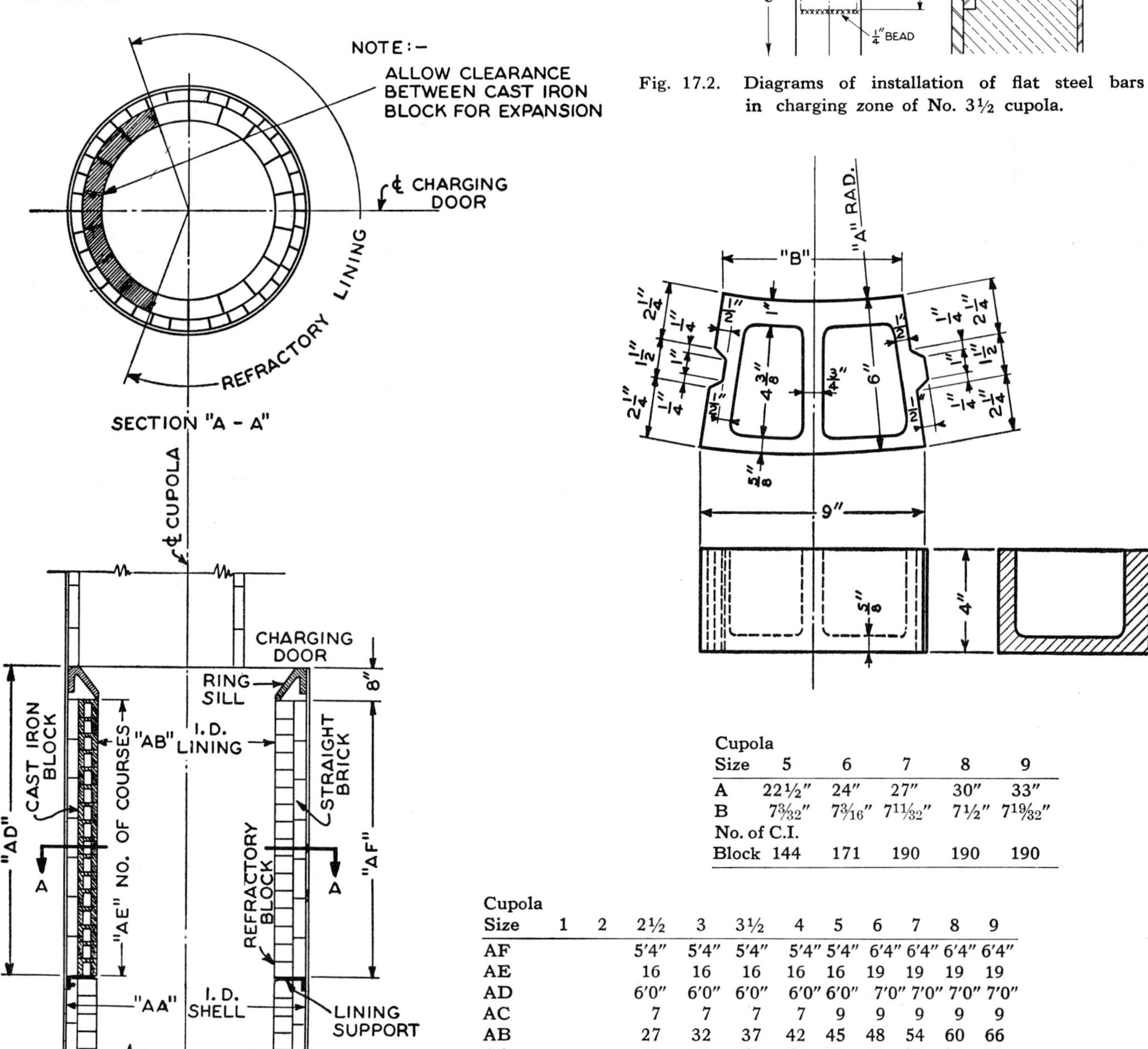

Cupola Size	5	6	7	8	9
A	22½"	24"	27"	30"	33"
B	7 3/32"	7 3/16"	7 11/32"	7½"	7 19/32"
No. of C.I. Block	144	171	190	190	190

Cupola Size	1	2	2½	3	3½	4	5	6	7	8	9
AF			5'4"	5'4"	5'4"	5'4"	5'4"	6'4"	6'4"	6'4"	6'4"
AE			16	16	16	16	16	19	19	19	19
AD			6'0"	6'0"	6'0"	6'0"	6'0"	7'0"	7'0"	7'0"	7'0"
AC			7	7	7	7	9	9	9	9	9
AB			27	32	37	42	45	48	54	60	66
AA			41	46	51	56	63	66	72	78	84

Fig. 17.1. Views showing installation methods and dimensions for lining charging zone with cast iron cupola block.

The burning away of the lining above the tuyeres normally is proportional to the temperature of the melting zone and the duration of the heat. Extreme burn-back either throughout the refractory lining or in localized areas generally results from one or more of the following causes.

One of the greatest causes of trouble with the lining of the melting zone is excessive blast. (Air under high pressure will have an abrasive effect on the lining and erosion will result.) Some of the iron will be oxidized and its solution in the slag will render the latter very corrosive. For these reasons, far better results are obtained by the use of a volume meter rather than by attempting to control the supply of blast air by means of the pressure gage alone (Chapters 6 and 25).

Bridging over the tuyeres or channeling of the air from any cause will result in extreme cutting due to blast abrasion and excessive oxidation at that point. Insufficient coke splits, lightweight or fine materials such as loose borings, rusty or burned iron all contribute to a higher iron oxide content and a greater refractory loss. Variation in the coke bed height by variation in coke splits, air blast, etc., will result in wider burn-outs and may result in deeper burn-back due to melting under oxidizing conditions. Any variation which affects the combustion reaction will affect the burn-out zone. For example, "hot blast" will result in a narrower but deeper zone of burn-out.

The nature of the mixture charged into the cupola has considerable bearing on the life of the refractory lining. A high percentage of steel scrap results in higher melting temperature and increased oxides, decreasing the life of the melting zone lining. Dirty scrap results in loss of lining life due to attack by the foreign materials on the lining and the necessity of using additional fluxing materials to remove the materials in the form of slag.

All materials charged into the cupola should be evenly distributed and held to reasonable size limits. Each charge and each coke split should be leveled off before succeeding charges are added. Failure to follow these precautions will result in channeling of the air blast, localized hot spots, excessive oxidation, etc., all of which contribute to excessive burn-back of the refractory lining.

The fluxing material also is important in its effect on the life of the lining. In general, materials which are more basic in character will attack the lining more rapidly than the less basic fluxes. If operations are such that a basic slag is required, it will be necessary to go to the basic or neutral types of lining which have gained impetus recently. Regardless of the flux used, it should be evenly distributed and be kept at least 6 in. away from the lining. The purity or analysis of the flux is important since burn-back is in direct relation to the volume of flux or slag which is developed in the melting operation.

Limestone which contains sufficient oxides to be barely self-fluxing is expensive regardless of its cost. Not only does it result in greater lining loss, but it requires a tremendous amount of heat to dissociate it and turn it into a slag fluid enough to be removed from the cupola. Dirty scrap or high-ash coke also increases the slag burden and lining loss.

Whatever the type of refractory lining—neutral, basic or acid; cupola block, brick, silica stone, monolithic (either gun patched or hand rammed) the lining will be no better than the methods and care that are used in installation. In this respect it should be pointed out that the reason a certain type of refractory lining works in one installation but not in another is many times due to the fact that the men involved in the successful application are obtaining the maximum benefits from the material through correct application, while the reverse is true where the material fails.

INSULATION

The cupola does not lend itself to insulation for two reasons; 1) the amount of heat that can be saved from radiation losses through the shell is small compared with the large amount carried out of the stack by the effluent gases, and 2) the strength of the refractory structure will be decreased because of excessively high temperature if the cupola is backed with insulation. The lining loss will be higher because of the higher heat retained at the surface of the refractory and because of the higher heat gradient through the refractory.

REFRACTORY INSTALLATION : STANDARD SHAPES

ACID (SILICEOUS) LININGS

The refractories constitute the main lining of the cupola. The steel shell merely holds the lining in place. The only exception is the water-cooled cupola, which will be discussed separately under basic linings.

The most generally accepted refractory for acid cupola linings is a high duty fireclay refractory. Refractory manufacturers make a large number of standard shapes from this material which are suitable for cupola linings. It is important to the cupola operator to utilize these sizes since they are considerably less expensive than special shapes made to the users' specifications. Some of these standard sizes are illustrated in Fig. 21.1.

Except for very small laboratory cupolas, the minimum refractory lining thickness should be 4½ in. As the cupola diameter or length of heat increases, the lining thickness should be increased.

Fig. 21.2 illustrates some of the lining arrangements possible using standard sizes. There are many other combinations possible; in fact, almost any lining thickness can be obtained by using various combinations of the standard sizes.

Attention is called to the arrangement of the component parts as shown in Fig. 21.2. Note that where two brick sizes are used to form the lining, the larger or thicker brick is placed on the inside of the lining. The thin brick (in most cases 9 in. splits or 9 in. straights) is placed against the shell. The purpose of this arrangement is to reduce refractory replacement costs. The lining must be replaced periodically. When this is necessary, the thin brick next to the shell (referred to as the back-up lining) usually does not need repairing. It is therefore only necessary to replace the inside lining, referred to as the working lining.

Before installing the lining it is necessary to prepare a mortar to bond the brick lining together and seal the joints. The mortar should be selected carefully. It must be at least the equal in refractoriness of the brick and should have good workability. Mortars that settle rapidly when mixed with water should be avoided. There are two general types available—"heat set" and "air set." These mortars may be obtained in either wet or dry form.

To prepare the mortar, turn the contents of the sack or drum into a clean mortar box, or if a small quantity is to be used, a clean wheelbarrow will be found useful. Add water to the mortar, mixing constantly with a mortar hoe until a rich creamy consistency is reached. More specific directions are found on the container in which the material is shipped.

The installation of the refractories is started on the base plate of the cupola. Figure 17.3 illustrates a typical lining, and the following procedure will serve as a guide to insure proper installation of any brick arrangement. It is advisable to put a heavy joint of a fireclay mixture (1/4-3/8-in.) on the bottom plate and on top of the tuyere cover plate. This procedure will expedite the replacement of the lining in this section since it will allow some leeway to compensate for irregularities in the thickness of the brick used for the replacement as against the thickness of the brick used in the original installation.

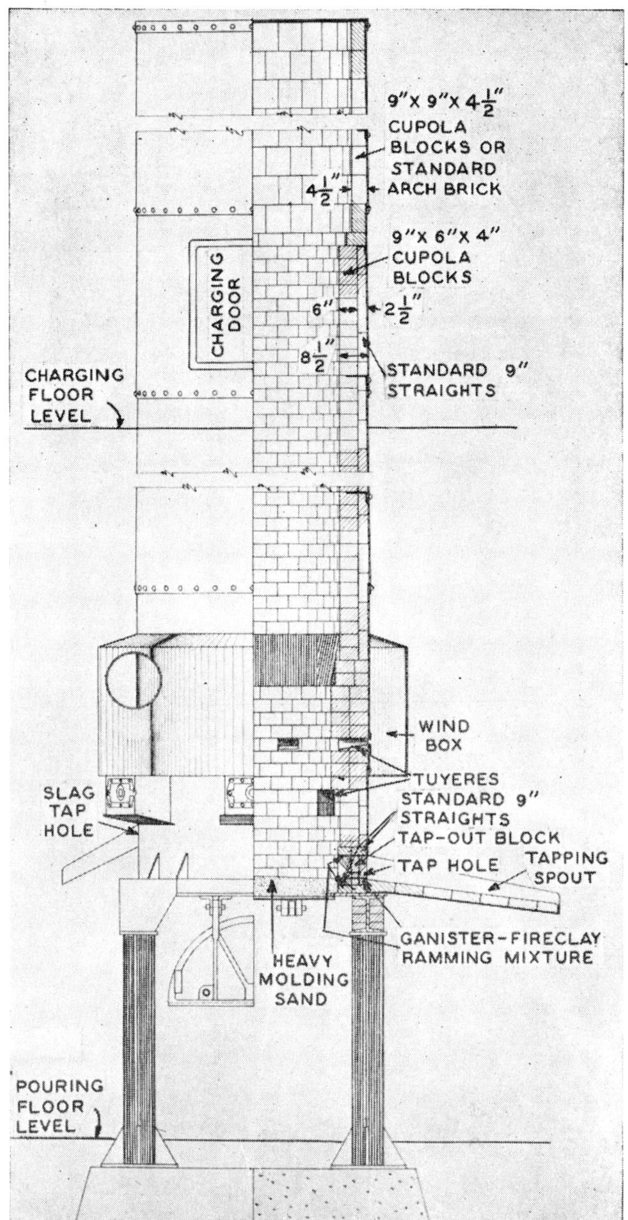

Fig. 17.3. Typical arrangement of cupola lining refractories.

Tap Hole

Before installing the first course of brick, set the tap hole brick in its proper location. Figure 21.5 depicts three varieties of the cupola blocks made and usually stocked by refractory manufacturers. The purpose of the two tap holes in one of the shapes illustrated is to provide a safety feature in case one tap hole freezes, or to afford a means to reduce a too high level of metal in the well when tapping continuously through a tap hole of a size related to the cupola melting rate.

It is desirable to use preformed refractory blocks which are available from most refractory manufacturers. Silica-fireclay ramming material, carbon-bearing plastics or ramming materials, or high duty fireclay material with graphite added, are available for ramming tap hole breasts and are still used in some cases.

The first course of 9 in. straights is installed, dipping each brick in mortar before setting in place. Since the 9 in. straights are set in a vertical position, the 9 x 4 1/2-in. face next to the shell must be dipped, also the bottom 4 1/2 x 2 1/2-in. face and one side of the 9 x 2 1/2-in. face. Set the brick firmly against the shell and up tight against the tap hole brick. Dip the next straight the same way and set in place, pressing it firmly against the brick already set.

It is very important to keep all brick joints as thin as possible. If a trowel can be inserted in any joint, the brick are not laid tightly enough. Continue to install the ring until the other side of the tap hole brick is reached. It is not necessary to start in this manner, especially when the tap hole is to be rammed, but this method will reduce cutting which can be time consuming. If the space left is too large to get one straight in, it is better to remove two brick and cut them than to install a small sliver of brick.

A good rule is, *never use less than a half-size brick.* If the area to be filled is smaller than this, it is better to cut several brick to finish the ring. This same rule applies when installing any other standard size. *Do not complete a ring of brick by using a thick mortar joint.* If a brick masonry saw is not available a mason's hammer will do a good job of cutting the brick. Draw a line and, holding the brick in one hand, tap lightly along the line with the sharp edge (scutching edge) of the hammer.

When an impression has been made along the entire length of the line, hold the large end of the brick firmly and tap the brick sharply along the line. Be sure the edge of the hammer is inclined slightly from the vertical, as illustrated in Fig. 17.4. After the brick has broken, smooth the surface before setting.

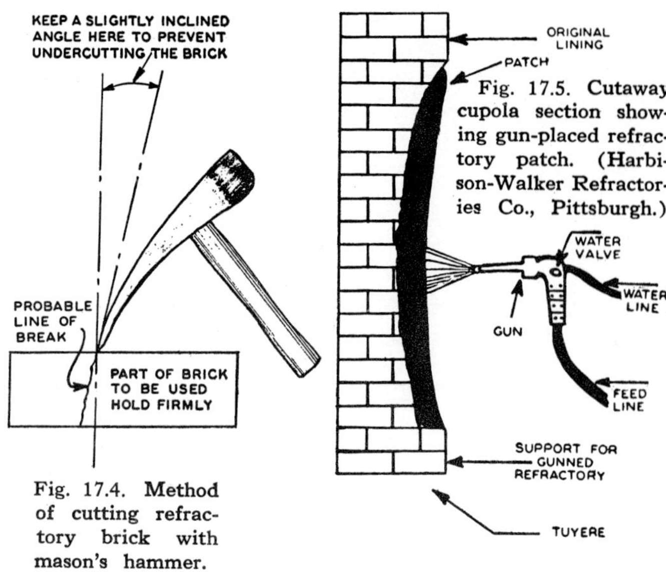

Fig. 17.4. Method of cutting refractory brick with mason's hammer.

Fig. 17.5. Cutaway cupola section showing gun-placed refractory patch. (Harbison-Walker Refractories Co., Pittsburgh.)

A good steel chisel can be used to cut brick, but the brick must be set on a flat surface. Tap lightly at first, increasing the sharpness of each blow as an impression is made in the brick. Some operators make rough cuts in this manner and finish dressing the brick on a grinder.

The working lining, which in the case of the example is of 6 in. cupola blocks, can now be installed. Dip the bottom side, back (large end), and one 6 x 4 in. side of the block. Set firmly in place against the back-up brick already installed, and tightly against the tap hole block. Continue around the ring, dipping each brick in this manner, tapping each one in place, and remember to install not less than half-size brick. Measure the area next to completing side of tap hole before setting last two blocks.

Continue laying both linings in this manner until the tuyere section is reached. Follow the same procedure around the slag hole block as outlined for the tap hole block. When setting the second course of brick start on the opposite side of the tap hole block to insure that all joints do not run in straight vertical lines.

Offset each course so that each vertical joint is staggered. The joints should appear like joints on a brick building when viewing them from the inside of the cupola. This applies to the back-up lining as well, although it is not as important as the face lining. Staggering the joints minimizes erosion.

In the example being used, a boshed section is started at the top of the tuyeres and carried up through the melting zone. When a lining is boshed it simply means that the internal diameter has been reduced by increasing the thickness of the lining. In this case the back-up lining of 9 in. straights has been replaced by 6-in. cupola blocks.

By decreasing the internal diameter it is possible to reduce the melting rate, concentrate the blast for better penetration, and protect the tuyeres from the metal and slag dropping into the well. While brick can be used for this purpose, it creates a problem for the operator since it will be necessary to stock more than one size of cupola block. A boshed zone can be established quickly and economically with a gun emplacement material, which will be discussed under a separate heading.

When the tuyere section is reached, the bottom tuyere plates should be firmly bedded on top of the brick lining, using the brick mortar mixed to a trowelling consistency. The correct consistency is about the same as for cement trowelling. If the tuyere is a one-piece assembly, bed it in place in the same manner. After the tuyeres are properly placed, fill in the void areas between them with brick cut to fit or ram with a high duty plastic refractory. The voids must be completely filled to prevent air entrapment.

Continue to install the lining up through the melting zone. If the melting rate of the cupola is to be reduced, the boshed lining will go this high. Step back then to the original lining used in the well, following the procedure outlined previously.

Above the melting zone the temperature is relatively lower, and the lining in this area will outlast the melting zone lining appreciably. The thickness of the lining above the melting zone may vary from 4½ in. for small cupolas and short heats to as much as 12 in. for large cupolas and long heats.

Various combinations of shapes for usual lining conditions are in Fig. 21.2; the number of brick required is shown in Table 21.1.

In the upper stack, a 2½ in. lining for small cupolas and 4½-in. for large cupolas is quite adequate. The brick may be of high or intermediate duty quality. An air-setting mortar, or a mortar consisting of half fire clay and half Portland cement should be used and should be installed following the same procedure outlined previously.

When the lining is completely installed, close the bottom doors and tamp in the bottom sand. The lining should be dried thoroughly before using. A slow-burning wood or coke fire built on the sand bottom will be sufficient if it is permitted to burn over a week end. It is not advisable to raise the temperature too quickly as the brick may spall or steam may form back in the lining and blow out the mortar joints.

Maintenance of Acid Cupola Refractories

The burning zone refractories and brickwork around the tap hole usually are consumed more rapidly than any other section. As a general rule, these areas will require maintenance after each heat.

For cupolas making short heats, one of the most common maintenance practices used is to permit the lining to wear back until a 9 in. split (9 x 4½ x 1¼ in.) can be inserted into the lining. Sometimes areas will burn out to a depth sufficiently large to insert a 9 in. straight (9 x 4½ x 2½ in.). To repair the lining with these sizes, clean out the area to be replaced, removing all slag, and dip the 9 in. splits or 9 in. straights in bonding mortar and set firmly in place. When the brick is properly installed the 9 x 4½-in. face of the brick should be against the old brickwork.

In foundries where the cupola is operated for longer daily runs, 8 hr or more, or where the operating conditions are particularly severe, it is a necessary and common practice to replace a full course of 9 x 6 x 4-in. cupola blocks for the height of the melting zone after each run. In this case, the back-up lining is not touched unless the operation has been of such severity that the burn-out has extended into it. It is then necessary to patch the back-up lining as well as to replace the full course of 6-in. blocks forming the inner lining.

Another maintenance practice is to use a hand-patching material. Most of these materials are silica, with sufficient high duty fire clay added to give good plasticity. This type of material is usually prepared one day ahead. Mix the material with approximately 12 to 13 per cent water in a clean mortar box.

When thoroughly mixed, permit it to stand in the box overnight and cover with wet sacks. To use simply slice it off in 2 or 3 in. slabs with a shovel and tamp into place with a mallet. A bench rammer is a good tool for this purpose. It is not necessary to hammer the material into a hard surface; simply tamp until all air has been evacuated between each layer.

Probably the most popular maintenance practice used today is gunning materials onto the cupola refractories. There are a number of good air placement guns on the market, and some excellent refractory materials. These materials are discussed under monolithic linings.

General Considerations

It is common practice to allow a ¼- to ½-in. expansion space between the cupola refractory lining and the shell. This space should be filled with ground fire clay, silica sand or other compressible refractory material. The expansion of fireclay brick at cupola operating temperatures will rarely exceed 3/32-in./ft. In a 48 in. I.D. cupola this amounts to a little more than an inch total expansion. The steel shell will expand and absorb a part of this expansion, and a certain amount will be absorbed in the brick joints.

When patching a cupola lining it is good practice to remove all the slag from the area to be repaired. The slag contains some low-melting compounds which will soften when the cupola is brought back to temperature. Patching material placed over this slag may slough away if the slag is of considerable volume. The slag should be carefully removed to prevent damage to the good brick behind it.

INSTALLATION OF BASIC LININGS

The operation of a cupola on basic practice does not require drastic changes in the procedure usually followed in acid practice, nor does it require a total change in refractory lining procedure. Probably the principal reason cupolas are converted to basic practice is to produce nodular iron.

Demand for hotter iron also plays an important role, and a shortage of good coke, resulting in the necessity of using high-sulfur fuels, sometimes results in conversion of the cupola to basic practice. In most cases one important change occurs when the cupola is converted, and that is an increase in the limestone charge. This, of course, is not the only change that occurs, but it is the one requiring a change in refractory lining procedure.

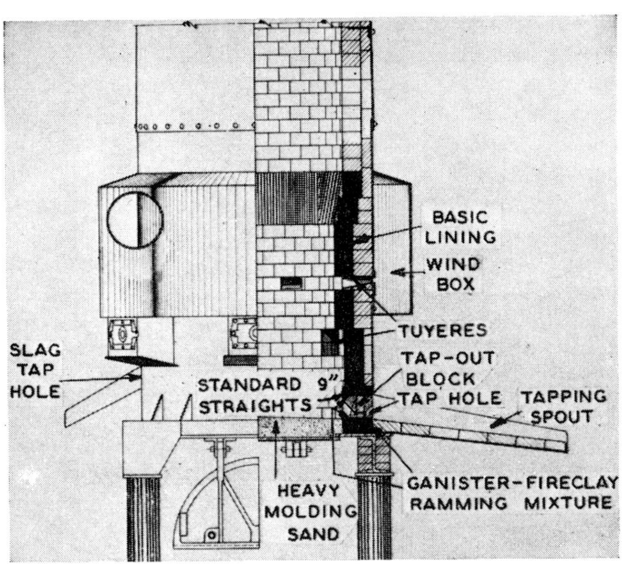

Fig. 17.6. Typical arrangement for cupola basic lining.

Limestone must be calcined into lime (CaO) before it is effective in the cupola. This calcining takes place in the area directly above the melting zone and extends into the melting zone where fluxing takes place. It is the melting zone and cupola well that must be protected against the basic slag.

Experience has shown that the best practice is to install the basic lining from the bottom plate to a height of 4 ft 6 in. to 5 ft above the tuyeres. The balance of the lining, including the bottom sand, is exactly the same as in the acid cupola. A typical lining is shown in Fig. 17.6.

The thickness of the basic lining is usually 4½ in., 6 or 9 in. Standard 9 x 4½ x 2½-in. arch brick may be used for a 4½-in. lining, special key brick for a 6 in. lining, and 9 x 4½ x 2½-in. key brick for a 9-in. lining. Another section will outline the physical properties of the basic materials, but in order to properly install basic refractories it is necessary to understand their expansion characteristics and their thermal conductivity properties.

Figures 17.7 and 17.8 show the values for the various commercially produced basic refractories. The two curves marked "I" and "II" are for chemically bonded magnesite chrome brick and high fired magnesite brick. They are most commonly used in basic installations. It is noticed that at cupola operating temperatures these refractories will expand approximately ⅛ to ¼-in./ft, and their thermal conductivity is approximately 75 per cent greater than high duty refractories.

In cupolas having less than 9 in. lining thicknesses, it is advantageous to install a 2 or 3 in. thick high duty fireclay brick course in back of the basic lining to compensate for the higher thermal conductivity. For lining thicknesses greater than 9 in., it is only necessary to substitute the basic lining for the high duty brick inner lining. Expansion joints are not provided in the well, but sometimes compressible material such as corrugated paper is placed between the lining and the shell to absorb the expansion.

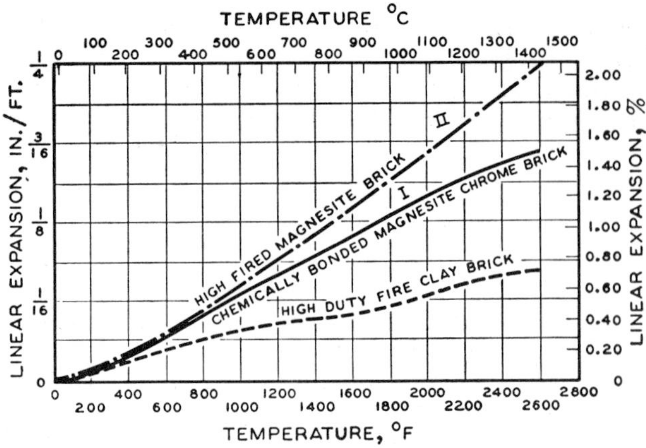

Fig. 17.7. Approximate reversible thermal expansion of refractories.

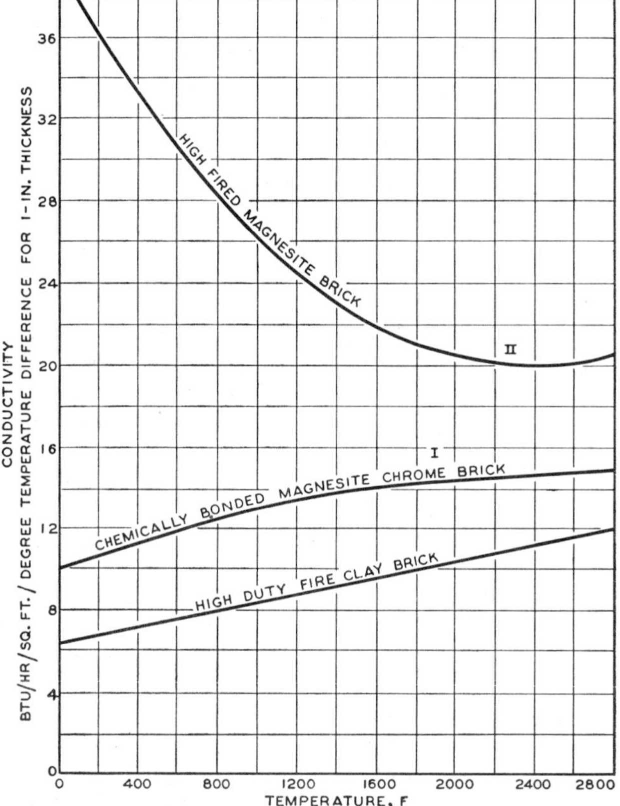

Fig. 17.8. Thermal conductivity of refractories, approximate.

In the melting zone expansion joints are provided by placing cardboard strips between the brick, both around the perimeter and vertically, allowing for an expansion rate in each direction of $\frac{3}{16}$-in./ft. For the slag hole and tap hole, high fired high magnesia or burned chrome magnesite refractories, as well as basic ramming mixes, carbon products, and silicon carbide blocks have given reasonably satisfactory, although somewhat variable, results. The basic brick linings are advantageously laid with dipped joints of air-setting high magnesia content mortar, or of air-setting chrome base mortar.

Installation Methods

Remove the old acid cupola inner or working lining from the bottom plate to a height of approximately 5 ft over the tuyeres. It will be necessary to go up to the reinforcing angle holding the upper lining in place. If 6 in. cupola blocks are removed, the special 6 in. basic keys can replace them. Standard 9 x $4\frac{1}{2}$ x $2\frac{1}{2}$-in. arch brick can be installed, which will give a $4\frac{1}{2}$-in. basic lining. Over this a $1\frac{1}{2}$-in. layer of basic patching material can be applied to bring the lining out to its original contour.

If 9-in. cupola blocks are being replaced, use standard 9 x $4\frac{1}{2}$ x $2\frac{1}{2}$-in. key brick, which will form a 9-in. lining. If a single course of 6-in. cupola blocks comprises the acid lining, install a course of 9 x $4\frac{1}{2}$ x $1\frac{1}{4}$ in. or 9 x $4\frac{1}{2}$ x 2 in. high duty fireclay straights against the steel shell, using the same mortar and procedure outlined under acid practice. A course of standard 9 x $4\frac{1}{2}$ x $2\frac{1}{2}$ in. arch brick installed against this lining will provide a $4\frac{1}{2}$ in. basic lining, and the composite lining will be the same as the thickness used in acid practice.

The basic brick must be installed with a basic mortar. The drums in which the material is shipped will be easily identified, but it is worthwhile marking the drums when they are received to prevent mistakes. Most of the mortars are shipped in dry form in moisture free steel drums. They contain a mineralizer that makes them dry hard. Be sure to mix only sufficient mortar to install about one third of the basic lining at a time. A wheelbarrow full is about the correct amount.

A clean barrow or mortar box is satisfactory to mix the mortar thoroughly with water to get a good dipping consistency. (See explanation of dipping consistency under acid linings.) Follow the same procedure outlined under acid practice until the lining is installed up to the tuyeres.

While this part of the lining is being installed, have some $\frac{1}{16}$-in. cardboard cut into strips slightly smaller than the thickness of the lining. If the brick are 9 x $4\frac{1}{2}$ x $2\frac{1}{2}$-in. arch brick and a $4\frac{1}{2}$-in. lining is being installed, the cardboard should be cut into pieces measuring $8\frac{3}{4}$ x $4\frac{1}{4}$ in. When the arch brick are set in place, the cardboard strip will fit neatly between adjacent brick.

Starting with the first course of brick above the tuyeres, expansion joints will be required since basic brick expand approximately twice as much as high duty fireclay brick. Assume that one ring of brick requires 60 pieces of 9 x $4\frac{1}{2}$ x $2\frac{1}{2}$-in. arch brick. Sixty pieces multiplied by the $2\frac{1}{2}$-in. dimension of the arch brick gives a circumference of 150 in. or $12\frac{1}{2}$-ft.

The arch brick will expand at a rate of about $\frac{3}{16}$-in./ft, or one complete ring will expand about $2\frac{3}{8}$ in. If a $\frac{1}{16}$-in. thick cardboard strip is placed between every other brick in the ring, $1\frac{7}{8}$-in. of the expansion will be provided for. The temperature of the steel shell will be at least 200 F, and the consequent expansion of the shell at this temperature will take up the balance of the brick expansion. The brick are installed in exactly the same manner outlined under acid practice, except that the cardboard strip is inserted between every other brick.

The basic brick will also expand vertically along the axis of the cupola, and this expansion must be taken into consideration or displacement of the upper lining may occur. Approximately 4 ft 6 in. of basic brick are to be installed over the tuyeres. At an expansion rate of $\frac{3}{16}$-in./ft this section of lining will expand or grow in the cupola about $\frac{7}{8}$-in.

For arch brick, 4 ft 6 in. of lining will require six courses of brick. It will, therefore, be necessary to insert two pieces of cardboard between each course of arch brick. After the first ring is completely installed over the tuyeres, lay the cardboard around the top of the ring and then set the next course on top.

After the final course of basic brick has been installed, replace the high heat duty brick rings up to the support ring. The lining must be thoroughly dried before the first heat is made. Correct drying procedure is outlined later in the chapter.

Tap Holes and Slag Holes

The slag hole can be a refractory block or it can be rammed up with a basic ramming mix, but one of the best materials in use is silicon carbide. It is neutral to the slag whether it is acid or basic. This is a very important consideration since many cupola operations which are supposedly basic are in actuality acid.

High silicon loss coupled with high lining loss are good indicators of this condition. The block can be inserted into the lining, using carbon paste, and the area around the slag hole, including all brick 1 ft on either side and two courses above and below, should be coated with a 1-in. layer. The carbon paste as received must be heated to make it plastic. Follow the manufacturer's recommendations carefully.

The tap hole need not be troublesome, although this is usually the weak spot in the lining. Use a high fired chrome magnesite brick (9 x 4½ x 3-in. straight) and build a box or breast wall around the tap hole. Use one course of these brick to span over the top hole opening, and cement every brick into place with the same mortar being used to lay the balance of the basic lining.

It may be necessary to cut the first brick along each side of the breast wall as in the procedure outlined for building an acid lined tap hole. After the breast and the wall have been built, insert a pipe of the desired tap hole diameter from the outside of the cupola and center it in the tap hole area. Coat the entire inner surface of this area with a very thin slurry of the basic mortar and ram around the pipe with a basic ramming mix.

The ramming mixes are dead-burned dolomite mixed with magnesite, or straight magnesite ground and sized, for maximum ramming density. They contain a mineralizer which imparts a good air-set to the material after it is rammed in place. Keep moisture to a minimum, never exceeding 10 per cent. The ramming mix can be prepared in a clean mortar box and requires only the addition of water. When properly mixed it should feel like damp molding sand. After the rammed tap hole has been dried for about 12 hr, the pipe can be removed and a burner set in place to give it a good ceramic set.

Cupola operators wishing to experiment with basic practice can do so by gunning about 2 in. of basic ramming mix over their acid lining. They will have to revise their slag hole and tap hole practice to comform with basic practice as outlined previously. This has been a very economical method used by many foundries to study basic practice under actual operating conditions. Where a gun is not available, a course of 9 x 4½ x 1¼-in. splits mortared over the acid lining has been satisfactory.

Daily Maintenance

Three general methods are being used for maintenance by patching. These are as follows:

1) Allow the lining to be slagged back until there is sufficient space for patching with a 9 x 4½ x 2½ in. straight brick laid with a high magnesia content mortar.
2) Hand patch after each day's operation with a basic ramming mixture. This mixture can be rammed to a dense monolith. Patching materials composed of fireclay and carbon have been used to advantage in wells and slag holes.
3) By means of an air-placement gun, various basic gun mixtures can be used for daily maintenance. The installation procedure is similar to the acid air placement operation discussed in Chapter 21.

General Considerations

1) When the basic lining is installed, a brush coating of high magnesia content mortar or ½ to 1½-in. of basic patch or basic gun emplacement material provides protection to the lining and minimizes wear during the first heat.
2) The same bottom sand used in acid operation can be used for basic operation. However, if a small basic heat is being made, it may be necessary to tamp a ½-in. layer of basic ramming mix over the bottom sand to maintain the basicity of the slag. For long heats or continuous operation, a basic material in the bottom is undesirable since it sets up very hard. This can interfere with the drop.
3) Gas or oil burners should be placed in the cupola after the basic lining is installed; or a wood fire will serve the purpose. Depending upon lining thickness, it will require from 8 hr to a day to thoroughly dry the lining, to establish satisfactory temperature equilibrium through the basic brick, and to allow the initial expansion to take place. This is a proper safeguard against thermal spalling of the basic refractories when the cupola is initially operated.
   Adherence to a thorough drying procedure will help prevent disintegration of magnesite and chemically bonded basic brick containing free magnesia. These refractories may slake when subjected to the action of steam. If ramming mixes are used to form tap holes or slag holes, a separate burner should be used for complete drying.
4) The cost of a basic lining is approximately three times that of a regular high duty fireclay brick lining. It is therefore important to study fully the economics of basic cupola operation.

MONOLITHIC LININGS

Introduction

Many cupola operators apply refractories by the air placement or "gunning" method. This process

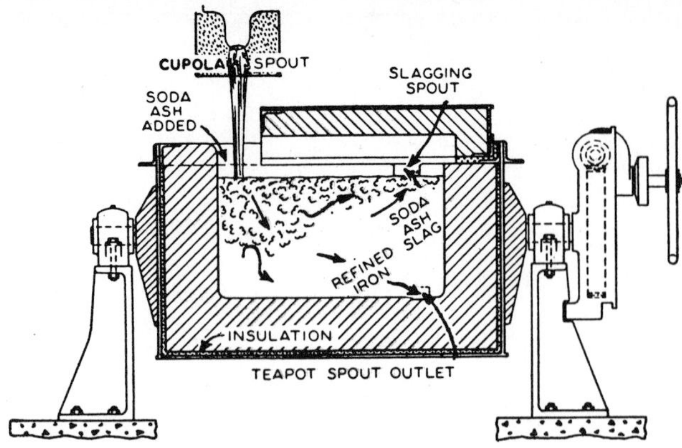

Fig. 17.9. U-shaped ladle is example of tilting type forehearth adaptable to desulfurizing practice.

takes its name from the fact that the refractories are forced onto the cupola wall by a piece of equipment that is air operated.

Equipment

This equipment, commonly referred to as a "gun," includes a feed hopper and pressure hopper. Dry refractory material is placed in the upper or feed hopper and introduced into the pressure hopper at regular intervals. The refractory mixture is swept by air through a feed hose to the nozzle of the gun. The nozzle is specially constructed in that it has a ring through which water is forced into the stream of dry material coming from the pressure chamber. The operator at the nozzle has a control valve which regulates the amount of water.

Acid Refractories

The composition of the air-placed refractory material is essentially the same as that used in hand patching, i.e., a mixture of fire clay and silica. In gun mixtures it is important that the fireclay portion has the ability to absorb water very rapidly. Since the dry refractory mixture and water are in contact for only a fraction of a second before striking the cupola wall, the clay must develop sufficient plasticity in this brief period to adhere to the wall and form a bed for the silica portion of the mix.

It is likewise important that the fire clay have good refractoriness. Finally, the sizing of the various ingredients must be carefully controlled in order to insure maximum density of the air placed material. Because of the necessity of close control over the various ingredients, most operators find it more economical to obtain gun mixes from refractory manufactures rather than making their own.

Application

Before applying a gunned patch, it is necessary to remove all slag and loose particles adhering to the refractory lining. Care must be exercised when removing such material not to break through the glazed finish of the existing refractory lining. This finish provides a good, strong base for the adherence of the patch. It is likewise important to provide proper support for the new patch before beginning the gunning operation (Fig. 17.5).

It must be remembered that the patching material requires considerable heat before vitrification takes place. At temperatures lower than the vitrification point the mixture has low strength, and any undue burden could destroy the patch. A ledge for the support of the patch is provided by the tuyere plate or a row of cupola block immediately above the tuyeres.

For proper placement of the gunned patch it is necessary that both air and water pressures be adequate. Low pressures may result in a low-density patch.

During the air placement of a refractory material, the operator must keep four principles in mind. First, it is important that he keep the nozzle of the gun at the proper distance from the wall. It has been found by experience that best results are obtained when the nozzle is kept between 2 and 3 ft from the cupola wall. Second, the operator must keep proper water control. Shooting too dry will result in excessive dusting and high rebounds. If the patch is too wet, it will slump or result in excessive burn-out because of loss of density. The third important principle of the gunning operation is the angle at which the operator holds the nozzle.

Rebounds are kept to a minimum when the nozzle is kept at right angles to the patch. Any deviation from the 90° angle results in a loss of particle impact and should be avoided. Finally, the operator should avoid the formation of laminations which are parallel to the hot face of the patch. Such laminations usually result in spalling and, of course, poor service life from the patch. This effect can be avoided by shooting downward and building the patch from the tuyere upwards. If this procedure is followed all laminations will be at an angle to the hot face, resulting in a more serviceable lining.

ACID LININGS — AUXILIARY EQUIPMENT

The important auxiliary equipment requiring refractory linings are spouts, forehearths, covers, transfer ladles, and holding furnaces.

Troughs and Spouts

Slag spouts for short heats require only a layer of 2 to 3 in. of a rammed ganister fireclay mixture. Where heats are long, mixtures of high duty fireclay and graphite, in plastic form, can be pounded into place and formed into any desired contour and thickness. A back-up lining of fire brick may be used to reduce the amount of plastic required.

The runout spout can vary in length from a few feet to 10 ft or more when tapping into receiving or transfer ladles. Generally, the spout is an open boxlike structure in which 9 x 4½ x 1¼-in. straights or 9 x 4½ x 2½-in. straights are set against the steel sides and bottom.

These brick can be either intermediate duty or high duty refractories, but a good general rule is to use the same quality that is stocked for cupola or ladle maintenance. This can simplify refractory inventory control. Over the refractories a ramming material should be applied to a thickness of 2 in. or more, depending on the length of the heat. Long heats may require 3 in. or more ramming material. The patching material used in the cupola can be applied to the spout.

However, if a gun emplacement material is used in the cupola, the material, as received, will not

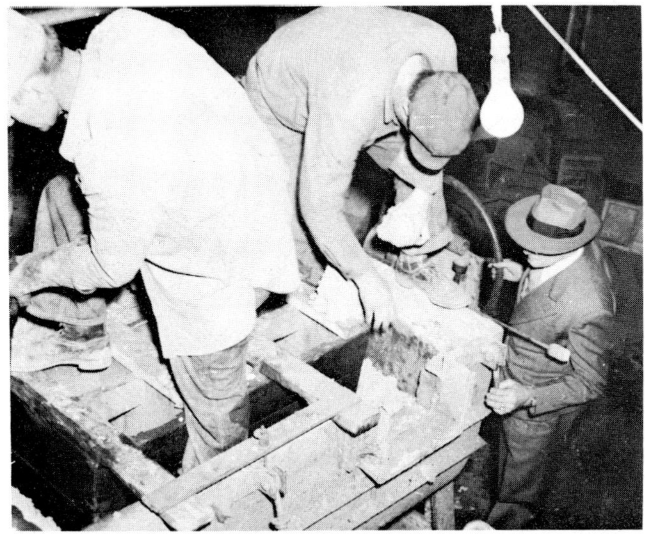

Fig. 17.10. Lining a U-shaped ladle with super duty plastic refractory using a form and pneumatic rammer. (Ironton Fire Brick Co., Ironton, Ohio.)

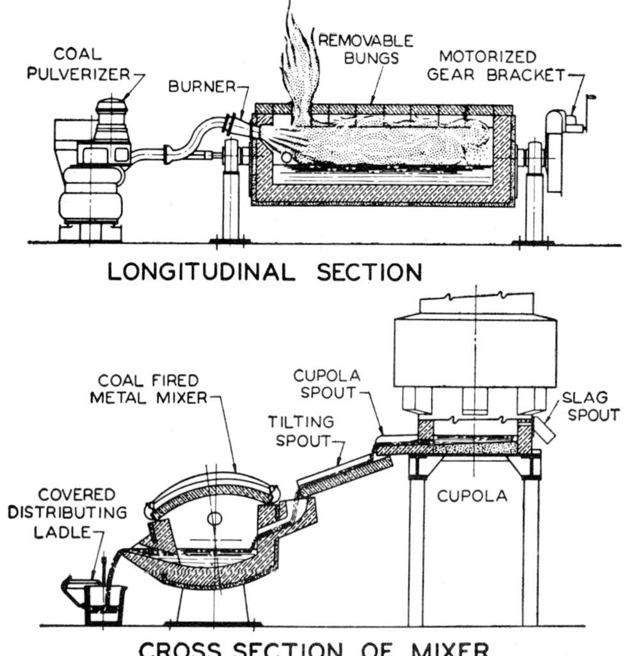

Fig. 17.11. Fuel fired forehearth or holding furnace requires refractories according to the melting and desulfurizing practices employed. (Whiting Corp., Harvey, Ill.)

work satisfactorily in the spout. It should be mixed with 12 to 13 per cent water, preferably in a sand muller or a lean mortar box. Cover with wet sacks and let it set overnight. The next day cut it off in slabs and tamp into place with a mallet.

Front Slagging Cupola Troughs

As the name implies, both the slag and the metal are tapped from the working side of a front slagging cupola. This is a very advantageous arrangement for continuous operation. A typical cross section of a front slagging cupola spout is illustrated in Fig. 2.7, page 21. Since hot metal continually is in contact with the refractories in a front slagger, dense, high duty refractories are necessary.

The Forehearth

A forehearth is a vessel interposing the cupola spout and the pouring ladle (Chapter 5, page 48).

Of the two types, the stationary and the tilting types, the stationary is disappearing from use in foundries and the tilting type (mixing ladle) is most commonly used.

The desulfurizing forehearth shown in Fig. 5.2 is the most common of the stationary type used in present times. This forehearth lends itself well to continuous desulfurizing practice in continuous flow systems. The elongated U-shaped ladle, Fig. 17.9, is the most popular of the tilting type forehearths, and also serves well for desulfurizing practice.

The refractory lining for the forehearth will depend on the intended use of the forehearth. For holding purposes a dense, high duty refractory lining is quite adequate, providing temperatures are not high. When hot metal is required or when desulfurizing with soda ash is practical, a dense, super-duty refractory may be necessary. If the forehearth is rectangular, standard size brick can be used.

The procedure outlined for cupola refractory installations will act as a guide in installing the forehearth refractories (Fig. 17.12). In most cases the refractory supplier will be able to supply a standard size whether the forehearth is rectangular or circular. An important point is to keep the mortar joints to a minimum thickness. Review the procedure for preparing a mortar for dipped joints and follow this procedure when installing the forehearth refractories. After each brick is dipped, slide the contacting surfaces together to remove entrapped air and then tap firmly.

Super-duty refractories in plastic form are also extensively used for lining forehearths. These materials (some impregnated with graphite) are shipped in cardboard cartons and are ready for use. To apply them the only tools required are a hand rammer, or preferably, an air ram. The material can be molded into any shape or form and to any thickness desired. It is best to work from the bottom up, applying the material in layers.

It is best to ram perpendicularly to the patch, maintaining the ram at a 45° angle with the horizontal. This will prevent over-ramming any particular layer and the entire lining will be more uniform. If a cover is used over the forehearth, it can be rammed in the same manner. If it is over 18 in. in diameter or 18 x 18 in. square, some metal or refractory anchorage should be provided to hold the material in place. The refractory supplier can offer assistance if necessary (Fig. 17.10).

The holding furnace is a fuel-fired forehearth, of large capacity, that provides the foundrymen with a means to obtain greater metal temperature and composition control than is possible in the conventional unfired forehearths. The refractories in these furnaces are usually super-duty quality or high alumina.

The choice depends a great deal on the metallurgy being employed, the nature of the slag, particularly the amount of desulfurizing agent used, and the tem-

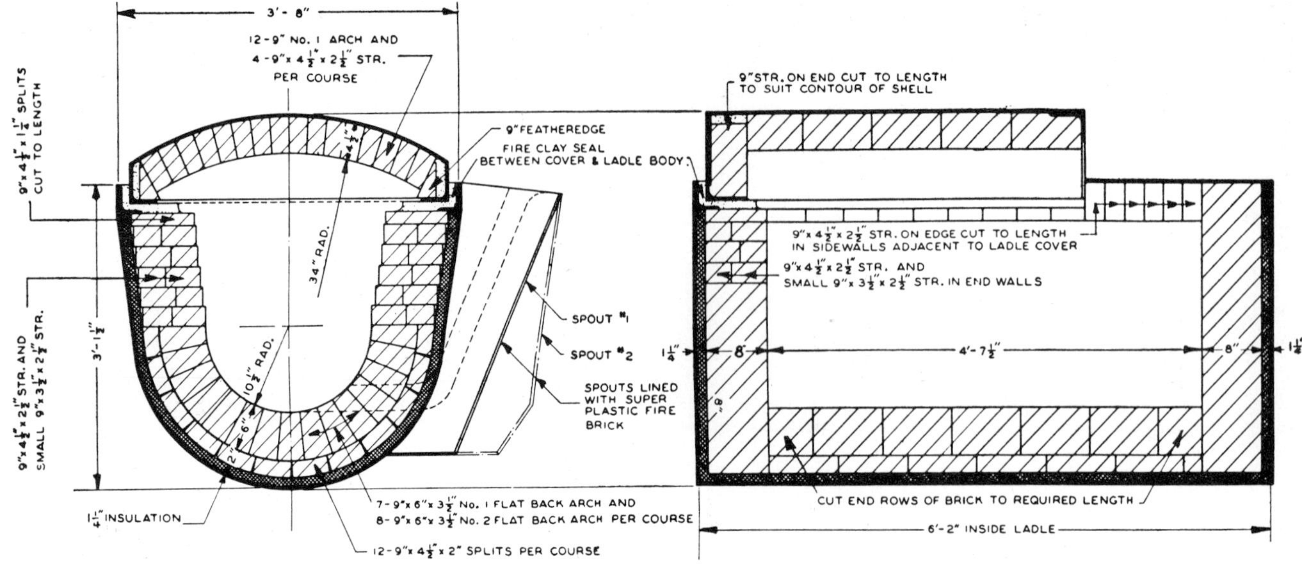

20"X 74" LADLE - 9¼" LINING

BRICK COUNT FOR LINING LADLE

Location	No. Brick Required	Description
Ladle Cover	60	9x4½x2½ No. 1 Arch
	36	9x4½x2½ Straights
	10	9x4½x2½ Featheredge
Alternate Cover Lining	775 lb	Super Plastic Fire Brick
Ladle Body	185	9x4½x2½ Straights
	170	9x3½x2½ Straights
	30	9x4½x1¼ Splits
	80	9x4½x2 Splits
	49	9x6x3½ No. 1 Flat-back Arch
	56	9x6x3½ No. 2 Flat-back Arch
	340 lb	Super Plastic Fire Brick, Spout No. 1
	480 lb	Super Plastic Fire Brick, Spout No. 2
	280 lb	High Temperature Cement
	220	9x4½x1¼ Splits Insulating Fire Brick

Fig. 17.12. Brick count and application of refractory lining in U-shaped ladle. (North American Refractories Co., Cleveland.)

perature of the metal. Since the refractories required are more costly than the usual foundry refractories, it is suggested that the refractories supplier be consulted.

A typical lining is illustrated in Fig. 17.11. When the brands are selected for the furnace, the installation procedure is the same as illustrated in the cupola lining discussion. In this furnace it is especially important that the joints of the working lining be held to an absolute minimum of thickness. The joints are the weak spots in the lining, and agents such as fluorspar will attack them quickly.

Transfer Ladles

This is a general title covering a large variety of ladles of the lip-pour and teapot-spout design. They generally are circular or oval in design, and are used for transporting metal from the cupola or forehearth to the mold.

The quality of the refractories for the transfer ladles is the same as for the cupola. Standard 9 in. arch brick or cupola blocks can be used, but the most popular lining materials are silica clay ramming mixes and plastic refractories containing graphite (Fig. 17.14). When the latter materials are used, they must be thoroughly dried by means of a gas burner or some other external heat source. One excellent way to do this is to build a 9 in. wall of high duty refractory, high enough to reach over the largest ladle when it is set on its side.

Burner openings are built in the center of the wall, using either 9 in. arch brick to form a circular opening or lintel tile such as 13½ x 9 x 2½-in. straights to form a square opening, or a special burner block may be required for a particular type of burner. The ladles are set on their sides against the wall, centering them with the burner openings. The burners are set in the wall from the other side. This arrangement will conserve the heat and concentrate it on the ladle lining (Fig. 17.13).

Fig. 17.13. Wall type heater for drying ladle linings. (Hauck Mfg. Co., Chicago.)

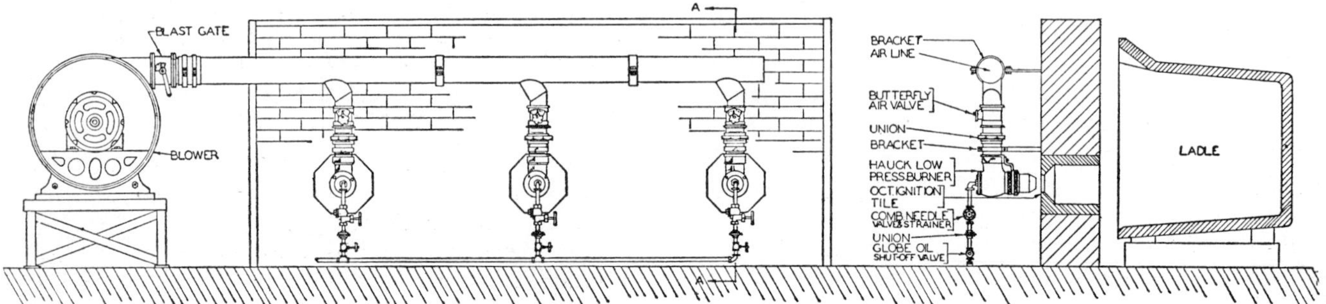

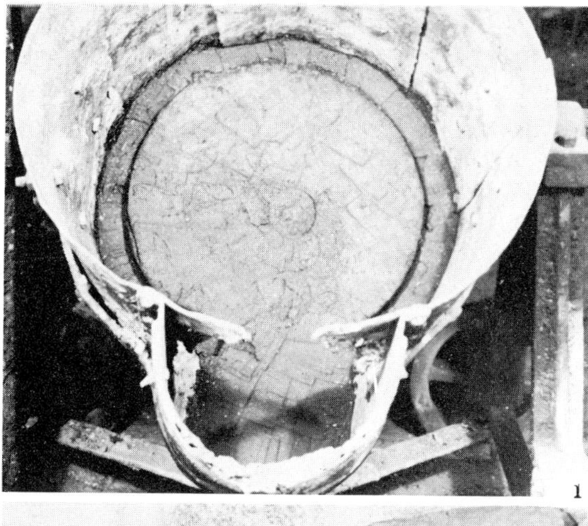

Fig. 17.14. *Procedure in lining ladle with plastic firebrick materials.* Bottom is tamped in (top *left*) leaving trench around outside edge. Slices (above) are placed in vertical position along sides, settled tightly in trench to provide sealed joint, and solidly tamped to contour of ladle to make smooth rounded surface.

. . . Peen joints (top *right*) to form valleys where slices abut. Tamp narrow strips into valleys (above) to obtain lining thickness and to seal joints against metal penetration. . .

. . Taper top edge; tamp in fillet between sidewall and bottom to form tight seal. . . .

. . Fashion pouring spout same way; build bridge across spout to form skimmer. Do not trowel smooth, but roughen entire lining surface to permit surface drying. After drying, apply ladle wash. *Mexico (Mo.) Refractories Co.*

To convert a lip pour ladle into a teapot ladle can be done economically. Figure 17.15 shows an easy, inexpensive method. The spout is made from regular high duty firebrick runner tile cut in half. The size tile depends on the stream of metal wanted.

When the cross-sectional area has been established, select a runner tile whose diameter gives an effective area at least double the required spout area. It should be remembered that sufficient free or open area must be retained between the ladle bottom lining and the

Fig. 17.15. Lip type ladle is converted to teapot type by embedding pouring tile in plastic ladle lining. (Laclede-Christy Co., St. Louis.)

lowest tile to permit free flow through the spout. The runner tile can be embedded in the sidewall lining and sealed with plastic fireclay or a thick mixture of air-setting bonding mortar.

The joints between the tile should be filled with an air set mortar, and the entire assembly can be brush-coated with a thin slurry of the bonding mortar. The entire assembly should be thoroughly dried before use. This is very important since the runner brick will absorb some of the moisture from the bedding mortar.

In addition to lining and repairing the cupola, the air-placement gun can be used to maintain the refractory linings in the spout and ladles. The refractory mixture described in the foregoing for cupola patching is also used in these applications.

When gunning the spout, the operation should begin at the end nearest the cupola. The gun should be kept in a constant left to right motion. As the trough is built up to the desired thickness, the gun is moved toward the outer end of the spout. All of the precautions mentioned for the cupola must be observed in gunning the spout.

The air placement of refractory linings in ladles is usually accomplished in two steps. Most foundries have found that the job is facilitated by gunning the bottom first and then the sidewalls. Where possible, the ladle should be turned on its side to gun the bottom. When this is done, the procedure already described is followed. After the bottom has been completed the sidewalls are installed with the ladle setting in the upright position.

TABLE 17.1. REFRACTORY CLASSIFICATION

Classification according to chemical nature and mineralogical composition

Chemical Nature	Mineralogical Composition	
Acid	Fire Clay	I) Fabricated Refractories (Fired or Unfired)
	Low Duty	A) Brick and Tile
	Intermediate Duty	a) Refractory
	High Duty	b) Insulating
	Super Duty	B) Special Tile & Shapes
	Special Super Duty	a) Refractory
	Alumina-Diaspore Series	b) Insulating
	50% Alumina	II) Monolithic Refractories
	60% Alumina	A) Mortars
	70% Alumina	a) Wet or dry
	80% Alumina	b) Air setting or heat setting
	90% Alumina	B) Coatings
	Kaolin	a) Wet
	Mullite	b) Dry
	Zircon	C) Castables
	Silica	a) Refractory
	Silicon Carbide	b) Insulating
Basic	Magnesia	D) Plastics and Ramming Materials
	Forsterite	a) Wet or Dry
	Spinel	b) Heat setting or high strength
Neutral	Chrome	
	Fused Alumina	
	Carbon	

REFRACTORY TYPES

Refractories are essential, not only to the foundry industry, but indeed to all industry. Without refractories, there would be no heat, light or power. There would indeed be no metals, no manufacturing, no transportation as they are known in modern industrial civilization.

Refractories are often defined as non-metallic structural materials that have the ability to resist destructive forces at high temperatures. These destructive forces may be abrasion, physical abuse, destructive slag or chemical attack, but always temperature is the common denominator in most refractory applications since destructive forces vary, often directly, with temperature.

There is no perfect refractory. Scores of refractory products are produced, each differing from the other in essential respects to meet that diversity of destructive forces imposed by modern furnace technology.

Ultimate success and economy in the use of refractories are predicated upon a comprehensive knowledge of refractory materials — their chemical, mineralogical, and physical properties, behavior under a wide variety of destructive forces, and the technology of their application.

CLASSIFICATION

In order to study refractories effectively, it is necessary to arrive at some method of classification. Many methods have been used. We shall base our classification on:

a) Chemical or metallurgical behavior.
b) Mineralogical constitution.
c) Physical form.

Table 17.1 classifies by these methods.

Chemical or Metallurgical Behavior

A metallurgical acid is defined as the oxide of a metalloid. The principal acids are silica (SiO_2) and phosphorus pentoxide (P_2O_5). A metallurgical base is defined as the oxide of a metal. The important bases are lime (CaO), magnesia (MgO), and the several oxides of iron.

Just as acids and bases in wet chemistry react to form salts, so acidic and basic refractories react to form compounds called slags:

$FeO + SiO_2$ .... $FeSiO_3$
$CaO + SiO_2$ .... $CaSiO_3$

It becomes at once apparent that the word refractory refers to use or application as much as to material. Environment then defines a refractory. Silica, alumina, and magnesia are excellent refractories, but in other environments may act as potent fluxes. Dolomite is used as a flux in blast furnaces – as a refractory in open hearths. In the same way, dolomite is used as a flux in the conventional cupola but as a refractory in the basic lined cupola which has been receiving so much recent attention. It might also be pointed out that in a boiler carbon is a fuel, but in the modern blast furnace or cupola it serves as a refractory.

In using this chemical classification, we are not unmindful of recent developments that tend to make these distinctions academic. We refer to the use and behavior of the family of spinels, particularly those containing magnesite and chrome, and the still more recent application of acid and basic refractories in combination (zebra construction) in open hearth steel furnace arches.

Mineralogical Constitution

Mineralogical composition is based on the essential constituent of raw material from which the refractory is manufactured. Such a constituent may be a chemical element (carbon), a compound (silicon carbide), an oxide (silica), or a combination of oxides (zircon or forsterite).

Chemical composition is of limited value in determining the commercial utility of refractories. Refractories of almost identical composition may differ widely in behavior. Chemical analyses are of value in control of raw materials and products, serve as a basis for classification, and do give an indication of melting behavior. Standard procedures for making chemical analyses have been worked out by the American Society for Testing Materials.

Most refractories are oxides or a mixture of oxides, along with accessory materials or impurities. Their basic behavior is a function of the mineral constituents, and ultimate behavior is based on a thermo-chemical-mineralogical relationship.

Over half of all refractories used are those of the fire-clay group, which are essentially a mixture of the oxides of silica (SiO_2) and alumina (Al_2O_3).

Physical Form

To make our classification more useful, we have incorporated that division which we have elected to call "physical form." In our definition of refractories, we might have been more explicit by referring to refractories as non-metallic structural materials – "in a variety of physical or commercial forms to make them applicable for use in furnace structures." It should be pointed out that the many mineralogical compositions can be manufactured in a variety of physical or commercial forms to facilitate their application. For example, fire-clay refractories of essentially the same chemical and mineralogical nature may be furnished in the form of brick and tile, mortars, coating materials, castables, plastics, etc.

All these mineralogical compositions, available in so many physical forms, make for a great variety of products. Multiply this by the brand names of numerous manufacturers and it is at once obvious why a logical method of classification is a must.

Classification is summarized by Table 17.2 tabulating the physical properties of refractories produced as brick and tile. These properties and their relation to foundry applications will be discussed.

METHODS OF REFRACTORY CONSTRUCTION

Refractory construction is classified according to material used and method applied, as:

1) Solid masonry construction
2) Suspended masonry
3) Monolithic construction

All three have a very definite place in the scheme of refractory application. Selection of method is determined by type of installation, service conditions, and many other factors. We will summarize briefly the development and evaluation of these methods in the light of modern refractory technology.

Solid Masonry

Solid masonry is the term used to describe a refractory structure or enclosure constructed of prefired refractory brick and shapes. Solid masonry construction had its inception in medieval times. Its origin and development unquestionably paralleled building construction methods through the centuries. It is little wonder that solid masonry and refractory construction should come to be thought of synonymously. This correlation persisted until some 40 years ago. It still persists in the mind of the layman.

Solid masonry has met the challenge of time. It is still the most used form of construction. For some types of applications, it still remains the best suited method. This is particularly true in metallurgical applications.

The conventional method of lining a cupola from top to bottom with standard cupola blocks and 9 in. series shapes is a typical solid masonry installation.

The use of insulating fire brick and insulating brick permitted many types of composite wall construction, resulting in better performance from solid masonry.

The standard shapes (or series) are more numerous and versatile than one may realize. The standard series are more economical, more readily available, and usually possess superior physical properties as compared to special shapes. Manufacturers' literature shows the almost unlimited variety of shapes available, as well as tables indicating the various ways and

TABLE 17.2. PROPERTIES OF REFRACTORIES[1]

[1]Hensen, W. H., "Special Refractories for Metal Melting," AFS Transactions, vol. 55 (1947).

Class	Type of Brick	Composition	P.C.E. or Fusion Point	True Specific Gravity	Approx. Weight in lbs. 9" Brick	Linear Coefficient of Expansion per °C	Thermal Conductivity BTU/Hr./-Sq.Ft./In./°F.*	Mean Specific Heat (cgs)	Deformation Under Load 25#/sq. in.	Constancy of Volume	Remarks
ACID	Silica	SiO_2 95–96%	31–33 Cone	2.3–2.4	6	See (A) Below	13.0 390–1832°F	0.265 70–1832°F	No deformation at 2732°F, 50psi	Low Shrinkage. Rev.† exp. to Melting Point	Strongly resistant to acid slags. Readily attacked by basic materials and fluorides.
ACID	High Heat Duty Fire Brick	Al_2O_3 35–42% SiO_2 52–60%	31–33 Cone	2.60–2.70	7½-8	53 x 10^{-7} 20 – 1200°C	400–2400°F 9.5	0.26 70°–1830°F	4.0+% @ 2460°F	2.0% Shrink. @ 2550°F	Rapidly attacked by basic slags, particularly iron slags. Moderately resistant to acid slags.
ACID	Super Duty Fire Brick	Al_2O_3 43–44% SiO_2 51–53%	33–34 Cone	2.65–2.75	7½–8	53 x 10^{-7} 20 – 1200°C	Approx. same as High Heat Duty	Approx. same as High Heat Duty	2.5 to 4.0% @ 2460°F	1% Max. Shrink. at 2732°F	
ACID	High Alumina Fire Brick	Al_2O_3 50–80%	34–39 Cone	2.80–3.40	8–9	53 – 65 x 10^{-7} 20 – 1425°C	Slightly more than High Heat Duty	Approx. same as High Heat Duty	Approx. same as Super Duty	0–3% Shrink. @ 2912°F	More resistant to alkali slags than fire clay brick; readily attacked by iron slags.
ACID	Kaolin	Al_2O_3 44–45% SiO_2 51–53%	31–34 Cone	2.60	7½–8	53 x 10^{-7} 20 – 1425°C	13.5 @2400°F	0.254 480–1832°F	1% @ 2800°F	0.5% Shrinkage @ 3000°F	Slightly more resistant than fire brick to slags, particularly basic slags.
ACID	Mullite	Al_2O_3 62% SiO_2 38%	38 Cone	3.03	8½	45 x 10^{-7} 20 – 1320°C	8.5 200–2600°F	0.175 70°–1475°F	0 @ 2650°F., 50 psi: 2.0% @ 3000°F, 50 psi	No appreciable change to 3000°F	Low solubility in glasses and some slags. Attacked by high iron slags.
ACID	Zircon	ZrO_2 67.1% SiO_2 32.9%	approx. 4400°F	4.6	12	42 x 10^{-7} 20 – 1550°C	13.5 390°–1832°F	0.132 100°F	Fails @ 2820°–2910°F	No appreciable change to 2820°F	Not readily attacked by acid slags. Readily attacked by basic slags and fluorides.
ACID	Silicon Carbide	SiC 89–91%	dissoc. @4082°F	3.13–3.22	9.5	45 x 10^{-7} 20 – 1100°C	66.0 @2000°F	0.186 70–1832°F	No deformation to 2732°F, 50 psi	No Shrinkage to 2732°F	Readily attacked by strongly basic slags, particularly those high in iron or calcium oxides.
NEUTRAL	Graphite	C 100%	above 5432°F	2.25	8	20 x 10^{-7} 20 – 1000°C	220. @ 2000°F	0.29 70–1832°F	None	No Shrinkage	Strongly resistant to all slags except those containing oxides readily reduced.
NEUTRAL	Chrome	Cr_2O_3 30–45% Al_2O_3 15–33% SiO_2 11–17% FeO 3–6%	3550–4000°F	3.8–4.1	11	80 x 10^{-7} 20 – 1000°C	12.1 @2400°F	0.22 @ 1832°F	No deformation @ 2600°F	1.3% Shrinkage at 2820°F	Neutral properties. Not readily attacked by acid or basic slags.
NEUTRAL	Fused Alumina	Al_2O_3 90–99.1%	38–41 Cone	3.80–4.00	11	70 x 10^{-7} 20 – 1000°C	18.0–20.0 @ 2000°F	0.174–0.304 32°–1832°F	1–2% @ 2732°F, 50 psi	No Shrinkage at 2732°F	Very resistant to acid slags, moderately resistant to basic slags; tendency to absorb.
BASIC	Forsterite	MgO 57.3% SiO_2 42.7%	40 Cone	3.3–3.4	9	110 x 10^{-7} 20 – 1500°C	10.3 @ 2400°F	0.22 70–200°F	No deformation to 2732°F, 50 psi	Negligible Shrinkage to 3000°F	Not readily attacked by basic slags; readily attacked by acid slags.
BASIC	Magnesia-Alumina Spinel	MgO 28.2% Al_2O_4 71.8%	3875°F	3.6	10	80 x 10^{-7} 20 – 800°C	14.5 @ 2400°F	0.25 70–1832°F			Moderate resistance to basic slags; low resistance to acid slags. Magnesia spinel sometimes shows slag absorption.
BASIC	Magnesite (Dead Burned)	MgO 83–93% Fe_2O_3 2–7%	3992°F	3.4–3.6	9½	147 x 10^{-7} 20 – 1425°C	13. 2400°F	0.278 70–1832°F	Poor load bearing property above 2450°F	No Shrinkage below 2900°F	Not readily attacked by basic slags; readily attacked by acid slags.
BASIC	Magnesia (Electrically fused)	MgO 94–96% SiO_2 2–3% CaO 1–2%	3992–4532°F	3.60	10	150 x 10^{-7} 20 – 1475°C	20.0 2000°F	0.292 32–2375°F	Poor load bearing property above 2732°F	Less than 1% below 3250°F	

* To change BTU units to C.G.S. units divide by 2903

(A) 430 x 10^{-7}, 20 - 300°C, 30 x 10^{-7}, 300 - 1100°C.

† Reversible

means of using these shapes in refractory structures. Design is simplified and performance enhanced by utilizing the available data.

The greatest advance in solid masonry, however, has been due to improved products. Refractory brick and tile have greater uniformity. Dimensional tolerances are much closer. Of even more importance, however, were the improvements possible in solid masonry by the refractory industry's progress in the development of mortars and coatings for service needs.

Suspended Construction

Suspended construction is the term used to describe a refractory structure or enclosure in which prefired brick and tile are assembled and held in place by suitably designed steel supports and suspension. Some 40 years ago the demand for improved construction methods that would permit greater latitude in the design of refractory enclosures led to the development of suspended construction. Initially this development was in the form of special tile and methods of suspending arches over fireboxes and grates where solid masonry was difficult. This led to the ultimate use of suspended refractory construction for complete refractory enclosures.

Monolithic Construction

Monolithic construction is a broad term used to describe any refractory structure or enclosure which is constructed to required form or shape by using monolithic type refractory materials (castables, plastics and ramming materials). Such enclosures, instead of being constructed by fabricated brick or shapes laid up by masons (solid masonry), are formed to required shape by casting or ramming as a monolithic.

Monolithic construction methods are finding greatly increased use in modern refractory practices. 'Monolithic construction has benefited by the many developments in the application of castables, plastics, and ramming materials. These products were first used as maintenance materials, but are now employed in a multitude of combinations in complete furnace enclosures.

Monolithic enclosures may employ castables which are mixed and poured like concrete or applied by gun placement. Plastics and ramming materials may be placed by ramming (hand or air hammer) or by gun placement. The hand placed daubing or the gun placed siliceous repairs in the melting zone of a cupola are good examples of monolithic installations.

Such monolithic enclosures include refractory and insulating castable enclosures as used in heat treating and annealing furnaces, castable and plastic combination boiler enclosures, acidic or basic lined cupolas, whether hand or gün placed.

WHAT REFRACTORIES DO IN THE CUPOLA

To answer this question we must study the behavior of refractories. There is no one perfect refractory. Each will react differently to the destructive actions imposed by industrial operating conditions. Choice will depend upon many factors and how a particular product will behave. The operating conditions might be summarized as:

1) Confining
2) Heating
3) Stressing
4) Melting
5) Fluxing
6) Disintegrating
7) Spalling

Confining

The primary purpose of the refractory lining in the cupola is to confine — to form an enclosure that confines the raw materials and the introduced heat of the process.

Heating

Heating incorporates a closely related and simultaneous combination of thermal effects. Heat energy generated flows into the refractory. Part of it is conducted through the refractory and lost to the surroundings by radiation and convection. Part of the heat energy is stored in the refractory. Part is radiated back into the cupola. The heat conducted through the wall is a function of the thermal conductivity of the refractory. Thermal conductivity is expressed in BTU per sq ft, per hr, per degree F, per in. thickness — generally referred to as "K" factor. Thermal conductivity varies with the nature of the material from which the refractory is made, the method of manufacture, physical structure (porosity) and temperature. Heat stored in a refractory is based on the weight, mean specific heat, and temperature change.

As refractories are heated they expand, and when cooled, contract. This effect is known as reversible thermal expansion. It introduces stresses on the refractory structure.

These stresses must be provided for in a cupola. Cupola shells have been ruptured by blocks laid too tightly against the shell.

In addition to these stresses, permanent dimensional changes may occur at high temperatures, as indicated by the reheat behavior described later in the chapter.

Melting

The melting behavior of fire clay refractories can be predicted on the basis of thermal equilibrium relationships of silica and alumina, previously described. The P. C. E. (pyrometric cone equivalent) value further indicates melting behavior.

In burning or firing fire-clay refractories a certain amount of glass is developed. At low temperatures this glass serves as a bond. This glass retains its rigidity to temperatures about 2000 F, after which the glass loses some rigidity and begins to act as a viscous liquid. This change is slow, however, and over a wide range of temperature the viscosity of the glass is so high that for all practical purposes it acts as if it were solid. Through this range the refractory will deform only if stressed. This particular phase of heating is best studied by hot-load tests.

With further heating the glass becomes more fluid and the brick sags. With still further heating the glass dissolves the solid or crystalline portion remaining, until melting is complete.

Melting refractories in the cupola is partly due to the high temperatures. Like other refractory failures, however, the temperature alone is only partly the cause of failure.

Fluxing

Fluxing is closely associated with melting behavior. The interaction of the mineral and glassy components of fire-clay refractories might in itself be termed fluxing. In general, however, fluxing refers to the chemical reaction between refractory and extraneous substances (liquid or solid). Fluxing action (or slag attack) is a function of many factors such as temperature, furnace atmosphere, chemical and mineralogical composition of refractory, physical structure and porosity of refractory, composition of flux, fluidity of flux, availability (mass action) of flux, etc.

In the cupola the "fluxing" action of the limestone, dirt on the sprue, ash in the coke, etc., at the temperatures encountered are largely responsible for melting zone failures.

TABLE 17.3. TEMPERATURE END POINTS OF AMERICAN PYROMETRIC CONES

Cone No.	End Point °F	End Point °C
10	2381	1305
11	2417	1325
12	2435	1335
13	2462	1350
14	2552	1400
15	2615	1435
16	2669	1465
17	2687	1475
18	2714	1490
19	2768	1520
20	2786	1530
23	2876	1580
26	2903	1595
27	2921	1605
28	2939	1615
29	2984	1640
30	3002	1650
31	3056	1680
32	3092	1700
32½*	3137	1725
33	3173	1745
34	3200	1760
35	3245	1785
36	3290	1810
37	3308	1820
38	3335	1835

* Not included in the tests of Fairchild and Peters. The temperatures given are approximate.

Fluxing is often the primary cause of refractory destruction, such as peeling or spalling. In these cases the reaction between flux or refractory may be such as to greatly alter the surface layer of refractory, causing this altered layer to peel.

Disintegrating

Gaseous attack while present is not a serious problem in cupola operation.

Spalling

Spalling is defined as "the breaking or crushing of a refractory unit due to thermal, mechanical, or structural causes, presenting newly exposed surfaces of the residual mass." This definition enumerates the three general types of spalling which, in turn, require defining.

Thermal Spalling results when refractories are unable to resist the stresses induced by unequal expansion or contraction usually associated with rapid temperature changes. Resistance to thermal spalling is related to reversible thermal expansion, heat transfer, elasticity, and texture of refractory used. This condition can occur in the melting zone of the cupola especially when sudden temperature changes are induced.

Mechanical Spalling results when refractories are unable to resist structural stresses. It is often called pinch spalling. The usual causes are pinching, inadequate provision for expansion, and improper drying. Mechanical strength, toughness, and dimensional uniformity of refractory are essential. This can happen when blocks are laid too tightly.

Structural Spalling is the result of alteration in the composition and/or structure of a portion of the refractory. This alteration may be induced by the action of heat, or the action of slags or gases. The structure, nature of bond, degree of burning, as well as composition of refractory, are the essential properties affecting this type of refractory behavior.

PHYSICAL PROPERTIES OF REFRACTORIES

Many standard tests are used to determine the physical properties of refractories. Standardization of tests has largely been the work of the American Society for Testing Materials, Committee C-8, consisting of qualified representatives of producing, consuming, and general interest groups. This committee is constantly formulating and revising standard and tentative specifications, classifications, methods of testing, and definitions pertaining to refractories. Some of these tests are described briefly. The publication of ASTM should be in every foundryman's library.

Pyrometric Cone Equivalent (P. C. E.)

Fire-clay refractories have no true melting point but soften over a range of temperature. The standard pyrometric cone equivalent (P. C. E.) is a time-honored method of determining softening behavior. Softening behavior (or refractoriness) is a function of time and temperature.

The standard method of determining P. C. E. is described in detail in ASTM Method C-24. It consists essentially of molding a small test cone from the refractory, mounting in a ceramic plaque with a series of standard pyrometric cones, and heating the plaque in a definite manner until the test cones soften and bend. The number of the standard cone which shows the same degree of deformation is reported as the P. C. E. These P. C. E. values indicate softening behavior. Refractoriness determined in this manner is a function of time and temperature. P. C. E. does not specify a service temperature at which a refractory may be used. It simply indicates softening behavior which is a valuable guide in refractory selection. This deformation will occur at a specific temperature since the tests are always made under standardized conditions. These P. C. E. end points are tabulated in Table 17.3.

Thermal Expansion

Thermal expansion is the term used to describe the property of expanding on heating, and contracting on cooling. If this heating is not carried to the point at which permanent high temperature volume changes occur, the refractory will return to its original dimension. This property is designated as "reversible thermal expansion." A number of methods are employed for determining co-efficient of thermal expansion of refractories.

Reversible thermal expansion is indicated as a function of dimensional change with temperature. This change may be expressed as a percentage, or in in./ft.

Reheat

The property of a refractory to show volume changes at high temperatures is referred to as reheat behavior. A refractory may exhibit volume stability and show no permanent change, or it may exhibit permanent reheat "shrinkage" or permanent reheat "expansion."

The standard procedure for determining "reheat" is ASTM Method C-113. The standard reheat tests on fire-clay refractories are conducted at 2460 F, and 2550 F. The reheat value is expressed in "per cent of contraction or expansion."

Hot Load Test

This test describes the behavior of a refractory under load at high temperature. The standard test for fire-clay refractories is described in ASTM Method C-16. In this test a 9 in. brick is placed on end in a furnace, loaded at 25 psi, and heated at a prescribed rate to a given temperature. This maximum temperature is maintained for a definite time and the furnace permitted to cool.

The subsidence is expressed in per cent and the temperature usually employed in testing fire-clay refractories is 2460 F and 2640 F.

The hot load of a refractory is very important in a cupola in that a refractory has to support its own weight as well as other forces upon it. A good example would be in a cupola melting zone where a softened refractory surface would be abraded away by the downcoming charge.

Panel Spalling Test

This test is conducted to determine the resistance of fire-clay refractories to the separate and combined effects of structural and thermal spalling under conditions believed to simulate the same type of spalling as encountered in service.

Spalling is defined as "the breakage or crushing of a refractory unit due to thermal, mechanical, or structural causes, presenting newly exposed surfaces of the residual mass."

Spalling is determined quantitatively by a series of standard procedures described in ASTM Methods C-38, C-107, C-122, and C-180. The test is conducted with movable panels of refractory approximately 18 in. square and 4½-in. thick. The panels are insulated on one side, and the other side is exposed to 1) a suitable heat treatment of 24 hr at 2910 F or 3000 F, and 2) a thermal shock treatment consisting of subjecting the exposed surface to an alternate heating and cooling cycle. Results are expressed in per cent of loss in weight of the refractory in the panel.

Mass

This is the collective term sometimes used in summarizing the collective properties of "apparent porosity," "water absorption," "apparent specific gravity," "bulk density," "true specific gravity," "true density," etc. Standard ASTM Methods C-20 (for apparent porosity and water absorption), C-134 (for bulk density), and C-135 (for true specific gravity), have been adopted.

To be more specific: 1) apparent porosity expresses as a percentage the relationship of the volume of the open pores to exterior volume; 2) water absorption expresses as a percentage the relationship of the weight of water absorbed to the weight of the dry specimen; 3) apparent specific gravity is the ratio between the weight of a brick (in grams) and the volume of brick less the volume of the open pore spaces (in cubic centimeters); and 4) bulk density is the ratio between the weight of a brick and its exterior volume, and is obtained by dividing the weight of the brick by the volume.

Strength

Refractories are subjected to many stresses such as compression, tension, impact, and abrasion that may occur during handling, transportation, installation, or in actual use.

Crushing strength and modulus of rupture are determined at room temperature by ASTM Method C-133. Crushing strength is that necessary to crush or shear by application of force at two opposite surfaces of a refractory brick or sample. The modulus of rupture is a measure of the transverse strength. It is determined by supporting both ends of a brick, or suitable sample, as a beam and applying the stress or load midway between the supports.

Crushing strength and modulus of rupture tests at high temperatures are useful, but no standard has been devised.

No standard tests for impact or abrasion have been devised, but considerable work has been done in adapting rattler test methods. Such tests are proving useful.

REFRACTORIES OF INDUSTRY

Having classified refractories, discussed their behavior and properties and, briefly, the general methods of behavior, we will discuss in greater detail refractories that are available to the foundryman, some of the details of manufacture as they affect application, and further details of application.

Fire-clay refractories constitute the largest group of refractories produced. Fire clays are widely available. They are produced in many areas — Ohio, Pennsylvania, Kentucky, Missouri and New Jersey being the largest producing areas. Fire clay refractories as a group are relatively low in cost. For economical as well as service reasons, the fire clay group is used to a large extent in almost every refractory enclosure.

For this reason, refractories will be divided into two groups: 1) fire clay; and 2) non-clay. The first group will be discussed in some greater detail.

Fire Clay Brick. The American Society for Testing Materials lists seven different classifications of fire-clay brick, designating them as low duty, intermediate duty, high duty, super duty, 50, 60, and 70 per cent alumina-diaspore fire clay brick. Another classification (not yet listed by ASTM) is known as special super duty fire clay brick. This brick is essentially a super duty brick burned to much higher than normal burning temperatures. The classified fire-clay brick are generally burned to about Cone 14 (2550 F - 1400 C), while the special super duty are burned to Cone 18 (2710 F - 1490 C), or above.

This fire-clay group of refractories covers a wide range of products. Chemically, they range all the way from 30 to 70 per cent alumina. The range in chemical and mineralogical characteristics is apparent.

Fig. 17.16. Dry pan and screen. Except for bottom construction, the dry pan is similar to the wet pan.

Fig. 17.17. Hand molding method of making cupola blocks. Heated drying floor shown in background.

This group constitutes a wide range of properties that find wide application in industry.

Not only chemically and mineralogically, but by virtue of differences in physical structure, the application of this group is still more diverse. In order to provide better understanding of this factor, some of the methods of forming or manufacturing these products will be described.

MANUFACTURE OF FIRE CLAY SHAPES

The raw materials are plastic, semi-plastic, and flint (non-plastic) fire clays, and previously fired material (calcine or grog) such as calcined flint clay or clean kiln breakage (bats), all of which are selected in accordance with the requirements of the class of refractory to be made. The grog, because it has been prefired and, therefore, does not shrink in subsequent firing, forms the skeleton of the body. The plastic or semi-plastic clays are used to make a moldable mixture when tempered with water and form a bond upon being dried and during the kiln firing. The many properties required in the final product are controlled by the formulation, preparation of the batch, and the methods of molding and firing.

The clays and grog may be ground and mixed in the required proportions with water in one operation in a "wet pan," which is essentially a revolving steel pan equipped with heavy steel-tired mullers set to ride directly on the pan bottom so that grinding takes place as the pan rotates. The materials may also be prepared by pregrinding them separately by suitable means. In common use is the "dry pan" (Fig. 17.16), which is similar to the wet pan with the exception that the bottom is formed of slotted plates. The rotating mullers crush and grind the charge and the product falls through the slots in the bottom of the pan into a collector. In many cases the material is screened so as to obtain definite particle sizes which are used in definite proportions in the mixture. From either the dry pan or the screens, the material is conveyed to storage bins.

The desired quantities of the ingredients for the batch are taken from the bins and mixed, and then tempered with water to form a moldable mass. This result may be accomplished in a wet pan with the mullers slightly raised to prevent further grinding, or in any one of a number of special muller-type mixers which are provided with plows. In some cases a pug mill is used. This machine consists of a trough in which is mounted a longitudinal rotating shaft provided with spiral blades.

Molding of Shapes

Three molding processes generally are used: 1) handmade or wood mold; 2) extruded or stiff mud; and 3) dry press, sometimes called power press.

Handmade Process

The clays are mixed and tempered with water, usually in a wet pan, to make a readily moldable mass, which is transferred to a molding table. A mass of the plastic mix is thrown into a wooden mold (Fig. 17.17) which may have metal liners and loose sides. The partially filled mold is then bumped against the table several times, and when it has been completely filled the excess "mud" is cut off and the top is slicked with a trowel. A pallet may be placed over the mold, which is then turned over. The mold is lifted off, the loose sides remaining on the shape. The sides then are removed carefully and the shape is slicked all around with a trowel. After partial drying on a heated floor, the shapes may be repressed in steel molds mounted in a machine, by which pressure is applied, thus insuring regular contours and sharp corners. With careful preparation and skillful manipulation, very satisfactory cupola blocks are produced by this method.

Extrusion or Stiff Mud Process

Less water is added to the clay-grog mixture than in the handmade process so that it leaves the mixer, usually a pug mill, in a very stiff plastic condition. The batch may be passed through a vacuum chamber to remove entrapped air, thus producing a body of improved homogeneity and higher density. The mix then passes into an auger machine from which it is extruded through a die in the form of a column which has approximately the same cross section as the shape

Fig. 17.18. The stiff clay blanks are pressed in steel molds to exact shape.

Fig. 17.19. The extrusion or stiff mud process involves forcing stiff clay through a die. The column of clay is cut by steel wires into blanks of desired size.

to be made (Fig. 17.19). The column of clay is cut by steel wires into blanks of the proper size, which are then pressed in steel molds to the exact shape desired (Fig. 17.18). The molded shapes are rigid enough to be handled without deformation.

Cupola block manufactured by the stiff mud process possess extremely high mechanical strength and denseness, and are, therefore, particularly resistant to abrasion and slag penetration.

Dry or Power Press Process

The raw materials and their preparation are somewhat the same as for hand molding and the stiff mud process. The tempering water is added in an amount barely sufficient to lubricate the particles and so that the mix may be formed under high pressure. The corners and edges of the molded shape are sharp, and the desired dimensions are more closely approximated than is possible by the other methods. Because of the low moisture content, dry press shapes are dried readily, the drying shrinkage is less, and lamination is minimized. Although the process is used extensively for the manufacture of the fire clay brick, cupola refractories so made do not have quite as high strength or denseness as, for example, those made by the stiff-mud process.

Drying

In drying fire clay refractories, the water originally used in tempering the batch is removed. The process requires considerable time and careful regulation of temperature and ventilation to prevent uneven shrinkage and cracking. The drying process is usually carried out on heated floors or in humidity or waste-heat drying ovens (Fig. 17.20).

Firing

The dried units are fired at high temperature either in periodic pyramidal or rectangular down draft kilns, or in continuous tunnel kilns (Fig. 17.21). This operation drives out the chemically-combined water of the clays, completes the shrinkage, and partially vitrifies the clays to obtain low porosity and high mechanical strength. The firing temperature is varied in accordance with the characteristics of the clays used in the mix, usually ranging between 2300 and 2600 F. The gradual rise in temperature to the maximum, and the cooling in any type of kiln usually requires a period of several days to a week. The time-temperature schedule may vary considerably depending upon the service for which the refractories are intended.

Fig. 17.20. Soft refractory shapes are placed on pallets and loaded on car for transfer to the drying oven.

Fig. 17.21. Car of refractory shapes entering continuous tunnel kiln for firing at high temperatures.

For cupola block, a high temperature and relatively long time are required to secure high mechanical strength and denseness.

Special Methods

The great demand for special shapes, and particularly shapes of specific properties, has resulted in the greater utilization of special methods.

"Air hammer" tamping processes are used extensively. These methods may be employed for conventional fire-clay mixes, comparable to "wood mold" mixes previously described.

A "special air hammer" process has been developed in which extremely high percentages of calcined grog, grain sized for maximum density, is used. This process permits the formation of shapes that show almost negligible shrinkage (1/16 in./ft as compared with 1/4 to 1 1/2 in./ft obtained with methods previously described). This permits the manufacture of special shapes to extremely close dimensional specifications, and bodies that compare to dry press process bodies in physical properties.

Table 17.4, showing approximate physical properties of high duty brick, indicates the effect of two different methods of forming.

There are other methods of forming refractories, particularly the non-clay group, but these methods are beyond the scope of this discussion.

TABLE 17.4. PROPERTIES OF REFRACTORY BRICK AND TILE (HIGH DUTY)*

	Dry Press	Stiff Mud
Pyrometric Cone Equivalent		
ASTM C24-46	32-33	32-33
Temperature Equivalent, F.	3090 - 3175 F	3090 - 3175 F
Reheat ASTM C113-46		
Per cent Contraction or Expansion at 2550 F	0 - 0.5% Contr.	0 - 0.5% Contr.
Hot Load Test ASTM C16-49		
Per cent Deformation High Heat Duty, 2460 F	2 to 4%	2 to 4%
Panel Spalling Test, ASTM C107-47		
Per cent loss—High Duty, 2910 F	2 to 6%	6 to 10%
Apparent Porosity ASTM C20-46	16 to 20%	10 to 13%
Water Absorption ASTM C20-46	7.5 to 9.5%	4.0 to 5.5%
Modulus of Rupture ASTM C133-49		
lb per sq. in.	700 to 1000	1400 to 1800
Cold Crushing Strength ASTM C133-49		
lb per sq. in.	1800 to 2500	3800 to 4800

* Data on a Missouri high duty brick.

Special Alumina Silica Refractories

In this classification are the sillimanite and mullite types usually made from kyanite, with an over-all alumina percentage of between 58 and 65 per cent. These brick are considerably more expensive than the alumina diaspore class, and are used where the service temperature of this latter group is exceeded.

In this classification are also the kaolin base refractories which are made from relatively pure china clay which has been heated to very high temperatures to render it volume stable at high application temperatures.

Also in this group are mullite refractories which have a true mullite composition with an alumina content of approximately 75 per cent. These brick are usually made from electrically fused mullite grain, with a bond which also develops theoretical mullite compositions on firing. These brick have extremely good compressive strength under load at high temperatures. They resist rapid heating and cooling cycles, and are resistant to certain types of slag attack. They are volume stable at higher temperatures than the refractories previously listed.

Refractories in this group may often find special application in the breast or tap-out section of the cupola.

Silica Refractories

Silica refractories constitute the second largest group of refractories produced. Silica brick are used in large quantities by the steel and glass industries. They are made from crushed sandstone or quartzite, bonded with a small amount of lime water. Silica brick have the advantages of being relatively low priced and have good load-bearing capacity at high temperatures close to their melting point. Because of their thermal expansion characteristics they have poor resistance to rapid heating and cooling, and for that reason are used primarily in furnaces where temperature is held constant for long periods of time.

Recently a new development in silica refractories has been made, known as the super duty silica type. This super duty silica brick is one in which the total alumina content is lower than in the normal variety, and as a result it has a somewhat higher use limit than the standard refractories.

No discussion of silica refractories can be complete without special reference to 1) natural stone, and 2) siliceous gun mixes.

Natural stone is found in many areas (the firestone of Ohio and the bauxite of Tennessee being typical examples). These stones are widely used in melting zone maintenance.

The siliceous gun mixes, consisting of a ganister of approximately 80 per cent silica and 20 per cent bond clay, are widely used as gun mixes for cupola melting zone maintenance. Such mixes are obtainable in premixed form, or are compounded by the user.

In discussing siliceous mixes, mention should be made of the wide range of miscellaneous local mixes ranging from comparatively high silica content to the high clay mixes or loams, some of which would render classification refractory-wise difficult. Such mixes are generally used in hand placed melting zone patches.

Magnesite Refractories

Magnesite refractories used for basic cupola operation are produced from calcined magnesite rock or from calcined magnesium carbonate recovered from sea water. In the heating process the CO_2 contained in the magnesium carbonate of the starting material is driven off to form MgO. The MgO granules are then bonded, sometimes with the addition of chrome ore, to form bricks and shapes. Some of these are fired to high temperatures, as in the case of other refractories, and some are chemically bonded by a process which requires no firing. Magnesite brick are used mainly where they are in contact with basic slags. These brick are considerably more expensive than fire-clay brick, and for that reason are used where the cheaper fire-clay brick will not give an economical life.

There is also a type of electrically fused MgO refractory produced from nearly pure magnesia, which has a higher use limit than normal magnesite brick and is suitable for use at very high temperatures.

Magnesite refractories in the form of brick and shapes, as well as in monolithic form generally gun applied, are finding extensive use in cupola melting zone service.

Dolomite Refractories

No discussion of basic refractories would be complete without including dolomite, a solid solution of calcium and magnesium carbonate which in pure form approaches the mineralogical composition of CaO.MgO, although all ratios occur in nature. Dolomite is widely distributed. Dolomite and dolomite-magnesia compounds are becoming extensively used in gun applied monolithic linings for cupola melting zone service.

Chrome Refractories

Chrome refractories are produced from natural chrome ore and, like magnesite, can be made either as fired or as chemically bonded brick. The chemically bonded brick always contain some MgO additions. Chrome brick are relatively neutral chemically, and do not react at moderately high temperatures with silica, magnesite, or alumina refractories. For that reason it is often used as a separator in furnace constructions between two refractories which would react with each other if allowed to come into contact. Very few chrome refractories are used in the iron foundry cupolas.

Forsterite Refractories

Forsterite is a basic refractory, usually made from olivine rock to which some MgO has been added to adjust the composition ratio to $2MgO.SiO_2$. Forsterite refractories can also be made by synthetic mixtures of MgO and SiO_2. They have not been used to any extent in cupolas.

Silicon Carbide Refractories

Silicon carbide is an electric furnace product used primarily as an abrasive. When this material is produced in refractory shapes it provides a very high rate of heat conduction, approximately ten times that of fire clay brick. Due to its hardness it is sometimes used where mechanical abrasion is severe and also where it is exposed to certain types of slag. Its property of high heat conduction, however, is probably its outstanding physical characteristic, and for this reason it is used widely for muffles and various air-cooled furnace and recuperator construction. Silicon carbide refractories have excellent resistance to cupola slags and are widely employed in slag hole blocks. However, silicon carbide is readily attacked by molten iron.

Fused Alumina Refractories

Fused alumina is another electric furnace product whose primary use is in abrasives. When compounded into refractory products it incorporates high heat conduction, but not so much as silicon carbide. Its heat flow is approximately 2.5 times that of ordinary fire-clay brick. It has a very high use limit in both oxidizing and reducing atmospheres, and is used where extreme temperature levels rule out other materials. Some fused alumina products are finding application in basic lined cupola furnace tap-outs.

Zircon Refractories

Zircon refractories are made mainly from the natural mineral zircon which is often found concentrated in certain beach sands. It has a high melting point and use limit, and is resistant to some types of siliceous slags. Zircon has been used only to a limited extent.

Carbon Refractories

Carbon is usually considered as a fuel (coke in the cupola being a good example). However, carbon does exist in many forms, both mineralogical and amorphous, from the finest gem diamond to soft unctuous soot.

Carbon in certain forms possesses an unusual combination of chemical and physical properties (high resistance to chemical attack and thermal shock). When used under the proper conditions of temperature and exposed to proper atmospheres, it serves as an excellent refractory.

Amorphous carbon and graphite are the chief forms used in refractories. Carbon has been used extensively in the hearth and crucible of the blast furnace. Carbon in amorphous or graphite form is generally used in carbon refractories. Carbon is made up in brick and tile shapes and also in the form of mortars and plastics.

TABLE 17.5. TYPICAL PHYSICAL PROPERTIES OF AMORPHOUS CARBON SHAPES

Form of Product	Carbon Shapes
Apparent Density, g/cc	1.50
Porosity, %	23
Strength, psi	
Tensile	600
Compressive	4500
Flexural	1250
Elastic Modulus X10[6], psi	1.25
Thermal Conductivity Btu/sq ft/sec/F	6
Mean Coefficient of Thermal Expansion, 70-212FX10[7]/F	13
Volume Shrinkage	none

Carbon has long been used in the foundry as a wash for molds, cores, ladles, linings, spouts, etc. It has been used for many years as an additive in fireclay mortars and plastics for similar applications.

Since carbon is a neutral material and does not react with either acid or basic materials, it can be used in both acid and basic practice. In addition, carbon has many properties which make it an ideal refractory. It is not wet by molten iron or slag; it is essentially unabsorbed by molten iron as produced in the cupola furnace; it is highly resistant to thermal shock; and it is resistant to abrasion and erosion by normal slag and iron. Carbon also possesses a very low coefficient of thermal expansion, which makes it easy to design a carbon lining for cupola practice that will remain structurally stable (Table 17.5).

Since the refractories in basic cupolas give short life it was natural, for economic reasons, that carbon be tried in this practice. Basic refractories commonly used for patching were replaced by carbon paste. Carbon paste as a tamped lining inside of a magnesite brick lining was used on the hot side. The first experience produced greatly increased run time between repairs and reduced refractory cost considerably.

Patching with carbon paste was also done in the well and tuyere zone. Carbon block well linings were likewise used. Carbon similarly applied to the acid cupola has been equally satisfactory. An additional advantage is that the cupola can be banked with coke between runs in place of dropping the bottom.

Basic cupola linings have advanced from the tamped carbon paste form to carbon brick inside of basic fire brick, and from there to a large carbon block lining inside of a carbon brick lining. The use of preformed, prebaked carbon block lining has proven superior to tamped paste. External shower cooling has been applied to the shell where all-carbon linings are used.

Carbon does an excellent job in the trough and skimmer for either acid or basic operation. When carbon paste is used to form a trough, the paste should be partially baked with a fire or open flame before use. A minimum thickness of 3 in. is recommended to gain sufficient strength in the mass of carbon so formed. Standard carbon shapes, laid up with carbonaceous cement, also can be used effectively, as can special carbon slabs.

The use of carbon around the tap hole has been a natural construction adaptation. Since most designs have a square tap hole, carbon brick can be laid to form such an opening. Carbon paste can be tamped around a form to produce the desired shape; or special tap blocks of almost any practical design can be fabricated.

Carbon, in paste form, can be tamped on the hot face of a ceramic or carbon brick lining in the well of either acid or basic cupolas. A minimum thickness of 4 in. is recommended, using a metal or wood form to retain the paste in position while heating with a fire or open flame to bake out.

Carbon brick or machined blocks or combinations of the two can be used with or without ceramic between the carbon and the outer shell.

Another intesting application of carbon in the paste form is as a ramming mix. It is contoured in the melting zone where it forms a monolithic patch. It has the property of baking to a dense form, approaching the prebaked brick, when subjected to the furnace temperature.

The biggest advantage of using carbon in the cupola is that, since carbon is a neutral material, it can be used with a refining slag which permits a charge of either scrap steel or pig iron. A carbon lined cupola can be used for either acid or basic practice. Part time basic operation of a carbon lined cupola obviously eliminates the necessity of installing an additional unit for such work.

Insulating Fire Brick and Insulating Brick

Both types are usually produced from fire clay which has been mixed with some type of combustible material such as sawdust. When fired, the combustible burns away leaving a porous refractory structure.

These products find no use in cupolas. The cupola does not lend itself to insulation for two reasons: 1) the amount of heat that can be saved from radiation losses through the shell is small compared with the large amount carried out of the stack by the effluent gases, and 2) the strength of the refractory structure will be decreased because of excessively high temperature if the cupola is backed by insulation. Also it is imperative that the lining be absolutely tight to prevent the penetration of slag and metal into joints.

Refractory Castables

Refractory castables, sometimes called refractory concretes, are similar to structural concrete in some respects. Refractory concretes consist essentially of an aggregate of crushed and grain sized refractory calcine or grog, and a cementatious bonding material or cement which may be some form of Portland, more often lumnite, and frequently special calcium aluminate cements.

The aggregate may be of any refractory material. The fire clay or alumina-silica base castables constitute the bulk of castables used. They are available for service temperatures of 2400 F to 3000 F.

For special service conditions, chrome, magnesia, olivine and other minerals may be used to prepare castables of specific physical properties. Refractory castables are finding some application in the charging zone of cupolas, and extensive use in sections of accessory equipment, such as hot-blast applications.

Insulating Refractory Castables

Castables may be prepared by using a porous refractory aggregate. The advantages of this type of insulating refractory castable are similar to the advantages of insulating fire brick. Just as in the case of prefired refractories which includes a class of insulating fire brick (intended primarily for backing up insulation), there is a group of insulating castables.

The general use of castables is being extended greatly due to their low cost of installation. Refractory concrete is mixed and placed in a manner similar to structural concrete, and is a desirable material to use in areas where skilled brick masons are hard to obtain. When the proper grade is selected for a given application, a castable will provide a volume-stable monolithic lining, in many instances giving equal or better service life than a lining of regular brickwork.

In the cupola installations refractory castables find their greatest use in hot. blast system dome linings, tube sheets, etc.

Plastic and Ramming Refractories

Another group of refractory products is known as plastic refractories or ramming mixes. These compositions are generally composed of clays or other binders mixed with crushed refractory aggregate and tempered with water to bring the mixture to proper working consistency. The plastic or ramming mix is installed by pounding or ramming into place.

Plastic or ramming mixtures are made in alumina-silica compositions with temperature use limits ranging from 2500 to over 3000 F. There are also compositions using fused alumina, chrome ore, magnesite, periclase, silicon carbide, and other refractory-base aggregates.

No discussion of castables, plastics and ramming materials would be complete without pointing out the great variation in the way they are used and the various materials available. In fact, these variations in material make it difficult even to adhere to our classifications. Again we should call attention to the carbon-containing plastics in cupola operation.

All are applied either by hand methods or gun application. Many of these groups lend themselves to application by either method.

Refractory Mortars

Many types of mortars are produced for laying up or jointing preformed refractory brick. There are two main types, those which develop their bond strength only when heated to temperature in the furnace — known as "heat setting" mortars — and those which develop a high bond on drying, called "air setting" mortars. Both types have their applications, and the best guide is to follow the recommendation of the manufacturer supplying the brick used with the mortar.

A general rule that should be adhered to is that the mortar should be equal or greater in refractoriness than the refractory with which it is used. The use of low fusion mortars or clays with high quality refractories is false economy.

REFERENCES

1. A. N. Kraner, "Refractories for the Basic Cupola," AFS TRANSACTIONS, vol. 60 (1952).
2. L. B. Wyckoff, "Effect of Slag on Furnace Linings," AFS TRANSACTIONS, vol. 60 (1952).

Safe Practices

These safety recommendations for the operation of a cupola should be deemed to constitute minimum standards for protecting employees.

Where protection is provided superior to that afforded by any applicable recommendation, such protection should be deemed to fulfill in a greater measure the purpose of these recommendations.

Mechanical Charging

The use of mechanical devices for charging cupolas not only saves labor but also reduces material-handling accidents.

Many foundry cupolas are now charged either by fully automatic charging machines (Chapter 4) equipped with crane or by forklift trucks equipped with tilting boxes. Some cupolas are equipped with doors or chain curtains which cover the charging opening. These should be kept closed except during charging.

The space underneath any cupola charging elevators, machines, lift hoists, skip hoists and cranes should be railed off or guarded in order to prevent material from dropping on workers below during charging operations.

ELEVATORS used to hoist barrows or buggies from the ground to the charging floor should be effectively guarded and equipped with safety appliances as required for freight elevators.

ELEVATOR OPENINGS at floor level to the elevator hatch should be protected by elevator gates, either mechanically or manually operated. Gates should be at least 6 ft high. . . . All hoistway openings should be safeguarded in accordance with local regulations.

GATE INTERLOCKS. All elevators should be either electrically or mechanically interlocked with the elevator platform so that it is impossible to start the elevator until the gate is in a closed position; also so that it is impossible to open the gate until the elevator is at floor level.

SAFETY BLOCKS. Elevators, other than hydraulic elevators, should be equipped with safety blocks operated by a speed governor control that will hold the elevator in case of cable failure or overspeeding.

HATCH LIMIT SWITCHES. All types of elevators should be equipped with upper and lower travel limit switches that will prevent the elevator from overtraveling.

ELEVATORS *should be effectively guarded with safety appliances to conform with local regulations and the requirements of insurance carriers.*

Manual Charging

Where cupolas are manually charged, a guard rail should be placed across the charging opening to prevent the operator from falling into the cupola while charging.

Where cupolas are charged with wheelbarrows or cars, a curb of the height equal to the wheel radius of the barrow or car should be provided to prevent the conveyance from falling into the cupola.

Hollow Vessels

Scrap material in the form of closed hollow vessels — such as cylinders, tanks, drums and the like — should be broken open before charging in order to prevent explosion in the cupola.

Charging Floor

Charging floors should be kept free of loose materials and a place should be provided for all equipment not in use.

Steel floor plates, if used, should be riveted in place and sufficiently substantial to prevent warping or upturning.

Standard railings should be provided around all floor openings. Since railings on the charging floor are likely to be exposed to considerable abuse, they should be constructed of heavy angle iron rather than of pipe. Angle iron is more easily repaired.

Interior Maintenance Work

When maintenance work is done inside a mechanically charged cupola, the mechanical charger should be locked out and warning signs posted indicating that work is being done inside the cupola.

With a manually charged cupola, warning signs should be posted, bars placed across the charge opening and locked in position. If there is a door on the opening, it should be locked closed unless there is an attendant on the charging floor.

In addition, these precautions should be taken:

1. A substantial screen or guard should be provided in the cupola and located above any men working therein, in order to protect them against falling objects. Such screens or guards should be constructed of not less than 1½ x 1½ x ¼-in. angle iron covered preferably with a screen having the strength equiva-

lent of a one inch mesh $\frac{3}{16}$-in. wire or not less than no. 12 U.S. Gage solid sheet steel. . . . Provision should be made for securely supporting such screens or guards by means of overhead slings or underpinning to resist any falling object.

2. All loose slag and bridges should be broken down and allowed to drop to the bottom of the cupola before beginning repairs on the cupola lining.

3. When the cupola is down for relining, the condition of the shell and the riveting should be inspected. A weak shell is unsafe.

4. In relining, ample clearance (at least $\frac{3}{4}$-in.) between the brick lining and the cupola shell should be left to allow for expansion and this space filled with dry sand to serve as a cushion, thus protecting the shell against severe stresses.

5. Before placing the coke charge for lightup purposes, a check should be made to determine that no one is in the cupola. *A coke charge buried a man for an hour and a half when a fellow workman inadvertently dumped coke into a cupola.*

6. Before starting up the cupola, the lining should be thoroughly dry, and all tools and equipment removed.

Carbon Monoxide

Sometimes backdrafts in the cupola cause the escape of carbon monoxide into working zones. The gas has no warning properties and thus may reach dangerous concentrations before man is aware of its presence.

Carbon monoxide warning alarms are commercially available and it is recommended that such a device be installed especially on charging floors which are not open to free circulation of outside air.

Blast Gates

Gates (Fig. 18.1) should be in the blast pipe that supplies air to the cupola. In order to prevent the accumulation of combustible gases in the air supply system and to minimize the explosion hazard, blast gates should be closed when the air supply fails or when the cupola is shut down. Gates should be located, in relation to the cupola windbox, to keep the duct volume to a minimum.

Motorized dampers may be installed so that they will close automatically when the air supply fails or is shut down.

Blast gates may be omitted if alternate tuyeres are opened to permit air circulation.

Where a Roots type positive displacement blower is stopped to shut off the air supply, the blower lobes act as an effective valve.

Tuyeres

On every cupola at least one tuyere should be of the safety type, provided with a small channel $1\frac{1}{2}$ x 2 in. below the normal tuyere level. The channel of this safety tuyere (Fig. 2.6, page 21) is provided with an easily fusible plate that will melt through should the slag and iron rise to an unsafe level.

Tapping

Tapping (Chapters 28 and 30) with safety requires skill and should be done only by thoroughly instructed men. . . . The tapout bar should never be held above

Fig. 18.1. Typical hand operated blast gate.

the level of the taphole, otherwise the bar might puncture the sand bed causing a *bottom runout.*

Obviously a continuous tap cupola eliminates the need for repeated tapping and therefore reduces the hazard.

Botting

When botting a taphole, spattering of molten metal will occur if the bot is thrust directly into the metal stream. The bot should be brought immediately about the stream of metal close to the taphole and aimed downward at a sharp angle. This procedure will keep spattering to a minimum. . . . An extra supply of bots ready for use should be kept within convenient reach of the cupola operator.

Slag Hole Shields

Where it is necessary to protect against the splashes or blowing of slag, the slag spout should be equipped with a shield or guard. The slag spot shield not only protects workers from sprays of molten slag but also prevents dispersion of slag wool.

Slag wool may be collected through a wet slagging system such as a water filled container or trough and flushed away (Fig. 18.2).

Dropping Bottom

When dropping the bottom (Chapters 9 and 30) by any method, no employee shall be allowed inside the danger zone unless protected by an enclosure or guard.

Dropping the bottom doors of a cupola requires extraordinary care. One of the best methods is to attach a block and tackle with a wire rope and chain leader to the props supporting the doors. The props

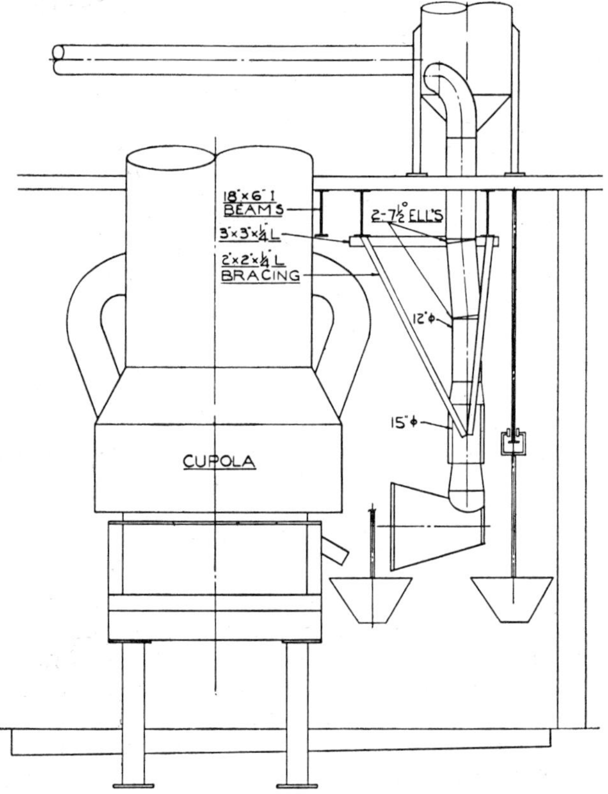

Fig. 18.2. Method controlling slag wool at slagging spout.

can then be pulled out by use of the block and tackle arrangement which can be actuated from a safe distance or from behind a suitable barrier to insure that the person dropping the bottom will not be burned by the slag.

Before the bottom is dropped, a careful inspection should be made of the area underneath the cupola to see that no water has seeped under the sand. A warning whistle or signal should be given and someone should be authorized to make sure that no one is in or can enter the danger zone.

If the cupola bottom doors fail to drop for any reason or if the remaining charge inside the cupola bridges over, employees shall never be permitted to enter the danger zone to force the doors or relieve the bridging. The doors can sometimes be opened and the bridging relieved by turning on the blast fan. The vibration produced usually corrects the condition. A mechanical vibrator attached to the bottom doors has also been found to be effective.

A heavy skull cracker may be dropped from the charging door. The weight must be heavy enough to overcome the yielding resistance of the cushion in the cupola bottom.

If these methods fail to produce the desired result, the doors or the bridging must be flame cut with a lance but only after the cupola is cooled to a safe temperature.

Water should never be introduced through the charging door to force the bottom with steam pressure. *The cupola blew up killing one person and severely injuring seven others when this was done in one foundry.*

Bottom Support

The cupola bottom should be supported by two metal props of the required structural strength and by screws or wedges.

Metal prop bases should be supported on a concrete footing or other fabricated footing of equivalent strength. Adjust to proper height by means of screws or wedges (Fig. 2.4, page 19). While the metal props are being adjusted, place temporary supports under the bottom doors to prevent their falling on any employee.

It is desirable to provide mechanical means for raising the bottom doors as shown in Fig. 2.5.

Drop

A cupola drag as illustrated in Fig. 9.11 (page 80) provides a convenient means for removing the cupola drop. With such a drag, the drop may be removed from under the cupola just after the bottom is dropped.

Special bottom door locking devices are available in case it is desired to catch the cupola drop in a container, car or skid as illustrated in Fig. 9.13. . . . Where these containers, cars or skids are apt to collect water, such as when stored outside, holes should be drilled in the bottom to insure removal of water.

Frozen Taphole

When the taphole, because of freezing, must be opened with an oxygen lance, take the same precautions against splashing metal as previously described.

Personal Protective Equipment

Toe protection. All persons handling heavy objects should wear safety shoes or foot guards.

Leggings : spats. Persons who handle molten metal should wear leggings or spats for the protection of legs and feet.

Pants should be cuffed over the leggings or spats in order to prevent molten metal from getting between the pants and the protective equipment. . . . Unless the pants are cuffed over, burns from molten metal will be more frequent and severe than if no protection at all were worn.

Clothing. When molten metal is being handled, as much of the body as possible should be covered by normal type clothing. . . . Clothing that is resistant to burning is advisable. Such clothing should fit closely at the neck and waist, and sleeves should not be rolled up.

Gauntlet type gloves should never be worn when handling molten metal. If gloves are required, only the safety cuff type should be used. They fit snugly and extend under shirt sleeves.

Eye protection. Persons working on a cupola, whether on the charging floor, tapping floor or inside the cupola, shall wear cup type goggles.

Head protection. Those doing maintenance work inside a cupola should wear hard hats to protect the head against falling objects.

CHAPTER 19

Calculating Charge

The principal objective of good cupola operation is the economical production of iron having a composition suited to the section sizes involved, the pur pose, of course, being to develop the desired physical and mechanical properties at a quality level commensurate with the type of castings required. The two chief factors leading to this desired end are the raw materials entering the cupola and a knowledge of how the cupola operation affects the chemistry of the charge. To begin with, therefore, it is highly desirable to know, insofar as is practically possible, the chemical constitution of the materials in the charge, that is, the metallic constituents, the coke, and the fluxing materials.

In comparison with the other main metallic raw materials, the composition of pig iron, as furnished in the designated grades, is reasonably well known and controlled, with the possible exception of its carbon content. However, it is advisable to check the shipper's analysis at a frequency commensurate to satisfy the needs. The composition of return scrap and gates is obtained from daily laboratory records of analysis. A knowledge of the chemical constitution of purchased scrap presents by comparison a formidable problem, particularly since for economic reasons it usually is necessary to employ the maximum percentage of this material without impairing chemical control of the molten metal.

A good method to show the economics of a charge is to graph the basic mix cost. Such a graph would show assumed mixes and cost per element of charge. From experience the additional cost of melting higher scrap and steel mixes must be determined for each individual operation. These extra costs might include coke, desulfurizer, hot blast fuel and ferro alloys. The extra costs must be added to the basic cost which gives a total mix cost for the various mixtures. As the market conditions and requirements change the data and curves must be recalculated. This must be done at frequent intervals.

Solving the problem of control of scrap is aided by having: 1) assurance of uniformity from the supplier; 2) careful inspection coupled with rejection of the shipment if not conforming to specifications; 3) additional segregation when feasible in the process of unloading; and 4) a reasonable knowledge of the average composition of the finally sorted materials.

After a period of training in the recognition of various types of scrap, crane operators and charging crews can offer an invaluable contribution to cupola control, as they see practically every piece of iron used during the course of operation.

MELTING STOCK

Pig iron, described in Chapter 11, is available in any desired silicon analysis up to about 4.00 per cent, together with a wide selection of manganese and phosphorus. High silicon silvery pig iron contains from about 7 to 17 per cent silicon. Purchased scrap, described in Chapter 12, includes gray cast iron; malleable cast iron; steel in the form of castings, plate scrap, railroad rails. rail fittings, structural scrap; and briquetted turnings and borings of both cast iron and steel. Home scrap consists of sprues, heads, gates and risers from one's own plant. Fluxing stone, fluorspar and soda ash are described in Chapter 15. Limestone and dolomite limestone should never contain less than 95 per cent calcium carbonate plus magnesium carbonate. The ferro alloys, described in Chapter 13, are available in lump or pig form, as briquettes for melting with the cupola charge, or in ground and shot form for spout or ladle addition.

Some alloys are bonded into briquette form with exothermic materials that, when added to the ladle, melt the contained alloy. Special analysis pig irons and silvery pig irons contain various alloys for use in the cupola charge. Home iron and steel scrap, as well as purchased iron and steel scrap, may contain useful amounts of alloy. Coke is described in Chapter 14.

APPROXIMATE ANALYSIS OF CAST IRON AND STEEL SCRAP

The classifications in Table 19.1 follow the grading specifications of cast iron and steel scrap in Chapter 12. The analyses are approximations only to guide in mixture making.

In estimating the analysis of scrap each pile should be considered separately giving consideration to such factors as the class of casting and, if possible, the producer. Age is a factor, since in recent years the use of alloys has increased steadily.

The loss or gain of elements, melted according to current good cupola practice, is shown in Table 19.2 as a percentage of the weight of each element charged, e.g., assume a mixture in which the charge contains a 2.50 per cent of silicon. With a 10 per cent silicon loss in melting, the estimated analysis of the iron at the cupola spout is 2.25 per cent silicon, i.e., 2.50— (10 per cent of 2.50) = 2.25.

TABLE 19.2. APPROXIMATE LOSS OR GAIN OF ELEMENTS IN ACID MELTING

Element	Approx. % Loss	Approx. % Gain
Silicon, in pig and scrap		
Si 3% in metal charge	7-12	—
Si 2% in metal charge	7-12	—
Si 1% in metal charge	7-12	—
Si 0.50% in metal charge	7-12	—
Lump Ferrosilicon	10-15	—
Manganese in pig iron and scrap	10-20	—
Lump Ferromanganese	15-25	—
Spiegeleisen	15-25	—
Chromium, lump ferro	10-20	—
Nickel, shot or ingot	2-5	—
Copper, shot or 3/16 and thicker scrap	2-5	—
Alloys in briquettes	5-10	—
Sulfur	—	40-60

TABLE 19.1. APPROXIMATE ANALYSIS CAST IRON AND STEEL SCRAP*

Type of Scrap	% *Si*	% *TC*	% *Mn*	% *P* max.	% *S*
No. 1 Mach. Cast lt.	2.00-2.50	3.40-3.60	0.50	0.30	0.14
and med.	1.50-2.00	3.25-3.50	0.60	0.15	0.14
No. 1 Cast hvy.	1.25-1.50	3.00-3.20	0.75	0.15	0.14
Automotive Cylinders	2.00	3.20	0.65	0.08	0.08
Truck and Tractor Cyl.	2.25	3.40	0.75	0.12	0.14
Agricultural Scrap	1.80-2.50	3.25-3.60	0.50-0.75	0.25-0.50	0.14
Pipe (Water)	1.25-1.85	3.40-3.65	0.35-0.45	0.30-0.70	.10-.12
Radiator Scrap	2.20-2.50	3.40-3.70	0.50-0.60	0.35-0.55	0.12
Brake Shoes	0.90-1.10	3.10-3.30	0.20-0.40	0.30-0.40	.18-.25
RR Car Wheel Chilled Fe	0.50-0.60	3.25-3.50	0.50-0.60	0.25-0.35	0.14
Malleable Scrap	1.10-1.50	2.20-2.50	0.30-0.50	0.10-0.15	.08-.12
Rails	0.20-0.30	0.60-0.80	0.70-0.80	0.05	0.05
Auto Steel	0.10-0.30	0.10-0.50	0.50-0.80	0.05	0.05
Structural Steel	0.10-0.30	0.10 0.20	0.50-0.80	0.05	0.05

*ALLOYING ELEMENTS (such as *Cu, Ni, Mo*) MAY BE PRESENT AND SHOULD BE DETERMINED BY ANALYSIS (*Cast Scrap* of CHAPTER 12, *page 98*).

TABLE 19.3. DAILY MIXTURE CALCULATION SHEET

Mixture No. Heat No. Cupola No. Date

			Carbon			*Silicon*			*Manganese*			*Sulfur*			*Phosphorus*		
Material Charged	%	lb/chg.	%	lb	% in Mix*	%	lb	% in Mix*	%	lb	Mix %*	%	lb	% in Mix*	%	lb	Mix %*
Pig Iron, Mall.	20	400	4.30	17.20	0.86	0.90	3.60	0.18	0.55	2.20	0.110	0.03	0.12	0.006	0.15	0.60	0.030
Pig Iron, Foundry																	
Silvery Piglets	4	80	2.50	2.00	0.100	7.5	6.00	0.30	0.65	0.52	0.026	0.05	0.040	0.002	0.10	0.08	0.004
50% Fe Si Lump																	
Purchased Scrap	26	520	3.30	17.16	0.858	1.90	9.88	0.494	0.50	2.60	0.130	0.12	0.624	0.031	0.35	1.82	0.091
Cast Iron Briquets																	
Steel Briquets																	
Steel Scrap	20	400	0.20	0.80	0.040	0.20	0.80	0.040	0.60	2.40	0.120	0.04	0.160	0.008	0.03	0.12	0.006
Returns	30	600	3.40	20.40	1.020	1.85	11.10	0.555	0.50	3.00	0.150	0.12	0.720	0.036	0.19	1.14	0.057
Other: *Mn, Cr, Ni Cu, Mo,* etc.			LATE *Fe Si* ADDITION 13.1 lb of 75% 3/8 × 12 M				9.81	0.49									
Total	100	2000		57.56	2.878		41.19	2.05		10.72	0.536		1.664	0.083		3.76	0.188
Analysis Charged %	(TOTALS DIVIDED BY WEIGHTS)				2.88			2.05			0.54			0.08			0.188
% Melting Gain or Loss					+0.44			−0.20			−0.05			+0.04			+0.010
Estimate Analysis (%) At Cupola Spout					3.32			1.85			0.49			0.12			0.198

*Per cent of element (*C, Si, Mn, S, P*) based on 2000 lb charge.

While Table 19.2 may be used to guide in mixture making, for a particular operation experience will establish the loss of elements during melting. Once established, these figures should always be used.

This is a method of calculating the cupola charge: The average composition of the ingoing charge, based on the respective weights (or percentages) and chemical compositions of the various metallic components used, is determined. Table 19.2 shows the changes in composition which occur during the melting operation expressed as "Approximate Loss or Gain of Elements in Melting." Then the losses (or gains) as indicated are subtracted (or added). The results obtained at this point should give a close approximation of the percentages of silicon, sulfur, manganese, and phosphorus (also alloys if any were present in the charge) to be expected in the iron at the cupola spout. Usually there is a carbon pickup in melting. Carbon control is treated in Chapter 22.

Table 19.3 is a convenient way to figure the cupola charge. Itemization should be self-explanatory. The possible exception is *Melting loss or gain*: Carbon pickup of 0.44 per cent represents the increase in carbon during melting, based on experience with a particular melting practice. Silicon and manganese losses were calculated at 10 per cent of the percentages of these elements in the charge *(Analysis Charged %)*. The increase in sulfur agrees with figures in Table 19.2.

The mixture was calculated by *weights* of the various components used. However, the calculation could just as well have been made on a "percentage" basis, the method to be used being dependent on the preference of the person making the calculation.

Careful attention should be given the layout of storage facilities to promote ease and economy of handling. All pig irons, silvery irons, each of the various grades or classes of purchased scrap, either cast or steel, home scrap, with and without alloys, as well as any special or unusual type of material, should be kept separated on the storage yard. Unless this is done with care, the efforts of the party responsible for calculating the cupola charges will be wasted.

In addition to the foregoing, the bins used for the storage of the metallic components of the charge, as well as those used for coke and limestone, should be emptied and cleaned at regular intervals. During these clean-up periods, non-metallic materials such as sand, cinders and other trash should be removed from the iron bins, and foreign material and fines should be removed from the coke and flux bins. Obviously, large quantities of foreign matter in the iron bins which find their way into the cupola charge have the same effect as inaccurate weighing, and this, in turn, may often result in poor uniformity of composition of the metal at the cupola spout

Table 19.4 shows analyses of typical castings.

TABLE 19.4. TYPICAL ANALYSES OF CASTINGS

	Composition, per cent								
Casting Type	Total Carbon	Silicon	Manganese	Phosphorous	Sulfur	Nickel	Copper	Chromium	Molybdenum
1) Gray Iron Castings									
Automobile Cylinders	3.30	2.10	0.60	0.12	0.10			0.30	
Truck & Tractor Cylinders	3.25	2.00	0.65	0.12	0.10	0.75		0.50	
	3.25	2.00	0.65	0.12	0.10			0.40	0.40
	3.25	2.00	0.65	0.12	0.10		0.75	0.40	
Auto. Brake Drums	3.40	2.00	0.70	0.20	0.10				
Auto. Clutch Plates	3.25	2.20	0.60	0.20	0.10				
Auto. Crankshafts	2.80	2.50	0.80	0.15	0.10	0.50		0.50	0.50
Farm Machinery Castings									
Light	3.40	2.40	0.55	0.60	0.10				
Medium	3.30	2.20	0.60	0.50	0.12				
Heavy	3.15	1.80	0.65	0.35	0.12				
Misc. Machinery Castings									
Light	3.50	2.50	0.50	0.30	0.10				
Medium	3.30	2.00	0.60	0.30	0.12				
Heavy	3.15	1.50	0.65	0.25	0.12				
Very Heavy	3.10	1.25	0.70	0.20	0.14				
Pipe, Water									
Pit cast	3.50	1.60	0.50	0.65	0.10				
DeLevaud	3.60	1.65	0.35	0.70	0.10				
Sand spun	3.60	1.10	0.45	0.65	0.10				
Stove Plate	3.50	2.40	0.50	0.80	0.12				
Radiators	3.50	2.30	0.50	0.50	0.12				
Grate Bars	3.25	2.00	0.60	0.40	0.10			1.00	
Pots, Caustic	3.50	0.70	0.50	0.15	0.10	2.50		0.40	
2) Chilled and White Iron Castings									
Chilled Car Wheels	3.50	0.55	0.50	0.30	0.12				
Chilled Plow Shares	3.40	1.40	0.60	0.40	0.12				
Chilled Mold Boards	3.50	0.80	0.60	0.30	0.12				
Chilled Glass Molds	3.50	2.20	0.60	0.20	0.10	1.00		0.30	
White Iron Bearings (Agr.)	3.40	0.75	0.70	0.25	0.12		1.00	1.00	
White Iron Crusher Plates	3.30	0.60	0.60	0.15	0.10	4.50		1.50	
3) Malleable Castings									
Light & Medium Section	2.50	1.40	0.45	0.15	0.14				
Heavy Section	2.35	0.95	0.40	0.15	0.12				

CHAPTER 20

Records

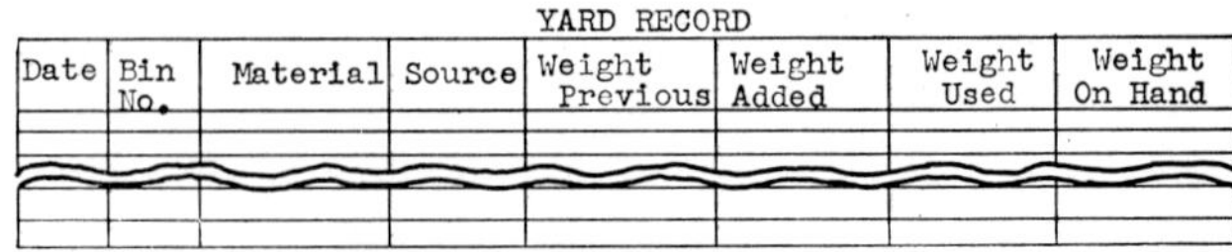

YARD RECORD

Date	Bin No.	Material	Source	Weight Previous	Weight Added	Weight Used	Weight On Hand

Fig. 20.2. Typical *Yard Record* form.

Records are a means to progress. They are often the basis for improvement and changes in technique, and if frequently and properly used they are an invaluable aid to the cupola operator and metallurgist. All daily records such as the mixture sheet, raw materials report, chemical and physical analysis sheet, chill test report, fluidity report, and the charts from recording equipment such as air weight, pressure, and temperature recorders should be filed in such a way that rapid and accurate comparison can be made. All records should be inspected periodically in an effort to minimize unfavorable trends or errors that may affect metal quality.

Many foundries have very concise melting logs that include all information on a single sheet, thus giving a complete history of the day's heat. A log such as this gives untold assistance to the cupola operator in his efforts to produce quality metal day in and day out.

The type and number of records used is strictly a matter of personal opinion, and can vary from simple forms in small foundries to very complicated ones in highly mechanized shops. Each foundry must determine its needs and set its records accordingly. Typical records that are recommended for efficient cupola control are –

1. Raw Material Record. The segregation of incoming materials is imperative since they vary from car to car. A "Yard Record" is a convenient way to keep them straight in cars, bins or piles, as the case may be. This record gives the history of each material as it is received, including the analysis grade and location, and it can also be used as a running raw material inventory. The total weights of material received and consumed can be taken from this record and reported to the accounting department. In the cases where forms have been set up by the ac-

DAILY MIXTURE CALCULATION SHEET

Mixture ______ Heat No. ______ Cupola No. ______ Date ______

Material Charged	Per cent	Pounds Per Charge	Carbon		Silicon		Manganese		Sulphur		Phosphorus	
			%	lb	%	lb	%	lb	%	lb	%	lb
Pig Iron, Low P Malleable												
Pig Iron, Foundry												
Silvery Piglets												
Returns												
Purchase Scrap												
Cast Iron Briquettes												
Steel Briquettes												
Steel Scrap												
Other												
Total												
Analysis Charged (Totals Divided by Pounds per Charge)												
Melting Loss or Gain												
Estimated Analysis												

Fig. 20.1. *Daily Mixture Calculation Sheet.*

CHARGING SCHEDULE

Date ______________

Cupola No. ______________ Heat No. ______________

Type of Iron ______________

Mixture No.				
	lb	lb	lb	lb
Pig Iron, Low P Malleable				
Pig Iron, Foundry				
Silvery Piglets				
Returns				
Purchase Scrap				
Cast Iron Briquettes				
Steel Briquettes				
Steel Scrap				
Other				
Total Weight				
Coke				
Limestone				
Fluorspar				
Manganese Briquettes				
Other				

Fig. 20.3. Example of *Charging Schedule* form.

counting department, this form would be unnecessary duplication.

Such a report provides the best reference and record for the calculation of mixtures and charge composition. Figure 20.2 shows a typical *Yard Record* used by one large production foundry.

2. Daily Mixture Calculation Sheet. The daily "Mix Sheet" is a practical way of figuring the charge composition. It is recommended that the charge be recalculated daily and filed in an orderly manner so that it can be used as a means of back-checking the mixture and estimated analysis. A recalculation on a new charge sheet should be made each time a different car, bin, pile or material is used, and a new mixture number should be assigned.

Actual material analyses are best to make computations. If not available, the figures in Table 19.1 can be used as approximations. Gain and loss of elements during melting are established for each operation through this set of calculations. The "Melting Gain or Loss" should be adjusted from time to time as changes occur in the operation of the cupola. Approximate per cent loss or gain of elements in cupola melting are in Table 19.2. Figure 20.1 is a simple *Mix Sheet* used by many foundries.

3. Charging Schedule. Each molding unit or floor foreman should determine the metal requirements for his section, and report this to the metallurgist or cupola foreman who makes the "Charging Schedule." After completion the charging schedule is given to the cupola charging crew or craneman. For double checking the intended analysis or the "Computed Mixture Analysis" is shown on the schedule. Figure 20.3 is an example of a *Charging Schedule.*

4. Cupola Record. All data pertaining to the operation of the cupola are shown on the "Cupola Record." Completeness of such a record cannot be overemphasized. The lining dimensions taken before and after the heat show the amount, location, and type of burn-out. In addition, a complete history of the bed preparation, lighting-off and burning-in is recorded along with other pertinent cupola data. The form also provides a convenient method for directing the cupola melting under the various conditions. A complete *Cupola Record* form is Fig. 20.4.

CUPOLA RECORD

Cupola No. __________ Date __________

Inside Diameter of Lining:	Before	After
Diameter of Well		
Diameter at Top of Main Tuyeres		
Diameter 6 inches above Top of Main Tuyeres		
" 12 " " " " " "		
" 24 " " " " " "		
" 36 " " " " " "		
" 48 " " " " " "		

Distance From Bottom of Tuyeres to:

Center of Tap Hole ______ Top of Sand Bottom at Tap Hole ______

Center of Slag Hole ______ Top of Sand Bottom at Slag Hole ______

Bed Preparation:

Light-up Time ______ Bed Height, Above Tuyeres ______

Weight of Coke in Light-up ______ Size of Bed Coke ______

Weight of Coke Fanned ______ Coke Brand ______

Weight of Coke, Full Bed ______ Weight of Limestone on Coke Bed ______

Remarks: ______

Filling the Cupola:

Number of Metal Charges ______ Number of Limestone Charges ______

Weight of Metal Charges ______ Weight of Limestone Charges ______

Number of Coke Charges ______ Time Filling Cupola: ______

Weight of Coke Charges ______ Start ______

Size of Coke in Fill Charges ______ Finish ______

Extra Coke in Fill Charges ______

Remarks: ______

Heat Records:

Time Blast on ______ Duration of Heat, Hours ______

Time on First Iron At Tuyeres ______ Tons Melted ______

Time on First Iron At Tap Hole ______ Down Time ______

Time of First Tap ______ Tapping Hours ______

Last Charge On ______ Heat Melting Rate ______

Blast Off ______ Lb Coke Used per Net Ton ______

Time Bottom Dropped ______ Melted ______

Remarks: ______

Fig. 20.4. Data of operation are kept on the *Cupola Record.*

TOTAL LADLE TREATMENT

Tap No.	Fore-hearth	Ladle					
	Soda Ash, lb	Chill Reducing Inoculant, lb	FeCr, lb	FeMo, lb	FeV, lb	F-Ni, lb	Other

Fig. 20.5. Alloying and inoculating procedures are entered on the *Total Ladle Treatment* record.

DAILY METAL CONTROL REPORT

KIND OF IRON ______________ DATE ______________

CUPOLA ______________

Pouring Time					
Mixture No.					
CHEMICAL TESTS					
Total Carbon					
Combined Carbon					
Graphitic Carbon					
Manganese					
Sulphur					
Phosphorus					
Silicon					
Nickel					
Chromium					
Molybdenum					
Vanadium					
PHYSICAL TESTS					
Brinell Hardness					
Chill Depth					
Transverse Str.					
Tensile Str.					
Deflection					
Spout Temp.					
Blast, oz					

Fig. 20.6. The *Daily Metal Control Report* records chemical and physical tests.

CUPOLA MELTING LOG | Cupola No. | Heat No. | Date

TIME AND MISC. RECORD	
Light Bed	
Start Charging	
Blast On	
First Tap	
First Slag	
Last Charge In	
Blast Off	
Total Time Blast On	
Total Down Time	
Net Melting Time	
Tons Melted Per Hour	
Coke Bed - Weight	
Coke Bed - Height	
Total No. of Charges	
Total Melt - Tons	
Total New Coke Used (Pounds)	
New Coke Per Ton of Melt (Pounds)	
Brand of Coke Used	

BLAST AND TEMPERATURE RECORD									
Time	Blast Vol. C.F.M.	Blast Press. oz.	Blast Off Mins.	Metal Temp. °F.					

CUPOLA CHARGES (in lbs.)

Material	% C	% Si.	% Mn.	% S	% P	Charges	Charges	Charges	Charges	Charges	Charges	Total
Pig Iron												
Remelt												
Steel Scrap												
Total Per Charge												
New Coke												
Reclaimed Coke												
Flux												
Gross % Carbon												
Gross % Silicon												
Gross % Manganese												
Gross % Sulphur												
Gross % Phosphorus												

Fig. 20.8. Typical *Cupola Melting Log* form.

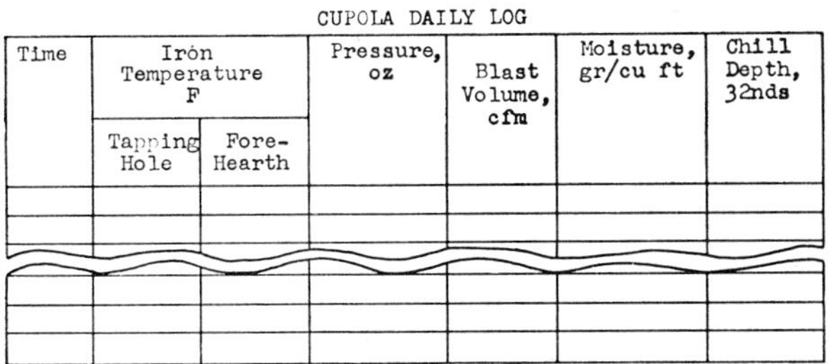

CUPOLA DAILY LOG

Time	Iron Temperature F		Pressure, oz	Blast Volume, cfm	Moisture, gr/cu ft	Chill Depth, 32nds
	Tapping Hole	Fore-Hearth				

Fig. 20.7. A running record of operation is provided by the *Cupola Daily Log.*

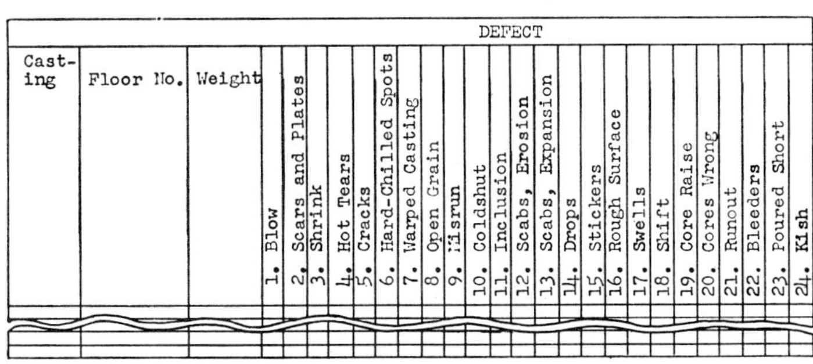

INSPECTORS DAILY REPORT

Date Cast ________ Date Inspected ________

Cast-ing	Floor No.	Weight	DEFECT 1. Blow	2. Scars and Plates	3. Shrink	4. Hot Tears	5. Cracks	6. Hard-Chilled Spots	7. Warped Casting	8. Open Grain	9. Misrun	10. Coldshut	11. Inclusion	12. Scabs, Erosion	13. Scabs, Expansion	14. Drops	15. Stickers	16. Rough Surface	17. Swells	18. Shift	19. Core Raise	20. Cores Wrong	21. Runout	22. Bleeders	23. Poured Short	24. Kish

Fig. 20.10. Enter casting defect data on the *Inspector's Daily Report.*

CASTING WORK SHEET

Shop Order	Pattern No. or Description	Av. Weight	No. of Pcs. Molded	Poured	Labor Cost Rate	Hr or Pcs	Amt.	Molder and Helper	Total Weight for Each Pattern	Bad Weight	Defect No.

Fig. 20.9. Molding floor work requirements and casting rejection data are recorded on the *Casting Work Sheet.*

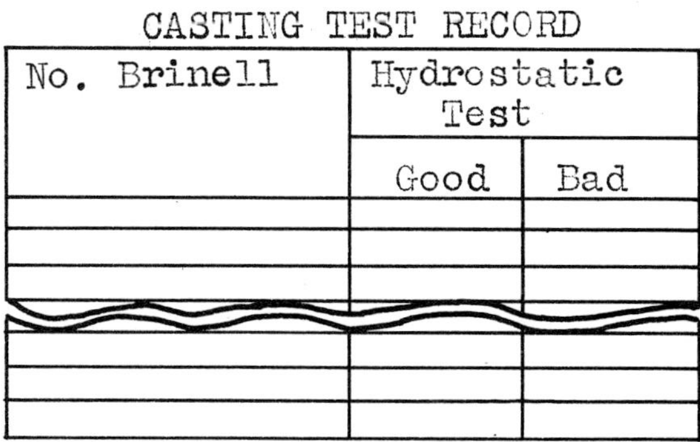

CASTING TEST RECORD

No.	Brinell	Hydrostatic Test Good	Bad

Fig. 20.11. For *Casting Test Record* results.

5. Cupola Daily Log. A running record of such phases of cupola melting as metal temperature, blast volume or weight, wind-box pressure, charges melted per hour, air moisture content, and chill depths is in the *Cupola Daily Log* (Fig. 20.7) and *Melting Log* (Fig. 20.8; Mechanical Charging Chapter 4, *page 41*).

6. Total Ladle Treatment. This record gives the alloying and inoculating procedure used at the cupola (Fig. 20.5). The *logs* in PARAGRAPHS 5 and 6 should be coordinated.

7. Daily Metal Control Report. The report is divided into two parts, chemical and physical tests. The form incorporates all the chemical and physical data of the iron melting in the cupola for a specific heat. The data should be obtained at a regular time interval throughout the heat. Taking the ladle analyses from only a couple of ladles is not sufficient because it does not show the trend of the cupola operation. The data on this form should be plotted daily to determine the variations of the operation. If the analyses and properties do not conform to the specification, steps should be taken immediately to correct such deviations. The average analysis from this record is used as the analysis of the returns in computing the cupola charge. Figure 20.6 is a typical *Daily Metal Control Report.*

The record forms referred to in this section are those that are considered necessary to good cupola practice. Since forms must meet individual foundry needs, those presented here are intended only as guides in making such forms. Some of them may need expansion, while others contain more detail than may be necessary. It is also recommended that as many of these forms as possible be combined into a single melting log that would present as complete a picture of the day's heat as is practical.

There are three additional records that aid the cupola foreman in producing an iron that is suitable for the particular casting that is being manufactured. These records are —

8. Casting Work Sheet. This report permits each molding unit or floor foreman to record his requirements and to determine the number and causes of casting rejections (Fig. 20.9).

9. Inspector's Daily Report. Casting inspection should be carried out prior to casting testing. The "Inspector's Daily Report" is the form provided for recording the casting defects (Fig. 20.10). These defects can be recorded by placing check marks or the number of such cases in the proper square. This report is then coordinated with the "Casting Work Sheet." Although a few defects are noted, the list is by no means complete. It would be advisable to conform to the needs of the individual foundry. When a defect occurs frequently, the metallurgist or cupola foreman, the molding foreman and the inspector should discuss the casting and defects and determine ways and means of eliminating the difficulties.

10. Casting Test Record. The "Casting Test Record" is the final check made on a casting before shipment (Fig. 20.11). If all the castings are tested and a serial number has not been cast into each one they should be numbered with paint. This will permit tracing the castings through the foundry in the event they are found to be defective after delivery.

CHAPTER 21

Refractory Lining Daily Maintenance

In order that the cupola furnace may contain the heat and molten products it must have a suitable refractory lining. Quality and uniformity are necessary in this lining to protect the structural components of the furnace, to insure consistent working dimensions, and assist a smooth stock descent with minimum contamination of the melt. The methods described in this chapter apply to cupolas with conventional refractory linings (Chapter 2, *page 16*). Special cupolas are treated in Chapter 3 *(page 23)*.

CUPOLA ZONES

From the standpoint of service conditions, the cupola is divided into four zones which, arranged in the order of decreasing severity, are: 1) the melting zone; 2) the crucible or hearth; 3) the charging zone; and 4) the zone above the charging door.

Melting Zone

The melting zone extends from the top of the tuyeres upward for a distance depending upon the height of the coke bed and the velocity of the blast air. The most severe conditions exist just above the tuyeres where oxidation of iron and other elements takes place and slag attack is most destructive. The high temperature in this zone increases chemical action and mechanical erosion. The extent to which the blast air penetrates into the coke at and above the tuyere level affects the refractory attack. The condition usually is worse in cupolas of smaller size.

Spalling (breaking or cracking of refractories to such an extent that fragments are separated, and new surfaces of the mass are exposed) is not likely to take place during the melting operation, but rather when the bottom is dropped—the cold air rushing past the extremely hot refractory establishes a condition of severe thermal shock. Thermal shock is aggravated by the introduction of streams of water to cool the furnace wall more quickly. Such a practice should be considered with caution since the saving in time may be heavily overbalanced by the cost of refractories destroyed.

Some abrasion by the moving components of the charge may take place at the top of the melting zone.

Crucible or Hearth

In the crucible or hearth of the cupola, the temperature is 300 to 400 F lower than that of the melting zone, and the lining is in contact only with molten metal, slag, and relatively static coke, so that the effects of temperature and abrasion are not serious. Unless the iron is badly oxidized, chemical reaction with the lining is not likely to take place, but some slag penetration is possible. Spalling will occur when the bottom is dropped, but usually to a lesser degree than higher in the cupola.

Charging Zone

The lining of the cupola in the charging zone is not subjected to very high temperatures nor to slag attack, but abrasion is very severe both from the impacts of the charging operation and the friction of the downward-moving solid charge. This condition is influenced by the method of charging. It is at its worst with certain types of mechanical charging, and perhaps scarcely noticeable in the careful hand-charging of small cupolas.

It is in this zone that a form of disintegration sometimes occurs which is caused by a gradual deposition of carbon in the pores of the refractories as the result of catalytic decomposition of carbon monoxide in the presence of iron at about 900 F. The reaction is: $2CO = CO_2 + C$.

Above Charging Door

Above the charging door, the conditions are not severe, the function of the lining being merely to protect the shell from heat of effluent stack gases.

THE ORIGINAL LINING

Materials

The materials most commonly used for the original cupola lining are fireclay refractories especially manufactured for the purpose. Monolithic linings are mixtures of fire clay and grog in suitable proportions, properly tempered with water, and rammed against the shell or a fireclay brick backing. Other refractories which are used to a small extent are the more costly super-duty fireclay, silica and high-alumina brick. Slabs of siliceous rock are used extensively, but chiefly for lining the melting zone. These materials are used for the conventional cupola, operated with an acid slag. For basic operation cupolas are lined with magnesite or dolomite brick or monolithic material for at least 4 ft above the tuyeres.

Generally one kind of fireclay refractory can be

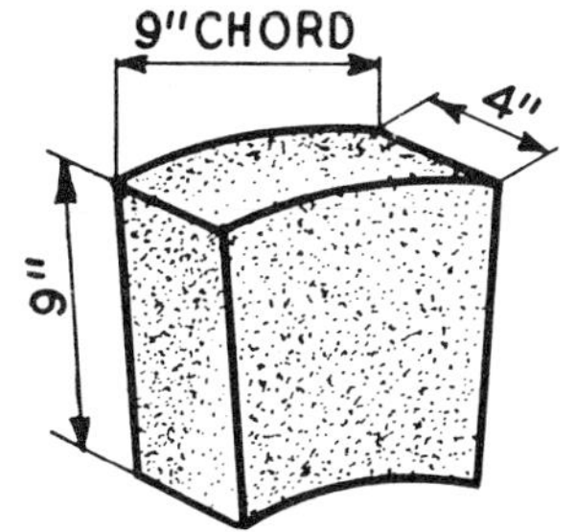

9" ROTARY KILN BLOCKS
(9" –) x 9" x 4"

Block No.	Inside chord in inches	Diameter in inches Ins.	Diameter in inches Outs.	No. of blocks to circle
48-66	$6\frac{17}{32}$	48	66	23
54-72	$6\frac{3}{4}$	54	72	26
60-78	$6\frac{15}{16}$	60	78	28
66-84	$7\frac{1}{16}$	66	84	30
72-90	$7\frac{3}{16}$	72	90	32
78-96	$7\frac{5}{16}$	78	96	34
84-102	$7\frac{13}{32}$	84	102	36
90-108	$7\frac{1}{2}$	90	108	38
96-114	$7\frac{19}{32}$	96	114	40
102-120	$7\frac{21}{32}$	102	120	42
108-126	$7\frac{23}{32}$	108	126	44
114-132	$7\frac{25}{32}$	114	132	46
117-135	$7\frac{13}{16}$	117	135	48
120-138	$7\frac{13}{16}$	120	138	49
123-141	$7\frac{27}{32}$	123	141	50
126-144	$7\frac{7}{8}$	126	144	51
132-150	$7\frac{29}{32}$	132	150	53
138-156	$7\frac{31}{32}$	138	156	55
144-162	8	144	162	57
150-168	$8\frac{1}{32}$	150	168	59

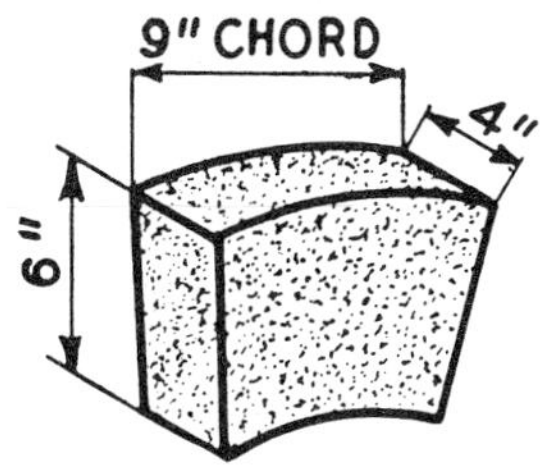

6" CUPOLA BLOCKS AND
6" ROTARY KILN BLOCKS
9" x 6" x 4"

Block No.	Inside chord in inches	Diameter in inches Ins.	Diameter in inches Outs.	No. of blocks to circle
30-42	$6\frac{7}{16}$	30	42	15
36-48	$6\frac{3}{4}$	36	48	17
42-54	7	42	54	19
48-60	$7\frac{3}{16}$	48	60	21
54-66	$7\frac{3}{8}$	54	66	23
60-72	$7\frac{1}{2}$	60	72	26
66-78	$7\frac{5}{8}$	66	78	28
72-84	$7\frac{23}{32}$	72	84	30
78-90	$7\frac{13}{16}$	78	90	32
84-96	$7\frac{7}{8}$	84	96	34
90-102	$7\frac{15}{16}$	90	102	36
96-108	8	96	108	38
102-114	$8\frac{1}{16}$	102	114	40
108-120	$8\frac{3}{32}$	108	120	42
114-126	$8\frac{5}{32}$	114	126	44
120-132	$8\frac{3}{16}$	120	132	46
123-135	$8\frac{3}{16}$	123	135	48

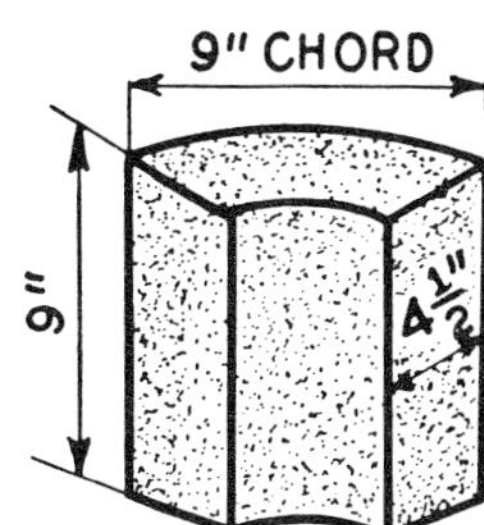

4½" CUPOLA BLOCKS 9" HIGH
9" x 4½" x 9"

Name of Block	Inside chord in inches	Diameter in inches Ins.	Diameter in inches Outs.	No. of blocks to circle
A	$5\frac{3}{4}$	16	25	9
B	$6\frac{5}{16}$	21	30	11
C	$6\frac{3}{4}$	27	36	13
D	$6\frac{15}{16}$	30	39	14
E	$7\frac{11}{32}$	40	49	18
F	$7\frac{21}{32}$	51	60	21
G	$7\frac{13}{16}$	60	69	24
H	8	73	82	29

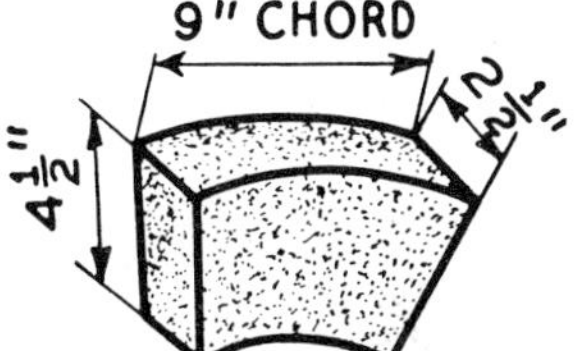

9" CIRCLE BRICK
9" x 4½" x 2½"

Brick No.	Inside chord in inches	Diameter in inches Ins.	Diameter in inches Outs.	No. of brick to circle
24-33	$6\frac{17}{32}$	24	33	12
36-45	$7\frac{3}{16}$	36	45	16
48-57	$7\frac{19}{32}$	48	57	20
60-69	$7\frac{13}{16}$	60	69	24
72-81	8	72	81	29
84-93	$8\frac{1}{8}$	84	93	33
96-105	$8\frac{7}{32}$	96	105	37
108-117	$8\frac{5}{16}$	108	117	41
120-129	$8\frac{3}{8}$	120	129	45

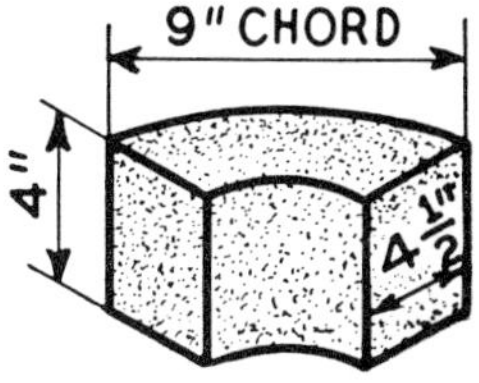

4½" CUPOLA BLOCKS 4½" HIGH
9" x 4½" x 4"

Block No.	Inside chord in inches	Diameter in inches Ins.	Diameter in inches Outs.	No. of blocks to circle
27-36	$6\frac{3}{4}$	27	36	13
32-41	$7\frac{1}{32}$	32	41	15

Fig. 21.1. **Standard types and sizes of cupola refractories.**

used for lining the cupola from bottom to charging door, provided the type selected can meet the severe requirements of the melting zone. Experience has shown that little, if any, economy is attained by using more than one kind of brick or block.

Properties

The properties that control the usefulness of fireclay refractories are 1) pyrometric cone equivalent (P.C.E.), which indicates the ability of the material to withstand high temperature, and 2) the density, or better, denseness, which affects the resistance to slag penetration, spalling, and abrasion.

The order of the P.C.E. depends upon the characteristics of the clays and grog used in the mixture from which the finished shape is made. The denseness is controlled by the nature of the clays and the proportions in which they are mixed, by particle

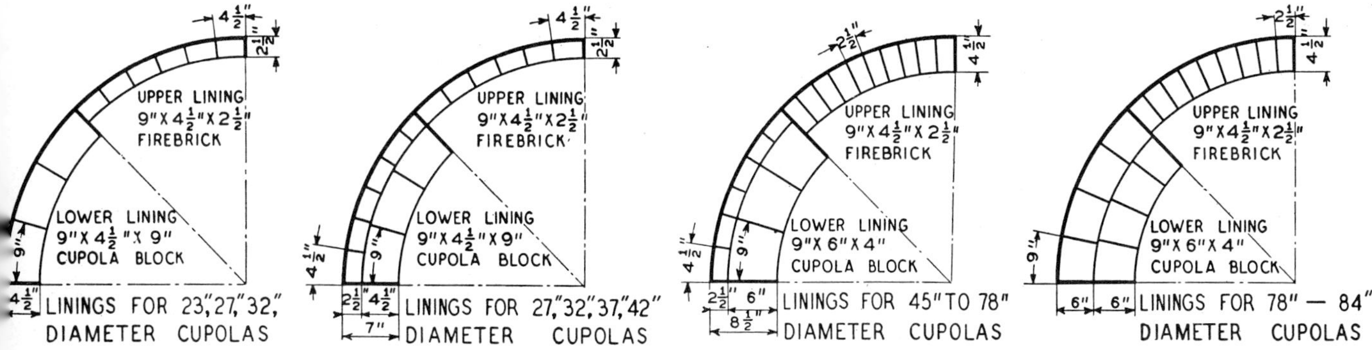

Fig. 21.2. Lining plan views: different size cupolas.

TABLE 21.1. **NUMBER OF BRICK AND BLOCK REQUIRED FOR CUPOLAS**

Consult refractory supplier for other available sizes. NOTE: For long runs, heavier linings are required.

	Lower Lining							Upper Lining				
				Number per foot					Number per foot			
Cupola No.	Shell Diam., in.	Thick-ness, in.	Size of Cupola Block	Cupola Block	9-in. Str. Brick	Fire clay, lb/ft	Total Weight per ft, lb	Thick-ness, in.	9-in. Str. Brick	Arch Brick No. 1	Fire clay, lb/ft	Total Weight per ft, lb
0**	27	4½	*18-27	12	..	15	303	...	..	...	..	....
1**	32	4½	*23-32	16	..	22	427	2½	31	...	12	215
2**	36	4½	*27-36	18	..	24	482	2½	35	...	14	243
2½**	41	7	*27-36	18	39	40	790	2½	39	...	16	271
3**	46	7	*32-41	20	43	44	869	2½	44	...	18	308
3½**	51	7	*37-46	21	47	47	932	2½	48	...	19	336
4**	56	7	*42-51	24	52	54	1059	2½	52	...	21	364
5	63	9	†42-54 †48-60	30 30	59	72	1422	4½	9	101	44	831
6	66	9	†48-60	63	61	76	1500	4½	15	101	47	879
7	72	9	†54-66	69	67	83	1643	4½	25	101	50	957
8	78	9	†60-72	75	73	91	1791	4½	36	101	55	1045
9	84	9	†66-78	81	78	98	1928	4½	45	101	58	1115
9½	90	9	†72-84	87	84	105	2065	4½	56	101	63	1203
10	96	9	†78-90	96	90	115	2265	4½	60	101	65	1235
11	102	12	†78-90 90-102	96 108	..	122	3400	4½	71	101	69	1322
12	108	12	†84-96 *96-108	102 114	..	130	3800	4½	82	101	75	1425

*Calliau Blocks; 9 in. across back, 9 in. high, 4½ radial.
†Cupola Blocks; 9 in. across back, 4 in. high, 6 in. radial.

**Alternate arrangement for Lower Linings (Cupolas No. 0 to No. 4 using standard arch and straight brick.)

Cupola No.	Shell Dia., in.	Thick-ness, in.	Shape — No. per ft	9-in. Straight Brick, No. per ft	Fire clay, lb/ft	Total Weight per ft, lb
0	27	4½	9″ No. 3 Arch— 6 9″ No. 2 Arch—40	—	18	317
1	32	4½	9″ No. 2 Arch—48 9″ No. 1 Arch— 7	—	22	383
2	36	4½	9″ No. 2 Arch—42 9″ No. 1 Arch—20	—	25	430
2½	41	7	9″ No. 2 Arch—42 9″ No. 1 Arch—20	39	40	700
3	46	7	9″ No. 2 Arch—32 9″ No. 1 Arch—38	44	46	794
3½	51	7	9″ No. 2 Arch—24 9″ No. 1 Arch—54	48	50	878
4	56	7	9″ No. 2 Arch—15 9″ No. 1 Arch—71	52	55	962

size, the method of forming or molding, and the time and temperature of firing. Refractory properties are detailed in Chapter 17 *(page 143)*.

Installation

The refractories are built up inside the cupola shell to form a container of uniform and ample thickness for the fuel and metal charges. The lining constitutes the real furnace, the steel shell merely holding it in place. It is first necessary to decide upon the thickness of the lining which must be at least 4½ in. thick for small cupolas and 7 in. for large ones. It is more economical in the long run to install thicknesses of 7 to 9 in., and for very large cupolas, 12 in. The lining is made up of cupola block of one or several of the tabulated sizes (Fig. 21.1) to form the required dia. Plan views of lining different size cupolas are in Fig. 21.2. Fig. 21.3 is a complete typical arrangement of the simplest straight 8½-in. lining. The number of brick and blocks for lining many size cupolas is in Table 21.1.

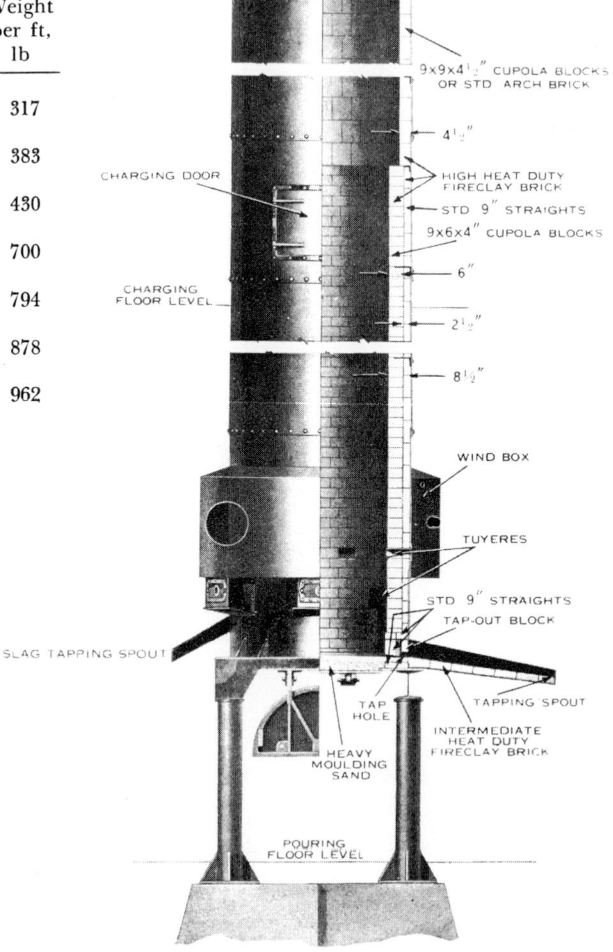

Fig. 21.3. Cutaway view showing typical arrangement of complete 8½-in. cupola lining.

In setting the refractory units, ¾-in. should be provided between the lining and the shell. As each course of block is laid, this space is filled with sand which absorbs the heavy expansion stresses produced when the lining is heated, thus preventing any distortion of the shell.

It cannot be over-emphasized that the cupola block must be laid up as close together as possible because the joints are most vulnerable to slag attack. Cupola block are used in preference to straight or arch brick because the units are larger and the number of joints in a given area is correspondingly smaller. The joints are made more resistant to slag penetration and erosion by the careful selection and proper use of the most suitable bonding material, a procedure to which too often, scant attention is given.

Bales and McCarthy state that cupola block have a longer service life in the well and melting zone when they are laid with super-quality refractory bonding mortar instead of ordinary fire clay, because the latter usually has a lower fusion point (P.C.E.) than that of the block. Fire clay has very little bonding power a few inches back of the hot face, and its relatively high shrinkage permits the penetration of slag and consequent erosion. High grade bonding mortars have a higher fusion point than the block; they form a better bond, and since the shrinkage is low the danger of slag penetration is greatly diminished. In any case, the bonding material should be mixed and the block placed so that the thinnest possible joints are obtained.

Each block is dipped in the bonding slip to cover the sides that are to be placed against other blocks. Strength and stability are imparted to the lining by offsetting the vertical joints of each course as shown in Fig. 21.3. The space between lining and shell is filled with sand as each course of block is laid.

In good cupola construction, shelves of cast iron or steel angles are provided at 5 to 10 ft intervals to help support the lining. The integrity of the remaining lining thus is maintained if sections fall out from accidental causes.

The erection of the cupola lining is started at the built-in supports adjacent to the bottom doors. Provision for the tap hole is made in the lowest courses, and for the slag hole in the next higher courses. The height of the slag hole above the tap hole depends on the volume of molten iron it is desired to carry in the well of the intermittent tap type cupola.

The tap hole is usually a round tapered orifice having a diameter depending upon the expected maximum melt rate. It has been customary for many years to tap out through a breast (Fig. 21.4) made of rammed refractory material. The breast must be made each day as a part of the patching and daubing operation described in Chapter 21. . . . The use of manufactured refractory block of the right quality and size in which one or two tap holes are made (Fig. 21.5) has been found more convenient in recent practice. This type of block is installed as a part of the cupola lining; it does not have to be replaced after each heat.

Similarly, the slag hole may be left or cut into the cupola lining at the proper height opposite the tap hole. It is best to use a slag hole block (Fig. 21.5), also installed as an integral part of the lining.

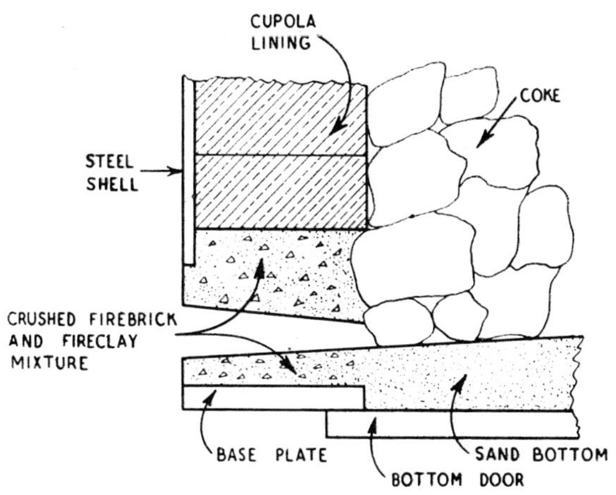

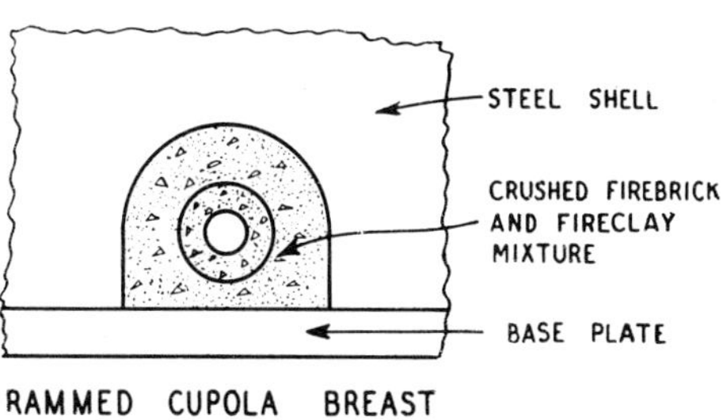

Fig. 21.4. **Sketch showing details of the cupola breast.**

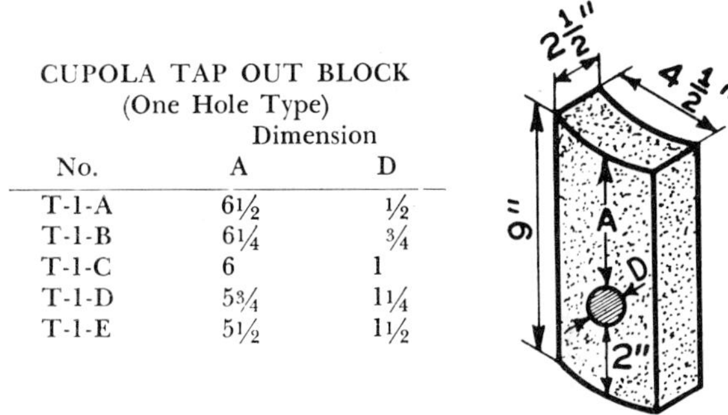

CUPOLA TAP OUT BLOCK
(One Hole Type)

No.	Dimension A	Dimension D
T-1-A	6½	½
T-1-B	6¼	¾
T-1-C	6	1
T-1-D	5¾	1¼
T-1-E	5½	1½

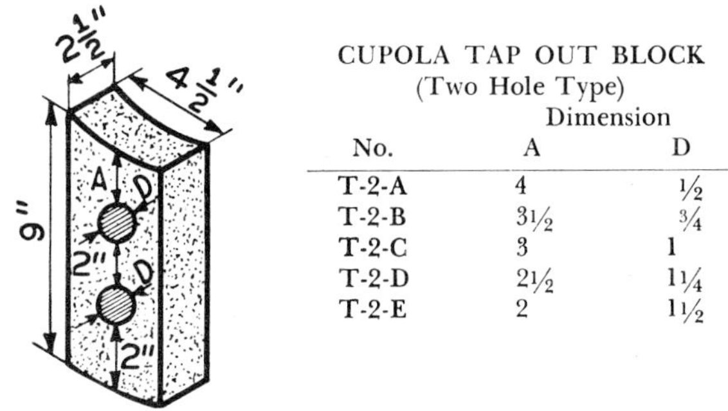

CUPOLA TAP OUT BLOCK
(Two Hole Type)

No.	Dimension A	Dimension D
T-2-A	4	½
T-2-B	3½	¾
T-2-C	3	1
T-2-D	2½	1¼
T-2-E	2	1½

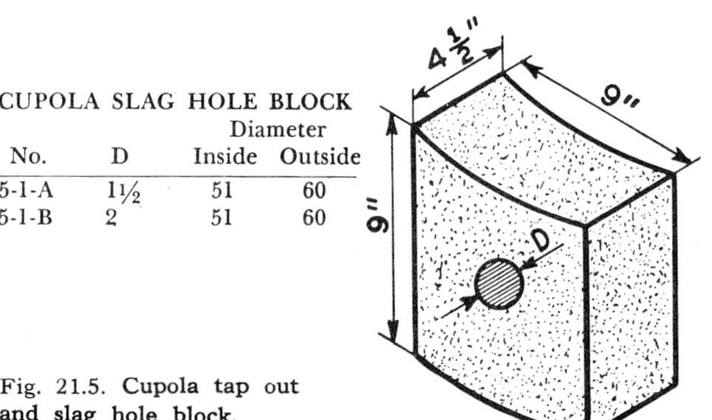

CUPOLA SLAG HOLE BLOCK

No.	D	Diameter Inside	Diameter Outside
5-1-A	1½	51	60
5-1-B	2	51	60

Fig. 21.5. **Cupola tap out and slag hole block.**

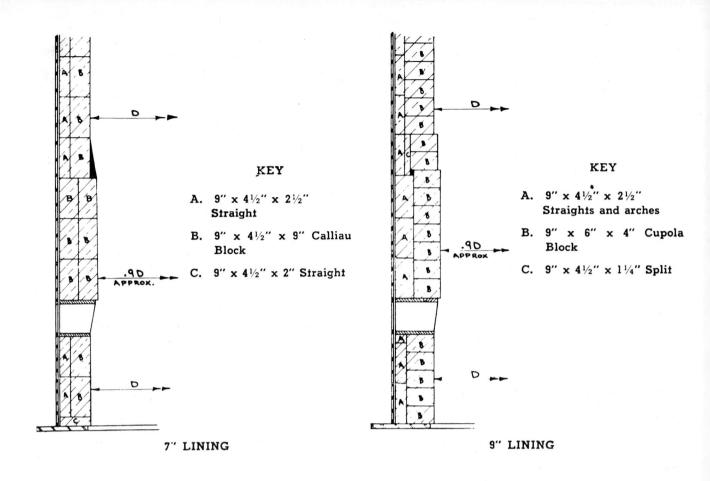

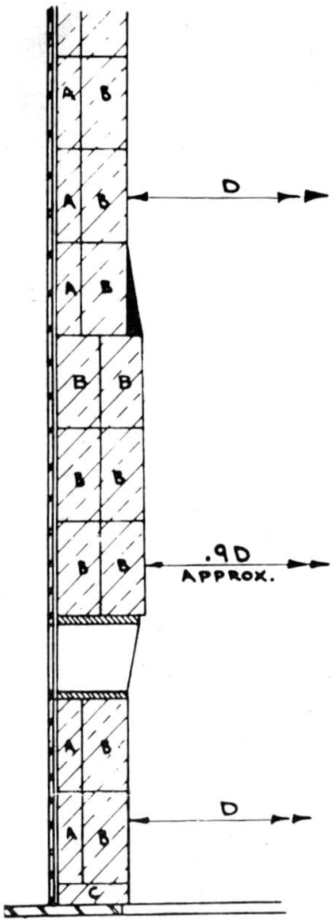

D
.9D
APPROX.
D

KEY

A. 9" x 4½" x 2½" Straight

B. 9" x 4½" x 9" Calliau Block

C. 9" x 4½" x 2" Straight

7" LINING

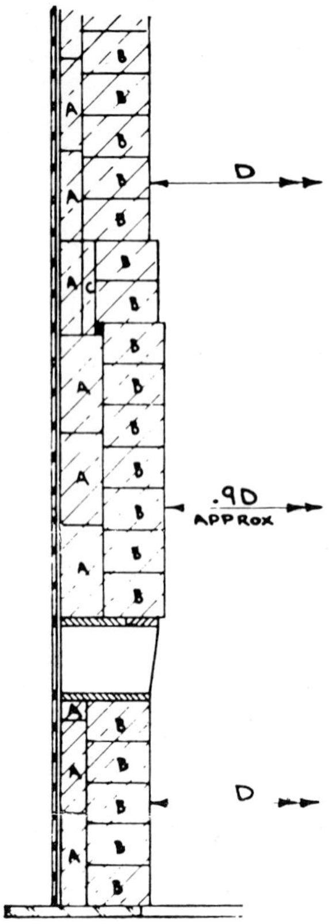

D
.9D
APPROX
D

KEY

A. 9" x 4½" x 2½" Straights and arches

B. 9" x 6" x 4" Cupola Block

C. 9" x 4½" x 1¼" Split

9" LINING

D
.9D
APPROX.
D

KEY

A. 9" x 4½" x 2½" Straights and arches

B. 9" x 6" x 4" Cupola Block

10½" LINING

D
.9D
APPROX.
D

KEY

A. 9" x 4½" x 2½" Straight

B. 9" x 6" x 4" Cupola Block

C.. 9" x 4½ x 1¼ Split

12" LINING

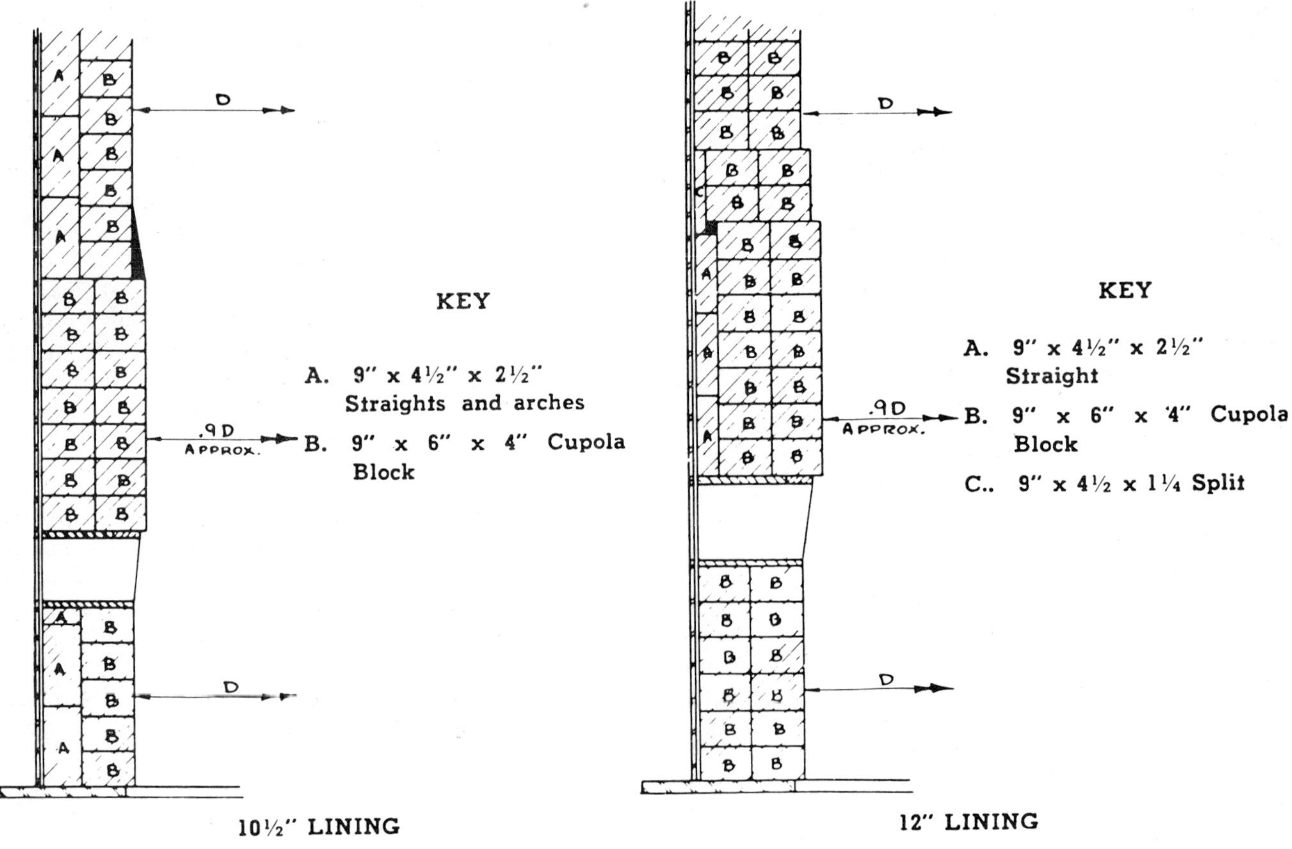

Fig. 21.6. Sketches showing several methods of building boshed-in cupola linings.

When the tuyere zone is reached, and the lining is even with the bottom of the tuyere elbows, the segments forming the lower part of the tuyeres are laid in place forming a continuous circle. The tuyere blocks or separators are then set in place and the spaces between the webs in the tuyere blocks are filled with ganister or crushed fireclay brick to protect them against heat. The top segments of the tuyeres are next laid in place forming a continuous shelf all around for the next course of brick or block. The tuyeres should fit tight against the shell to minimize air leakage.

Boshed-in Lining

A boshed-in lining is used to ensure better penetration of the blast, or merely to assure good clearance for the metal and slag as they drop past the tuyeres.

In such practice, the ID of the cupola immediately above the tuyeres is reduced to a dimension less than that of the area above the melting zone. Fig. 21.6 illustrates methods of building such boshed-in linings. Refractory consumption will increase by the use of this lining practice; other benefits must be gained to offset the added cost.

The bosh is made by extending the three to eight courses of block above the tuyeres by means of thicker brick or extra split brick placed against the shell, thus causing the block to overhang from 2 to 6 in., depending on the size of the cupola. From that point upward the lining is tapered backward gradually to the normal diameter. The angle of slope of the bosh is important. At the top of the bosh where the diameter is increased gradually to the normal diameter the slope of the bricking should be not less than 60° from the horizontal.

Lining to Charging Door

After tapering the lining back to its normal diameter, course after course of block is laid straight up to the top of the charging door. In many cases cast iron block, which offer better resistance to the impact and abrasion of the fuel and metal charges, are used in place of the clay refractories opposite to and for a few courses below the charging door.

Stack Lining

Above the charging door, where but a single lining is required, circle brick or Calliau block are laid directly against the shell because the temperature in the zone is not sufficiently high to cause excessive expansion, and therefore no cushion is required.

Drying the Lining

After the lining has been completed it should be brought to temperature as slowly as possible. Otherwise, with extremely high temperature suddenly applied, the block will become red hot on the face while the other parts are still wet, and excessive spalling will take place, especially when the block are hard and dense in structure. Even in preliminary drying some cracks are bound to appear, but these can be patched and thus prevent the penetration of metal and slag which would materially shorten the service life of the lining.

In some plants an elaborate drying process is carried out by closing the bottom doors of the cupola and making a sand bottom in the regular way. Shavings are charged and pieces of wood placed on them, the larger pieces standing around the cupola wall. Coke is then charged and the shavings are ignited. A slow fire is maintained, preferably for several days during which the moisture will be removed gradually without harmful effect on the lining.

Installation of Monolithic Linings

As the name implies, a monolithic lining is a single solid refractory wall of uniform structure built against the cupola shell from bottom plate to or above the charging door. Thus the joints inherent in a lining constructed of brick or block are eliminated, and herein lies the principal advantage of a monolithic lining. The material used is a highly siliceous ramming refractory or a plastic refractory of the clay-grog type. It is rammed as tightly as possible between the cupola shell and a wooden form. The specification in regard to wall thickness is the same as for block linings, but allowance should be made for shrinkage, keeping in mind that while fireclay refractories are prefired, the firing of a rammed lining is completed only when the first melting operation is carried out.

The high temperature cannot be applied as uniformly as in a kiln and, therefore, the face will be sintered and perhaps glazed while the lining adjacent to the shell is still relatively soft. However, rammed linings have given very satisfactory service and some operators claim for them longer life and lower cost than can be attained with brick or block linings.

A review of foundry literature shows that monolithic linings are used to a greater extent in Britain and continental Europe than in the United States. In England a clay-bonded ganister is preferred to clay-grog mixtures.

Preparation of Plastic Batch

The batch for a monolithic lining is prepared in the same manner as the material from which refractory shapes are made. Careful attention must be given to the selection of materials, formulation, and mixing. For the last purpose, a muller-type mixer, such as used for mixing foundry sand, is well suited. The amount of water used is kept to the minimum required to develop the proper degree of plasticity to insure maximum cohesion. Too much water in the mix will prevent tight ramming and cause trouble in drying.

Installation

The lining is formed by placing the moist material, in small quantities at a time, between the cupola shell and a circular wooden form having a diameter slightly less than that of the desired lining to allow for shrinkage. The wooden form must be centered properly in the cupola to provide equal thickness of lining around the circumference. The plastic material is packed as tightly as possible by hand, or preferably with a pneumatic rammer. Only 4 or 5 in. of the lining, clear around the cupola, is rammed at a time. The form is then pulled up a few inches and the next layer is rammed in.

Provision is made at the outset for the breast or the setting of tap-hole and slag hole block. At the proper

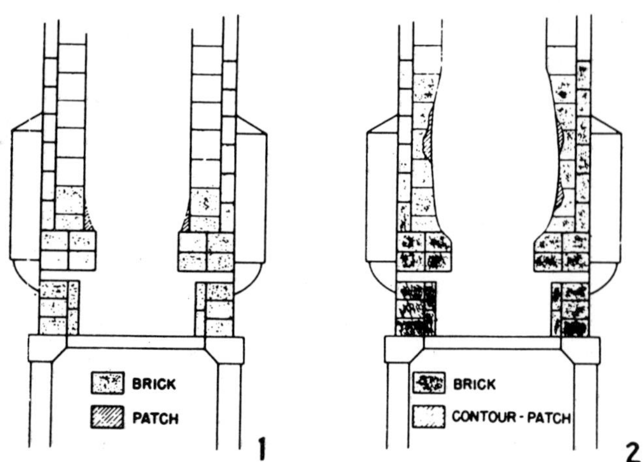

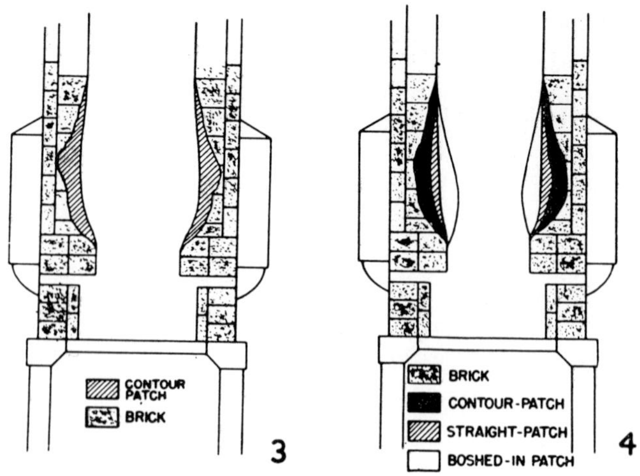

Fig. 21.7. Methods of patching burn-back area in cupola melting zone: 1) original brick lining prior to service; 2) burn-out and patch after first short heat; 3) burn-out and patch after first long heat or second or third short heat; 4) contour patch compared with straight patch (not recommended) and boshed-in patch (not recommended).

height the tuyeres are set, as in the case of a block lining, and the remainder of the lining is rammed straight from the tuyere level to the charging door. After the form is removed the overhang above the tuyeres is built and the entire lining face is troweled smooth. The lining must be well vented with a wire or rod to aid the escape of moisture during drying.

Drying Monolithic Linings

The service life of a monolithic lining depends almost entirely on the care with which it is dried. Haste at this stage spells disaster. For the first 2 or 3 days a current of air should be passed through the cupola to bring about slow evaporation of the moisture. A small fire is then placed in the bottom, but the flame should not come in contact with the lining until it has been warmed and all free moisture has been expelled. The next step is to stand a row of bricks on end in a circle and light a coke fire about 9 in. deep inside the circle. Coke is added from time to time and temperature of 300 to 400 F is maintained until the lining is perfectly dry. This point can be determined by drilling a small hole into the lining and inserting therein a glass rod. If there is no condensation of moisture on the rod when it is removed, the lining can be considered dry.

The fire is then made up to the melting zone and the temperature increased to 2200 F. All air inlets at the bottom of the shaft and the tuyeres are closed, and the whole is allowed to soak as long as possible. When this operation is carried out properly, the lining will be hard and free from cracks and spalls, and have the appearance of lightly-burned fire brick. It then will be ready for the regular melting operation.

LINING REPAIR

Conditions in the upper parts of the cupola are not so severe and these areas seldom have to be relined more often than once a year or two. However, conditions are very severe in the melting zone. No refractory has yet been developed which will withstand for more than a few hours the high temperature plus the corrosive action of the slag and oxidizing atmosphere. This results in a lining burn-back of several inches depth just above the tuyeres. This burn-back usually makes it necessary to patch or repair the lining of the melting zone after every long heat (Fig. 21.7).

The burn-back is normally proportional to the length of the heat and the temperature of the melting zone. Relative refractory consumption may be increased by excessive blast, excessive flux, high proportions of steel scrap, small cupola diameter, and uneven charging.

In order to patch a cupola properly it is necessary to chip away adhering slag and coke so that the patch can adhere to a firm refractory foundation. Without sufficient chipping the glossy slag layer does not bond readily to the patch material and is inclined to soften during the following heat, causing the patch to fall off.

The chipping is readily accomplished with such hand tools as a pick or chipping hammer (Fig. 21.8), or may be done with a pneumatic chipping hammer.

Patching Methods

There are four principal methods of patching cupola linings.

1) Brick.
2) Natural silica stone.
3) Rammed monolithic plastic.
4) Gun placed monolithic lining.

Each of the methods has certain advantages under certain conditions. The length of heat and the severity of attack, the number of cupolas to be patched, and proximity to natural materials are some of the factors that determine the best method of patching from the standpoint of cost and performance.

Patching With Brick

When repairing with standard fireclay refractory shapes, the nature of the repair will depend upon the extent of the burnout. The preferred practice is to use that combination of shapes which will give the most stable construction and may indicate the use of standard 9-in. circle brick and sometimes arch brick as well as straights and splits. These are installed with daubing mud or plastic refractory, using the proper amount to hold the fireclay shapes in place and to fill up all openings that cannot be filled with the shapes. Every advantage of extra anchoring and support should be taken, and this is made easier if the proper ledge or base has been provided above the tuyeres.

It is desirable to remove the first two courses above the tuyeres if the burnout justifies it and replace with new blocks. This practice provides a good foundation on which to make the repair. If the burnout is less severe, it is desirable to cut back an adequate ledge in this area to give a good foundation to support the repair.

Mortar

Perhaps the most important consideration is the preparation of the daubing mud, and every operator will agree that nothing done in the foundry finds a wider selection of materials and methods than does the preparation of daubing mixes. The materials employed are silica ganister (a high silica rock called quartzite), sand, refractory grog, fire clays, and just clays or loams. The choice of materials too often is dictated by what happens to be at hand. About all that can be definitely stated is that they are some form of alumina-silica mixture, and as such their behavior might be anticipated by a study of the silica-alumina phase equilibria relationships. Unfortunately, this is only one factor in trying to ascertain what any such mixture will do in service.

The other factors of grain sizing, method of mixing, method of tempering, type of service to which subjected, are also of such importance that it is difficult to use daubing mixes on the basis of thermo-mineralogical considerations, which in the first place are based on equilibrium conditions not always, if ever, obtained in the use of these materials.

Perhaps the most widely used mixtures are made up of ganister and fire clay. These mixtures vary from 3 to 1 (ganister: fire clay) on down to predominantly fireclay composition. Perhaps the best practice, if there is a best practice, will employ a ratio approaching 2 to 1 of silica to clay. This will depend upon the nature of the clay, and particularly its plasticity and its shrinkage characteristics. The latter may be compensated for by the addition of fireclay grog to these silica clay mixtures. The use of low grade clays, loams, and materials of low refractoriness should be avoided.

A very important consideration is the proper grain sizing and grain distribution in preparing these mixes. Every refractory manufacturer is well aware of the effect of grain sizing of silica or ganister in manufacturing refractory products. The use of the proper combination of coarse and fine grain size ganister generally will give best results.

Tempering and Preparation

Perhaps of no less importance than composition and materials used is the method of tempering and preparation. It is an economy to provide for mulling or thorough mixing of the daubing mud. Without proper mixing the optimum properties of the material used cannot be obtained. Variable results almost always follow.

The amount of water used will depend upon the nature of the raw materials and the manner in which the daubing mud is to be applied. It is desirable to mix the mud well in advance of the time

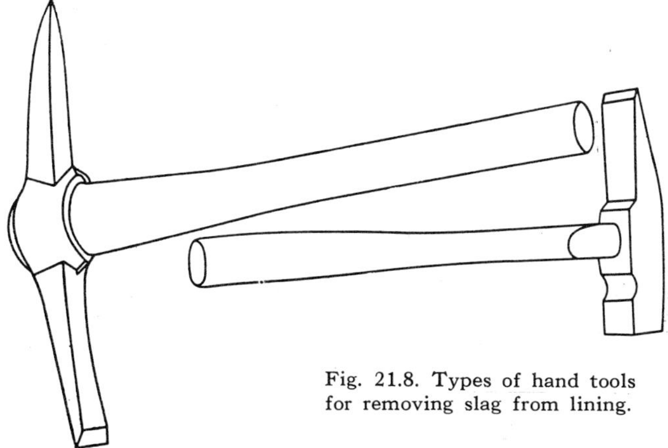

Fig. 21.8. Types of hand tools for removing slag from lining.

it is to be used to allow for the development of the maximum plasticity and workability of the clays contained in the mix. As to the method of using, some operators use a fairly wet (thin or sticky) mud and apply by throwing in balls on the surface to be patched and pressing the fireclay shapes into place.

Others use a drier mix and hammer or force the refractory shapes into place. Some operators prepare a very stiff mix and tamp it into mortar boxes until it is required. It can then be cut off in slices and hammered into place. Some favor the use of these drier mixes (as dry as compatible with proper installation) since the dry mixtures are subject to less drying and burning shrinkage.

In laying brick it is important that the brick be surrounded by mortar to be sure there are no voids. Then the inserted brick should be pressed or tapped firmly against the bricks beside and below it to press out any excess mortar and minimize joint space. Since the mortar is not as dense or refractory as the brick it is advantageous to hold the amount of mortar as low as possible.

Some typical mortar mixes are: 1 part clay: 2 parts crushed brick; 2 parts clay: 3 parts sand.

Patching With Natural Silica Stone

Natural sandstone, firestone, or mica schist can be used in many cases to economically patch the cupola. Several foundries report that the use of sandstone is the accepted practice in their plants, and that the results have been very satisfactory both in cost and lining life.

In order to make the substitution successfully the patching must be done by an experienced man. The irregular shapes and sizes require some additional care in order to obtain a solid patch. The training of such a man is not a difficult task, and any tender who is experienced in patching with brick can make the substitution with only limited additional instructions.

In some cases the use of sandstone results in a better lining life and reduced patching cost. These reductions are due to the high fusion point of the sandstone, P.C.E. 32, and to the ease with which the slabs of sandstone can be laid. It is not uncommon for pieces as large as 6 to 8 in. square and 2 to 4 in. thick to be used. A typical chemical analysis of firestone is—

	Per Cent		Per Cent
Silica (SiO_2)	93.13	Magnesium Oxide (MgO)	0.25
Alumina (Al_2O_3)	3.86	Calcium Oxide (CaO)	0.10
Ferric Oxide (Fe_2O_3)	0 11	Loss on ignition	1.43
Ferrous Oxide (FeO)	0.54		

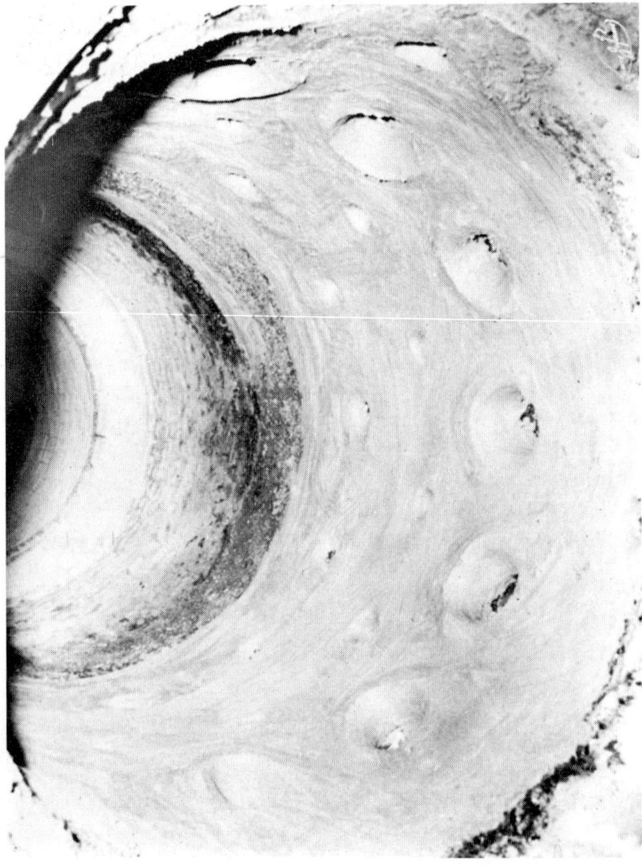

Figs. 21.9 and 21.10. Views (looking up from bottom) of cupola patched with natural sandstone. Top: after laying stone; bottom: after finishing with a clay slurry.

The daubing material used in laying up firestone should consist of approximately 60 per cent fire clay and 40 per cent silica sand, ground firebrick, or firestone. These components should be mixed thoroughly with only enough water to give a plasticity that will adhere to the cupola wall. Care should be taken to prevent the freshly patched areas from slipping during the early part of the heat.

It is important, as is the case with any patching material, that the cupola walls be chipped clean of all adhering coke and slag. It is good practice to chip the cupola walls until the face of the back-up refractory is showing.

After the cupola has been completely chipped down the daubing material is thrown against or pounded onto the cupola walls to a thickness of approximately 2 in. The sandstone is then pressed into the daub to a depth that will make it secure from slipping. It is necessary to fit the pieces of sandstone as closely together as possible and at the same time leave room for expansion as the freshly patched area is heated. Figures 21.9 and 21.10 show patching with natural sandstone.

It is recommended that the sandstone be predried to a temperature in excess of 200 F, or slowly dried to that temperature after installation. This treatment prevents excessive spalling during the drying-out period early in the heat.

A more desirable patch is obtained if the cleavage planes or grains of the sandstone are in the horizontal direction, that is, at right angles to the axis of the cupola, when laid-up. This method of laying-up reduces spalling and the resulting increase in the slag burden as the pieces of sandstone spall-off and fall into the cupola well. In most cases the cost of quarrying the sandstone in this manner is prohibitive, and it is the usual practice for the cleavage planes of the slabs of sandstone to run parallel to the cupola axis. In locations where natural sandstone is available as a low cost patching material it can be used successfully.

Patching by Ramming Monolithic Material

Some foundries patch by ramming a tempered mixture against the cupola wall. A mixture of ganister, sand, and clay is frequently used. The components are mixed in a muller and tempered to the minimum moisture content to develop sufficient plasticity for good ramming. Specific recommendations for one such mixture for cupola patching and ladle lining are

Ingredients	Screen Distribution
50% Silica Ganister,* 3/8 in. x D	On 28 mesh 53-55%
30% Silica Ganister, 1/8 in. x D	28 - 65 mesh 14-15%
14% Silica Flour, 140 mesh	Thru 65 mesh 33-36%
6% Western Bentonite	
Approx. 7% Water	

* Ganister as defined by the refractory producers is a dense high silica rock (quartzite).

Size distribution is considered important to obtain the best density, strength, and spall resistance.

Some other mixtures used successfully are

1) 50% ganister, 30% silica sand, 20% clay.
2) 35% coarse sand, 35% fine sand, 10% fine graphite, 20% fire clay.

One method of installation is by ramming with a pneumatic rammer behind a skeleton form. As one layer is completed the form is raised a few inches and another layer rammed.

Another method of application involves daubing or sticking balls of the mixture together against the walls.

Some plants use a natural clay with no mixing. In some localities such natural clays can be found that are properly balanced for good plasticity and refractoriness and are very inexpensive.

Still another alternative is the use of slices of tempered mixture either synthetic, natural, or proprietary plastic in drums or boxes. Sheets of plastic of desired thickness are placed around the wall, hand rammed into place, and later compressed with a pneumatic rammer. Some of the commercial plastics have better than average resistance but usually cost more than the natural or homemade preparations. The cost must be balanced against performance.

GUN PATCHING

Cupola linings were first applied successfully with pneumatic guns in late 1948. Since that time their use has increased till a large proportion of the cupolas in this country are patched by this method. Machines are manufactured by several companies and are used to blow a variety of mixtures.

The equipment consists essentially of a pressure hopper containing the material under air pressure, a rubber hose through which the dry material is blown, and the nozzle from which the material is discharged as water is sprayed into it.

Some of the machines use a double hopper that permits continuous filling while blowing. Others use only a single hopper with more capacity which can be refilled only by stopping the blowing. The machines vary slightly in details of agitation equipment to facilitate smooth discharge. In Fig. 21.11 a pressure hopper is filled from an overhead storage bin. A cupola wall is being patched by gun in Fig. 21.12.

The acid mixture blown is essentially a combination of ganister, sand, and clay. Sizing of the components is important to obtain the desired density and compactness, and the quality of the clay is important to insure efficient application and good refractoriness. Formation of a glaze is generally considered more desirable than a material of exceptional refractoriness. Proprietary mixtures for gun application are marketed by a number of manufacturers who have made an effort to incorporate these various requirements.

Some foundries have worked out satisfactory homemade mixtures from local materials. The following are some typical mixtures.

1) 50% ganister, (1/4 in. x D), 30% silica sand, 20% clay (50 mesh).
2) 75% amorphous silica (half coarse and half fine), 25% clay.
3) 50% silica pebbles, 25% sand, 25% clay.

Proper preparation is necessary for any refractory patch, but the preparation required for the air-placement process may differ somewhat from previous practice. In the first place, the sand-blasting effect of the equipment used in air placement provides somewhat greater leeway in the amount of chipping. Because this is true, there is then the danger that too many liberties may be taken with the preparation or that the operation becomes careless and leads to a poor patch.

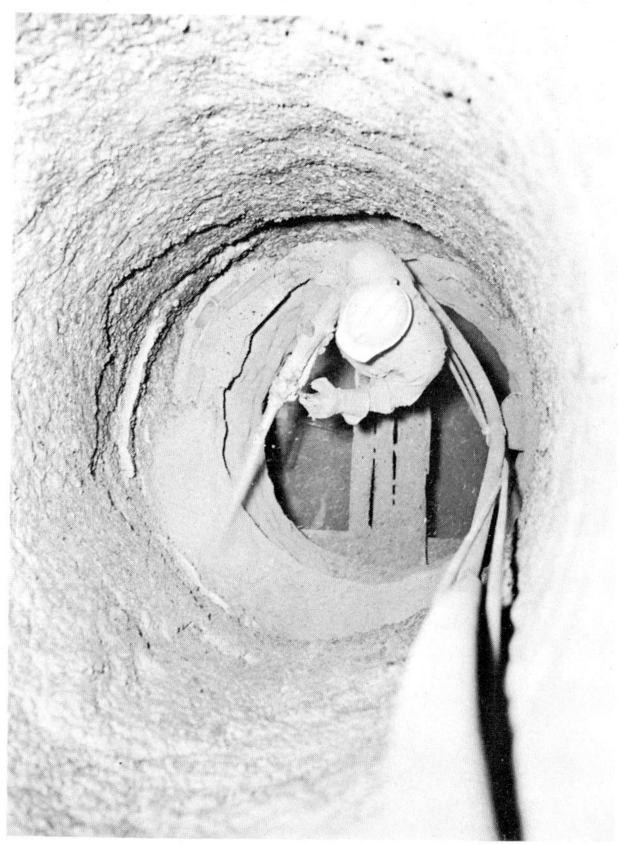

Figs. 21.11 and 21.12. Cupola patching with pneumatic gun. Top: discharging material from storage bin to pressure hopper; bottom: gun application of patch to cupola walls.

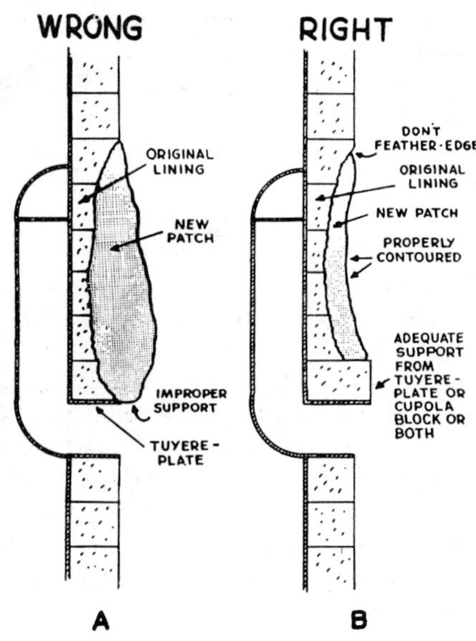

Fig. 21.13. *A* is a monolithic patch without sufficient support; slumping or bridging can result. *B* shows how the extended tuyere plate or one row of block can give proper support for the monolithic lining.

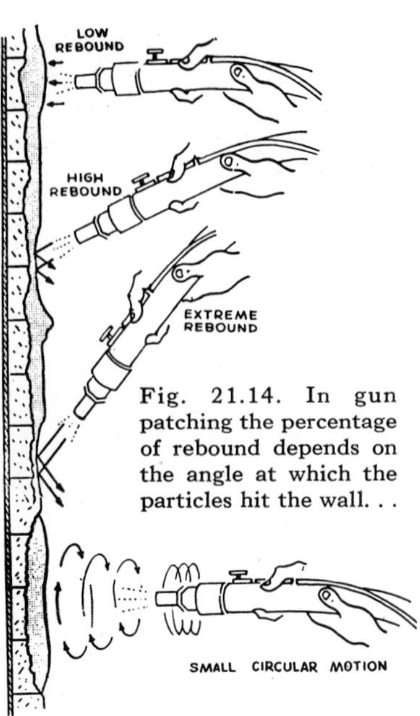

Fig. 21.14. In gun patching the percentage of rebound depends on the angle at which the particles hit the wall. . .

. . A small circular motion, with gun head held to provide 90 degree impact, results in minimum rebound.

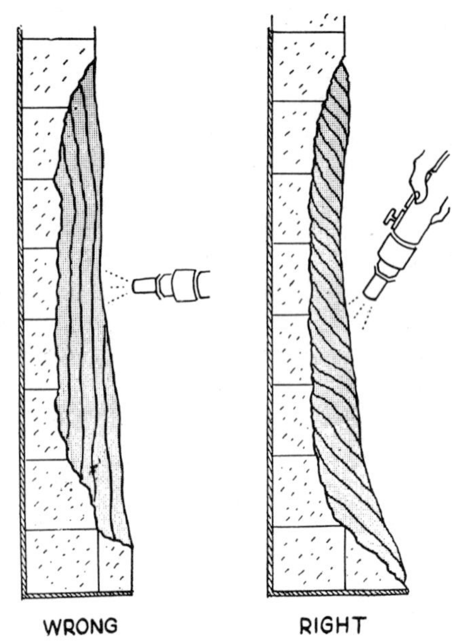

Fig. 21.15. Working above zone to be patched, the gun operator can develop horizontal layers minimizing spalling.

Users of air placement equipment are informed that in preparing a cupola two things are important. First, it is not desirable to remove the glazed finish left from the previous day's operation. In other words, it is not desirable or necessary to break through the ceramic bond which has developed during the previous heat. The glazed portion is monolithic material which has been fired or sintered in place and is, therefore, the best part of the lining. It will be a hard shell ranging from ½-in. to the full thickness of the lining, depending upon the composition of the refractory and the intensity of heat at the wall.

Adherence of the patch is not a problem with air placement, as it might be in hand patching of the same cupola. On the other hand, it is necessary to avoid leaving patches of slag or loose coke on the cupola wall. Therefore, the chipping operation should be checked from two standpoints: first, to avoid loose coke or excessive slag deposits on the wall which will permit the subsequent patch to drop or slump; second, to avoid breaking through the glaze and patching against low strength, unglazed material which may not provide sufficient support to prevent spalling of the new patch. The gun operation is such that patch material will adhere to almost any solid surface, but, it must have something solid on which to adhere.

A second factor of importance in air-placed patching is the amount of support provided for the green-patch material. The refractory has low strength through a given range of low temperature before being heated to the temperature at which glazing or vitrification takes place. During this period it can support its own weight, but should not support excessive burdens from above or behind. Therefore, a ledge is provided to furnish support for the load. This may be provided by the upper tuyere plate as shown in Fig. 21.13.

In some operations it may be found that the tuyere plates have burned away to the extent that adequate support is not longer available. Or the design may be such that the tuyere plate cannot provide sufficient support because of the degree to which the refractory must overhang the tuyere plate. In these cases it is desirable to start with one row of cupola block or brick immediately above the tuyeres so that a solid formation is available for subsequent blowing or air-placement of the patch. Ignoring this problem may lead to a slumping or screening and blocking of the tuyeres during the early part of the heat. Some foundries compensate for this slump through the use of excessive secondary flux. This usually results in unnecessary refractory loss.

Contour patching has been mentioned but is of particular importance in air placement patching, and should be stressed as one of the important factors controlling optimum results. Air placement is well adapted to contour patching because the shape of the cupola can be controlled with accuracy and ease. Such a contour before and after patching is in Fig. 21.7.

Operation of Air Placement Equipment—Effect on Refractory Quality[4]

Aside from the composition of the material used and the cupola operational influences upon refractory life, there is also a relationship between the technique of handling the gun and the refractory life. There is a certain degree of "know-how" involved to obtain the maximum results from the process. Ignoring some of these rules may result in a low quality patch in spite of the fact that the equipment is designed to be as foolproof as possible.

Probably, the most common source of difficulty with air placement equipment for patching cupolas is a lack of proper air pressure and air volume. The equipment is pneumatic; it transports material through air flow and deposits the refractory on the wall of the cupola as a result of air velocity. The density of the patch must depend largely on the available air pressure and volume.

The theoretical maximum density of solid silica is 2.65 grams per cc. The maximum dry packed density that has been obtained in a monolithic type material with close control of particle shape and distribution is 2.27 grams per cc, or a porosity of 14 per cent. Wet packed density will be somewhat lower than the maximum dry packed density. The exact density obtained will then depend upon the distribution of the particles and the particle shape plus the imposed effect of velocity and air pressure.

Air and Water Pressure

Lack of sufficient air pressure or incomplete utilization of the air available to the machine will result in a low-density patch. It will also result in surging or slugging, which prevents proper moisture control of the patch. It should be recognized that density of patch is related to the kinetic energy or the energy imparted by velocity. The velocity is related to the size and shape of the materials being thrown, or in other words, to the flowability of the material. However, the fundamental factor is the air pressure of air volume available, all other factors being equal.

The earlier models of air placement equipment were not capable of handling materials at high pressure without plugging or bucking, but with the present designs operating pressures from 45 to 65 psi are common and desirable. This has led to some modification of the materials because the higher pressures permit the use of better compositions, and in turn change the requirements for permeability of materials.

Low water pressure, like low air pressure, can lead to a poor patch and undesirable refractory losses. The reason for the loss in this case, however, is different. Air pressure or air volume is related to the density of the patched material as placed in the cupola. Water pressure controls the ability to wet the clay particles and develop enough stickiness or tackiness for adhesion to cupola walls. Wetting agents may be used in the gunning operation to reduce rebound and produce a stronger bond in the refractory material.

If water pressures are inadequate, only the outside layers of the refractory coming through the material hose are wetted. The rebound is high. If the water pressures are low, there will be a tendency toward erratic wetting of the materials, resulting in wet and dry spots. The wet and dry spots, in turn, cause spalling of the lining together with apparent slump and increased refractory loss. Best results are obtained with water pressures in excess of 50 psi. Auxiliary pumps and water tanks are available to increase the existing plant water pressure when necessary.

A similar difficulty is encountered while operating with a worn material hose gasket. The material hose gasket directs the stream of material in such a way as to expose it to water to obtain maximum wetting and slaking of the clay. If the restriction or guiding gasket in the material hose becomes worn the material will scatter as it passes through the water chamber of the gun, resulting in improper slaking of the clay. The end result of a worn material hose gasket is the same as for low water pressure and may lead to confusion of the two problems.

The moisture control of the patch on the cupola wall is almost automatic. If the material is too dry it will rebound, and if it is too wet it will wash off. However, even with this semi-automatic feature, there is still a range of moisture content from 8 to 9 per cent "on the wall." In some cupola operations it may be necessary to control to within the limits of this semi-automatic range. If insufficient water is used, the dry strength of the patch will be low. The effect may be compared to that from insufficient water in a molding sand (reduced dry strength). If the patch is too wet, the result may be cracking and low density. These difficulties will be emphasized if the permeability of the material being used is not properly controlled by the manufacturer because improper permeability would narrow the permissible range for moisture.

Moisture Control

There is less danger of getting material too dry than too wet. When material is shot too dry, both the rebound and the dust will be excessive. The operator will have a natural tendency to increase the moisture to reduce the dust. However, in some operations, the operator may carry this to extremes and run too wet to obtain absolute freedom of dust and prevent rebound. In most operations this change is insignificant, but in the really tough melting jobs the loss of density may be noticeable to the extent that a good patch is not obtained. The operator should avoid putting in a "soft and wet" patch followed by shooting dry material into the soft matrix to dry it up, causing low density and spalling.

The ability of the patch to operate with excessive water will depend partly on the severity of the melting operation and partly upon the thickness of the patch. Thicker patches normally indicate a more severe cupola operation and require less water than thin patches which can dry quickly. When properly controlled, air-placed patches require no "air dry" before using.

Gun Technique

When installing air placement equipment for patching, the engineer tries to train the operator to use the proper motion in handling the gun head. The proper technique of handling the gun head is difficult to describe on paper in spite of the fact that it is simple to demonstrate. However, the principles involved can be pointed out. When shooting the refractory against a cupola wall the normal laws of rebound must be considered. If the particle hits the walls perpendicularly, it will tend to bounce straight back.

With a plastic mix such as that under discussion the rebound straight back will be small because the cushioning effect of the previously placed patch will allow the particle to imbed itself and remain on the wall. However, in departing from the 90 degree angle and approaching the 45 degree angle the amount of rebound will increase because the plasticity of the previously placed patch is incapable of withstanding the shearing action which develops when a particle is being bounced at a 45 degree angle (Fig. 21.14).

The motion in handling the gun is designed to keep the particles shooting directly at the wall to minimize rebound and obtain maximum density. The easiest way to do this is with a small circular direction of motion in front of the operation. Such a motion will minimize both the piling up and skidding away of material. The small circular motion working relatively close to the cupola wall will develop maximum density with minimum rebound. However, it will produce an uneven appearance, with the result that some operators will then stand back and spray at rather wide angles to get a smoother surface. The smoother appearance is undesirable and unnecessary.

When materials are shot in such a way as to give a high rebound (wide angle), segregation will result because the finer particles will adhere and the coarser particles will tend to bounce away. The result of segregation on the cupola wall is a change in the composition of the material, resulting in unsatisfactory refractory life. Like hand patching, the best gun patching is not necessarily the "prettiest."

Patch Finishing

Tendencies to "featheredge" the patch in an effort to obtain a "prettier" or smoother finish should be discouraged. Some operators like to finish off the patch, toward the upper range of the melting zone, by tapering off to a knife-edge. Such a patch accomplishes nothing because the amount of burnout at that point is too small to warrant a patch. However, it is worse than just unwarranted, because the thin featheredges on the patch are subject to expansion during the drying process.

The expansion and contraction will result in curling of the upper edges of the melting zone patch, pulling that portion of the patch away from the wall. Frequently, such a patch will pull away from the wall all the way into the main body of the patch. Early sloughing or slumping of the upper zones of the monolithic patch may result. It is much better to finish the patching where there is still a reasonable thickness of patch to be installed. This still leaves an indentation or groove at the top of the melting zone, as shown in Fig. 21.13, but this is harmless because there is little burn-out at that point.

Gun placed patches should never be smoothed, trowelled, hammered or butted-off. Techniques of this type will cause scabbing, buckling and loosening of the adhering surfaces of the patch. Slumping, sliding or disintegration will result. Scabs, similar to sand-mold scabs, may form during heating of the patch prior to reaching the vitrification temperature.

One of the important factors in proper gun-patching is control of the direction of the planes of cleavages of layers which can be generated. Spraying or painting the patch, with a side-to-side motion (or an up-and-down motion) will result in a layer effect. If these layers are parallel to the shell of the cupola it will mean that the cleavage or planes of weakness between layers will be parallel to the melting direction of the cupola. Such a layer effect can result in spalling or scabbing away of monolithic material as drying and vitrification progresses. Such spalling is comparable to that obtained with firestone when the grain of the stone is placed parallel to the shell of the cupola. When gun patching, spalling can be avoided by utilizing the recommended circular motion and working around the periphery of the cupola. The patch should start at the tuyeres and build toward the top.

If the operator will stay above the work so that he is shooting downward as he is placing the patch, he will automatically place the layers vertical to the cupola shell (shown in Fig. 21.15). The result will be minimum spalling and scabbing of the refractory material. For this reason the operator should be provided with proper scaffolding which will permit him to stay above the work and eliminate placing the material in layers parallel to the shell or above the gun level.

There are a few tricks of the trade which can be used to further improve monolithic linings. The outstanding one is the use of secondary materials to increase the rate of glazing. Such additions may be made to the water tank used in conjunction with the air-placement equipment. When a water tank is available, it becomes a simple matter to introduce molasses in the ratio of 1 to 30, 1 to 20, or 1 to 15 (by volume) to the water.

Another material of value is waterglass or sodium silicate. It can be added to the water tank in the ratio of one gallon of silicate (50 per cent purity) to 15 gallons of water. Both molasses and silicate provide a greater stickiness to the patch and reduce rebound. Molasses is valuable in this respect in that it improves the dry strength of the lining and helps to support the lining in position until vitrification can take place at the elevated temperatures. Sodium silicate has this effect and also provides an earlier sintering or glazing of the lining, thereby increasing the refractory life for many applications. Painting the patch with either molasses or waterglass has been tried but such practice is not satisfactory.

MAINTAINING BASIC REFRACTORIES

Basic linings may be installed and maintained by methods similar to those for the usual acid linings. Basic refractories are merely substituted for clay refractories in the basin and for 3 to 5 ft above the tuyeres.

For the original lining various standard brick shapes of either magnesite or dolomite may be used. The mortar must also be either magnesite or dolomite. Clay mortar must not be used with basic brick where high temperatures are expected; the acid clay will flux away the basic brick.

Basic linings may be patched with brick, rammed monolithic, or gunned monolithic. Magnesite brick, dead burned or chemically bonded, are very resistant but high in cost. Commercial magnesite mortars are usual for steel temperatures, but may have insufficient plasticity. Sufficient plasticity may be gained by a 1 to 3 per cent addition of western bentonite.

For rammed patches either granular magnesite or dolomite work satisfactorily. Bond may be improved with bentonite. Dolomite is much cheaper and glazes well, but is less stable over long shutdown periods, holidays, etc.

For patching with a pneumatic gun either dolomite or magnesite proprietary mixtures may be used. Because of the density of basic materials some adjustments on the gun may have to be changed from acid practice.

LINING CONTOUR

Lining contour is an important consideration in refractory maintenance. There are three fundamentally different shapes about which opinions vary: 1. straight or cylindrical, 2. boshed in, 3. natural contour. Their differences are shown in Fig. 21.7 *no. 4*.

The straight or cylindrical shape illustrated in Fig. 21.3 is the simplest, easiest to maintain with dimensional accuracy and concentricity, especially when patching with brick.

The boshed-in lining shape is illustrated in Fig. 21.6. . . . An extra thickness of lining (usually 5 per cent of the inside diameter) is carried 2 to 3 ft above the tuyeres. This boshed-in lining can be maintained well when patching with brick or stone that is anchored in. Such a protruding lining is not practical when patching with gunned or rammed monolithic material. Lining consumption per ton of melt is inclined to be higher, but better overall protection on long heats is generally claimed because of the extra lining thickness in the critical area. It is generally agreed that some lining projection above the tuyeres is good. It is generally recommended that the basin diameter should be about 10 per cent greater than the diameter just above the tuyeres in order to prevent slag and metal droplets from being deflected into the tuyeres.

The contoured or natural lining shape is rounded out in the melting zone following the natural trends of the burn back as shown in Fig. 21.13A. Increased diameter for 1 to 3 ft above the tuyeres allows for the pressure of expanding combustion gases and tends to reduce the refractory consumption. However, the reduced lining thickness provides less factor of safety on long heats. This contour is especially adapted to gun patching. Application with the gun makes it easier to obtain such a shape and the concave lining is less inclined to slump down or spall off.

Regardless of the contour chosen, uniformity in both dimensions and contour is important for day to day consistency in performance. After each patching the lining diameter should be measured in certain established locations. Dimensions should be recorded and watched by the operator. Otherwise the liner can easily allow the lining to drift to undesirable dimensions or contours, or possibly to eccentricity with the cupola shell. An adjustable measuring stick (Fig. 21.16) is a valuable tool for measuring and controlling cupola diameters.

LINING EFFECT ON OPERATION

Consistent operation and control requires a consistent refractory practice and use of materials of sufficient quality.

Irregular dimensions can cause irregular melting capacity. On a small cupola particularly a few inches of extra lining on each side can reduce considerably the cupola area and potential melting capacity.

As previously explained some contours can be unfavorable to operating efficiency. Projections or humps in the charging zone can cause "hang ups" and interfere with charge descent. If the lining is not projected over the top of the tuyeres, slag can

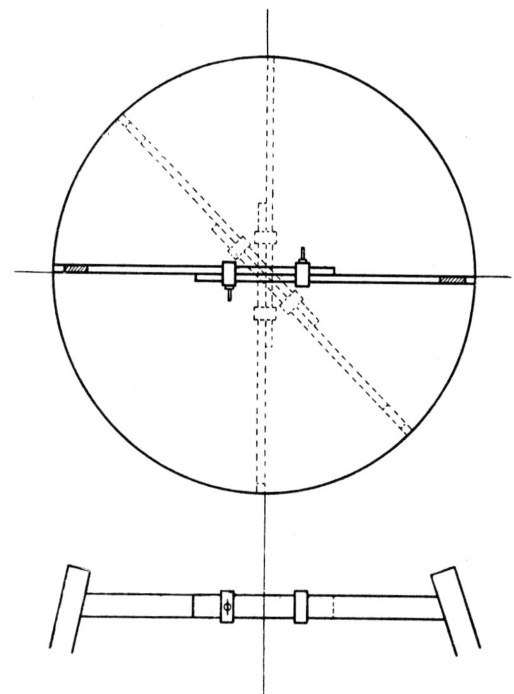

Fig. 21.16. **Adjustable measuring stick used to control cupola diameters after patching.**

be deflected into the tuyeres where it will eventually interfere with air supply and distribution. If the contour of the melting zone is varied from boshed-in to contoured-out, some irregularities in behavior can be expected.

One of the most important effects of refractory behavior is on the slag and cleanliness of the tuyere area. The lining that is fluxed away drips down into the slag, and being on the circumference must drop past or near the tuyere areas. If the refractory quality is good and the application sound, refractory consumption will be gradual and properly balanced by the flux. Tuyere area may be kept fairly clean and the cupola have good permeability.

On the other hand, if refractory consumption is excessive a viscous slag is inclined to be chilled in the tuyere areas, forming a bridge and interfering with good blast penetration. Refractory consumption may be high because refractory quality is poor, or because application technique has not been good. Patches or sections of linings may slide, slump, or spall from the wall because of improper "chipping down" or preliminary preparation, improperly anchored brick or stone, or from monolithic material insufficiently bonded, too wet, or improperly applied. This falling out of patches of lining can suddenly change an efficiently operating furnace into a "sick" cupola and jeopardize the metal shell.

For these reasons it is important that cupola supervision pay close attention to all patching techniques and materials, bearing in mind that a few short cuts in patching today can cause trouble tomorrow. Observation of the lining condition after the drop or before chipping down often gives useful indications of lining performance and operating conditions.

OPERATIONAL FACTORS EFFECT ON LINING ATTACK

The combination of conditions in the melting zone of the cupola make some lining attack inevitable regardless of the type of refractory However there are many factors that affect the refractory consumption and may be regulated to give best refractory performance provided they are consistent with other objectives. Disregard of some of these factors can easily cause unnecessarily high refractory cost.

In general, the burning away of the lining is considered to be proportional to the length of the heat and the temperature of the melting zone. Degree of oxidation is a powerful factor in fluxing away the hot refractory.

Excessive blast is a potential cause of high refractory consumption, by creating more oxidizing gases at higher pressure and by driving turbulent particles of slag, flux and metal against the lining. The same effect of excessive blast can be produced in sections of the cupola as a result of reduced permeability on one side because of irregular charging, bridging, or viscous slag.

Tuyere area and condition can influence refractory consumption in the melting zone. Too much tuyere area can result in insufficient blast penetration and excessive air up the face of the lining. Insufficient tuyere areas can cause excessive chilling and prove hard to keep open. Unequal dimensions and conditions among the several tuyeres can cause uneven introduction of air and greater burn-back in spots.

Lining consumption can be greater in both the melting zone and basin if an excessive amount of flux is used in an acid cupola. Likewise if flux amount is insufficient to prevent bridging and loss of permeability, lining attack may be increased. Careless charging of flux can build up high concentrations in spots against the lining, where refractory will be attacked by the local excess of basic flux. Likewise, high concentration of the more reactive secondary fluxes such as fluorspar and sodium carbonate can increase refractory loss.

The nature of the charge has considerable influence on refractory attack. High proportions of steel scrap decrease lining life, especially when it is thin and rusty. Thin oxidized or burnt cast scrap also increases attack.

Refractory consumption has been decreased considerably by the use of water cooling behind a thin refractory lining. The higher priced neutral linings of carbon and graphite are almost completely resistant to the corrosive factors that cause refractory consumption, and may effect refractory savings where the first cost can be justified. These special linings are discussed in Chapter 17.

SPECIAL REFRACTORY APPLICATIONS

Carbon Refractories

Carbon refractories are used as essentially complete linings in some special cupola applications as described in Chapter 17. They are often used in critical areas such as the well, slag hole, slag trough, etc.

Carbon has unusual physical characteristics that make it an excellent refractory material. It is chemically neutral and resistant to both acid and basic slags; it has a low coefficient of thermal expansion; high mechanical strength is maintained at elevated temperatures; resistance to thermal shock is high; the fusion point of carbon is much higher than cupola operating temperatures. Low carbon irons and oxidizing conditions at high temperatures reduce the service life of carbon refractories.

The cost of carbon refractories, several times that of clay refractories, is easily justified where long heats or continuous operation is desired. Carbon refractories are available in standard brick shapes as well as special blocks, carbon pastes and ramming mixes. A back up lining of standard or insulating brick shapes is often used in conjunction with carbon materials to offset the higher thermal conductivity of the carbon. When the lining is over 9 in. thick, blocks may be used to reduce the number of joints. Blocks up to 1500 lb have been fabricated for large installations where handling equipment is available.

Carbon well zone linings are also constructed by ramming carbon paste onto a backup lining of blocks or bricks. Carbon paste generally requires slight warming to improve plasticity for ramming. The surface to be patched must be clean and a thin coating of tar may be applied to make the patch adhere. Cold ramming mixes also have been developed and are much easier to handle and install.

The pastes depend on bitumastic binders for cold strength and care must be exercised in heating large masses of the material to prevent slumping. Some support frequently is necessary; it may be a wood or steel form, or merely the bed coke to support a patch in the well section.

Carbon taphole blocks, either machined or rammed, are widely used for basic or neutral slag conditions, especially for long heats. When a rammed material is employed, it is rammed around a steel pipe which is left in place. The portion of the taphole over which the metal flows need not be carbon.

Tap Hole and Breast

Since the tap hole and breast areas are important factors in maintaining uninterrupted performance they require careful supervision. Specifications vary according to the tapping system employed. With intermittent tapping the taper, dimensional accuracy and neatness of the hole are important to facilitate "botting up", but slag resistance is not important since slag is not eliminated through the tap hole.

On the other hand, with continuous tapping and front slagging the tap hole area must resist the continuous discharge of slag. Dimensional accuracy or hole shape is not important since the metal level is determined by the dam height. Only the vertical height need be maintained. Corrosion of the tap hole can decrease the necessary differential between the top of the hole and the iron dam.

There are two general methods for forming the tap hole: 1) special tap hole blocks; 2) rammed plastic.

Tap Hole Blocks

Special refractory blocks are made with holes of required dimensions (illustrated in Fig. 21.5). A wide variety of dimensions and hole sizes are available from a number of brick manufacturers. Some plants use a two hole block, with one kept closed and available in case of a freezeup. Fireclay blocks are most popular, but a number of plants use special low porosity or high density refractories for better slag resistance and longer life. Magnesite and chrome-magnesite tap hole blocks are manufactured for use in basic cupolas.

These blocks can be replaced daily, or every few days as needed. They are simply filled into the brick lining with tight joints, good mortar, and overlapping joints whenever possible.

Rammed Breast and Tap Hole

A number of plants form the breast by ramming monolithic material into an opening left in the front brickwork, as Fig. 21.4 shows. A tap hole of suitable size and shape is formed by ramming around a wooden plug, metal bar, or pipe. The hole should be gently sloped down for draining. For intermittent tapping the outside of the hole is generally flared considerably to form a good seat for the bot plug. Tap holes should be tapered out to prevent clogging with small particles of coke, refractory etc. Tap hole size should be properly adjusted to melt rate and tapping cycle.

In front slagging additional consideration must be given the trough section behind the slag knife where both metal and slag are contained. On long acid heats higher density clay brick are sometimes used in this area and for the slag knife. The more expensive high-alumina brick (90 percent + alumina) offer good slag resistance, and are sometimes justified for slag knives that may be retained for several heats.

On basic operation this section of the front slagging trough is generally lined with magnesite or chrome-magnesite brick, and frequently faced with a replaceable layer of dolomite plastic.

Carbon paste is very useful in this area and is frequently used over the basic brick. A slow heating period is essential to develop the density of current carbon ramming mixtures.

Beyond the slag knife no slag is present, and the basic cupola trough need be no different from an acid cupola trough.

Sand Bottom

Almost all American cupolas drop hinged bottom doors at the end of each heat or when patching is required. This principle requires a refractory bottom of sufficient strength to support and contain the molten metal, but still weak enough to fall out at the end of the heat. Several inches of foundry sand is generally used. The operation is fairly simple, but neglect of certain basic principles can cause serious delays.

The bottom doors should fit snugly. If cracked or warped they should be replaced promptly. Numerous 1/4- to 1/2-in. vent holes should be provided for the escape of gas. If not provided entrapped steam can blow up sections of bottom sand, causing a serious runout. Vent holes must be cleaned at regular intervals.

The door joints are daubed to insure a snug fit. Sometimes a row of brick is used around the edges of large cupolas. The doors are closed and held in place by props, which are wedged upward from a firm floor bottom. The number of props should increase with the size of the cupola. Figure 2.5, *page 20*, is an outside chain hoist for closing the bottom doors. Other arrangements pull the doors up with an inside chain block or with a charge crane, where available.

A wide variety of sands are used successfully for cupola bottoms where ramming technique, drying time, etc., have been worked out for the sand used. A large proportion of plants use a sand straight from a foundry system. Sand from slinger floors and large castings is very suitable. A number of plants make minor modifications to a system sand or a shakeout sand by adding new sand and possibly clay or bentonite. Some plants with no suitable molding sand available make up a synthetic bottom sand with additions of clay or bentonite to a suitably sized base sand.

Many differences in sand properties may be compensated by differences in ramming intensity. For consistent performance the sand should be rammed with consistent technique and sand properties should be maintained with reasonable control. Tests for moisture, permeability, and green strength at least once a week are desirable to minimize bottom troubles. Many plants find it advisable to make tests on bottom sand each day. Close supervision is as important as laboratory tests.

A survey of 35 plants indicated a wide variety of sand properties successfully used. Moistures ranged from 3 to 8 per cent. Permeabilities ranged from 30 to 180—over 65 is generally recommended. Green bonds ranged from 4 to 14 psi, and dry bonds from 40 to 150 lb. Clay contents from 4 to 15 per cent were reported satisfactory. Grain fineness numbers ranged from 35 to 90.

Moisture should be held to a practical minimum and sand should be mixed uniformly. The bottom sand should be screened through a coarse riddle (about No. 4) to eliminate sand lumps and pieces of iron or nails that may cause metal to run through the bottom doors. The bottom sand should always be measured by volume or weight to insure proper bottom thickness and well capacity.

The sand is dumped into the cupola through the charging door and spread evenly over the bottom. It is rammed into a wide fillet against the lining with two or three rammings with the peen end of a hand rammer. The sand bottom is slanted toward the tap hole at a slope of about 1 in. per ft., as Fig. 21.17 shows. If the sand strength is too high and/or the sand is rammed too hard the bottom might be difficult to drop. The depth of sand varies from about 3 in. for a 30 in. cupola on short heats to 9 in. for 96 in. cupolas on long heats.

For continuous operation, 12-15 in. sand is used by some operators; others employ special materials such as high alumina ramming mixes, sand with a topping of basic material, or sand in combination with brick. Special bottoms can be difficult to drop.

Many plants ram the breast while patching the cupola. This provides a better opportunity for denser ramming and longer drying. On some small cupolas with no kindling tuyeres the breast opening is left open to enable lighting the bed through the breast opening. After lighting the bed the breast is rammed around a metal bar, which is then withdrawn. Rammed breasts should be thoroughly dried and preheated before use.

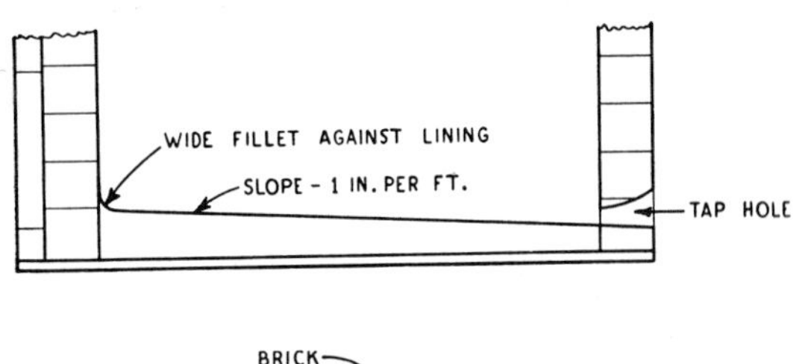

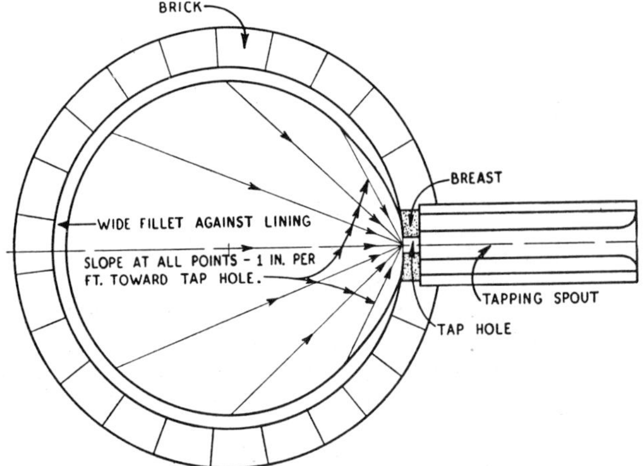

Fig. 21.17. **Plan and section views showing method of placing cupola bottom.**

A variety of materials are used for rammed breasts. The simplest of materials is a homemade mixture of sand and clay or ganister and clay along the lines described for monolithic lining and patching. Some proprietary plastics are used. Some advantages in longer life are claimed for the clay-graphite plastics. The presence of graphite in the mixture gives better slag resistance and less tendency toward adherence to slag or metal.

On basic cupolas dolomite and magnesite mixtures have been rammed for breasts. Very small bentonite additions (1-2 per cent) are sometimes necessary for sufficient bond.

Carbon paste has been used successfully on some of the more basic slags. This material is more difficult to apply but has unusually long life and frequently can be used for several heats.

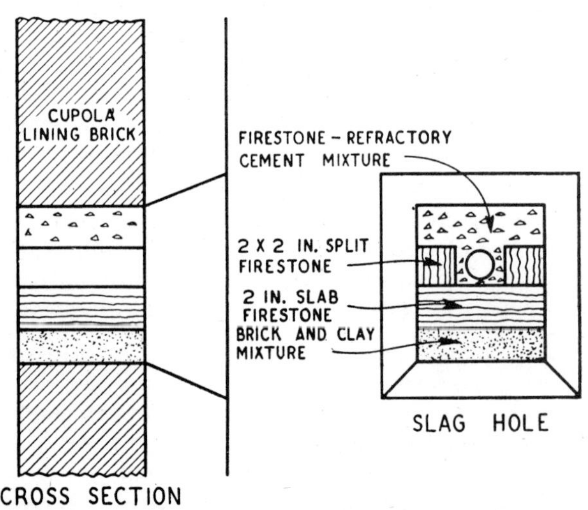

Fig. 21.18. **Special slag hole construction method. Hole is rammed over firestone slab which resists slag attack.**

After preparation the tap hole is usually stopped up temporarily with loose sand, a stock core, or blacking tempered with kerosene. Some operators like to blow through the tap hole until a few minutes before melting starts to get maximum preheating. After melting has been started and the desired volume of metal has been accumulated the tap hole is opened and the first metal tapped.

Slag Hole

In back slagging the slag hole is very important since all the slag of the heat must pass through this small refractory area.

Just as on the tap hole, the slag hole may be either of refractory blocks or of rammed monolithic. More consideration must be given slag resistance. Ordinary clay refractories have only a limited life where all the slag is discharged.

A high proportion of foundries use slag hole blocks of carborundum (silicon carbide). Carborundum is very slag resistant and may last for several heats, but is readily attacked by metal if allowed to run over the slag hole. Carborundum slag hole blocks are available from several manufacturers in a number of sizes, and with rectangular, round, or tapered holes.

Some slag holes are rammed by similar techniques described in breast construction. Clay graphite plastics are popular where slag holes are rammed, in order to get better slag resistance from the included graphite. Figure 21.18 shows special slag hole construction with a hole rammed over a special firestone slab which takes the brunt of the slag attack.

Basic slags are more corrosive to slag hole refractories. Rammed dolomite gives reasonable performance on short heats. Carbon paste has proved sufficiently resistant for long heats with highly basic slags.

Trough

Troughs carrying the metal from the cupola to the forehearth or ladle are usually lined with clay brick with an inner lining of mud, plastic, or rammed monolithic.

Some plants depend chiefly on a thick lining of brick or fitted trough tile, with only a thin layer of mortar or mud to seal. Others use only a thin backing of brick and depend chiefly on a considerable thickness of rammed material. Homemade mixtures of clay and sand tempered to mud consistency may be applied simply, but must be dried and resurfaced carefully because of shrinkage cracks.

Rammed mixtures of sand and clay tempered to minimum moisture can be rammed to high strength and density with a minimum of drying.

One such successful mixture consists of 80 per cent ganister, 14 per cent silica flour, and 6 per cent bentonite. Some advantages are claimed for clay-graphite plastics for trough linings.

REFERENCES

1. *Practical Hints in Cupola Operation,* Whiting Corp., Harvey, Ill.
2. Ray A. Witschey, "Cupola Refractories," *Foundry,* April, 1947.
3. N. J. Dunbeck and T. E. Barlow, "Patching the Cupola," AMERICAN FOUNDRYMAN, October, 1949.
4. T. E. Barlow and P. D. Humont, "Gun Placed Silica Cupola Lining," AFS TRANSACTIONS, vol. 61 (1953).

CHAPTER 22

Composition Control
Mixture Manipulation

It is well known that uniformity of metal composition is dependent upon a great many factors. The components of a metal charge melt progressively and the drops of molten iron trickle through the bed into the well of the cupola (Fig. 22.1, ZONE E). Obviously, mixing is necessary to produce uniform iron and may be accomplished 1) by accumulating two or more molten charges in the cupola well; 2) by continuously tapping the metal as fast as it melts into a forehearth holding two or more charges; or 3) by a combination of holding in the cupola and tapping into a receiving ladle. No matter which scheme of accumulation is used, care should be taken to assure the continuous mixing or blending of at least two charges.

No Forehearth or Reservoir Ladle in System

If the metal handling system, regardless of the tapping method used, does not include a forehearth or reservoir ladle having a capacity of at least two or three charges of iron, the mixing must be done either in the well of the cupola or in a transfer or pouring ladle outside the cupola. In some instances it may be possible to adjust the well depth to fit a given size metal charge. However, in cases where the cupola well depth is fixed, it will be necessary to adjust the charge size to fit the well capacity. The depth of the well, from the top of the sand bottom to the bottom of the slag hole, required to hold two charges (fixed weight) of molten iron is determined as follows:

1 cu. in. of iron weighs 0.26 lb

Coke in the well occupies approximately 50 per cent of the volume

Iron in the well occupies 50 per cent of the volume

Using weights in lb and dimensions in in.,

$$\frac{2 \times \text{weight of 1 metal charge (lb)}}{0.26} = \text{Volume of 2 charges (cu. in.)}$$

$$\frac{\text{Volume of 2 charges (cu. in.)}}{50} \times 100 = \text{Volume of well (cu. in.)}$$

Area of well = Area of circle of the diameter of cupola in well zone

$$\frac{\text{Vol. of well (cu. in.)}}{\text{Area of well (sq. in.)}} = \text{Depth of well (in.)}$$

The tuyeres are located 4 to 8 in. above the slag hole (Fig. 22.1, ZONE D).

Sand bottom to slag hole = Depth of well.

Conversely, the above calculation can be used to advantage for determining the proper size or weight of charge to use in a cupola of fixed well depth.

With intermittent tapping and back slagging, the cupola well should be allowed to fill up completely with iron and the slag run off through the slag hole in each tapping cycle. Tapping the cupola when the well is only partially full should be avoided unless the amount of iron tapped out in this manner into a particular transfer or pouring ladle is sufficiently great to insure good mixing. Furthermore, tapping the cupola when the well is only partially full may result in the accumulation of an abnormally large volume of slag. This condition has a definite effect on the operation, and if allowed to continue for long periods of time will lead to trouble.

With continuous tapping and back slagging, the vertical distance between the tap hole and slag hole should be adjusted so that there are at least two charges of molten iron in the cupola well at all times. Assuming that there is no forehearth or reservoir ladle in the metal handling system, it will, obviously, be necessary to use a tilting spout. With this arrangement the amount of iron tapped may vary over a relatively broad range and the capacity of the transfer or pouring ladle need bear no particular relationship to the weight of the cupola charge. The reason for this is that the amount of molten iron in the cupola well remains constant, inasmuch as it cannot be tapped out any faster than it is melted. In contrast, the arrangement with intermittent, back-slagging cupolas is generally such that the molten metal can be and frequently is practically all removed during each tapping cycle.

With continuous tap, front slagging cupolas, the amount of molten iron in the well and front-slagging spout is relatively small, hence mixing of molten iron must be done outside the cupola, and the receiving ladles used must be able to hold at least two charges of iron.

With Forehearth or Reservoir Ladle in System

A forehearth or reservoir ladle which holds the equivalent of two or three cupola charges, whether it be of the stationary or tilting type, is an important aid to uniformity of metal composition. This applies

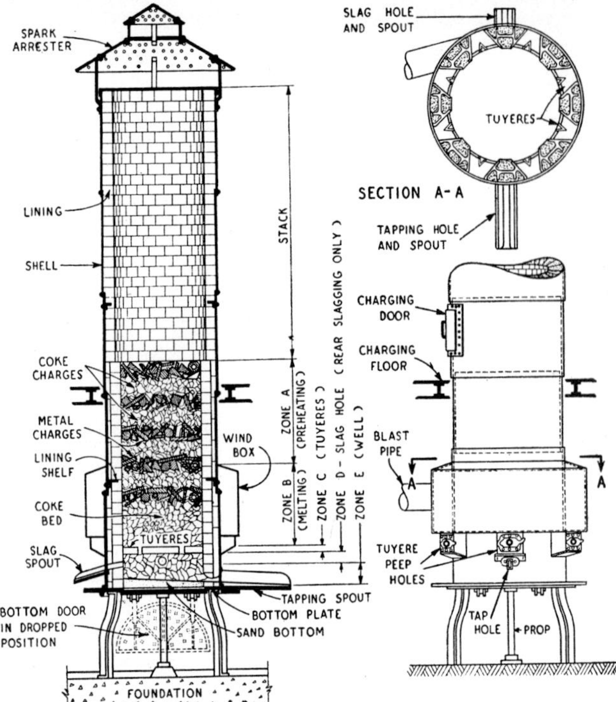

Fig. 22.1. Views of the cupola showing various details, sections and zones.

to cupolas tapped intermittently as well as to continuous tapping. With intermittent tapping, a forehearth of sufficient capacity may make it possible to use a cupola charge size greater than ⅓ to ½ of the well capacity. Thus, there will be no sacrifice in uniformity of metal chemistry, and economies in cupola charging can be realized.

It is well known that changes in melting rate and shutdowns bring about changes in both metal temperature and composition. These irregularities in the operation can occur while a ladle is being transported to the pouring area and the iron poured off. The use of a forehearth makes it possible to eliminate or minimize the number of shutdowns, and in this way the irregularities in metal composition caused by the shutdowns can be avoided. Some judgment must be used in connection with the amount of iron allowed to accumulate in the forehearth after each ladle is removed. If the forehearth holds as little as two cupola charges, it should be allowed to fill up completely each time any iron is taken out. If it holds as many as eight or ten cupola charges (which is actually the case in some installations), it is permissible to "tap" the forehearth when it is only one-half full or even less.

ADJUSTMENTS IN FIRST CHARGES

When using any given cupola mixture, the metal tapped at the beginning of the heat is frequently higher in total carbon than after equilibrium conditions have been reached. In order to compensate for this condition, many operators use a higher percentage of steel in the first few charges than in those used later. The amount of extra steel used in the first charges may be so great that some additional silicon will be required to keep the silicon content of the metal within the desired range. The number of charges in which more than the usual percentage of steel will be required is best determined by experience and careful observation of results obtained.

At times the first iron tapped is not hot enough to be used. Some of the reasons for this are that the refractories in the cupola well and ladles in the metal handling system have not been preheated to a sufficiently high temperature. Consequently, with intermittent tapping, iron may be tapped out before the well has been filled. With continuous tapping, a forehearth ladle may be tapped before the established minimum amount of iron has been allowed to accumulate. These irregularities in the operation may result in non-uniformity of metal composition at the start but can be overcome, at least in part, by using smaller charges at the beginning of the heat. Generally speaking, this should cause no great inconvenience as there is usually some extra time available before wind time while the charges used to fill the cupola are being made up.

CARBON CONTROL

Silicon and manganese losses during melting will vary, depending on the degree of oxidation, slag chemistry and the percentage of these elements in the charge.

The increase in sulfur and phosphorus contents is usually fairly uniform for a given operation, and the percentages present in the iron at the cupola spout are functions of the amount present in the materials charged, including the coke and fluxes.

The amount of carbon in cast iron has more influence on the physical and mechanical properties of the castings than any of the other ordinary elements entering into the chemistry of the iron (Alloying elements and inoculants bring about certain changes due in part to their influence on the amount of graphite or combined carbon in the iron, and in part to the effect resulting from being taken into solution by the matrix).

The equation for calculating carbon equivalent

$$CE = TC + \frac{Si + P}{3}$$

indicates the relative effect of these elements on the eutectic composition. Their relative effect on the properties of the iron is of approximately the same ratio, but only over narrow ranges of compositional change.

The percentage of total carbon exerts about three times as much effect on the properties of the iron as do either silicon or phosphorus. In other words, the foregoing equation indicates that a change in carbon necessitates an inverse change in silicon and/or phosphorus of approximately three times the magnitude if the same structure and hardness are to be maintained in castings having equal cooling rates.

Silicon content of iron can be increased when necessary by the addition of ferrosilicon after the iron has been melted. Conversely, for some applications an excess of silicon (as determined by chill test) can be compensated for by the addition of some sort of carbide stabilizer such as ferrochromium.

Sulfur can be increased or decreased after the metal has been melted. Manganese can be increased and likewise phosphorus if desired. In contrast with the elements just mentioned, it is practically impossible to increase or decrease the carbon content of the iron after it has been tapped from the cupola. This applies particularly to the composition range covering the bulk of commercial gray iron castings. Furthermore, in certain applications, such as permanent mold irons, a deficiency in total carbon cannot be satisfactorily compensated for by an increase in silicon. An excess of total carbon in these applications cannot be taken care of quickly as there is no practical method of reducing the carbon content without resorting to the use of special procedures and equipment; the silicon cannot be reduced and, in some of the irons in question, the addition of stabilizing alloys or inoculants is out of the question due to detrimental effects on the finished product. From the foregoing, it is obvious that every effort must be made to control the melting operation so that the total carbon in the iron at the cupola spout will be in the range suitable for the type of castings being produced.

There are a great many factors which affect the amount of carbon pick-up (or loss) during melting, a few of which are listed as follows:

1) Percentage of carbon in the charge.
2) Percentage of silicon in the iron at the cupola spout (or in the charge).
3) Percentage of phosphorus in the iron at the cupola spout (or in the charge).
4) Amount of coke or other fuel used.
5) Type of coke or other fuel used.
6) Size of pieces of coke or other fuel used.
7) Combinations of fuels used.
8) Amount and type of fluxing material used.
9) Melting temperature.
10) Melting rate as expressed in terms of percentage of "normal" rated output for a given size cupola.
11) Uniformity of melting rate
12) Air blast temperature.
13) Moisture in air blast.
14) Method of tapping the metal from the cupola.

From the foregoing, it is evident that it would be quite difficult to write a simple rule indicating the percentage of carbon in the iron at the cupola spout which will adequately include the many variables which enter into ordinary cupola practice. However, within reasonable time each operator can establish an empirical formula which applies to his particular operation. To do this, accurate laboratory records must be kept in which the effects of changes in percentage of carbon in the cupola charge, the percentages of silicon and phosphorus in the iron at the cupola spout (or in the charge), and all other variables which enter the operation are carefully noted and properly correlated. For example, one such set of records kept in connection with the operation of 48, 60 and 72 in. ID front slagging cupolas has resulted in the development of an equation for calculating the percentage of carbon in the iron at the cupola spout. By this means the operator can predict the percentage of carbon in the iron at the spout regardless of the relative amounts of steel, cast scrap, and pig iron in the charge, provided that certain practices are followed and certain conditions exist. The equation is

1) $\text{T.C.} = 2.4\% + \frac{1}{2}\,\text{C} - \frac{1}{4}\,(\text{Si} + \text{P})$

The definitions of terms used and necessary conditions are tabulated in Fig. 22.2.

In addition, it has been found advantageous to apply a factor ("f" for example) to the constant 2.4 appearing in the equation. By inserting values in the equation, it can be solved for "f." If the value is "1" and the temperature of the metal at the cupola spout is about 2750 to 2825 F, the operator can consider the coke being used as satisfactory. If the value for "f" is greater than unity the coke is unusually good, and if less than unity the coke is less satisfactory.

For convenience, *Equation 1)* has been put into the form of the alignment chart shown in Fig. 22.2. It can be looked upon as containing three unknown quantities, namely "(Si + P)," "C", and "T.C." and

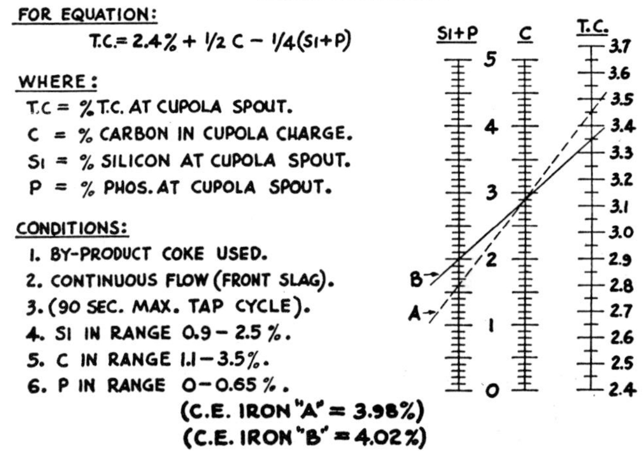

Fig. 22.2. Alignment chart for carbon contents of cupola-melted irons.

these terms appear as headings over the vertical scales in the alignment chart. The chart is used by assigning values to two of the unknowns and solving for the third. It contains all solutions for Equation 1), and any one of the three unknowns can be determined after assigning values to the other two. This is done by placing the chart on a flat surface and drawing a line (or laying a straight edge) between the two points representing known values on any two of the three vertical scales. The figure sought will be found along the straight line where it intersects the third vertical scale. Suppose, for example, that it is required to produce an iron with 1.8 per cent silicon, 0.2 per cent phosphorus, and 3.35 per cent total carbon at the cupola spout. Having this information it is necessary to determine "C," or the percentage of carbon in the cupola charge. The value of "(Si + P)" is 2.0, and the value of "T.C." is 3.35. The line, labelled "B" in the chart, drawn between these two points intersects the scale headed "C" at the 2.9 level. From this it is known that there must be 2.9 per cent carbon in the charge in order to produce iron of the required composition at the cupola spout.

Examination of the equation reveals

1) Any change made in "% carbon in cupola charge" increases or decreases the "% T.C. at cupola spout" by an amount equal to ½ the charge.

2) Increasing the percentage of silicon and/or phosphorus in the melt analysis reduces the carbon pickup during melting. Numerically the reduction is equal to ¼ the increase in the percentages of these elements. Conversely, a decrease in the percentage of silicon and/or phosphorus will increase carbon pickup by an amount equal to ¼ the decrease in percentages of these elements.

Lines labeled "A" and "B" respectively in the alignment chart show graphically the effect of an increase or decrease amounting to 0.40 per cent in silicon plus phosphorus in the iron at the spout. Reducing the silicon plus phosphorus from 2.0 per cent (line "B") to 1.6 per cent (line "A") and maintaining 2.9 per cent carbon in the charge, in both cases (see vertical scale headed "C") has increased the total carbon from 3.35 to 3.45 per cent, or a gain of 0.10 per cent (see vertical scale headed "T.C."). The carbon equivalents of the irons represented by lines "A" and "B" are 3.98 and 4.02 per cent, respectively, and for practical purposes these would be considered the same. However, this difference in carbon equivalent could be compensated for by a late addition of silicon to iron "A."

The equation illustrated is applicable only to the cupola operation used in the example. However, there is no reason why modified, but general similar equations cannot be formulated for other types of cupola operations, provided reasonably constant operating conditions are maintained.

SAMPLING FOR CHEMICAL ANALYSIS

Chemical control of the cupola operation requires proper sampling. Unless representative samples of the molten iron are taken the results become meaningless. Iron to be sampled for total carbon determination should be cast in the form of white iron spindles ⅛-in. OD. They are cast in a split chill mold containing two or more cavities of the proper size. The spindles can be readily crushed in a hardened steel mortar with a pestle of like material, or with one of the small type air hammers that employs a hardened steel head. All the carbon in the spindle is in the combined form, and hence total carbon can be accurately determined. This method is definitely preferred over the drilling of graphite bearing irons, where carbon is lost through chipping out of the graphite flakes and it is difficult to obtain a representative sample. Where total carbon has to be determined in a casting under conditions where a sample cannot be obtained from a ladle of molten iron, best results are obtained by breaking off a small, clean piece of the casting and using the entire piece for the total carbon determination.

Combined carbon varies inversely with the casting section. It is best, therefore, to determine the combined carbon in a sample of the casting obtained as mentioned above.

The same type of crushed white iron sample as used in connection with the determination for total carbon can be used to advantage for determinations of silicon, sulfur, manganese, phosphorus, and alloys. This entirely eliminates the need for the cores or molds generally used to pour the pieces from which "drilling samples" are obtained. Furthermore, the white iron samples dissolve more rapidly than samples containing graphitic carbon and, consequently, the time required to complete the analyses in the laboratory may be reduced.

The use of chill tests, fluidity or flowability tests, tensile strength, transverse strength, hardness, and other tests as well as studies of the microstructure of the iron are invaluable aids to the cupola operator. These tests are discussed in detail elsewhere.

The appearance of the cupola smoke and slag is an excellent guide to conditions inside the cupola. No set of rules can as yet be written stating just what might constitute an ideal appearance, but with experience changes which might be taking place inside can be detected and corrective measures taken before results of chemical analysis are normally received from the laboratory.

CHAPTER 23

Preparing Charge
Charging

The importance of a well-planned iron yard layout, good separation of all of the various types and grades of iron, fuels and fluxes, as well as good housekeeping in the storage area, have all been referred to in Chapter 19 "Calculating the Cupola Charge."

Melting stock should be sized according to the diameter of the cupola in order to prevent "hanging" and "bridging." The maximum dimension of metal pieces should not exceed one third of the inside diameter of the cupola at the melting zone. If rectangular shapes are being used, the greatest length will be a diagonal and not the length of the longest side of a particular piece. For example, in a 72 in. ID cupola, the maximum dimension should not exceed 24 in. Using 24 in. square pieces would not be satisfactory as the length of the diagonal of such a piece is 34 in. A 17 in. square has a diagonal of 24 in., so this is the maximum size square piece to be used in a 72 in. cupola.

Coke size has a definite bearing on the cupola operation, with uniformity of size being an important factor in coke quality. In many cases an otherwise good coke is seriously damaged because it is crushed in handling at the foundry, particularly if it is unloaded from cars or moved from storage piles by means of clamshell buckets. Where such handling cannot be avoided, a continuous screening operation in the coke handling system has been found effective.

CHARGING FLUX MATERIAL

When the bed is burned through evenly, and not until then, is the cupola ready for charging. In order to provide a large volume of fluid slag as soon after the start of the heat as possible, an amount of limestone equal to two to four times that used on each charge is placed directly on the coke bed or in the first few charges. This compensates for the ash from the coke bed, loose refractories, etc. Some operators use from 4 to 6 lb of fused soda ash per ton of metal on each charge used in the initial fill of the cupola, in addition to the regular charge of fluxing stone.

SEQUENCE OF CHARGING

The general rule is to charge fluxing materials on the coke and, if possible, at least 6 in. away from the cupola walls. In order to prevent excessive losses through oxidation, ferro alloys, including those in briquetted form, are placed on the coke near the center of the cupola. The metallic components are added next, and a definite sequence for placing them either in the cupola or in the charging buckets should be established and maintained. Such a sequence makes for a more uniform operation, and in many instances will permit maximum carbon pick-up commensurate with the type of charge being used.

With hand charging good results have been obtained by placing the portion of the cupola charge containing the lowest percentage of carbon next to the coke charge, and the portion containing the highest percentage of carbon furthest from the coke charge. Components containing intermediate percentages of carbon are placed between. The steel will be the component containing the least carbon, and the pig iron will probably contain the most. The intermediate components will be returns, home scrap, and purchased scrap.

CHARGING METHOD AFFECTS OPERATION

Observations made in connection with one 48 in. ID cupola and two 60 in. ID cupolas indicate that the manner in which the cupola is charged has a definite effect on the operation. When these cupolas were changed over from hand charging to mechanical charging with cone-bottom buckets, an increase in temperature of the iron at the cupola spout was immediately apparent, other factors being the same.

One explanation for this improvement lies in the fact that the cone-bottom buckets distribute the charges in a manner which results in less packing or lower density of the stock near the center of the cupola, which in turn permits better blast penetration and more uniform combustion of the fuel over the entire cross section of the cupola. On the other hand, some authorities feel that a large portion of the cupola blast, following the line of least resistance, passes out of the stack along the refractory lining. Advantage may be taken of this condition by placing the coke charge in the bottom of the buckets. By distributing the charges in the manner achieved with the cone-bottom buckets, a large portion of the coke slides to the cupola lining. It is here that it comes into contact with the air blast and, consequently, a relatively high thermal efficiency is obtained.

The first step in the charging operation consists of accurate weighing of the coke, pig iron, home scrap (heads, gates, risers and defective castings), purchased iron scrap, steel scrap, fluxing materials (limestone, fluorspar and soda ash), silvery pig iron, and any alloys that may be required. Since the molten iron is no more uniform in composition than the accuracy

Fig. 23.1. **Pendant type monorail scales can be moved to various storage bins, where charges are made up by hand.**

with which the components of the charge are selected and weighed, the need for accurate scales and careful weighing in the storage yard and on the charging platform cannot be over-emphasized. Weighing equipment must be checked frequently and kept in good order by qualified scale repair men. One good procedure consists of engaging the services of professional scale repair men to make periodic inspections of all weighing equipment. In addition to this, all scales should be checked daily, over the range in which they are used, with standard scale weights. This subject must be given considerable thought and attention by top management as well as the cupola foreman, as there is no substitute for accurate weighing.

Too frequently, when the analysis "gets off," investigation reveals that the iron yard scale or some other scale is out of order. The weighing equipment must be rugged and accurate, sensitive over the range in which it is to be used, and intelligently chosen for the job it is intended to do. One set of scales will not be satisfactory for weighing all of the materials entering into the charge. For example, 50 lb of 50 per cent lump ferrosilicon cannot be weighed accurately on a set of scales designed for heavy loads where the smallest division on the dial represents 25 lb, and the tare weight of the charging car and bucket may be 3,000 or 4,000 lb. For weighing materials used in quantities up to about 50 lb an ordinary spring scale has been found satisfactory. For weighing "concentrated" materials such as silvery pig iron and spiegeleisen in quantities of 50 to 150 lb, a portable platform scale of 500 lb capacity is recommended. Coke may be weighed on the same type of scales and the equipment need not be expensive or elaborate. Containers used for coke may be scrap steel drums cut in two with handles welded to each half. The gross weight is marked on each container and, for convenience and ease of handling, the coke is weighed in batches of 100 lb or less. Plant layout and conditions will determine, at least to some extent, the type of weighing equipment to be used.

In foundries where all components of the charge are loaded by hand, the pendant type, monorail scales, as in Fig. 23.1, have been found satisfactory. This equipment is provided with push button controls so that the scales and charging buckets can be raised, lowered, or moved to any storage bin in the iron yard.

Air used in the cupola melting process should be looked upon as a most important raw material. When melting 200 tons of iron in a cupola, about 5,200,000 cu ft of air will be required. Air at 14.7 psi atmospheric pressure and 60 F weighs 0.0764 lb per cu ft. By means of simple arithmetic it is evident that for every pound of iron melted, practically 1 lb of air is required. Emphasis has been placed on the importance of accurate weighing of the metal, coke, limestone, and other materials comprising a cupola mixture. However, to insure uniformity of operations, it is just as important that the raw material, air, used in quantities nearly equal in weight to the tonnage of iron melted, be metered or weighed with the same care and accuracy as the other components of the charge. Melting Control is detailed in Chapter 25.

CHAPTER 24

Coke Bed

The preparation, height, and burning-in of the coke bed are among the most critical items in the operation of a cupola. It is commonly agreed that any effort to economize on these phases of operation may lead to costly melting difficulties.

The most valuable asset that any melting department can have is a conscientious supervisor who watches all necessary details and has the knowledge and intelligence needed to recognize minor variations and trends as they occur, and is able to correct them before they become serious. The importance of careful supervision and planning in eliminating daily variations cannot be overemphasized.

The coke bed may be hand picked to advantage. This should involve selection of uniformly large pieces to permit free flow of air. Use of burned coke from the previous day's drop should be prohibited.

While chemical and physical properties of foundry coke of different producers will vary, this general specification should give good results—

Fixed Carbon	92 %	min.
Volatile Matter	1 %	max.
Ash	7 %	max.
Sulfur	0.8%	max.
Shatter (per cent on 2 in. screen)	92 %	min.

Some operators consider an ideal coke size to be 1/12 the effective diameter of the cupola. The Cupola Fuels chapter (14) is a guide to selecting the proper coke for a particular cupola operation.

The method of lighting-off and burning-in of the coke bed is a matter of personal preference governed by the equipment available and the cost involved. *The cheapest way is the best way* as long as satisfactory results are obtained. The most popular methods are:

Lighting-off	Burning-in
1) Wood Kindling	1) Natural Draft
2) Gas or Oil Burners or Torches	2) Induced Draft
3) Electric Igniter	a. Compressed Air
4) Externally Ignited Coke	b. Blower

WOOD KINDLING

When igniting the bed with wood kindling, slabs of wood or other combustible material are laid carefully on the sand bottom to absorb the impact of the additional wood and coke as they are charged. It is considered good practice to stand slabs of wood against the lining to form an inverted cone, and then to place the smaller miscellaneous pieces of wood into the cone to a depth slightly above the top of the tuyeres. Slabs and strips should be charged in a crisscross fashion to provide adequate air space. The slabs standing upright protect the lining against damage by the additional wood and coke as they are charged. It is important that the kindling wood be dry. Sawmill scantlings, waste from wood or pattern shops, scorched bottom boards, or any well dried, soft, easy burning wood make excellent kindling material. The use of hardwoods should be discouraged because they burn too slowly to properly ignite the bed coke. Metal plates, fittings, nails and trim should be removed from all kindling as they tend to chill the molten first iron. Small metal parts may cause a freezeup of the tap hole as the first tap is made.

Tuyere covers are left open and the wood is ignited, either through these openings or the open tap hole, by a gas or oil torch, or by burning oil-soaked rags. When the wood is burning freely, and not until then, a third, half or three-quarters of the coke to be used in the bed is forked in carefully. This step in the bed burning-in process is most important. Unburned coke in the cupola well can lead to cold iron and erratic operations that are practically impossible to overcome in a day's heat.

For an hour or so the burning of the bed proceeds by natural draft until it has attained a bright, even, cherry-red color throughout. The bed burning should be observed from time to time from the charging door. Any low spots or holes in the bed should be filled promptly with coke so that the whole bed burns evenly. Burning-in may be hastened by using a partial blast for a few minutes at the finish. The use of the full blower volume is considered poor practice due to the possibility of localized burning at the tuyere area. Therefore, the blower should be set to deliver a minimum amount of air, or the tuyere peepholes should be left open to reduce the effective air volume to a point where the air is fed evenly through all the tuyeres, and no bright spots or excessively localized fast burning zones are observed.

When all wood has been consumed (not until then) and the top of the bed has attained an even cherry red color (showing that bed has been burned through), the bed should be leveled carefully to the standard height measured with a metal gage rod or chain hung from the sill of the charging door (Fig. 24.1). After the bed is leveled, charging should be begun at once.

GAS OR OIL BURNERS: TORCHES

Probably the most widely used method of bed burning, among large production foundries, is the use of gas or oil burners or torches. The bed is ignited with burners or torches inserted through separate holes that are cut in the sides of the cupola shell

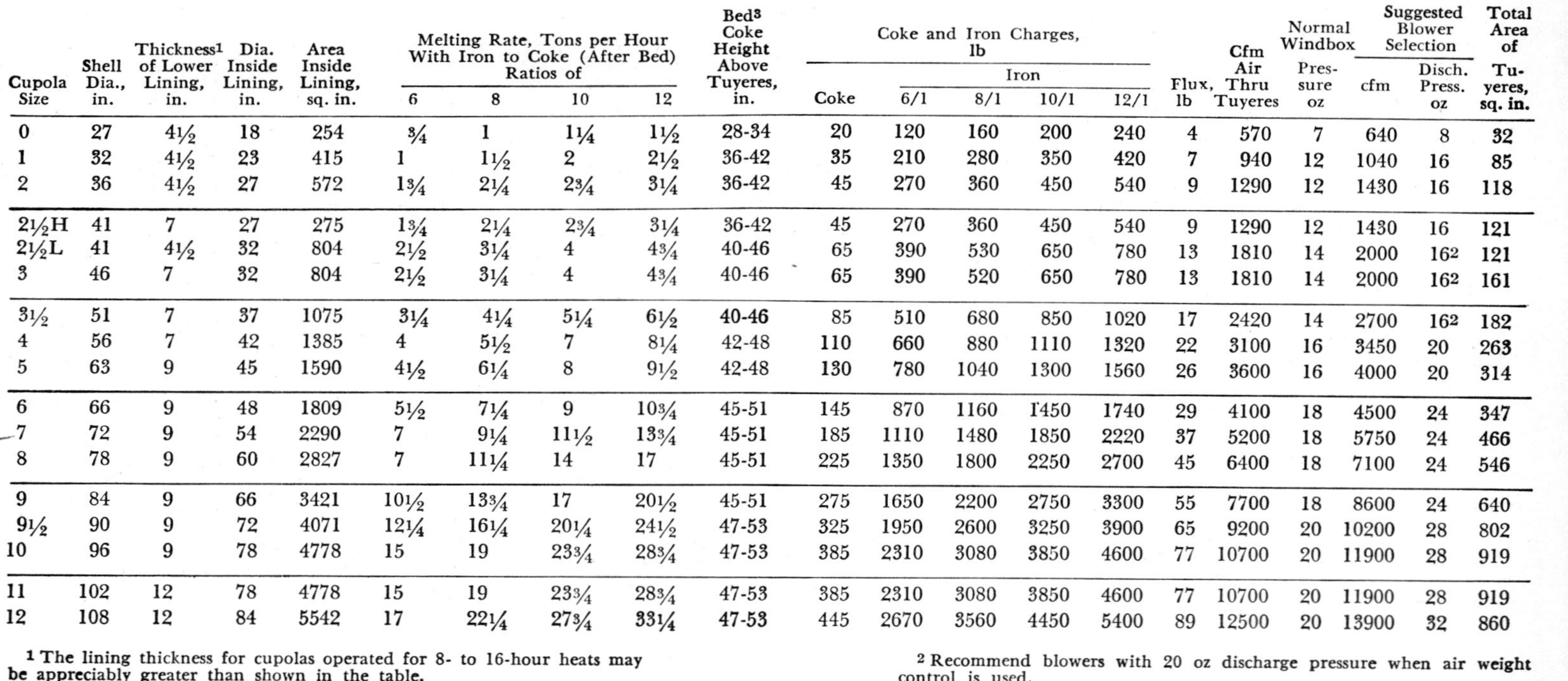

Fig. 24.1. Gage for measuring height of cupola bed.

and lining. The burners are placed in these holes, which are located approximately 4 in. above the sand bottom and evenly spaced around the circumference of the cupola shell. The number of burners used is a matter of preference, but usually four burners are used for cupolas larger than 54 in. diameter.

In lighting the bed in this manner it is considered good practice to build coke tunnels by hand in front of each burner to allow the burner flame to penetrate the bed. Many foundries using this method form the foundation for the tunnels by placing 4 in. pipe in the burner holes. The hand-picked uniform coke is then placed in such a way that the tunnels will not cave in after the pipe are withdrawn and the burners started. This assures that the burner flame will penetrate the entire bed and that an evenly burned bed will be attained.

This method of bed burning has some decided advantages that should be considered in selecting the bed-burning practice to be used.

Advantages

1) Breast and tap hole are formed before the bottom doors are closed.
2) Permits repair man to make breast under normal cool working conditions.
3) Breast is thoroughly dried during the burning-in of the bed.
4) Permits preheating of lining and sand bottom.
5) Eliminates blanket of charcoal formed during wood-burning operations thus minimizing freeze-ups.
6) Gives more positive control over bed burning, thus reducing the danger of an unevenly burned bed as is often encountered when the blower is used.
7) Reduces the possibility of overburning the bed.
8) Short burning-in time. Some foundries report 20-30 min bed burning practice on cupolas as large as 72 to 84 in. diameter.
9) Less chance for variation in practice.
10) Less ash formed.

Disadvantages

1) Must have semi-skilled man to burn bed.
2) Bed building is time consuming and tedious.
3) Greater cost.

TABLE 24.1. GENERAL CHARGING DIRECTIONS FOR CUPOLAS

Cupola Size	Shell Dia., in.	Thickness[1] of Lower Lining, in.	Dia. Inside Lining, in.	Area Inside Lining, sq. in.	Melting Rate, Tons per Hour With Iron to Coke (After Bed) Ratios of				Bed[3] Coke Height Above Tuyeres, in.	Coke and Iron Charges, lb					Flux, lb	Cfm Air Thru Tuyeres	Normal Windbox Pressure oz	Suggested Blower Selection		Total Area of Tuyeres, sq. in.
					6	8	10	12		Coke	Iron 6/1	8/1	10/1	12/1				cfm	Disch. Press. oz	
0	27	4½	18	254	¾	1	1¼	1½	28-34	20	120	160	200	240	4	570	7	640	8	32
1	32	4½	23	415	1	1½	2	2½	36-42	35	210	280	350	420	7	940	12	1040	16	85
2	36	4½	27	572	1¾	2¼	2¾	3¼	36-42	45	270	360	450	540	9	1290	12	1430	16	118
2½H	41	7	27	275	1¾	2¼	2¾	3¼	36-42	45	270	360	450	540	9	1290	12	1430	16	121
2½L	41	4½	32	804	2½	3¼	4	4¾	40-46	65	390	530	650	780	13	1810	14	2000	16[2]	121
3	46	7	32	804	2½	3¼	4	4¾	40-46	65	390	520	650	780	13	1810	14	2000	16[2]	161
3½	51	7	37	1075	3¼	4¼	5¼	6½	40-46	85	510	680	850	1020	17	2420	14	2700	16[2]	182
4	56	7	42	1385	4	5½	7	8¼	42-48	110	660	880	1110	1320	22	3100	16	3450	20	263
5	63	9	45	1590	4½	6¼	8	9½	42-48	130	780	1040	1300	1560	26	3600	16	4000	20	314
6	66	9	48	1809	5½	7¼	9	10¾	45-51	145	870	1160	1450	1740	29	4100	18	4500	24	347
7	72	9	54	2290	7	9¼	11½	13¾	45-51	185	1110	1480	1850	2220	37	5200	18	5750	24	466
8	78	9	60	2827	7	11¼	14	17	45-51	225	1350	1800	2250	2700	45	6400	18	7100	24	546
9	84	9	66	3421	10½	13¾	17	20½	45-51	275	1650	2200	2750	3300	55	7700	18	8600	24	640
9½	90	9	72	4071	12¼	16¼	20¼	24½	47-53	325	1950	2600	3250	3900	65	9200	20	10200	28	802
10	96	9	78	4778	15	19	23¾	28¾	47-53	385	2310	3080	3850	4600	77	10700	20	11900	28	919
11	102	12	78	4778	15	19	23¾	28¾	47-53	385	2310	3080	3850	4600	77	10700	20	11900	28	919
12	108	12	84	5542	17	22¼	27¾	33¼	47-53	445	2670	3560	4450	5400	89	12500	20	13900	32	860

[1] The lining thickness for cupolas operated for 8- to 16-hour heats may be appreciably greater than shown in the table.

[2] Recommend blowers with 20 oz discharge pressure when air weight control is used.

[3] Height of bed coke varies as square root of blast pressure.

4) Some expense involved in preparation of equipment.
5) Possibility of burnout through burner hole if not botted properly.

After the cupola bed is ignited the burner or torch holes are botted up with rammed breast mix.

Many foundries ignite the bed in this manner, and when it is thoroughly ignited the fuel is cut off but the compressed air is left on until the entire bed has attained bright cherry-red color. The bed is then leveled off, measured, and the cupola is charged. Natural draft works well with this method of bed-burning but is somewhat slower.

INDUCED DRAFT

The use of induced draft in the bed burning-in practice is reported as a satisfactory method by several foundries, but needless to say, it should be carried out with considerable care.

In this method a wood fire is kindled, the blower turned on, and half to three fourths of the required bed coke is added immediately. It is considered good practice to leave the tuyere peepholes open and to set the blower to deliver a very small amount of air, thus minimizing localized burning. The blast is continued until the top of the bed is burning uniformly to a bright cherry-red color. Care should be taken to obtain an even burning-in. The blower is turned off and the remainder of the bed coke is added and the bed is leveled in the usual manner.

Some difficulty is encountered in establishing the desired bed height with a measuring rod because the coke occasionally seems to pile loosely, only to pack during the fill-up to a height that is lower then the desired operating bed height.

KINDLING TUYERES

Some cupolas are equipped with kindling tuyeres which open into the cupola at the top of the sand bottom. Usually there are four such tuyeres equally spaced around the shell. They are connected to the wind box so that a gentle blast can be applied through them if necessary. This method with gas or oil torches or wood kindling preheats the bottom sand and well very nicely. In addition an evenly burned bed is obtained.

With this method it is necessary to keep main tuyere valves in good working order so that most of the draft for igniting the bed comes through the kindling tuyere.

The kindling tuyeres are stopped up with a suitable ramming mix when the bed burning-in is complete.

ELECTRIC IGNITER

The electric coke igniter, also available for lighting the bed, has not met with great acceptance. The method for operation of this type of ignition is best obtained from the manufacturer.

BURNERS INSERTED IN TUYERES

Use of gas burners inserted through the tuyeres is another satisfactory method of lighting the bed. Before placing any coke on the cupola bottom, lengths of pipe are placed in the tuyere openings through the peepholes, slanted downward and wedged in place against the tuyeres. About two-thirds of the bed coke is placed in the cupola. The pipes are then carefully removed to maintain the channels formed in the coke bed. Gas burners are used to ignite the bed. They are inserted through separate tuyeres into the respective channels. When the adjacent coke has been ignited, the burners are withdrawn and if necessary placed in other channels until the entire bed is ignited.

GAS OR OIL TORCH IN BREAST OPENING

It is an acceptable practice in smaller cupolas to leave the breast open and after the coke has been charged, ignite it with a gas or oil torch through the breast opening. Depending on the size of the cupola, one or more channels are formed by carefully arranging pieces of coke placed along the bottom from the breast to the back of the cupola to permit even ignition of the bed. When the lower layer of coke has been ignited, the torch can be removed and the breast made.

EXTERNALLY IGNITED COKE

To accelerate the burning-in operation, a few foundries use this procedure: A portion of the bed coke is ignited outside the cupola in a special grate-bottomed container. The ignited coke is dumped in place through the charging door. The bed is built up, leveled off, and when its height has been checked, the cupola is ready for charging.

DISCUSSION OF PRACTICES

It is recommended that the preparation and burning-in of the coke bed be carried out carefully, even if the day's heat is delayed. No phase of cupola operation is more important than to have a properly prepared and burned-in bed. It is a rare occasion when a poorly prepared bed can be corrected during the course of a day's heat. It is much more economical to take extra time and care to get off to a good start than to take the risk of losing the entire day's production because of bad metal.

After the coke bed has been made and lighted it is important that it be burned evenly and thoroughly throughout the entire bed. Localized hot spots should be eliminated by adjusting the burners and/or air supply. It is good practice to keep the bed as level as possible during the burning-in period with the addition of coke forked onto the bed where low or hot spots develop.

Most competent melters burn the bed until it attains a bright-cherry color throughout the entire bed. It is an accepted practice, however, to top the burned bed with from 6 to 12 in. of green coke after it has attained the proper color. Care must be taken to prevent overburning.

The bed is always leveled off to a standard height measured by a rod hung from the charging door sill. The standard bed height is always used regardless of the weight of the coke required. However, the weight of coke used in the bed should be recorded for accounting purposes.

IDEAL BED HEIGHT

It is suggested that the competent operator avail himself of the information in Chapter 34 on "Thermochemical Principles." A knowledge of the theory of combustion and its application to the cupola is helpful in establishing the routine for efficient cupola operation. Nevertheless, that all-important dimension, the height of the coke bed above the top of the tuyeres, must be determined by experimentation.

Table 24.1 shows suggested bed heights based on cupola diameter and normal windbox pressure. For conventional operation the correct bed height in inches will probably fall in the range of 10½ times the square root of the windbox pressure, and this value plus 6.

Example—Cupola operates at 16 oz windbox pressure then $10\frac{1}{2}\sqrt{16} = 42$. Therefore, the proper bed height for these conditions will be between 42 and 48 in. For a given pressure the suggested bed height is the starting point for a series of experiments. From the results, determine the optimum bed height for the cupola in question in this way:

First Day

1) Level off the bed to the suggested height.
2) The tap hole is left open and, after the bed has been burned-in properly and the cupola is full to the charging door sill, the blast is turned on. A steady, continuous stream of molten iron should flow through the tap hole in about 8 to 10 min after the blast is turned on.
3) A longer time interval accompanied by a dribbling stream of cold iron indicates that the bed is too high.
4) A shorter time interval and a fair sized stream of cold iron indicates that the bed is too low. When the bed is excessively low oxidation of the iron is likely to occur, with the emission of short, fast sparks from the stream of molten iron.
5) After running out a few hundred pounds of iron for test, the tap hole is botted up and the heat proceeds as usual.

Second and Subsequent Days

The procedure is repeated, using a higher or lower bed as indicated by the first trial, but with all other variables in the cupola operation remaining unchanged.

During the trials, the bed should be varied in about 3 in. steps for small cupolas up to 48 in. inside diameter, 4 in. steps for cupolas up to 66 in. diameter, and 6 in. steps for large cupolas.

The data are recorded in tabular fashion to permit easy comparison daily throughout the test:

Time

A) Hour and minute of "blast on."
B) Elapsed time to appearance of first droplets of molten iron at tuyere peep holes.
C) Elapsed time to first steady stream of molten iron at open tap hole.
D) Elapsed time to botting up the tap hole.
E) Elapsed time to first tap of iron.

Temperature

Temperatures should be read with an accurate optical pyrometer.

A) Temperature of iron at time "C" above.
B) Temperature of iron at time "E" above.
C) Temperature of iron at 15 min. intervals throughout the heat.

If the first trial indicates a low or high bed, succeeding trials of higher or lower beds, as the case may be, should be made until a satisfactory bed height is attained. Trials at that height should be continued for several days. Again the bed should be successively raised until it is too high, and in a like manner at a later date, trials should be made with lower beds to the point where the bed is too low. In this manner the upper and lower extremes and the optimum bed height can be established.

Having found the optimum bed height, the maintenance of metal temperature at the cupola spout throughout the heat indicates that the weight of the coke charge has been properly chosen. Table 24.1 contains recommendations for coke charges of proper weight in relation to cupola diameter, but these values may require some modification for a particular operation.

When the proper bed height has been determined the metal and coke charge and the weight or volume of air should be held constant, for a trial period, in order to check the bed performance. During this trial period the temperature of the iron at the cupola spout should be determined with an optical pyrometer every 15 min, and the readings should be recorded in tabular form to permit comparison of day-to-day operation. If the bed gradually builds up to a height greater than the optimum, the temperature of the iron will fall and the melting rate, as shown by the size of the stream of iron at the spout, will decrease. If the bed gradually burns down to a height lower than the optimum, the temperature of the iron will be lower, the melting rate will increase slightly, and the iron will be oxidized to an extent shown by an increase in chill depth. Thus an abnormally high or low bed occurring during a heat is indicated by the same symptoms that are used at the outset in the determination of the optimum bed height.

When the optimum bed height and the proper weight of the coke charge have been established, and the resulting cupola practice is producing an iron of the proper temperature and analysis, it is recommended that this bed height be established as routine and should be rigorously maintained.

Many foundrymen prefer to start the melting operation with the tap hole botted up. This is good practice, but when experimenting to establish the height of the coke bed, the tap hole should be left open to permit close observation of the first iron.

In using Table 24.1, the weight of the coke charge depends on the diameter of the cupola and the weight of the iron charge is derived from that of the coke charge by means of the iron-to-fuel ratio. For example, the recommended coke charge for a 37 in. diameter cupola is 85 lb. The metal charge is then 680 lb for a ratio of 8 to 1; 850 lb for a ratio of 10 to 1, and so on. These ratios refer to metal and coke in the charges only, and do not take into consideration the overall metal-to-coke ratio which includes the weight of the bed coke.

MAINTAINING PROPER BED HEIGHT THROUGHOUT HEAT

A procedure of experimentation for determining the proper bed height is recommended in the foregoing. This experiment extends over a period of several heats, and the best height of the coke bed for the beginning of the heat can be established in this manner. However, many things can happen during an extended heat to change the bed height, and any change in bed height nearly always results in cold metal. It is obvious that the cupola operator should have some means of correcting this condition in the least possible time.

If the metal temperature falls during the heat, considerable damage may occur before adjustment of the coke charge will register in increased metal temperature. Many operators charge a constant weight of air throughout heat, and this is desirable so long as the bed height remains the same. The air is just as much a part of the charge as the coke and metal.

Unless there is an obvious cause for cold metal, such as a shutdown, it is nearly always the result of the bed height and air input becoming unbalanced. Fortunately, in most cases the weight of air can be adjusted to match any change in bed height in a few minutes, and the effect will be an increase in the spout metal temperature.

Assuming that the correct bed height has been established and the proper weight of air is being charged through the tuyeres, sometimes during the heat a drop of 50F may occur in metal temperature. If there has been no shutdown, the air input and bed height have become unbalanced. What is not known is whether the bed is too high or too low. This can be determined as follows: the weight of air charged should be reduced by 5 to 7 per cent, and if this is done the tapping temperature of the metal will either increase or decrease depending upon the condition of the coke bed. If the coke bed is too low, the decrease in air input will be followed within 5 min by an increase in metal temperature. On the other hand if the coke bed is too high a further drop in metal temperature will occur. In the latter case the air charge should be increased 5 to 7 per cent above the normal input. The metal temperature will then increase because of the faster burning rate of coke. This procedure will avoid extended periods of cold metal.

While the above procedure will avoid cold metal, it is desirable to re-establish the normal melting rate to meet shop demands as soon as possible. To do this, in the case of a low bed, enough coke should be charged to raise the bed from 4 to 6 in. In case of a high bed the coke charge should be reduced by the same amount. As soon as the coke change has had time to reach the coke bed, the air input should be adjusted to normal. With a continuous flow of metal at the spout and automatic air weight control available, this means of control becomes very simple. In this connection, the radiation pyrometer recorder described in Chapter 8 is valuable since the operator has a running record of the spout metal temperature.

CHECKING COKE BED PERFORMANCE

Because of the high temperature of the melting zone, the lining is eroded in a band several inches wide at the operating height of the coke bed. The bed performance can be checked by observing the extent of the cutting when the cupola is cold. In most cases this severely eroded band will be from 18 to 24 in. above the top of the main tuyeres, and it is this height of coke that is equal to the height at which it is desired to carry the combustion zone.

The observant cupola operator will make daily notes of the refractory burnout sustained. These daily notes serve as an excellent guide to proper bed performance, and in many cases will give indications of melting irregularities that can be eliminated before they become serious enough to affect the metal quality.

Careful examination of the refractory burnout after a day's heat (after cupola is cool) is an excellent way to check performance of the coke bed.

Checking the performance of the coke bed during actual operation is not as simple as observing the eroded refractory band mentioned above, but there are several fundamental symptoms that indicate improper bed performance. These symptoms usually occur before any appreciable damage is done to the molten metal. The alert cupola operator will learn these symptoms and peculiarities of cupola melting and will make the necessary adjustments at once.

Probably the most apparent symptom of irregular bed performance is a sudden change in metal temperature without apparent cause. In most cases this sudden change is due to a low coke bed. The first indication will be a sudden rise, followed within a few minutes by a gradual but definite drop in metal temperature. This drop in temperature will continue until the air input and the operating bed height are put in balance again.

The color of the slag is another factor that can be used to advantage in checking the bed performance. Normal acid cupola slags are a grayish-green color when the bed height and air input are in balance. If the slag gradually changes from the normal grayish-green to a dull black color the bed has fallen below its normal operating height and the necessary steps should be taken to reestablish the proper air input and bed height ratio. Should the slag become a very light green or cream color it is an indication that too much flux is being used.

In addition excessive loss of silicon and manganese, together with low carbon pick-up and sudden changes in melting rate are almost sure signs of an improper bed performance. Chill tests caught regularly will be helpful in recognizing these changes. In any of the foregoing events the precautionary steps should be taken as soon as possible in an effort to eliminate erratic bed performance which may cause cold or oxidized iron.

In each case of faulty bed performance the symptoms are similar and their remedy is simple for the alert, well-trained operator. The addition or subtraction of coke is one method of correction, but the immediate correction is to adjust the air input, as mentioned in a foregoing section.

RECORDS RELATIVE AND ESSENTIAL TO PROPER BED PERFORMANCE

The practice of maintaining a daily record of those factors that are pertinent to bed performance is considered time well spent. It is these records that keep the well-trained operator alerted for signs of trouble, and aid him greatly in his effort to produce a quality iron for each heat.

The Records section (Chapter 20) is recommended as a guide for selecting melting record types that fit particular needs.

CHAPTER 25

Melting Control

The cupola is fundamentally the most important unit in the equipment of a gray or malleable iron foundry. The quality of the metal taken from the tap hole depends to a considerable extent upon the way the cupola is operated. If too much air is used in proportion to the coke consumed, fuel is wasted, the gases are relatively cold, and there is an ever-present danger of oxidation which means not only loss of metal but poor castings. The oxidation loss of silicon and manganese in such a case also must be considered because these elements are expensive, and the composition of the metal tapped will be adversely affected. On the other hand, if too little air is used the fuel will not be completely consumed and the temperature will not be sufficiently high to produce the desired quantity or quality of metal.

Proper regulation of the cupola during melting decreases costs throughout the foundry. Poor cupola operation will result in poor iron, and good castings cannot be made from such material. It has been the experience of foundrymen that the number of defective castings, other conditions being normal, will be reduced materially with efficient melting.

The cupola is a furnace of determinable design and construction, and certain basic principles of operation are applicable in every case. Therefore, when two cupolas of the same design in the same foundry consistently vary in performances, the fact should not be taken for granted but considered a challenge to the knowledge and ingenuity of the operator. Some difference in construction or operation will account for the variance in performance of the two cupolas, and the cause must be sought out and corrected. The operator should have faith in the fundamental laws of chemistry and physics upon which the performance of his cupola depends, and strive to use them to the best advantage rather than accept the irregularities of performance as being due to some unsolved mystery. Identical cupolas operated on alternate days can be made to produce identical results.

COMBUSTION PRINCIPLES

When the bed has been burned through and leveled off and the fill-up completed, the blast is turned into the tuyeres and this reaction occurs:

(1) $C + O_2$ (from air) $= CO_2 + 14{,}550$ Btu per lb Carbon

The heat produced is the maximum, and consequently it is this reaction that is necessary for the most efficient cupola operation. The extent to which this reaction can be made to take place is determined by the analysis of the coke, the height of the coke bed, the weight of the coke charges, and the accurate regulation of the air supply by either weight or volume. The oxygen in the air supply should be consumed completely by the time the gases reach the top of the coke bed, since free oxygen in the melting zone will cause melting losses due to the oxidation of iron, silicon, and manganese.

Carbon dioxide, like oxygen, also will react with the coke. Thus some of the carbon dioxide initially formed reacts with the carbon with which it is in contact, to a greater or less extent, depending upon the temperature, to form carbon monoxide according to the equation:

(2) $CO_2 + C = 2\,CO - 5{,}850$ Btu per lb Carbon

It should be noted that this reaction is accompanied by an absorption of heat. The net heat produced is, therefore, the difference between the heat generated in the first reaction and the heat absorbed in the second. The maximum combustion efficiency that can be attained practically depends upon the extent to which Reaction 2 can be limited.

The first reaction takes place very rapidly, even at a comparatively low temperature, while the second is much slower and does not reach its maximum velocity below 1800 F, and therefore it takes place higher in the combustion zone. The faster Reaction 1 can be made to go, that is, the higher the burning rate of the coke, the more heat will be developed initially and in usable form.

Since the rate of reaction in either case increases with temperature, the hotter the carbon dioxide and coke become the more carbon monoxide will be produced. Therefore, a high carbon monoxide content in the effluent gas does not connote incomplete combustion, but may actually be the result of higher temperatures existing within the combustion zone which have affected the carbon dioxide-carbon monoxide equilibrium even in the face of supposedly constant fuel and air inputs into the cupola. The cupola is actually melting faster and delivering hotter iron under these conditions.

Under certain conditions Reaction 2 is reversible. At temperatures above 1800 F, provided sufficient time is available, the reaction proceeds almost completely to the right, while at about 900 F (the temperature of the upper part of the stack) the reaction proceeds to the left, the carbon monoxide breaking down into carbon and carbon dioxide to an extent depending upon the catalytic effect of the iron present.

Carbon monoxide combines with free oxygen to form carbon dioxide according to the equation:

(3) $2\ CO + O_2 = 2\ CO_2 + 10{,}200$ Btu/lb C

Carbon monoxide formed in Reaction 2 is oxidized to carbon dioxide in Reaction 3 when free oxygen is made available by the use of a second or third row of tuyeres, as in the balanced-blast cupola, and the heat that was lost in the original formation of the carbon monoxide is regained.

The gases pass through the bed and up the stack with tremendous velocity. As a result, all three of the reactions take place simultaneously.

Chapter 33 is a complete technical discussion of combustion in the cupola.

Current Theory of Combustion in Cupola

The ideal combustion efficiency is attained by burning all the oxygen of the blast air to carbon dioxide. Practically, some carbon dioxide must be reduced to carbon monoxide. Therefore, since the goal sought in cupola operation is the most efficient relationship between melting rate and temperature, the selection and stabilization of the proper ratio of carbon dioxide to carbon monoxide in the effluent gases is most important.

The theory on which the use of auxiliary tuyeres and the balanced-blast cupola is based is that, by the admission of additional air above the main tuyeres, the carbon monoxide present will be burned immediately to carbon dioxide with the generation of heat and consequent increase in the efficiency of the combustion process.

The most desirable ratio of carbon dioxide to carbon monoxide in the effluent gases for a given type of iron is a debatable question and must have further study. One school, represented by users of the balanced blast cupola, inclines toward low carbon monoxide to promote combustion efficiency. Another school, using the conventional cold blast cupola, advocates 10 per cent or more carbon monoxide in the effluent gases to avoid excessive oxidation and consequent high melting losses.

Application of Combustion Reaction

Because the gases pass through the stack at such high velocity, the combustion reactions which take place simultaneously cannot go to completion. This results in a condition, which is called dynamic equilibrium, under which the composition of the effluent gases become relatively constant and reflects the conditions present in the melting zone. At a distance below the charging door where the ascending gases have not met the incoming air from that source and have cooled to 600 to 900 degrees F, it is good practice to draw off a sample and analyze it for carbon dioxide. From this value can be computed the carbon monoxide, as shown in Chapter 33. Since the metal to fuel ratio is known, the required blast air can be calculated by the method explained in Chapter 33.

The combustion reactions show that a given weight of coke requires a definite weight of air to burn it to a certain desired ratio of carbon dioxide to carbon monoxide, or to put it another way, it takes so much air to burn effectively so much coke. Therefore, it is not good practice to add more coke in an effort to secure hotter iron without properly increasing the blast volume just as the coke additions reach the top of the bed.

For a given operation there is a certain height of the coke bed at which the combustion process will work to best advantage. This is known as the *optimum bed height.* In practice the optimum bed height properly determined by experimentation for each operation (described in Chapter 24), will yield iron at the highest temperature possible for a given metal to fuel ratio.

The yardsticks of good cupola operation are: 1) clean molten iron produced at the desired melting rate, and at a temperature which is best suited to the type of castings under consideration; 2) iron of the desired analysis within normal limits; and 3) normal losses of iron, silicon, and manganese.

Conservation of Waste Heat

The cupola acts as a heat recuperator. The hot gases leaving the melting zone preheat to a considerable extent the overlying charges of iron and coke. This is the reason for the high heat efficiency of the cupola as compared with other metallurgical furnaces. To derive the full benefit of the preheating process the effective height of the cupola, that is, the distance from the tuyeres to the charging door, must be sufficient. It is generally considered that the best effective height lies between 16 and 22 ft, depending upon the diameter of the cupola. Vial developed the following formula for expressing the relationship between the height and diameter.

Cold Blast	Hot Blast
$H = 2D + 5$ ft	
H = Height in feet	$H = 2\frac{1}{2}D + 5$ ft
D = Diameter in feet	

The height may exceed this relationship in special cases, but Vial's formula provides a rule of thumb means of determining the height necessary to insure proper blast penetration.

Tuyeres

The shape and size of the tuyeres should be selected to insure the uniform distribution and adequate penetration of the volume of blast air necessary for the efficient combustion of coke. Unfortunately, the most careful calculations are often upset by the obstructing action of the coke which lies immediately in front of the tuyeres. When the tuyere area is too small, the velocity of the air is increased and, while the penetration may be good, the cooling effect may be excessive and the power required to operate the blower will be increased. If the tuyeres are too large, the velocity will be decreased and the penetration will be less, often resulting in the presence of a cone of unconsumed coke in the center of the cupola.

The tuyeres should not be placed too high above the sand bottom of the cupola if the coke consumption is to be kept low and the iron hot. However, when tapping intermittently, or in absence of a forehearth or receiving ladle, the tuyeres should be sufficiently high above the slag hole to prevent the air stream from impinging upon the molten iron.

The air passes through the tuyeres horizontally and immediately seeks an upward path. Thus coke lying below the tuyeres is not burned and, therefore, furnishes no heat. The hot iron from the melting zone loses some heat as it passes through the relatively cold coke, and sometimes it has to be pigged because it is too cold to pour into molds. This can be prevented by allowing the iron to accumulate in the well before making the first tap, since in this way the dead coke is heated to the temperature of the iron. It has been noted that when other conditions are the same, the hottest first iron is taken from cupolas having relatively low tuyeres. However, if the tuyeres are set too low, the blast will cool the molten iron in the well of the cupola.

If upper tuyeres are used, they should be placed close enough to the lower tuyeres so that the heat produced by the combustion of carbon monoxide can be utilized efficiently. If the upper tuyeres are too high a second melting zone will be formed, with accompanying deterioration of the cupola lining.

Varying Melting Rate : Blast and Iron-Coke Ratio

For a cupola of given size, an increase in air will increase the coke consumption in the melting zone, hence the bed should be higher with more air and faster burning of the coke, and the bed should be lower for less air and decreased coke consumption. The desired spout temperature of the molten iron depends on the quantity of heat produced and, therefore, on the rate at which the coke is burned. The air supply and the coke consumption can be varied in proper relation to one another so as to increase or decrease the melting rate, and at the same time retain the desired melting conditions.

A regular relationship exists between air input, iron to coke ratio, spout temperatures, and melting rate. The combustion process will automatically establish a new norm whenever the blast is increased or decreased, if proper adjustments in iron to coke ratio and air input are made simultaneously. This is the solution to successfully varying the melting rate of a cupola at any time during the heat.

Cupola capacity can be varied considerably from the normal or rated output.

Shop demands vary from season to season, and proper air input and bed height for sustained slack and heavy production periods should be determined. The varying demand for iron throughout any heat and the required blast and bed conditions for that demand will follow the same pattern.

The ideal procedure for slower melting is to reduce the coke charges in anticipation of slowing down the blower so that the bed will have burned itself down to the desired lower operating height at about the time the blast volume is reduced, and vice versa for faster melting. Actually, the bed height can be measured only at the beginning of a heat. Hence, the optimum conditions to be met when the melting rate is changed during the heat must be derived from data accumulated over long periods of slack and heavy production.

In practice, limited variations in the rate of melting are practicable, but wide variations are dangerous. The test for the proper adjustment of air volume, coke consumption and bed height when increasing or decreasing the output is the maintenance of the desired spout temperature and chemical analysis of the iron. Experience prescribes for each iron certain chill characteristics, as measured by the chill test described in Chapter 31, which can be taken readily at every tap or from every ladle of iron. Chill tests provide a rapid and frequent estimate of the characteristics of the iron. From day to day, typical chill coupons should be analyzed chemically to interpret and standardize the meaning of the various depths of chill.

By increasing the air input it is possible to suddenly increase the output and, for a time, the temperature of the iron. The bed will tend to burn down to a lower operating level, and if continued too long without the addition of more coke the metal will be oxidized, since the bed will be too low to consume all the incoming oxygen. This is particularly true if the cupola is being operated at the highest thermal efficiency with a high metal-to-coke ratio. However, the highest thermal efficiency is very frequently and justifiably sacrificed by using more coke to produce hotter iron.

In this case an excess of coke is present, so it is possible to suddenly increase and maintain the air input up to the limit of that excess. Increasing the air input without increasing the coke will tend to decrease the carbon picked up by the melting iron. Experimentation is necessary to determine how long such an air increase can be maintained without adding more coke.

Slower melting can be achieved by 1) using a larger coke charge without changing the air input, and 2) by decreasing the air input without changing the coke charge. Either procedure results in a slower combustion rate, hence slower melting. Both procedures tend toward higher carbon pick-up by the molten iron. In the first procedure, the steel component of the metal charges can be increased at the same time the coke is increased to offset the tendency toward greater carbon pickup in melting. Experience and careful observation of the chill tests are necessary to obtain uniform temperature and chemical analysis. The second procedure does not permit any great amount of steel to be added to offset carbon pick-up because the amount of available heat has not been increased.

Melting Rate — Summary

To summarize, slower melting in the cupola can be achieved by using 1) more coke or 2) less air, and the rate of melting can be increased by using 1) more air or 2) less coke. Within reasonable limits, the rate of melting a saturated iron (where the charge and molten iron are of about the same analysis) can be varied without affecting the characteristics of the molten iron.

Any variation in cupola practice when melting sensitive lower carbon irons is to be discouraged, except under the most careful observation and control. The rate of melting low carbon irons can be increased successfully only by using more air, and the output can be decreased only by simultaneously using more coke and increasing the steel in the metal charge to offset the tendency toward higher carbon in the melting iron. When tapping intermittently, the length of each tap should be the same and should be timed with a stop watch, but for such irons continuous tapping is to be preferred.

SHUTDOWNS DURING THE HEAT

Frequent starting and stopping the cupola is not recommended because it tends to produce cold iron. Each shutdown is accompanied by a short interval of high carbon monoxide concentration at and near the melting zone, during which the melt picks up considerably more than its normal quota of carbon. This is particularly noticeable on the first tap of lower carbon iron following even a short shutdown.

The carbon pickup is less with higher carbon iron. The best practice is to keep the cupola running and have a large enough crew to handle the iron at all times, but as this is not always practicable, pouring conditions should at least be regulated to accumulate several frequent shutdowns into a single and longer shutdown. This minimizes temperature drop and variations in analysis.

Melting nearly ceases if the blower is shut off. In short shutdowns (15 min) the cupola can be botted or, with a front slagger, let stand. CAUTION – Open one tuyere cover during any shutdown to guard against an explosive gas mixture of carbon monoxide and oxygen backing into the windbox. For a prolonged shutdown, as at the noon hour, an extra charge of coke may be added in time to reach the bed just at the noon hour to maintain the bed height during the interim. The tap hole is left open and the front slagging spout is drained. One tuyere cover is opened. Melting is resumed by closing the tuyere cover and turning on the blower. With extra coke on the bed, the usual temperature of the iron will be attained promptly.

In melting high test iron, shutdowns should be avoided altogether, but when they are unavoidable, the first tap after a shutdown should be pigged or used for less important castings.

Extra Coke Between Metal Charges

A single extra (or spreader) charge of coke can be used between the last charge of one mixture and the first charge of a different mixture, to indicate the transition and help separate one iron from the other. . . . The sudden increase in bed height will decrease the melting rate.

FACTORS CONTROLLING METAL TEMPERATURE

The temperature of the molten iron from a given cupola is a function of iron carbon ratio, the blast volume and blast temperature. Proper regulation of air input and the iron to coke ration insure at all times molten iron of desired temperature. The graphs in Chapter 33 can be used to determine the best relationship between air input and iron to coke ratio for any melting rate and temperature required.

When hot blast is used, molten metal temperatures may be raised or lowered quickly by raising or lowering the blast temperature. The molten metal temperature change can be accomplished without any change in either the air input or the iron to coke ratio.

SELECTING THE CUPOLA

The molten iron capacity and the slagging procedure determine the principal dimensions of the cupola. Capacity is indicated by the inside diameter of the melting zone at the operating height of the coke bed where the iron is melted, or by the rated output in tons/hr for a cupola of fixed ID. Use Table 24.1 as a guide for determining the dimensions necessary to produce a given output. A cupola is said to be rear slagging when the slag flows off through a spout at the rear, or front slagging when the slag and molten iron flow together through the tap hole at the front.

The inside diameter of a cupola is established by the demand rate of metal in tons/hr and the hr length of the heat.

It is desirable for some shops to have two cupolas, so that one can be operating while the other is being repaired for the next day's operation. Water cooled cupolas can be operated for more than one heat. However, because of excessive heat losses, water cooled units are impractical in smaller sizes.

Because a cupola can be lined down to a smaller size, if only one unit is to be installed it should be larger than necessary to satisfy the demand rate, to permit some increase in capacity and melting rate.

MAINTAINING UNIFORM COMBUSTION

Theoretically, the bed height should be regulated so that all the oxygen supplied in the blast is consumed just as it reaches the top of the bed, and the weight of the coke charges should be adjusted so that the bed height is maintained throughout the heat. It is most important to hold the bed at its proper height, especially during long time intervals between charging and the beginning of melting. In general, the correct coke size is the largest that will insure complete combustion of oxygen to carbon dioxide at the top of the bed. It has been reported that the best combustion efficiency is obtained with coke ranging in size from 1/10 to 1/12 the diameter of the cupola.

The thickness of the coke charge varies from 3 in. for a very small cupola to as much as 9 in. for a cupola of diameter 54 in. or larger. Table 24.1 gives pertinent data relative to the size of both the coke and iron charges.

Each coke charge should be weighed. A scale is a small investment and pays for itself many times over in better control of melting conditions and coke savings. Due corrections for variation in moisture content should be made when necessary. However, if no scale is available, a measure can be devised to hold the required volume, but it should be checked regularly to see that the prescribed weight standard is maintained.

Coke recovered from the drop should not be used in the coke bed. It is not as desirable as new coke for the charge, principally because it has been broken into small pieces which carry a coating of ash and slag. If there are not other uses for it, it may be used in small portion in the charges, or preferably in the last charge at the end of the heat. It is well to note that the coke in the drop has not entered into the combustion process. The total coke consumed during a heat is the weight of coke charged, plus the weight of the bed coke, minus the weight of the coke recovered from the drop.

FLUX CHARGE

With manual charging, limestone, dolomite, fluorspar, soda ash, and proprietary fluxing materials are spread evenly over the coke charge, about 6 in. from the cupola walls to reduce attack on the lining. With mechanical charging, such distribution of fluxing materials is not possible. The limestone charge may vary from 20 per cent of the coke charge in certain acid practices to over 50 per cent of the coke charge in certain basic operations.

All heats should be fluxed and slagged. Fluxing stone should be added to the bed and to all charges. The bed should be fluxed with two or three times the material added to each charge so that the bed coke will be promptly supplied with slag to hasten the establishment of normal melting conditions.

Sand, dirt and iron oxides associated with the metal charge, and the oxides of silicon, iron and manganese, formed in the cupola, together with the coke ash and eroded portions of the refractory lining combine chemically, and fuse at cupola temperatures to form a viscous or gummy natural cupola slag. Such a slag blankets the coke surfaces in the melting zone and retards the combustion reactions. It solidifies at a comparatively high temperature and is quickly frozen by the incoming blast, forming a bridge over and under the tuyeres which blocks off the cupola and slows up the melting rate and, finally, with long heats, causes cold melting accompanied by excessive oxidation of the metal.

Fluxes accelerate the formation of a larger volume of a more fluid, chemically-active slag which continually flushes the surfaces of the coke in the combustion zone. Thus, a more intimate contact between the blast and the fuel and between the drops of iron and the incandescent coke surfaces is established, which promotes better melting conditions and increases the melting temperature.

Another important function of the flux is its action in accelerating the combustion reaction

$$CO_2 + C = 2\,CO$$

This reaction is accelerated to a limited extent by both of the alkaline earths, CaO and MgO, but to a more pronounced degree by the alkalies, especially by sodium carbonate (soda ash). Thus, the melting and super-heating zone is restricted to a narrower, hotter zone. This increases the melting temperature and reduces the time and extent of exposure of the drops of iron to the blast in passing down to the hearth, thereby preventing oxidation of the metal.

The flux forms a more actively refining slag bath by which sulfur and metallic oxides in the drops of iron trickling down through the slag are removed, and which protects the metal in the hearth from oxidation by the blast. Finally, fluxing agents and slag liquifiers serve to maintain fluidity at lower temperatures, thus facilitating the flow-off of excess slag through the slag hole.

METAL CHARGE

The total weight of the metal charge is derived from the weight of the coke charge in accordance with the desired "fuel ratio," that is, the ratio of pounds of metal to pounds of coke per charge. Suggested metal-to-fuel ratios are shown in Table 24.1.

Melting stock should be sized according to the diameter of the cupola, and in no event should the diagonal dimension of the metal pieces exceed one-third the diameter of the cupola. Uniform charging and sizing of the cupola burden promotes the most efficient operation.

CHAPTER 26

Basic Slag Cupola

The operation of cupolas having basic slags has had as its principal objective the production of low sulfur and/or high carbon irons. With good cupola practice in acid melting, it is well known that there is always an increase in sulfur and, in most cases, an increase in total carbon. High carbon irons, in acid practice, are produced from mixtures containing high percentages of pig iron in the cupola metal charge.

The exception in acid melting would be the utilization of high hot blast temperatures (800 to 1200 F; 425-650 C) where high steel percentages (50-70 per cent) can be incorporated in the metal charge. Carter and Carlson[1] clearly demonstrate the effect of steel size and per cent used in an acid metal charge (Fig. 26.1). The basic cupola is capable of reducing sulfur to extremely low levels, and can achieve carbon pickups greatly in excess of what can be accomplished in regular acid cupolas using comparable raw materials.

From this, it is evident that high carbon irons can be produced in the basic cupola from metal mixtures containing high percentages of steel, which in itself has the advantage of making low phosphorus irons available in applications where such irons are needed. Furthermore, high percentages of purchased scrap and returns may be used without danger of producing irons with excessively high sulfur; thus, in many cases eliminating the necessity of desulfurization after the metal has been melted.

The basic cupola is now being used for making the base iron for nodular iron, as low sulfurs are easily obtainable along with the higher carbon levels that are usually desired. This type of cupola is currently being used in the U.S. and in Europe for producing a base iron for the first stage of producing basic oxygen steel. A few basic cupolas are producing gray iron metal where low sulfur, low phosphorus and high total carbons are required.

The advantage of using a basic slag operated cupola is the ability to use low cost charging materials to produce gray iron or other base irons that require low phosphorus or low sulfurs with varying total carbon ranges. In many cases 100 per cent steel charges consisting of steel turnings, sheet metal and thin section steel stock have been used to produce good gray iron compositions.

Disadvantages of using a basic cupola for normal cupola operation where the metal desired does not require low sulfur or phosphorus levels are:

1. Silicon losses are greater than in an acid cupola where one may expect 10-20 per cent losses, whereas a basic cupola will range from 30-40 per cent with a hot blast installation to 60 per cent with a cold blast operation. The silicon loss is dependent on the slag basicity being maintained in the operation. The higher the slag basicity, the greater the silicon losses.

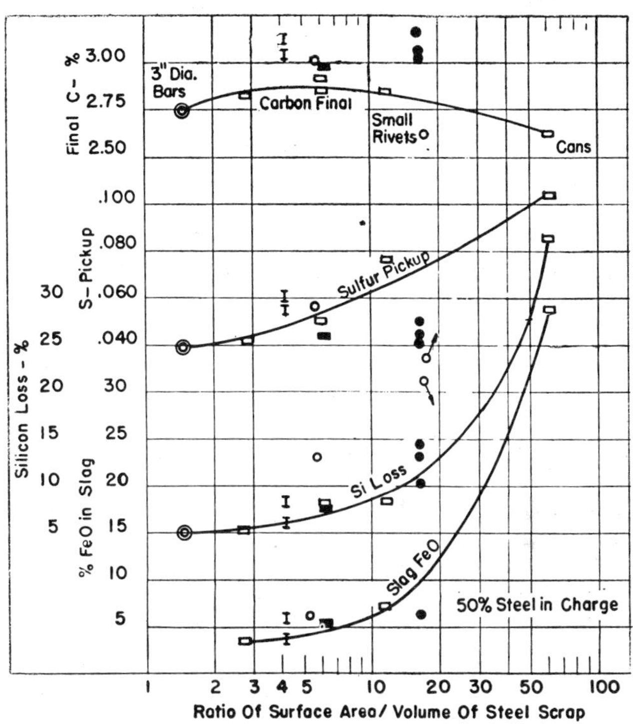

Fig. 26.1. Effect of variation in composition, size, and shape of steel and cast scrap.[1]

2. Refractory costs on basic operated cupola will average at least two to three times that of an acid cupola. This primarily is due to the high cost of the types of refractory used in its operation. Water cooling the cupola will reduce these costs, but they will still exceed those of an acid cupola for ton of metal melted.

3. Cost of fluxing material will exceed that of an acid operated cupola.

4. Cold blast basic operated cupolas require more coke per ton of iron melted, *consequently have slower melting rates,* than acid operated cupolas of the same diameters. Hot blast equipment reduces the amount of coke required in a basic operation and increases the melting rates.

5. Metal analysis is more difficult to control in basic than acid cupolas; for this reason only the best practices can be tolerated. This has been summed up by Carter:[2] "From the standpoint of chemical control, the basic cupola is generally more complex and requires more careful supervision. Its complexity increases with the amount of work done by the basic slag. From the standpoint of sulfur control and a

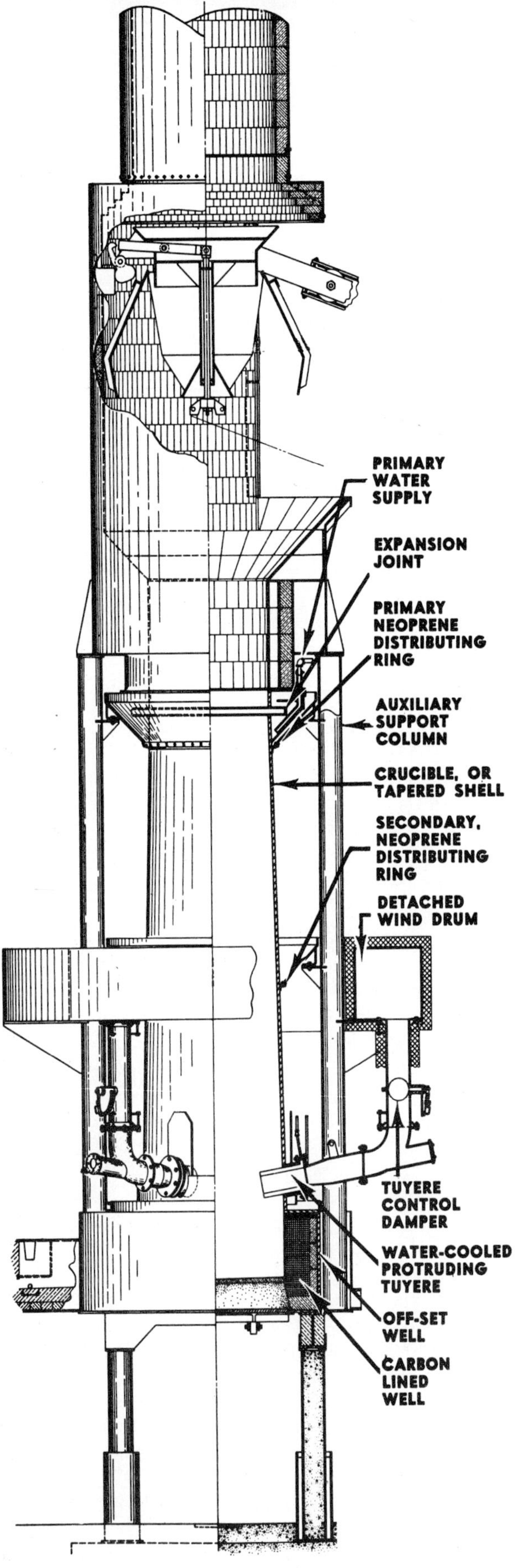

Fig. 26.2. Basic design of water cooled cupola.

sufficient manganese to sulfur ratio, control of the basic cupola is superior. *Carbon control appears to be better on a high carbon iron,* almost equal on a medium carbon iron, and more difficult on a low carbon iron. Silicon consistency (not loss) can be made equal to acid performance but is inclined to be a little more difficult to control because of greater losses. However, in basic operation, the charge frequently consists of more scrap of less predictable chemistry, or more silicon is added as concentrated alloy because of more steel. These less consistent charge materials increase the risk of chemical variations within themselves, irrespective of the basicity. A receiving ladle of sufficient capacity levels out many of these irregularities."

Trends in basic cupola operation have been toward water cooling the cupola shell either with an external water curtain on the shell, or with some type of water glands internally in the melting zone. Carbon refractories are being used to a greater extent due to longer life and neutral characteristics in regard to operating a neutral or basic slag. Hot blast equipment and higher blast temperature ranges (1000-1200 F; 540-650 C) are seriously considered for basic cupolas due to economic reasons, metallurgical control and melting rates. Most basic slag operated cupolas have been constructed to provide a greater distance from the sand bottom to the bottom of the tuyeres. *It is felt this was done for four reasons:*

1. There is a greater volume of slag generated within the cupola due to a larger amount of flux material being charged.
2. Some operators feel that if a deep head of slag is retained in the cupola well the iron loses sulfur and the FeO is reduced as it passes through the slag layer.
3. The blast furnace, being a basic operated melting unit, has a deep hearth and it may have been natural to follow this design.
4. To some operators a deep well was essential to produce high carbon iron from low carbon material.

Carbon pickup as related to the depth of the cupola well has not been fully resolved up to this time. Preliminary findings indicate that the cupola well depth may be an important factor in carbon control.

Various designs have been used in building cupolas to be operated with a basic lining or with a basic slag. Current designs are essentially that of a normal cupola with some modifications being made for each individual installation. There has again been some differences of opinion on cupola construction in regard to using a straight or tapered shell from the cupola well to the charging door, external or internal water cooling for the cupola, or heavy or light metal stock for the shell.

Fleming[3] and Löbbecke[4] carried on extensive work in establishing proper cupola shell design. They concluded that the cupola shell should be made in the shape of a cone expanding downward towards the tuyeres. The designs developed performed satisfactorily in regard to metal temperatures and metallurgical control (Fig. 26.2).

Their reasons for adopting the tapered shell are:

1. Reduced heat losses in combustion zone.
2. Simple construction insures a good water curtain.
3. Reduced amount of iron oxide rich slag that would contact the insulating slag adhering to the

cupola shell, thus preventing the adhering slag from melting off due to lowering of its melting point.

4. Design assists in obtaining center combustion.
5. Construction helps prevent secondary melt zone.
6. Easy removal of any skull formation.

It is possible that the tapered shell would cost more than a straight shell. . . . The straight shell construction has been used satisfactorily and water adherence has been no problem. Such a shell retains slag on the inner wall easily as there is no sloping away at the bottom allowing easy slippage of the created lining. If a partial lining is used the refractories are easier to lay up in the melting zone.

External and internal water cooling of the cupola shells is more thoroughly covered in the Special Cupolas and Accessories Chapter 3. Many prefer an externally water cooled shell as they wish to see what is occurring during the melting operations. External sections are easier and cheaper to replace than internal glands. Both methods of water cooling the cupola are being used with the same beneficial results.

The thickness of the cupola shell has been varied from thin steel shells to 5/16 to 5/8-in. to thicker shells of 3/4-in. or better. Both types of shells are being used in production and each type appears to be satisfactory. However, the heavier shells are used primarily to provide adequate strength to the cupola shell in case of water failure and to simplify construction over a straight shell where support has to be obtained from other locations.

Evidence of section size influencing the heat transference rate has not been fully established although there are some indications that the thicker shells may be more prone to develop cracks. Most of the thin shelled cupolas usually incorporate a thin refractory lining about 1/2 to one in. thick in the melting zone to assist in obtaining hotter iron on the first tap, and to encourage an early buildup of slag on the internal cupola wall.

On water cooled cupolas the cupola wells have been offset by increasing the shell well diameter about 4 to 6 in. below the tuyeres. This arrangement allows the well diameter to be flush with the upper lining or shell after it is lined and prevents severe lining erosion in the well.

The cupola well depth from the sand bottom to the bottom of the tuyere openings usually is increased, over that of a conventionally designed cupola, to handle the large slag volume generated in basic operation.

The tuyere design used in a basic lined cupola is usually the conventional type. There has been a tendency to adopt the round type tuyere in basic operations, although this is not required to obtain good operations in a lined cupola. In recent years protruding water cooled tuyeres, fabricated or cast from copper, have been adopted in basic and acid melting. The adoption of this type of tuyere has been due to the advent of the water cooled cupola shell where the lining has been partially or completely removed. The tuyeres are exposed in a liningless cupola and become exposed, during melting, in a partially lined cupola. The result is that the tuyeres burn off and cause the cupola blast to travel up the side wall of the cupola; in order to prevent this a water cooled tuyere was used.

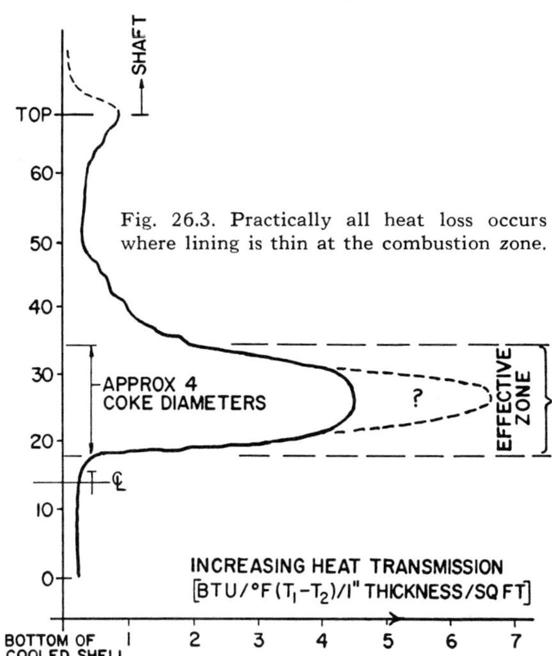

Fig. 26.3. Practically all heat loss occurs where lining is thin at the combustion zone.

TABLE 26.1. SHIFT of COOLING LOSSES With CHANGE of BLAST VELOCITY in TUYERES In LININGLESS HOT BLAST CUPOLA

Blast Velocity	100 ft/min		345 ft/min	
Cooling Loss	Btu/hr	%	Btu/hr	%
Shell	1,646,720	43.0	1,297,536	34.6
Tuyeres	2,182,400	57.0	2,452,224	65.4
Total	3,829,120		3,749,760	

Removal of the cupola lining has also resulted in higher heat transfer rates which results in somewhat lower iron temperatures unless a proper slag wall is built on the inner shell. The protruding tuyere minimizes the side wall wind travel thus helping to retard heat losses and excessive metal or slag buildup on the inner wall. Experimental tuyeres made of steel and gray iron have been tried, but copper appears to be the best due to its high heat conductivity.

The distance that tuyeres should protrude within the cupola and the degree of slope downward that they should have is still subject to individual opinions. Fleming,[3] Löbbecke,[4] Levi[5] and others have modified the degree of slope and the amount of protrusion with varied results. They all agree, that increased air velocity through the tuyeres of a water cooled cupola, over that of the conventional lined cupola, is necessary to obtain good metal temperatures, good metallurgical control and good combustion in the center of the cupola.

Fleming established that protrusion should be at least 2 1/2 coke diameters at 932 F (500 C) with coke being 8 per cent of the cupola diameter. His results indicated that such a protrusion – along with proper air velocities through the tuyeres – allows the cupola to form a thin lining on the shell, combustion occurring in the center of the cupola with the minimum amount of heat losses from the water cooled projecting tuyeres (Fig. 26.3).

Löbbecke's work on shift of cooling losses, as shown in Table 26.1, shows the effect of air velocity on cooling losses. Löbbecke found that with proper air ve-

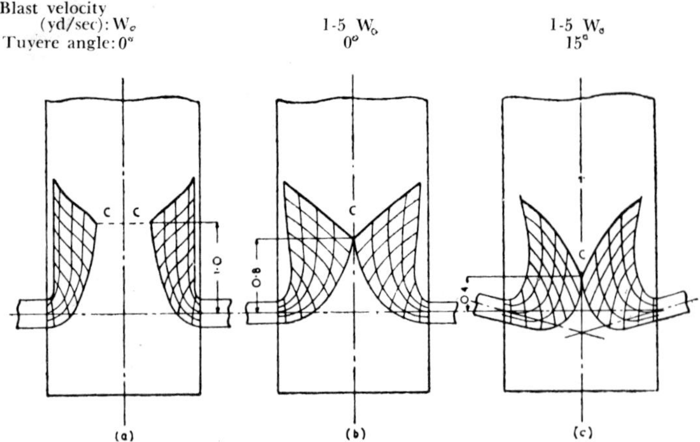

Fig. 26.4. Theory of blast velocity in tuyeres and angle of tuyeres on combustion.[4]

TABLE 26.2. AIR VELOCITY through TUYERES in FT/MIN

Original	*Revision 1*	*Revision 3*	*Revision 4*
At 650 lb/min and 600 F (315 C)			
2700	3680	7350	14,700
At 800 lb/min and 850 F (455 C)			
4100	5600	11,200	22,500

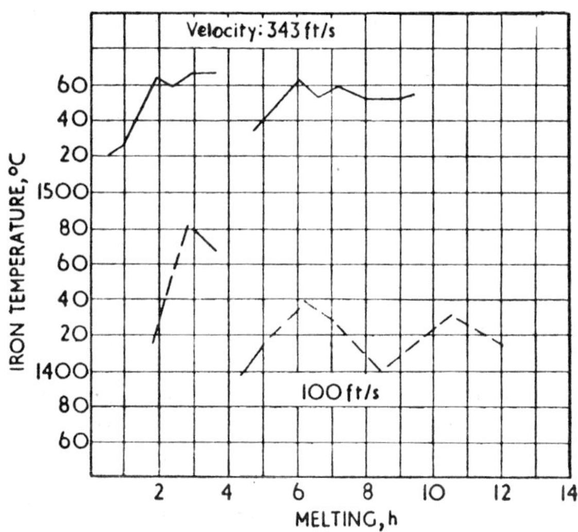

Fig. 26.5. Effect of blast velocity in tuyeres on iron temperatures in a liningless cupola.[4]

locities through the tuyeres and a conical shell, protruding tuyeres minimized the secondary melt zone which created iron and slag skulls and obtained the results that Fleming listed.

All protruding tuyeres, sloped downward to avoid a buildup in the tuyere opening, assist in maintaining proper water flow in the tip of the tuyere where normal failure usually occurs and the other advantages just covered. The slope has varied from 7 to 15 degrees. Experiment results indicate that certain blast velocities can be specified for each liningless cupola diameter at which blast will penetrate to the center of the cupola and produce optimum combustion conditions. Also noted is that as the blast velocities increase, the combustion zone moves downward in the cupola shaft; from this it was concluded that it should become possible to further increase combustion, and hence melting conditions, by a suitable inclination of the tuyeres (Fig. 26.4).

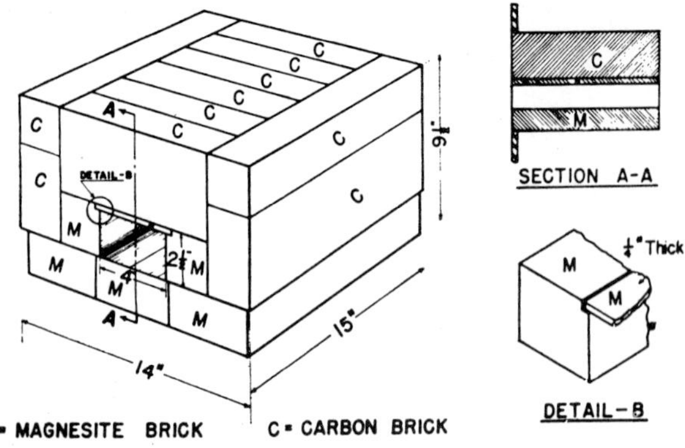

Fig. 26.6. Dual refractory taphole for front slagging. Contruction consists of magnesite brick bottom and sides, with carbon brick top. Sides are backed with carbon brick and top is faced with 1/4-in. thick wafer of magnesite as shown in Detail B.

By placing inserts in standard 7 1/4-in. dia. tuyeres, Fleming increased blast velocities from 25 ft/sec to 85 ft/sec and 115 ft/sec. In the 34 in. dia. hot blast cupola he was using, it was found that the 3 in. inserts (85 ft/sec) produced the best results on the lower melting rates, 4 in. inserts (115 ft/sec) on the higher melting rates.

Using a 3.5 ft dia. cupola, Löbbecke carried out the same type experiments with higher air blast velocities through the tuyeres and a 500 C (932 F) hot blast. Air velocities used varied from 100.4 ft/sec to 525.6 ft/sec. Levi[5] operated with air velocities of 68.3 ft/sec to 375.0 ft/sec (Table 26.2). With the lower velocities both experienced a double melting zone and cold iron but, as Levi approached 375 ft/sec in a 7.33 ft dia. cupola, excellent results were obtained with a reduced amount of coke. Löbbecke in his 3.5 ft dia. cupola found that 342.8 ft/sec gave his best operation (Fig. 26.5). *In all cases higher blast velocities through the inclined tuyeres gave lower silicon losses, better iron temperatures and less skulling.*

The cupola spout or trough and breast designs are usually altered in a basic slag operated cupola only to the extent to provide adequate frame work for the refractories required. Special refractories constructions are treated here (Chapter 26).

The type of metal trough used will be dependent on the method of slagging. In front slagging, construction can be of normal design as expressed in the Tapping and Slagging Chapter 28. In the rear slagging type or the syphon rear slagging method, a normal constructed spout — such as employed in intermittent tapping — may be used.

Auxiliary equipment such as hot blast, blast control, and pressure controls are the same on basic cupolas as on conventional acid cupolas. The trend on hot blast has been toward the higher ranges of 1000 to 1200 F (540-650 C).

Refractories for basic cupolas or basic slag operated cupolas are treated in Chapter 17. . . . Some of the refractories[6] — other than basic brick or ramming materials used — may be carbon paste or brick, tar-bonded dolomite, brick or paste, and high alumina.

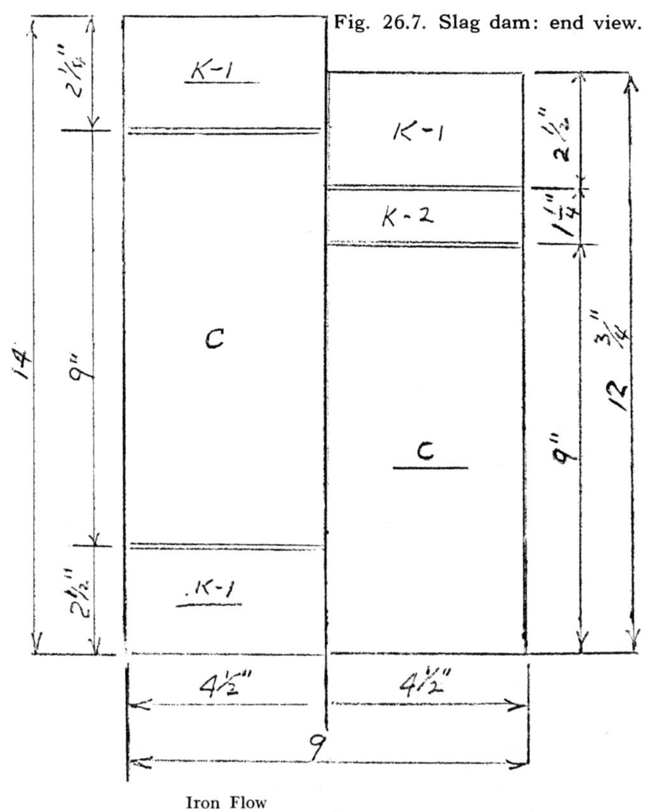
Fig. 26.7. Slag dam: end view.

Iron Flow

C = Blast furnace carbon block 18 in. long
K-1 = Korundal brick 18 in. long
K-2 = Korundal split brick 1¼ × 4½ × 9 in.
Cast iron C.E = 4.40-4.55 approx.
Slag basicity = 1.00-1.05

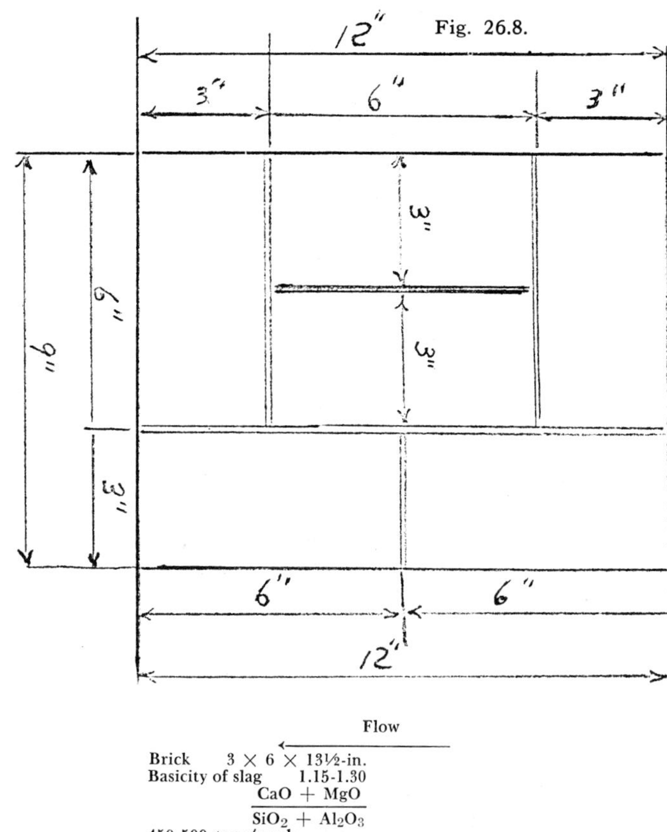
Fig. 26.8.

Flow

Brick 3 × 6 × 13½-in.
Basicity of slag 1.15-1.30 $\frac{CaO + MgO}{SiO_2 + Al_2O_3}$
450-500 tons/week

These refractories have been used in front slagging cupola troughs and cupola wells to withstand the severe erosion at the slag metal interfaces. Some of the applications that have been used in front slagging are shown in Figs. 26.6, 26.7 and 26.8.

A normal basic lined cupola has a basic lining extending 5 to 10 ft above the tuyeres and is acid lined from there to the charging door. The cupola can be either basic or neutral. Basic refractories expand 3/16 in./ft whereas acid expands 1/16 in/ft. The thermal conductivity of basic refractories is approximately double those of acid refractories. It is these factors which have to be considered when a basic cupola is lined. Provision in the melting zone should be provided for expansion and it usually is accomplished by inserting cardboard strips or other suitable material between the bricks. Due to the lower operating temperatures in the cupola well and the possibility of leaks, this practice is not required. Because of heat conduction rates it is advisable to use an insulating brick or acid refractory adjacent to the cupola shell.

Hard burned magnesite brick containing 88 per cent magnesite is most generally being used in the melting zone. High fired chrome magnesite refractories are being used in cupola breasts troughs and cupola wells but are not considered for the melting zone due to the possibility of chrome contamination. Other materials of value may be forsterite and chemically bonded magnesite brick.

If a 12 in. lining is considered, a 6 in. inner lining of basic brick should be used with a 6 in. acid lining against the shell. If the burnout is greater, compensation will have to be made during the repair. The basic brick is advantageously laid with dipped joints of air setting high magnesia content mortar.

Two general methods of daily maintenance:

1. Allow the lining to be eroded back after several heats and put in brick patching.
2. Hand or gun patch with a basic ramming mix.

The cost of lining a basic cupola is approximately three times that of an acid cupola. Refractory consumption rates vary from 38 lb/ton of melt to better than 100 lb/ton of melt. Usually figure a cost of about $3/ton for refractories.

An insulating brick or acid refractory should be used against the shell to avoid damage from heat conduction. If the cupola well is water cooled this may not be required.

The cupola well can be lined with basic brick, rammed basic material, carbon brick or carbon paste. The type of refractory used in the melting zone or cupola well will influence the slag basicity and this should be considered at all times. Carbon has no effect, whereas the basic refractories are important.

SLAG BECOMES BASIC in composition as the sum of lime (CaO) and magnesia (MgO) exceeds the sum of silica (SiO_2) and alumina (Al_2O_3). Acid slags contain higher percentages of silica and alumina than lime and magnesia. The basicity of a slag is expressed as *basicity ratio:*

$$\text{(a)} \quad \frac{CaO + MgO}{SiO_2 + Al_2O}$$

Variations are:

$$\text{(b)} \quad \frac{CaO + MgO}{SiO_2} \quad \text{and} \quad \text{(c)} \quad \frac{CaO}{SiO_2}$$

Fig. 26.9.

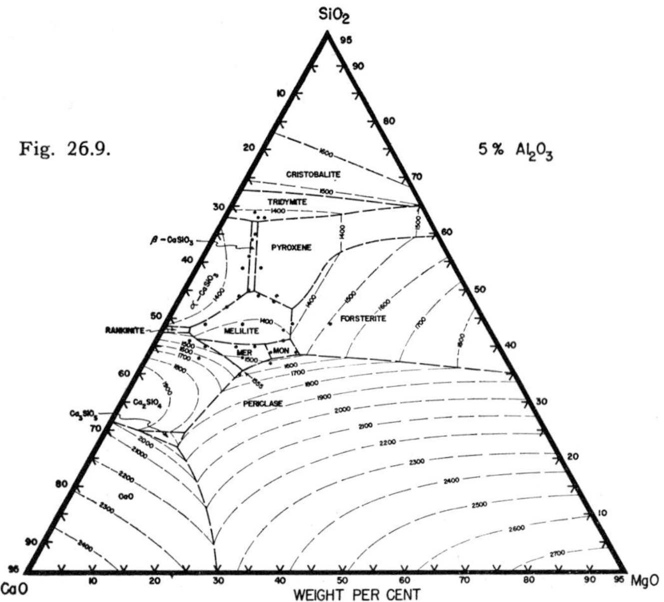

Liquidus diagram at 5 pct Al_2O_3 in the system CaO-MgO-Al_2O_3-SiO_2. Light lines are isotherms of the liquidus surface, heavier lines are primary phase boundary curves, and dots represent compositions of mixtures studied. Temperatures are in °C. Mer, merwinite ($Ca_3MgSi_2O_8$); Mon, monticellite ($CaMgSiO_4$); rankinite, $Ca_3Si_2O_7$; melilite, solid solution of akermanite ($Ca_2MgSi_2O_7$) and gehlenite ($Ca_2Al_2SiO_7$); pyroxene, solid solution largely of diopside ($CaMgSi_2O_6$) and clinoenstatite ($MgSiO_3$); tridymite and cristobalite are forms of SiO_2; forsterite, Mg_2SiO_4; periclase, MgO.

Some writers claim that alumina is amphoteric, may react either acid or basic, and should not be included in the ratio as in *(b)*. Others say that because of the low desulfurizing ability of MgO it should not be in the ratio as in *(c)*.

As an excess of CaO becomes available reactions take place between the metal and slag which cannot occur with an acid slag. As explained in the Fluxing and Slag Control Chapter 29, PART II, flux is added to an acid cupola primarily to remove coke ash, lining, etc. No chemical reactions occur between the metal and slag. The primary function of a basic slag is to remove sulfur from the metal. This is accomplished by the reaction

$$C + CaO + FeS \qquad CaS + Fe + CO$$

THE FLUXES ADDED to basic slag cupolas include limestone, dolomite, dolomitic limestone, bauxite, fluorspar, both briqueted and as received from mines, and calcium carbide. After the materials calcine or breakdown in the cupola the compounds CaO, MgO and CaF_2 are available to combine with SiO_2 and Al_2O_3 to form the basic slag. The sources of SiO_2 are coke ash, silicon oxidation and small amounts from the fluxes and basic linings. The sources of Al_2O_3 are coke ash, bauxite and small amounts in the basic lining.

When cupolas have sufficient lining it is common for flux charges to be void of dolomite, a source of MgO since the lining provides MgO. With unlined cupolas, dolomite is ordinarily included in the flux charge.

Examination of the three phase system CaO, Al_2O_3, and SiO_2 in Chapter 29, PART II, reveals relatively low melting points for slags of acid composition, 1300 to 1400 C (2372-2552 F). Increasing the per cent CaO, increases the melting point of the slag up to ranges between 1500 to 1600 C (2732-2912 F). To reduce these melting points to those compatible with good cupola operation fluorspar, dolomite or bauxite must be added. In the U.S. it is common practice to provide MgO, either through the lining or dolomitic limestone. Small amounts of fluorspar insure good slag fluidity.

It is now necessary to examine the quaternary system CaO, Al_2O_3, MgO, SiO_2. . . . A four variable system consists of a solid with three components at the base forming an equilateral triangle and the fourth component extending vertical from each apex. To simplify interpretation of this system, planes may be sliced through the solid at fixed levels of any one of these components (Figs. 26.9 and 26.10). Notice that this interpretation does not account for the effect of fluorspar, iron oxide and manganese oxide. All of these compounds depress the melting points of the complex compounds present in the slag. As may be noted in Figs. 26.9 and 26.10 some of the complex compounds that may be present in basic slags are –

Complex Compound	*Melting Point*
$(CaO)_2 \cdot SiO_2$	3866 F
$MgO \cdot Al_2O_3$	3876 F
MgO	5070 F
$(CaO)_2 \cdot Al_2O_3 \cdot SiO$	2894 F
$(CaO)_3 \cdot MgO \cdot SiO_2$	2876 F
$(CaO)_3 \cdot (SiO_2)_2$	2673 F
$(CaO)_3 \cdot MgO \cdot (SiO_2)_2$	2660 F

Changes of one to 5 per cent in any one of the four components SiO_2, CaO, MgO, or Al_2O_3 may result in a complete change in the complex compounds present in the slag, depending upon the original analysis. In order to continuously produce iron with low sulfur analysis, slag composition must be such that low melting point complex compounds are present, or else excessive quantities of slag fluidizers such as fluorspar must be added.

Factors responsible for changes in slag analysis are:

Factors affecting SiO_2 Change in –

1. silicon from iron
2. amount of or chemistry of ash in coke
3. amount of dirt, sand, core butts, etc., in charge

Factors affecting CaO and MgO

1. Change in flux sizing
2. Stabilization of lining loss

Factors affecting Al_2O_3

1. Change in amount of or chemistry of ash in coke
2. Stabilization of lining loss

The most significant change in slag chemistry results from drastic changes in silicon loss from iron, emphasizing the need for good practices in basic cupola operation.

The oxidation of silicon, Si, to silica SiO_2 results in weight increase of 2.15 or for every pound of silicon lost from the metal, 2.15 lb of silica is available to enter the slag.

In lined basic cupola operation, a relatively stable lining contour is formed one to 3 hr after tapping.

This will deprive the slag of MgO and CaO and force an increase of flux components bearing these two compounds, in order to maintain a constant slag analysis. Most basic monolithic linings contain 50 per cent MgO, 35 per cent CaO, with the balance SiO_2, Al_2O_3, Fe_2O_3, etc. The largest variation from lining stabilization will be seen in per cent MgO.

Examples — for seven operating foundries — of slag analysis, flux charges and sulfur content in the iron are listed in Table 26.3.

Cupola bottoms used in basic cupolas are the same as in normal acid cupolas. Where long heats are run and the bottoms are used for months at a time, brick and rammed refractories are used. In daily heats or heats that will run for several days a regular sand bottom is used, but the depth will be increased up to 12 to 15 in. Proper ramming of the sand bottom is required to prevent erosion and failure on long heats. In some cases a rammed basic material has been put over the top of the silica sand bottom to protect it from the first basic slag that may be generated at the start of the heat.

The operation of a basic cupola or basic slag operated cupola is sensitive to charge material changes and distribution of the metal, flux and coke charges. This sensitivity is due to the effect of slag properties on the metal composition and cupola operation.

The weighing of the metal components[7] and fluxes is critical because, as the ingoing total carbon level and silicon varies from fluctuations in the metal charge, the resulting metal melted will also vary. Since the slag chemistry is dependent on the amount of flux used, this is a critical material and should be weighed accurately for good results. Coke and metallics also affect slag chemistry but not as greatly as the amount and type of flux used in lesser quantities.

The size of the metal used in length, width and thickness is similar to that of acid operated cupolas. Thin section steel will give lower carbon results than the heavier melting stock with the same slag basicity.

The amount of silica entering the cupola has an important bearing on the slag basicity and should be controlled or compensated for in the charging operations, particularly on wet operating days where excess dirt or extraneous material is carried in with the charging materials.

The most important phase of melting in an acid or a basic cupola is the distribution of the metal, flux and coke charge within the cupola. The generation of FeO in a basic cupola has adverse effects and should be avoided as much as possible. In all cases attempts should be made to keep the sidewalls of the cupola the denser area within the cupola. This forces the blast to the center of the cupola and minimizes sidewall wind travel, generation of high FeO contents and secondary melt zones, areas of skull formation, and low silicon and manganese losses.

High slag basicities will give high total carbons, low sulfurs and higher silicon losses. The reverse occurs with low slag basicities. Slag (being basic in nature) wipes the coke free of ash, which is acid, allowing the metal to have intimate contact with the coke surfaces, which determines the amount of carbon that will

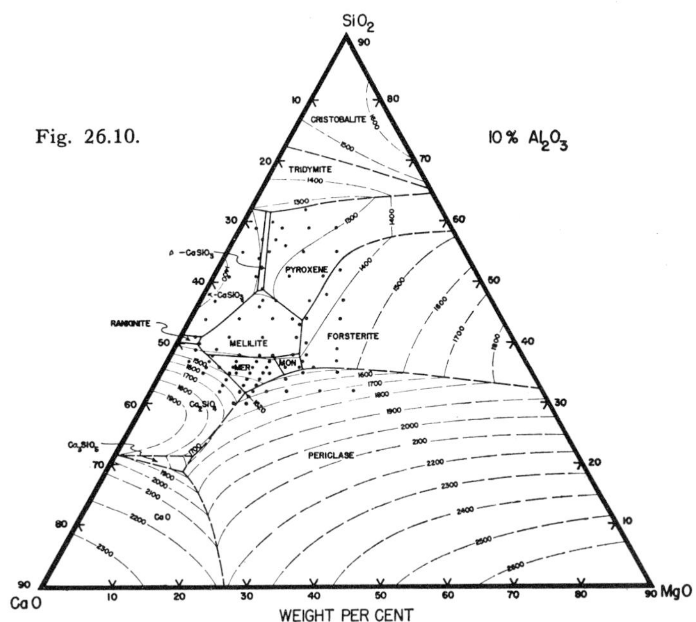

Liquidus diagram for the 10 pct Al_2O_3 plane. Anorthite, $CaAl_2Si_2O_8$; mullite, $3Al_2O_3 \cdot 2SiO_2$.

be picked up in the melting zone. The amount of carbon picked up in the cupola well has not yet been resolved. The degree of slag basicity is not always the factor which determines desulfurization, silicon loss or carbon pickup. Since all of these are chemical reactions, temperature plays an important part. With higher slag and metal temperatures — and the same contact time — the sulfurs will be lower and the carbon higher (Fig. 26.11).

The secondary melting zone problem (referred to in this Chapter 26) should be more fully explained. . . . The use of water cooling in the melting zone has at times led to difficulties, as evidenced by the formation of a ring of partially fused slag and metal adhering to the cupola lining at an abnormal height. These rings frequently form near or just above the water cooled section of the melting zone, occasionally they can be higher, and indicate the presence of a *secondary melting zone.*

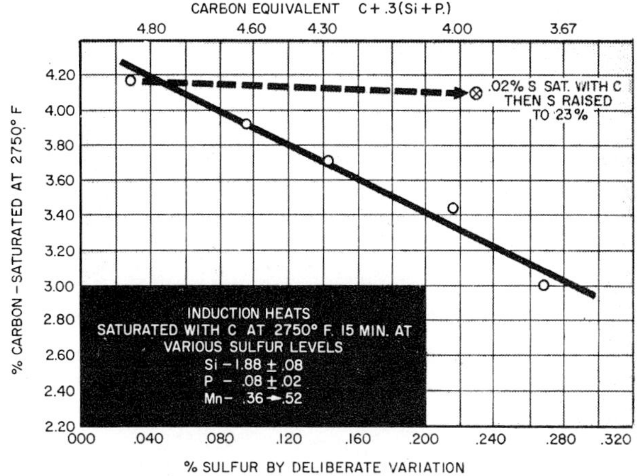

Fig. 26.11. Effect of sulfur on carbon solubility, the results of induction heats in which sulfur level deliberately was varied and the bath saturated with an excess of carbon at 5 sulfur levels.

It seems reasonable that some of the unreacted air entering the tuyeres passes upward along a relatively cool surface in the water cooled melting zone, this being a path of low resistance. Just above the top of the coolers, where there is a refractory lining in the cupola, this air becomes hot enough to ignite the coke and partially melt some of the metal, thus generating the *secondary melting zone.* This condition is undesirable because at least part of the iron melted in the upper melting zone drips for some distance through air containing free oxygen. The iron oxide formed eventually finds its way into the slag and thus reduces the desulfurizing panes of the slag. As a result, the sulfur content of the iron will be high and the carbon will be low, in effect defeating the purpose of basic operation (Fig. 26.12).

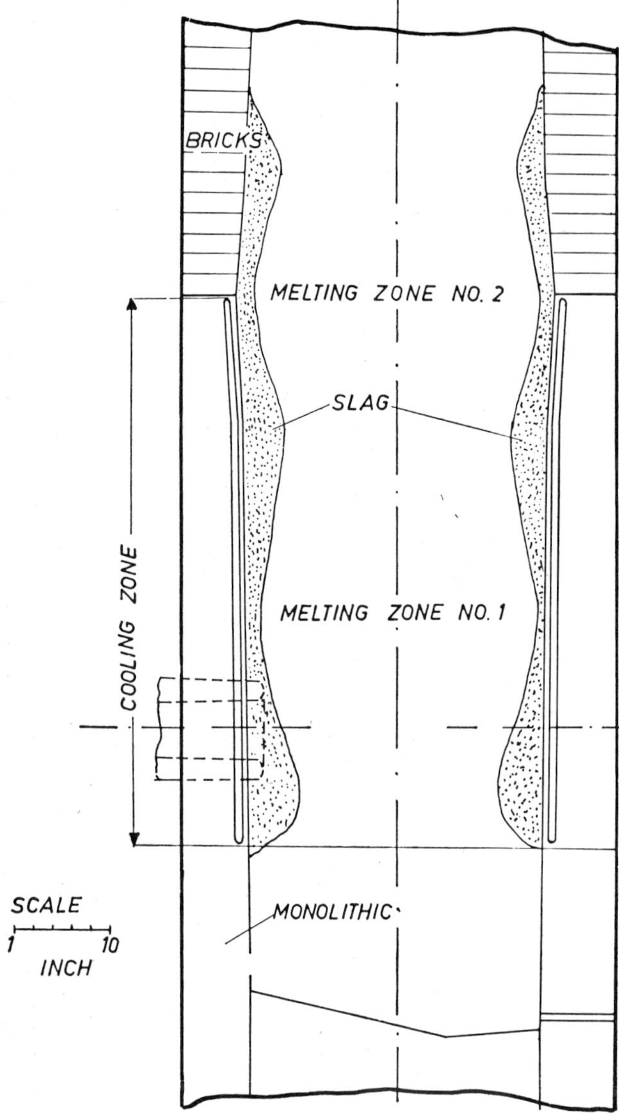

Fig. 26.12. Double melting zone liningless cupola.

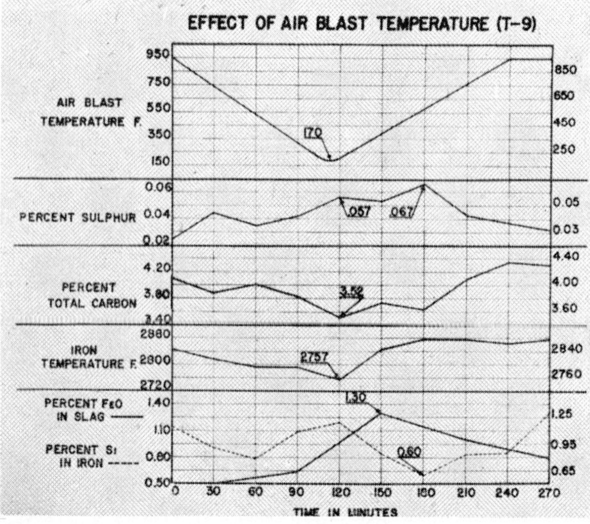

Fig. 26.13. Effect of air blast temperature on metal composition, metal temperature, and percentage of *FeO* in the slag.

The presence of a *secondary melting zone* has been established by many operators and has been overcome by installing projecting tuyeres with high air velocities and, in some cases, with a conical designed shell. All of these modifications, along with proper metal, coke and flux distribution, force the air to the center thus eliminating the cause of the problem.

Table 26.4 compares the acid and the basic cupola. Typical metal and coke charges for basic cupolas are:

Example 1

Charge		Analysis
Steel	3900 lb	TC ..3.13 -3.49 %
Pig Iron	700 lb	*S* 0.037-0.074%
Ductile returns	400 lb	*Si* ....0.50 -1.25 %
Coke	750 lb	Slag ranges: SiO_2 16-20%; MnO 1.24-1.92%
Fluorspar	75 lb	MgO 17-30%; CaO 34-50%; Al_2O_3 10-11.5%
Limestone	250 lb	FeO 0.63-1.30%
metal temp. 2680 F (1470 C)		

Example 2

Charge		Final analysis after inoculation of 75% *FeSi*
Pig Iron	200 lb	*Si* ...1.00%
Steel	1200 lb	*S* 0.05%
Auto cast	550 lb	*Mn* ..0.90%
Spiegel	50 lb	*P* ...0.15%
Coke	300 lb	TC ..4.10%
Dolomitic stone	150 lb	

air blast temp. 950 F (510 C)

Example 3, AS CAST NODULAR MIX

Charge		Analysis
Steel	1700 lb	TC ..3.82 -4.00 %
Ductile returns	800 lb	*Si* ....1.25 -1.50 %
	2500 lb	*S* 0.010-0.015%
Coke	290 lb	*Mn* ..0.45 -0.50 %
Calcium stone	105 lb	*P* ....0.02 -0.03 %
Dolomitic	75 lb	
Spar	35 lb	

hot blast temp. 600 F (315 C)
metal temp. 2820-2860 F (1550-1570 C)
cfm 5000-6800

Example 4, AS CAST NODULAR BASE IRON

Charge		Analysis
Steel	1050 lb	*Si* ....1.00 -1.40 %
Returns	550 lb	TC ..3.70 -4.10 %
Coke	245 lb	*P* 0.025%
Stone	120 lb	*Mn* ..0.45 %
Spar	24 lb	*S* 0.020-0.025%

Slag: SiO 24-30%; CaO 39-44%; MgO 12-18%; Al_2O_3 9-12%; FeO 1 max. %; MnO 0.40-0.80%

room temp. blast
cfm 3100-3400
metal temp. 2840-2860 F (1560-1570 C)

Example 5, AS CAST NODULAR BASE IRON

Charge		Analysis
Steel	1000 lb	*Si* ....1.15 -1.40 %
Pig	1000 lb	TC ..4.49 -4.70 %
Returns	1000 lb	*S* 0.008-0.019%
Coke	450 lb	*Mn* ..0.30 -0.40 %
Stone	150 lb	Slag: SiO_2 30%; CaO 45%; MgO 17%; Al_2O_3 6%
Spar	48 lb	

cfm 6200
room temp. blast
metal temp. 2830-2900 F (1555-1595 C)

TABLE 26.3

Plant	Base Iron % Carbon	Base Iron % Sulfur	Type of Cupola	Flux % Stone	Flux % CaF_2	Flux % CaC_2	% CaO	% MgO	% SiO_2	% Al_2O_3
1	3.50-3.80	.025-.040	no lining	9.5	0.5	0	47-52	6-7	26-29	8-10
2	3.70-4.00	.010-.020	lined	4	2	3	52	15	25	6
3	3.80	.040	no lining	11	3	0	32	18	37	10
4	3.90-4.15	.018-.020	no lining	13.75	3.5	0	66	3.5	27	3.1
5	3.80	.020-.025	lined	5	2.5	1	42	22	27	7
6	3.80	.010	no lining	10	3.3	0	62	nil	24.5	10.5
7	3.80	.014	no lining	8.6	1.4	0	46	13	28	10

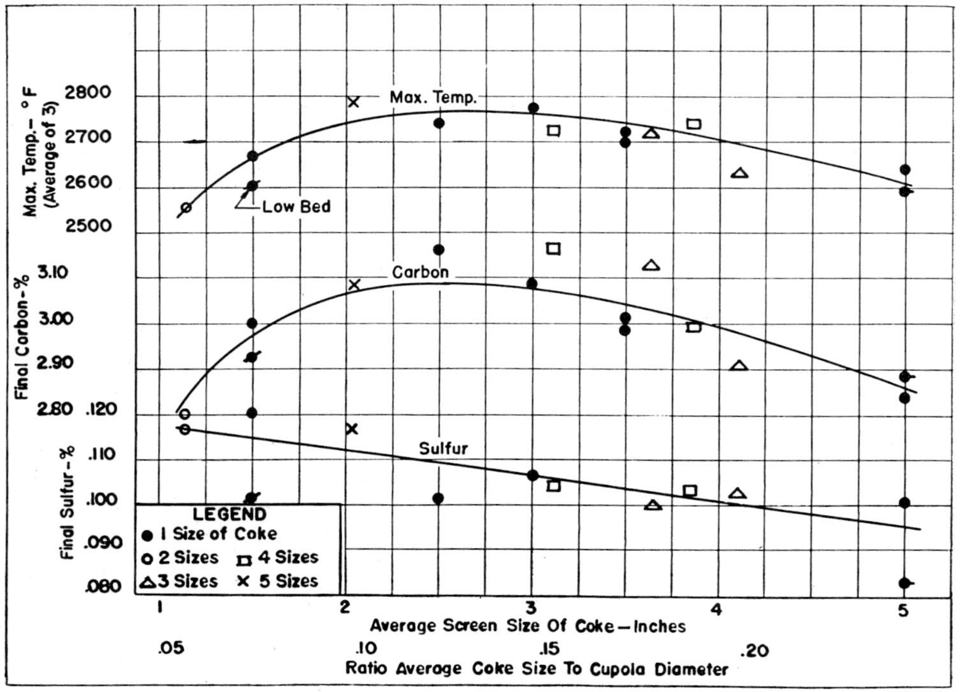

Fig. 26.14. Effect of coke size on temperature, carbon, sulfur.[1]

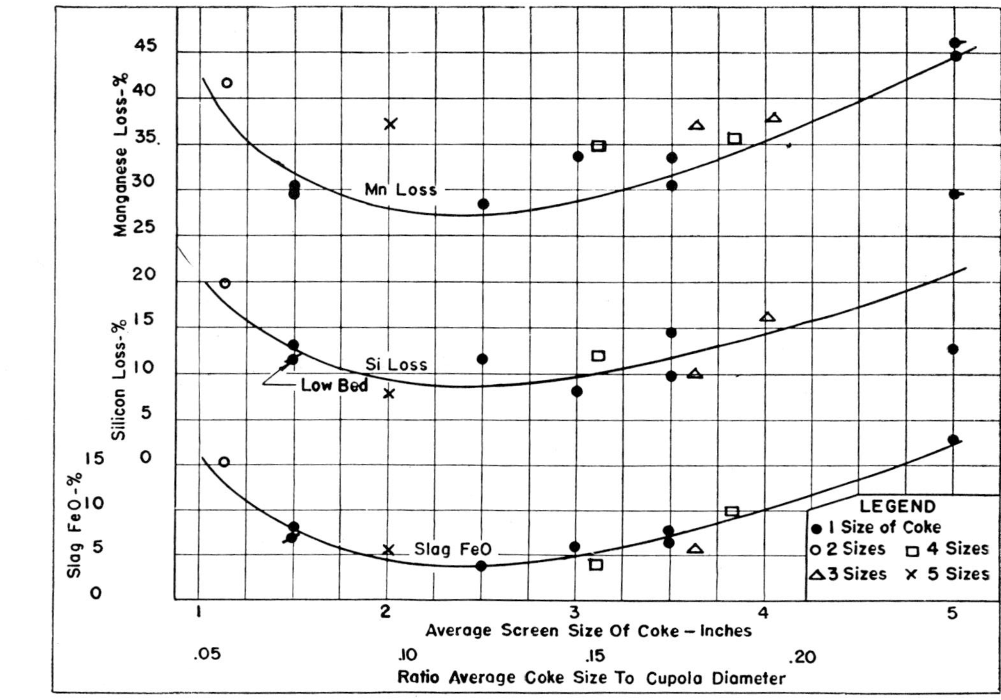

Fig. 26.15. Effect of coke size on oxidation losses.[1]

THE MAIN USE OF A BASIC CUPOLA is in producing a high carbon, low phos and sulfur metal. Carter ran a series of induction heats where the sulfur level was deliberately varied and the bath saturated with an excess of carbon at five sulfur levels.

At 0.270 per cent S, carbon could not be dissolved above 3.00 per cent. At 0.140 per cent sulfur, maximum carbon was 3.70 per cent. With a low sulfur of 0.030 per cent, carbons near 4.20 per cent were obtained. On one low sulfur saturated heat, sulfur was added and went into solution easily to a 0.230 per cent level. This result verifies the fact that sulfur will keep out carbon, but carbon will not keep out sulfur.

On the basis of the usual carbon equivalent formula, carbon equivalents of 4.80 were obtained on the low

TABLE 26.4. ACID and BASIC CUPOLA COMPARISON

Materials	Acid	Basic		Acid, %	Basic, %
Steel, lb	700	700	TC charged	2.48	2.18
Auto Cast, lb	600	1300	TC at spout	3.34	3.52
Pig Iron, lb	700	None	TC pickup	0.86	1.34
Coke, lb	300	300	S charged	0.061	0.092
Dolomite, lb	90	90	S at spout	0.135	0.119
Blast Temp., F	room	800	S pickup	0.074	0.027

Cupola Slags

	CaO, %	MgO, %	SiO_2, %	Al_2O_3, %	FeO, %	Basicity	
Acid	21.0	8.0	53.0	14.0	2.0	0.43*	0.55**
Basic	35.0	10.0	36.0	14.0	0.4	0.90*	1.25**

$$*\text{Basicity} = \frac{CaO + MgO}{SiO_2 + Al_2O_3} \qquad **\text{Basicity} = \frac{CaO + MgO}{SiO_2}$$

sulfur, whereas equivalents with the high sulfur contents were below 4.00. This fact explains why high carbon content is hard to maintain when high sulfur is used or large proportions of scrap are melted. It further explains why basic cupolas running very low sulfurs can produce some carbons above 4.00 per cent (Fig. 26.11).

The effect of hot blast in cupola melting in regard to total carbon pickup is explained by W. Levi's graph (Fig. 26.13).

THE TYPE OF MATERIAL USED in an acid cupola has a great effect on carbon pickup and follows the same trend in a basic cupola. A series of heats run by Carter in an acid cupola shows the effect of steel sections such as tin cans, rivets, one in. plate sections, ⅜-in. plate and $^3/_{16}$-in. plate. As the material became thinner and the ratio of surface area to volume increased, sulfur absorption increased, silicon loss increased and FeO in the slag increased. In a basic cupola the results are the same, but with adjustments in coke and fluxing practice good metal can be produced (Fig. 26.1).

The depth of slag carried in the cupola well can influence the amount of carbon pickup and is somewhat dependent on the basicity and temperature of the retained slag. Desulfurization is a function of basicity, time and temperature; therefore, if the sulfurs are lowered in the metal by passing through a hot deep layer of slag, the carbons will raise through contact with the coke present in the well. If the factors of time, temperature and basicity are all on the low side, the minimum of carbon will be picked up in the well due to poor sulfur removal (Table 26.5).

Coke can influence carbon pickup in a basic cupola for the same reasons presented for an acid cupola. To get maximum carbon pickup, the ash content of the coke should be as low as possible and the fixed carbon should be as high as possible. In the area of coke size there are opinion differences that may be due to cupola size, cold or hot blast, type of charging equipment in use, and other factors. Normally a coke size of 8 to 12 per cent of the cupola diameter produces the best operation. Lower sizes produce lower iron temperatures; larger sizes follow the same trend. Total carbons follow the same pattern if the other cupola variables are maintained (Figs. 26.15 and 26.14).

TABLE 26.5.
EFFECT of FLUX on SLAG-METAL RELATIONS

Same Metal Charge—100% Return

Flux Charge	SiO_2	Al_2O_3	FeO	MnO	CaO	MgO
1. 3% Limestone	35.4	10.1	1.9	1.9	34.1	16.2
2. 4% Lst., .5% Sp.	32.4	11.7	1.2	0.6	39.0	15.1
3. 6% Lst., 2% Sp.	30.6	7.8	0.7	0.8	42.3	15.2

(Slag Composition: SiO_2 through MgO)

	Metal Sulfur	Slag Sulfur	Basicity Ratio	Slag Color
1.	.069	0.46	1.42	Br. Blk.
2.	.051	0.62	1.67	Med. Br.
3.	.022	0.7	1.88	Light Br.

REFERENCES

1. *Some Variables in Acid and Cupola Melting,* Sam F. Carter and Ralph Carlson, AFS TRANSACTIONS, vol. 62 (1954) p. 267.
2. *"Cupola Handbook," AFS* 1954, Chapter 15, p. 87-90, Carter.
3. *The Controlled Slag Hot Blast Cupola,* D. Fleming, AFS TRANSACTIONS, vol. 66 (1958) p. 113.
4. *From Conventional Lined Cupolas to Liningless Hot Blast Cupolas,* (development of the hot blast cupola), E. L. W. Löbbecke, The British Foundrymen, vol. 51 (July 1958) p. 331.
5. *Our Basic Cupola,* W. W. Levi, THE IRON WORKER, vol. 18, no. 2 (Spring 1954) p. 14.
6. *Basic Refractories for Cupola Service,* M. W. Demler, AFS TRANSACTIONS, vol. 60 (1952) p. 385.
7. *Optimum Composition of Blast Furnace Slag as Deduced from Liquidus Data for The Quaternary System CaO-MgO-Al_2O_3-SiO_2,* E. F. Osborn, R. C. DeVries, K. H. Gee, and H. M. Kraner, A.I.M.E. Transactions (Journal of Metals, January 1954), vol. 200, p. 33.

CHAPTER 27

Melting Malleable Iron

In the majority of cases the cupolas operating in the malleable iron industry are used as the primary melting unit, with a second furnace, either an air furnace or electric furnace, acting as a holding furnace. This method of melting is called "duplexing" and provides for a continuous supply of metal at the proper temperature and analysis.

Malleable iron cupolas which are used for melting iron to be poured directly into the mold are in most cases very similar to those used in the duplexing process. The general construction details are the same as those of cupolas used for melting gray irons.

Comparison of typical analyses for a medium strength gray iron and a standard malleable iron emphasizes the compositional differences (Table 27.1).

TABLE 27.1. ANALYSES COMPARISON

Component	Gray Iron	Malleable Iron
Carbon, %	3.0 – 3.2	2.25 – 2.70
Silicon, %	1.9 – 2.50	0.8 – 1.5
Manganese, %	0.4 – 0.7	0.5 max.
Phosphorus, %	0.1 – 0.7	0.2 max.
Sulfur, %	0.12 max.	0.13 max.
Alloys	as needed	Chromium very low

TABLE 27.2. MALLEABLE MELTING MIXTURES

Charge Material	Cupola to Air Furnace, %	Cupola to Electric Furnace, %
Pig Iron, malleable	10 – 25	0 – 6
Pig Iron, silvery	5 – 10	4 – 12
Steel Scrap	20 – 30	28 – 40
Sprue & Returns	40 – 60	40 – 60
Ferro Alloys	as required	as required

CHARGE MATERIALS

Metallics

The major difference in a cupola charge producing white cast iron compared to gray cast iron is the lower carbon in the charge. This is due to the mottling tendency of a higher carbon iron. A lower carbon is necessary at the spout of the cupola both in direct pouring or duplexing of the molten metal.

No general cupola charge is universally used. Various malleable iron producers use silvery iron ranging from 10 per cent silicon to 22 per cent silicon with managanese from one to 4 per cent. Some producers use 50 per cent ferrosilicon as their source of silicon. Usually there are two factors governing the silicon material used: 1. Uniformity and the quality of iron at the cupola spout, 2. The economic question.

Some producers believe that a given per cent of virgin metal is necessary to produce the best castings. Some charges will carry up to 10 per cent of a 1.75-2.25 per cent malleable pig iron.

The quality and quantity of steel scrap varies widely with various producers. Chromium can be specified in the silvery irons and ferrosilicon to a point where it is not a problem. However, the selection of steel scrap is one constant concern and chromium and other alloys such as tin, arsenic, nickel, molybdenum, titanium, antimony, lead, etc., must be held to a minimum. Sulfur is another element that most foundrymen dread to see go over 0.15 per cent max. That means the practical elimination of screw stock from the charge. Both chromium and sulfur affect the annealability of the white iron. Many strive for less than 0.02 per cent chromium in the iron as poured. The use of boron as an addition to the white iron in amounts of 0.001 to 0.004 per cent has greatly lessened the dread of a higher chromium, since boron does counteract chromium.

The use of baled sheet steel scrap in weights from 100 lb to as high as 700 lb is common practice in many shops. This is usually clean and low price material. Other forms of steel scrap include flashings, plate, agricultural, punching, shearings and briquetted steel turnings. Briquetted malleable iron borings also are used.

All materials in a cupola charge should be sized to a maximum dimension of less than one-third the diameter of the cupola, inside the lining. Large material will cause bridging of the charge or *hang-ups* which seriously impair control and require extra coke for safety against excessive oxidation. This is more serious in malleable practice as compared to gray iron, since the operation is closer to the oxidizing range in malleable iron melting. Any condition which will upset the balance toward the oxidizing side is bound to have a serious effect on the production of a satisfactory iron.

Cupola mixtures for malleable melting use up to 50 per cent steel and up to 35 per cent pig iron. Typical mixtures are shown in Table 27.2.

Coke

Coke is one of the most important, if not the most important, material in the cupola charge. This is more true in malleable than in gray iron melting, due to the fact that the coke must not only be of a satisfactory structure to melt the iron and heat to the proper temperature, but it must also act as a recarburizer to the charge and give a uniform carbon pickup. A good malleable coke must be a superb fuel and have special characteristics.

A satisfactory coke should have a high heat value, be strong enough to withstand reasonable handling and charging service, strong also under high heat conditions to properly support the burden, and of a good size to provide the necessary voids for the passage of the blast and hot gases. Small coke and mixtures of small and large coke retard blast penetration and cause channeled flow of the gases at the furnace wall. Then, instead of melting uniformly across the whole cross-sectional area of the cupola, the melting is confined to a narrow ring around the periphery of the cupola. This upsets the equilibrium of the operation as it requires more coke to prevent oxidation and affects the melting rate adversely.

Most foundrymen prefer a low carbon pick-up coke since malleable iron is produced from a duplex process within the range of 2.40-2.60 per cent carbon.

Flux

The amount of limestone and special flux should be sufficient to keep the slag free flowing. Usually 20 to 30 per cent of the weight of the coke in limestone is sufficient. Some foundrymen figure in terms of 40 to 60 lb per ton of iron. Some recommend about 2 lb of soda ash per ton of melt to increase the fluidity of the slag and help keep the cupola melting clean and hot. Where the melting rate is high and the charge of a rusty and dirty nature, small amounts of fluorspar are also found advantageous. Usually 3-5 lb per ton will show good results.

The slagging operation is one of the most important factors to keep under close control. The color and viscosity of the slag are indicative of the quality of the iron being made. Light colored slag indicates an excess of flux and possibly coke; a black slag indicates the danger of excessive oxidizing conditions because of poor fluxing or a deficiency of coke. Cupola *hang-ups,* caused either from poor charging practice or poor slag conditions, can produce oxidized iron. A normal slag usually will have a dark green color, indicating normal operating conditions.

CHARGING PRACTICE

The sequence of charging a cupola usually takes into account the melting point of the raw materials. The highest melting material — *steel* — usually is placed on top of the limestone. Best results are obtained when the metal charge is level and all holes in the charge are filled up. No red spots should show around the periphery of the cupola. The hottest iron with the lowest oxidation is produced by placing as much as possible of the coke in the center of the charge.

CUPOLA OPERATION

The operation of a cupola for the melting of white iron is not much different than that carried out for the melting of gray iron. Metallurgical control of all factors involved must be closely watched to maintain the most uniform iron possible, owing to the small leeway in composition normally available.

Good control of the melting involves every phase of the operation, from the chemical and physical analysis of all raw materials entering the charge to the analysis of the metal poured into the mold. Charts showing by graphic representation the actual operating conditions throughout the melting day are most helpful. Factors to be plotted might be carbon, silicon, spout temperature, tons/hr, blast volume, etc.

As previously mentioned, when melting iron in a cupola in the production of malleable iron the major difference is the lower carbon iron at the cupola spout. This calls for a lower carbon metal charge and increasing the iron to coke ratio. The leaner coke ratio results in a higher degree of oxidation during melting. The silicon and manganese losses can run high, depending on the percentage and nature of the steel scrap used. The higher oxidation loss frequently results in increasing the tendency of the iron to shrink, and causes hot tears and cracks. Higher oxidation also raises the freezing point of the metal and has an adverse effect on fluidity, thus increasing the tendency for the iron to misrun.

To overcome the higher oxidation losses, many malleable foundries have installed hot blast equipment. There are several advantages to be derived from the use of the hot blast, but the principal one is the lessening of the oxidation of the metal.

Humidity blast control is another tool used by the malleable foundry to maintain quality. Moisture control throughout the year, holding to a range of 3 to 4 grains per cu ft has helped the foundryman reduce his casting losses and maintain a more uniform metal.

Slag control consists mainly in maintaining the fluidity at the desired level for minimum fluxing of refractories and ease of running the cupola at maximum efficiency. The iron and manganese oxide content is higher in the slag in a malleable cupola compared to a gray iron operation. This produces a black or darker green colored slag; it is difficult to control from the standpoint of color.

Sulfur is picked up from the coke during melting, and generally is higher than that obtained in gray iron practice. Most malleable iron operated cupolas do not melt as hot as for gray iron, and that is one reason for the higher sulfur. Some foundries desulfurize with sodium carbonate in a forehearth, and reduce sulfur up to 30 per cent of the sulfur content otherwise obtained.

AIR FURNACE and ELECTRIC FURNACE OPERATIONS

Duplexed malleable iron is melted in the cupola and refined in electric induction, electric arc or air furnaces. The metal charge for duplexing varies from cold melt practice, in that larger proportions of steel and less pig iron are used. This arises from molten metal being carburized as it passes through the cupola and comes into contact with the incandescent coke.

In cold melt practice all carbon must be charged with the metal. Generally, the cupolas are operated to provide molten iron at low temperatures (2700-2750 F, 1482-1510 C) to avoid excess carbon pickup. The iron flows from the cupola into the electric or air furnaces, where it is superheated to 2800-2900 F (1538-1593 C) and refined preparatory to casting. Minor corrections in composition can be made in the refining furnace. Basic process control, however, is in the cupola.

CHAPTER 28

Tapping Slagging

There are three general methods of tapping and slagging cupolas. The oldest method, still in use in many cupolas, particularly in those of smaller diameter operating for relatively short melting campaigns, is that of intermittent tapping coupled with rear slagging. More recently, especially in the case of large tonnage cupolas melting for protracted periods, continuous front tapping procedures are employed, in one case coupled with continuous front slagging and in the other with continuous rear slagging, the latter employing a siphon arrangement. Each of these methods will be described in some detail.

INTERMITTENT TAPPING — REAR SLAGGING

With intermittent tapping and rear slagging the iron and slag flow from the cupola through two separate and distinct tap holes. These holes are generally located 180 degrees apart, although the distance between them circumferentially may be any convenient and practical distance. Furthermore, in some foundries it may be desirable to tap part of the iron directly into the pouring ladles, and part of the iron, at a different time in the heat, into a forehearth ladle for mixing and treating with a desulfurizing agent. Under these conditions, the cupola may be provided with two tap holes.

The breast and tap hole are prepared and installed in accordance with any of the approved methods discussed in detail in Chapter 21. The breast should be made of the best refractories obtainable, the type being governed by particular shop conditions such as metal temperature, duration of the heat, etc. Prepared mixtures and some special clays are available for making tap holes, their use being a matter of individual preference.

For the type of operation in question the tap hole should preferably be in the form of a truncated cone with the large diameter toward the outside of the cupola. This permits easy removal of the forming plug after the breast material has been rammed into place, and likewise facilitates insertion and removal of bots during the actual tapping operation. The bottom of the tap hole should be on the same level as the top of the sand bottom.

With intermittent tapping it is important that the breast and tap hole be thoroughly dried and well preheated before melting starts. This can be accomplished with a gas or oil torch placed in the cupola spout while the coke bed is being ignited and burning through. In addition to this, the tap hole may be left open while burning of the coke bed is being hastened by a gentle blast from the blower. The hot gases from inside the cupola preheat the tap hole still further. The practices just described also dry and preheat the refractories in the cupola spout.

The tap hole may be left open or "botted shut" at the start of the heat, as desired. If it is left open the stream of iron is allowed to run over the spout until a clean tap hole is assured and the iron has reached a satisfactory temperature. (One undesirable feature of starting with an open tap hole is the shower of sparks blown through shortly after the wind is turned on and until the hole is closed.) The flow of iron is then stopped by inserting a bot in the tap hole. The iron continues to melt and accumulates in the well until slag or metal appears at the slag hole, which was left open. The cupola is then ready for tapping.

The first tap is made promptly, and in intermittent tapping, after the ladle or other receptacle is filled, the tap hole is closed. Succeeding taps follow according to the demand for iron, but in each tapping cycle, enough metal should be accumulated in the well to bring the slag above the level of the slag hole, from which it is removed before making the next tap. In each cycle the tap hole may remain open until all the iron has been tapped, or the metal may be taken in several successive short taps, as required. In connection with the latter, care must be taken to avoid the accumulation of an abnormally large volume of slag in the cupola well, because this condition has a definite effect on the operation and, if allowed to continue for long periods of time, may lead to trouble.

BOTTING METHODS

When the heat is started with the tap and slag holes closed, both may be botted with a stock core "backed" at the outside of the cupola with bot clay pressed firmly into place. Dry, well-burned molding sand, with or without additions of some carbonaceous material, may be used by some in preference to the stock cores mentioned. In either case the purpose is to use a material with relatively low hot strength which can be easily "picked" out at the proper time. With this type of practice the tap hole

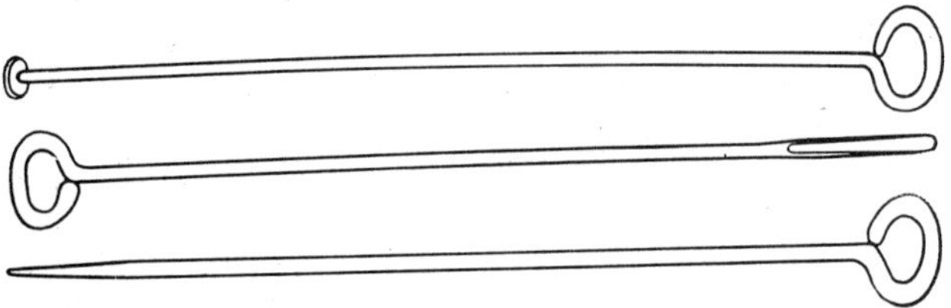

Figs. 28.1 and 28.2. Botting the cupola (above). Cupola tapping and botting tools: a bot stick and two types of bot pick (below).

must be opened in time to prevent iron and slag from entering the tuyeres. At the same time, there must be a reasonable accumulation of molten iron in the well.

Some operators tap out at a definite length of time after the wind is turned on. This is determined by experience and a knowledge of the well capacity. Another procedure is to tap out when a predetermined number of charges have been placed in the cupola after the blast is turned on at the start of the heat. Regardless of the method used, observations should be made at frequent intervals through the peep-hole covers on the tuyeres in order to avoid difficulties which might occur at the start of the heat. After about 30 min of operation, during which time a quantity of molten slag has accumulated, the slag hole is opened and it is not closed again during the heat. From this point on the tapping and slagging procedure is the same as that previously described.

A bot stick and two types of bot pick are shown in Fig. 28.2. The stick is a convenient length, usually a 3 ft rod with a metal disc of approximately 2 in. diameter welded to one end to hold a cone of botting mixture. The bot is forced in place by firm hand pressure applied through the rod. The bot can be picked out with the pointed rod, or it can be cut off with a downward sweep of the chisel-ended rod, care being taken not to enlarge the tapping hole and thereby cause difficulty later in the heat. Figure 28.1 is of a cupola being botted; botting tools are at left of operator.

The slag hole is formed in an opening in the brickwork, similar to the breast, by the procedure used for making the tap hole. The hole is from ¾ to 1½ in. in diameter at the inside of the cupola, tapered outward to promote the flow of molten slag. Most cupolas are provided with a short cast iron slag spout which is lined with brick and faced with a rammed lining in the same fashion as the tapping spout. Refractories manufacturers provide slag hole blocks (Fig. 21.5), which may be rammed in place in the same manner as taphole blocks.

Carbon and carborundum slag hole blocks can be used, or the slag hole can be formed by means of standard shapes made from these materials. They last for several heats, but care must be exercised not to run iron over the slag hole, as it erodes both carbon and carborundum. Good refractory practice is essential in the slag hole area because, generally speaking, refractories are attacked much more rapidly by molten slag than by molten iron.

CONTINUOUS TAPPING — FRONT SLAGGING

During the past few years, there has been a growing interest in front-slagging cupolas.* With this arrangement iron and slag flow from the cupola simultaneously through the same hole, thus eliminating the conventional slag hole used with intermittent tapping.

Before any operator can consider front slagging, the cupola must be checked to determine that the tuyeres are sufficiently high above the sand bottom so that when the air supply is reduced or shut off during the course of the heat the metal which backs into the cupola does not raise the slag level inside to a height where slag will run into the tuyeres. Furthermore, there may be a greater accumulation of slag inside when operating at low blast pressures than when operating at high blast pressures, and provision must be made for the storage of this relatively large amount of slag.

Figure 28.3 is of a schematic drawing of the construction of a front slagging spout, with a series of horizontal lines showing levels of both slag and iron inside and outside the cupola under various operating conditions. A brief study of the drawing will indicate that the principle of the front slagging spout is that of a simple U-tube in which the air pressure inside the cupola, plus the downward pressure of molten slag inside the cupola, are balanced against a head of molten iron outside the cupola.

In constructing the spout the required head of metal is provided by installing the refractories so that location "A" is above the top of the tap hole a distance designated as "X." Starting from location "A" (highest point in the trough on side of slag dam away from cupola), the bottom of the

*W. W. Levi, "Cupola Operation," AFS TRANSACTIONS, vol. 58, p. 6 (1950).

trough should be level for a distance of about 4 or 5 in., and dimension "X" should be kept as small as possible for reasons given later in this discussion.

In actual practice, it has been found that the "ideal" front slagging spout would be designed so that

1) Slag will start flowing from the cupola at the beginning of the heat in no more than 20 min after tapping out.
2) The cupola can be operated satisfactorily over its entire range of melting rates without an unduly large accumulation of slag inside when melting slowly, and without leakage or "blowing" of air through the tap hole when melting rapidly.
3) There will be a minimum accumulation of slag inside the cupola regardless of melting rate.

Based on the foregoing, the following equation can be written for conditions representing maximum air pressure inside the cupola

(1) $X + D$ (in.) $= \frac{1}{4}$ Max. C (oz) $+ \frac{1}{3}$ S (in.),

where

"X" is vertical distance in inches from top of tap hole to point "A."

"D" is maximum depth in inches of metal flowing over point "A."

"C" is air pressure in ounces inside cupola. *This is not the same as windbox pressure.* It has been determined experimentally that the pressure inside the cupola always is less than the windbox pressure and, consequently, the windbox pressure readings can be used only for rough approximations of "X." Some of these differences in windbox pressure and actual pressure inside the cupola are shown in connection with Fig. 28.3 in the tabulation of *Pressure Data and X Values.* The data were obtained in connection with both 72 in. balanced blast and 72 in. conventional type cupolas. The column headed "Windbox (W)" indicates actual windbox pressure in ounces, and the column headed "Cupola (C)" indicates the corresponding wind pressure in ounces inside the cupola. Columns headed "X (W)" and "X (C)" show calculated values of "X" based on windbox pressures and actual pressures inside the cupola, respectively. From the above, it is evident that if windbox pressure readings are used in the equation, the calculated value of "X" will always be greater than needed in actual practice.

"S" is depth in inches above the top of the tap hole of layer of molten slag inside the cupola.

Iron weighs 0.26 lb per cu. in. Therefore, a head of 1 in. of iron will about balance 4 oz (0.25 lb) of air pressure.

Molten slag weighs about one-third as much as iron. Therefore, a head of 1 in. of iron will about balance a 3 in. head of slag.

Attention is again called to the fact that Equation (1) represents a condition corresponding to the maximum cupola air pressure for which the spout is designed. The slightest increase in pressure beyond the maximum would result in leakage of air through the tap hole, which indicates that *at* maximum pressure the depth of the slag layer "S" is approaching

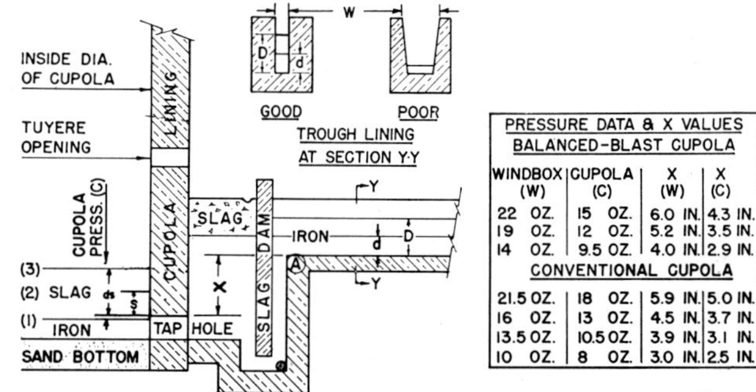

PRESSURE DATA & X VALUES			
BALANCED-BLAST CUPOLA			
WINDBOX (W)	CUPOLA (C)	X (W)	X (C)
22 OZ.	15 OZ.	6.0 IN.	4.3 IN.
19 OZ.	12 OZ.	5.2 IN.	3.5 IN.
14 OZ.	9.5 OZ.	4.0 IN.	2.9 IN.
CONVENTIONAL CUPOLA			
21.5 OZ.	18 OZ.	5.9 IN.	5.0 IN.
16 OZ.	13 OZ.	4.5 IN.	3.7 IN.
13.5 OZ.	10.5 OZ.	3.9 IN.	3.1 IN.
10 OZ.	8 OZ.	3.0 IN.	2.5 IN.

(1) SLAG-IRON INTERFACE - ANY BLAST PRESSURE WHEN SLAG IS FLOWING.
(2) TOP OF SLAG LAYER - HIGH BLAST PRESSURE.
(3) TOP OF SLAG LAYER - LOW BLAST PRESSURE.

Fig. 28.3. Schematic drawing showing the construction of a front slagging cupola spout.

zero. This being the case, the term ($\frac{1}{3}$ S) in Equation (1) can be dropped and the equation re-written

(2) $X + D$ (in.) $= \frac{1}{4}$ Max. C (oz)

In Fig. 28.3 the depth of iron flowing over point "A" has been indicated as "d" under conditions of slow melting, and as "D" when melting at a high rate. By keeping the passage for iron in the trough narrow at section "Y-Y" in the manner labeled "Good," the depth of molten iron at location "A" will be appreciably affected by variations in melting rate. The depth will be proportional to both melting rate and cupola pressure, and can be made to provide a fully compensating and automatic balance for pressure changes inside the cupola.

In order to accomplish this, the width of the channel, dimension "W," in section "Y-Y" would have to be such that for every increase or decrease of 4 oz in cupola air pressure ("C" in Equation 2), there would be a corresponding increase or decrease of 1 in. in metal depth at point "A." It would actually be wise to make "W" a little greater than the minimum needed to fully compensate for pressure changes, because it is conceivable that an increase in melting rate resulting from an accidental improvement in coke ratio (with no change in air rate) might stop the flow of slag from the cupola.

For existing cupolas with front-slagging spouts, values for "D" and "C" in Equation 2 can be determined experimentally over the range of melting rates and air pressures used. Based on the data obtained, gradual changes can be made in "X" and "W" in Fig. 28.3 until an almost ideal design for the front slagging spout is developed for any cupola operation.

For new and untried installations, the procedure for determining "X" as described by T. W. Curry* has been found to be very satisfactory. The highest operating pressure expected during the heat is used as a basis for determining the distance from the top of the tap hole to the bottom of the trough at point "A." This distance, in inches, should be somewhat less than one fourth of the expected maximum windbox pressure. The height of the dam calculated and set in this manner will, in all probability, be high

*Assistant to the President, Lynchburg Foundry Co.

enough to prevent "blowing," but may be too high to allow slag to discharge through the tap hole. It is well to keep the spout construction at point "A" in the form of a 4-in. ridge across the spout in case adjustments are necessary.

After the cupola is tapped slag should appear on the surface of the metal in front of the tap hole in a maximum of 20 min of elapsed time from the first tap. If no slag appears, the height of dam is lowered about 1/4-in., and time is allowed for the liquids to establish themselves at the new level created. This procedure is repeated until slag does appear on the slag spout, and no further adjustment need be made if the slag will discharge from the cupola in sufficient volume to run over the slag spout in about 10 min after it makes its first appearance.

This, then, establishes a working height of the dam, and it should be measured carefully from some fixed point on the spout frame. The new, adjusted height becomes the height of the dam, as previously described, for the next day's heat. Adjustments on the second heat may again be necessary and, if any are required, the new height is measured from the same fixed spot. This procedure is repeated on subsequent heats, or until an average height is obtained which will allow the cupola to begin slagging in not more than 20 min, and will efficiently seal the tap hole from "blowing."

Experience gained in using the front slagging spout would naturally allow the proper height at point "A" to be determined quickly and efficiently. On a new spout, this can generally be done in three consecutive heats by making one small adjustment at the beginning of each. It would be expected that one inexperienced in the use of the front slagging spout would perhaps require more than three heats to establish the proper height, but this need not interfere with the melting efficiency in any way during the experimental work. Usually the adjustments described do not require more than one hour's time after the first tap is made, and the dam height established in this manner is more versatile and efficient than any calculated setting.

With front slagging no definite relationship need exist between the melting rate of the cupola and the size of the tap hole. For example, a 2 in. diameter hole will serve satisfactorily whether the cupola is melting 5 or 25 tons per hr. The tap hole may be either circular or rectangular in cross section, and with front slagging, it is felt that the rectangular hole with the long dimension in the horizontal plane offers more resistance to the cutting action of the slag than does the round hole.

It has been definitely established in front slagging cupolas that slag and iron flow through the tap hole in two separate layers with the slag on top and the iron toward the bottom as might be expected. From this, it becomes evident that for any given value of "X" the only way to increase the slag-carrying capacity of a rectangular tap hole is by increasing the width. This also increases the iron-carrying capacity. Increasing the height of the tap hole increases its iron-carrying capacity but leaves the slag-carrying capacity unchanged.

FRONT SLAGGING SPOUT REFRACTORIES

It is of utmost importance to select and properly install good refractories in the front-slagging spout. Once established, the dimension "X" must not vary more than 1/4-in. during an entire heat. The top of the tap hole is subject to slag attack, and the refractories at point "A" are subject to erosion by the iron. Failure of the refractories at either of these two points results in a decrease in distance "X." This may allow leakage of air through the tap hole, which will make it necessary to reduce the air pressure or stop the operation for repairs.

Front-slagging cupolas possess many advantages over those tapped intermittently, including uniform carbon pick-up, which is one of the essentials of carbon control. Other advantages include hotter iron at the cupola spout, no need for a slag hole with the usual loss of air blast, and better housekeeping because no slag wool is generated. Furthermore, the occasional shutdowns generally necessary for repairing the slag hole can be avoided, and the flow of metal from the cupola may be stopped by simply shutting off the blower, thus eliminating the need for bots in the breast hole. This not only makes a safer operation, but also it is practically impossible to run cupola slag into the pouring ladles, as frequently happens with intermittent tapping when the man tapping the cupola leaves the breast hole open a little too long or a bot accidentally comes out.

In addition to the advantages just mentioned, it is easier to produce low carbon irons from front slagging cupolas, because at no time after tapping out is there any appreciable accumulation of molten iron in the well, and the small amount which does accumulate remains at a constant level since the metal flows out as fast as it is melted.

After the last charge is in the cupola, the same procedure is followed at the end of the heat as is discussed in connection with the intermittent tapping—rear slagging cupola, up to the point where the last iron has been melted. At this time the air blast is shut off and there will be several hundred pounds of iron and some slag remaining in the cupola well and slag spout. These are removed by opening the slag spout drain and may be separated by lightly plugging the slag spout drain as soon as slag appears at the hole.

With some cupolas the arrangement is such that this last iron can be used, while in other cases it is collected under or at the side of the cupola in a suitable pig mold. After all of the iron and slag have drained out the bottom doors are dropped, and when the lining has cooled sufficiently the cupola is ready for patching and preparation for another heat.

CONTINUOUS TAPPING — REAR SIPHON SLAGGING

A variation of the usual front or rear slagging system is that in which slag is removed from a hole in the rear, but in which a slag dam is employed to keep the hole continuously covered, giving a uniform flow of slag and complete lack of slag wool. This type of slagging practice is applicable to any continuous operation in which a front iron dam can be used. This dam (10 in. above the tap hole top in a typical installation) holds back iron in the cupola to a level depending upon cupola pressure. The slag hole is then located slightly above the iron level but at the rear of the cupola or at any other convenient location.

A slag box is built onto the cupola at this point, and when lined with refractory is given a dam to hold back slag in the cupola much as the front dam holds back iron. It must be remembered that it will take considerably more height to hold back cupola pressure with a slag column than with iron.

It is common practice with this type of slagging system to melt 30-45 min before opening the slag hole, which has been previously closed with a molding sand plug. This assures a sufficient quantity of hot slag to warm up the system and avoid a freeze-up. After the system is completely warmed up it is not uncommon to allow a shutdown for as much as 30 min and find, upon starting up, that slag will immediately start to flow. If, however, the level of iron in the cupola is raised by a higher dam or lower pressure so that it can cover the slag hole, the iron will throttle the slag and prevent slagging until a sufficient thickness of slag has been built up to push the iron down again.

Since neither air nor slag comes into contact with the iron taphole, the life of this block can be long. In some instances 10,000 tons have been run through a block without any repair or maintenance. The size of a block is shown in Fig. 28.4.

Daily maintenance is required for the slag hole. It is generally built up of standard shapes, and after

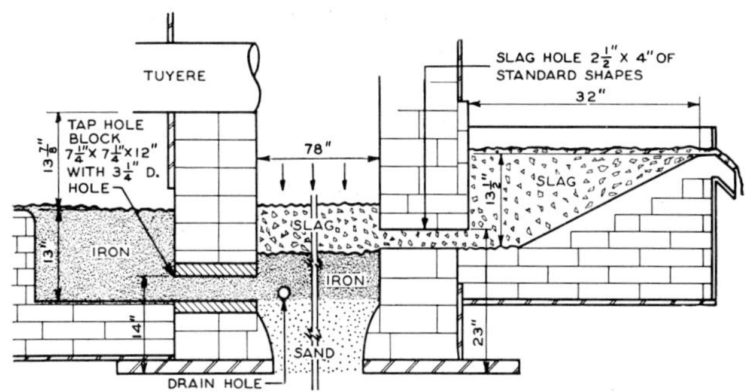

Fig. 28.4. **Sketch showing details of tap hole and slag hole in continuous tapping-rear siphon slagging operation.**

each 16 hr heat is usually repairable with a ramming type refractory for several more runs. However, if the slag dam is allowed to drop sufficiently to allow air to escape through the hole, it will erode rapidly.

Such a condition if not too extensive can be cured without shutdown by inserting a properly sized bar in the hole (since no iron is present) and ramming refractory against it. Lacking this, a drain hole can be opened, allowing sufficient slag to drain from box so that the repair can be made. However, such repairs should not be necessary if proper care is taken. For example, if the pressure begins to rise, an extra inch or two of refractory on the slag dam will compensate for the increased pressure.

CHAPTER 29

Fluxing
Slag Control

PART I

In the process of cupola melting a certain quantity of non-metallic material accumulates as a residue or dross called "slag." Coke ash, oxidation products, fluxed refractory lining and extraneous "dirt" all contribute to form the slag.

Without some adjustment the slag that is naturally formed is very viscous and sticky as a result of excessive concentration of acid constituents like silicon oxide, and a deficiency of basic constituents like lime.

The addition of basic materials like limestone or dolomite is needed to flux or liquefy the slag and facilitate its elimination from the cupola. By definition, a flux is a substance which reacts with slag to lower its fusion point, thereby increasing its fluidity and improving its refining value.

Without such a basic flux a cupola could not operate long before the viscous pasty slag would choke up the interstitial spaces in the coke and build up a bridge in the areas chilled by the air from the tuyeres.

USUAL FLUXES

The most popular flux for cupola slags is the natural rock limestone, which is principally calcium carbonate ($CaCO_3$). Other forms of calcium carbonate such as oyster shells, marl, chalk, and the pure mineral calcite may be used if more readily available.

Dolomite and dolomitic limestones, containing a proportion of magnesium carbonate ($MgCO_3$) along with the calcium carbonate, are used satisfactorily. Some minor advantages have been reported for dolomite over limestone, but they have been used interchangeably. Purity and size are usually more important than the differences in composition.

As the limestone descends toward the melting zone it is calcined to lime, which is calcium oxide. As the basic calcium oxide contacts the gummy and insufficiently fluxed acid silicon oxide, the two combine to form a fluid calcium-silicate slag. This properly balanced fluid slag liberates itself from the coke, drips freely through the coke interstices, accumulates in the well or hearth, and flows freely from the cupola.

SPECIAL FLUXES

Several more active basic materials are sometimes used as supplementary fluxes. Sodium carbonate (Na_2CO_3) or soda ash in the form of lumps, fused pigs, or pellets is an effective fluxing agent. A proportion of sodium carbonate added to the limestone adds further fluidity to the slag. It has been reported that from the standpoint of fluidity 1 lb of sodium carbonate is roughly equivalent to 2-5 lb of limestone. Some operators regularly use some sodium carbonate to supplement the limestone. Still more use sodium carbonate additions on the first few charges to be sure that the first slag is very fluid and that the cupola bed and hearth areas are adequately flushed for a good start.

Sodium carbonate is frequently used as a slag medicine. Because of its relatively low melting point, sodium carbonate melts higher in the stack and trickles down over the coke, reacting with any bridged masses of insufficiently fluxed slag.

Fluorspar, a calcium fluoride mineral (CaF_2), is likewise a powerful fluxing agent that is sometimes used in small proportions along with limestone, to improve slag fluidity and cupola cleanliness. Fluorspar is also a good medicine for a cupola badly bridged or choked up with gummy slag. Excessive use of these strong fluxes after the bridge has been removed can result in severe refractory attack. Because of its corrosive effect on acid refractories fluorspar must be used carefully.

Calcium carbide has been used for a number of years as a special and powerful fluxing agent. A special carbide, with an adjusted composition, has been developed with lower fusion and combustion temperature to permit this material to melt and burn in the cupola bed. In amounts up to 5 per cent of the metal charge, its effect is to produce hotter iron, increase melting rate and reduce coke requirements.

The use of carbide may be particularly beneficial when high proportions of scrap are used or when poor quality coke must be employed. Carbide increases the fluidity and desulfurizing ability of both basic and acid slags. Its quick melting characteristics may be of particular benefit in providing proper slag control and hotter temperatures at the start of a cupola heat.

Although some of the results obtained with carbide are beyond those normally associated with fluxes (Chapter 15), the dissociation of carbide produces lime which enters the slag and many of the reactions are primarily those of a flux. CaC_2 also increases carbon pickup and reduces sulfur (Chapter 16).

COMPOUND FLUXES

There are a number of commercial fluxes marketed for improvement of cupola slagging. These are usually combinations of various strong basic fluxing agents made up in convenient briquet form. Advantages have been reported where the special fluxes corrected the particular slag deficiency that was causing a problem. When the slag condition is already good and the cupola is kept clean and efficiently operated, benefits from special fluxes may not be expected to be as great.

SLAG CONDITION EFFECTS

The most noticeable effect of slag condition is the ease with which it flows from the cupola. When the slag flows from the cupola sluggishly it is inclined to lag behind and build up in the cupola to the point of clogging up the tuyeres and causing serious trouble. Slag fluidity studies have shown that the fluidity of acid slags is roughly proportional to the total bases, of which lime is the principal variable. If the slag is viscous and stiff, increased stone will improve the fluidity, but a thorough search should be made to determine why an abnormal quantity of flux is needed. It is much better to anticipate and eliminate sources of additional slag than to compensate for them.

Another condition that can result from improper fluxing is "bridging." If the slag droplets are viscous and insufficiently fluxed as they pass the tuyere zone, the sluggish slag is chilled by the rush of the incoming cold air and builds up on the cupola walls as a bridge. Such a protrusion usually forms just above the tuyeres, but might also form below the tuyere if the slag level is allowed to climb too high in the hearth. Such a bridge reduces effective cupola area, and obstructs blast penetration, causing slower melting, and colder iron.

Combustion efficiency is affected by slag condition. If the slag is not adequately fluxed, the build-up of slag around the coke and in the interstitial spaces, as well as the subsequent bridging, interferes with even blast penetration and efficient combustion of the coke.

The degree of oxidation may be affected by extremes in slag composition since oxidation is influenced by combustion reactions as well as bridging.

Carbon pick-up may also be affected by fluxing practice. The effect on carbon content is more conspicuous on low-carbon charges that are more dependent on carbon pick-up from the coke. A viscous, insufficiently fluxed slag tends to coat the coke and obstruct carbon absorption. A more basic flux produces a more fluid, more basic slag that effectively cleans the slag away from the coke, leaving its surface cleaner for absorption and combustion. Some operators on low-carbon irons regularly adjust carbon levels by flux modifications while maintaining a fixed metal charge.

LININGS AFFECTED BY FLUX

In describing the need for fluxing, the results of inadequate limestone have been implied. On the other hand, excessive amounts of basic flux have some undesirable consequences in the cupola lined with conventional acid refractories. A more basic slag seriously attacks the acid refractories, especially in the hearth, tap hole, and slag trough of a front-slagging cupola, or the slag hole of back-slagging operation. Basic or neutral refractories are necessary if a basic slag is to be maintained.

The cupola slag serves as a protective blanket to the incoming air, and collects non-metallic impurities after it has cleansed the coke. Slag droplets are oxidized and reduced, along with metal droplets in their descent. Having an inclination to reach an equilibrium with the metal in contact with it, slag condition and composition has some diagnostic value in giving an insight into cupola or metal conditions.

In acid operation the purpose of the slag is essentially limited to these physical functions. However, in basic operation the slag has a chemical refining function in addition to these physical requirements. Desulfurization and carbon pick-up depend considerably on the composition of the basic slag. The advantages and costs of basic operation are described in Chapter 26, and a discussion of basic slags is in this Chapter 29, PART II. Although the principles apply to both types of slags, the details in this discussion apply to acid slags.

AMOUNT OF FLUX

In acid practice the cupola operator must adjust the amount of flux added to give the advantages of good fluxing without the cost of excessive refractory attack. This optimum amount of flux is not the same on all cupolas or under all conditions. The proper amount has been found to vary as much as from 1½ to 10 per cent of the metal charge under extreme conditions. However a majority of the larger cupolas operate with flux amounts 2 to 4 per cent of the metal charge, while on smaller cupolas the optimum amount usually ranges from 3 to 7 per cent of the metal charge. Since the flux is the smallest ingredient of the charge it is often given little consideration.

Frequently the various ingredients of the metal charge are carefully calculated and the air weight controlled, while a few shovels of limestone are carelessly thrown to the most convenient side of the cupola. Although it is hard to prescribe exactly the proper amount of flux, reasonably close estimation can be made if charge conditions are studied. Some trial and error adjustments will be necessary.

A more detailed analysis of sources of slag is given in Chapter 29, PART II. Now sources of slag will be discussed sufficiently to suggest some empirical adjustments that may be made by the operator to meet varied conditions.

Coke ash is one definite source of slag. The more coke used, the greater is the quantity of flux required; likewise, the higher the ash content of the coke, the more flux needed. Many operators base the amount of flux on the coke charged, usually 20 or 25 per cent of the charge. Under most average conditions this proportion proves satisfactory, but is not accurate for some exceptional circumstances where other factors become very important. With a metal to coke ratio of 6 to 1 and a 10 per cent ash coke, the slag from coke alone would be 16.6 per cent x 10 per cent = 1.66 per cent of the metal melted, and would require about that amount of limestone (1.66 per cent or 33 lb/ton) to flux that part of the slag. If metal to coke ratio were 12 to 1 only half that amount of slag would be formed and stone might be cut 16 lb per ton.

On the other hand, if a coke with 15 per cent ash were used instead of the 10 per cent ash coke, the flux would need an increase of 16 lb per ton. A second source of slag is the oxidation products. Since silicon is the principal element oxidized the acid silicon oxide is the predominant slag product. Iron and manganese oxides are also formed but in smaller amounts. Higher silicon irons and more oxidizing conditions should have slightly more flux.

A third source of slag is the refractory lining that is consumed or fluxed away during the day's melt. With water cooled or neutral linings, relatively little slag may be contributed from the lining. On larger cupolas operated for long periods the lining consumption per ton of metal melted is usually relatively low. On smaller cupolas the lining consumption is frequently the largest source of slag, and more flux is needed where refractory consumption is high. Likewise, poor refractory quality or erratic lining practice can cause irregularities in slag condition The amount of refractory to patch divided by the total day's melt represents the refractory addition per ton. Each pound of refractory requires approximately 1 lb of limestone to flux it.

A fourth source of slag is dirt and sand that may be attached to return scrap or included with purchased cast scrap. On rainy days it is easy for make-up magnets to pick up much dirt, sand, and mud from the bottom of storage bins. This extra dirt is predominantly sand, hence acid in nature, and requires additional flux. Each pound of extra sand should have 1 or 2 lb of extra limestone. Changing from clean scrap to dirty scrap without some flux adjustment can cause slag troubles and irregular performance. It is far better to prevent such extra dirt from entering the cupola. Some foundries find it advantageous to clean all return scrap in order to reduce the slag volume and to maintain conditions favorable to consistent slag control.

FLUX CONDITIONING AND CHARGING

In addition to adding the proper amount it is important that the flux used be of the proper size and purity. Since limestone is usually an inexpensive natural product, its condition is frequently neglected. It is generally agreed that size should be in the range of ½ to 3 in., and preferably ¾ to 2 in. Stone too small may be blown out of the cupola, whereas lumps too large may be calcined too late and too low in the cupola to give best results.

Acid impurities in basic fluxes should be held to a minimum. Since 5 per cent SiO_2 as an impurity would require 5 per cent of the lime content to neutralize the impurity, fluxing efficiency is reduced more than 10 per cent. A good limestone should contain less than a 2 or 3 per cent maximum silica content. In many plants lots of limestone are regularly analyzed for SiO_2 to insure the purity.

The flux should be evenly charged and not allowed to concentrate on one side of the cupola. Localized or heavy concentration of flux in one spot or too near the lining can cause increased lining attack. However, flux reasonably distributed toward the perimeter of the cupola helps keep the tuyere areas clean and the cupola operating efficiently. A smaller amount of flux properly distributed may be better than larger amounts improperly distributed.

Slag condition may be appraised and controlled by a number of simple tests and observations, as well as by partial or complete chemical analysis. One of the simplest tests is the fluidity apparent in running down the slag trough or from the slag hole. Conspicuous differences in fluidity can be expected to be reflected in variations in cupola performance.

If the slag becomes sluggish or unusually fluid the cupola operator should check the amount of flux being added as well as its condition and distribution. If the flux is being added as prescribed, then he should check the cleanliness of the charge, charging practice and refractory practice in a search for unusual sources of slag variation.

SLAG TESTS

Fluidity molds have been used to assign a quantitative value to the fluidity of the slag. The liquid slag is run into a mold consisting of a basin and a standardized channel. The distance the slag flows into the channel before it is stopped by solidification is a measure of its fluidity. Fluidity studies have indicated that the viscous slags with insufficient fluidity are usually low in lime and high in silica content. Slags with a higher ratio of lime to silica are more fluid. Such tests make it possible to record a measure of fluidity for control purposes.

Another simple routine slag test is observation of color. Since color is affected by cooling rate, size of sample, etc., it is important that slag samples for observation should be collected in the same manner. Slag granulated in water troughs has a tendency to be lighter in color than pancakes cast directly from the molten stream. A slag color considered favorable by many foundries is a dark olive green to greenish black. Blacker slags generally contain more iron and manganese oxides, indicative of more oxidizing conditions. Lighter colored slags generally indicate higher lime and lower iron oxide contents.

No one particular color necessarily represents the best composition for all cupola operations. Furthermore, slag colors are affected by many minor variations. However, varying slag colors on the same cupola indicate varying cupola conditions and results. A number of foundries pour slag samples at regular intervals for observation tests. By associating a given color with desirable operation, abnormal slag appearance immediately suggests that something is wrong. A few foundrymen report that critical castings are not poured when the color of the slag is outside of the desired working range.

Slag analyses are not necessary for good slag control, and a complete chemical analysis requires too much time for immediate corrective value. But occasional analyses are valuable to check the various visual tests. The following is the usual composition range for acid slags:

Acid Constituents
40-50% Silicon Oxide (SiO_2)

Neutral
10-20% Aluminum Oxide (Al_2O_3)

Basic Constituents
25-38% Calcium Oxide (CaO) (+Magnesium Oxide, MgO, and Sodium Oxide if present)
1-8% Iron Oxides (FeO plus a trace of Fe_2O_3)
1-5% Manganese Oxide (MnO)

A number of foundries analyze as a routine only one or two of the most indicative slag constituents like silica and iron oxide. These are probably the most significant since silica content would indicate fluidity and lime to silica ratio, while iron oxide would indicate the degree of oxidation. Spectrographic methods of slag analysis have been developed which can be reported within a couple of hours and make possible routine slag analysis and control.

Along with a detailed discussion of the factors affecting slag composition as well as the effect of slag composition on cupola performance and metal chemistry, a number of slag analyses are given in PART II.

PART II

PART I of this Chapter 29 states that a slag residue accumulates in the cupola, coming principally from the coke ash, oxidation products, refractory lining fluxed away in melting, and dirt and sand on the charge material This slag is inclined to be very viscous at cupola temperatures because of a relatively high fusion point resulting from an unfavorable excess of the acid constituent SiO_2. The need for the addition of basic fluxes was described for the purpose of lowering the fusion point of the slag and increasing the fluidity and the ease of elimination from the cupola.

The physical importance of proper fluxing and good slag fluidity has been emphasized as necessary to keep an open, efficiently operating cupola. Sluggish, insufficiently fluxed slag tends to close up interstitial space and to build up as a bridge on the cupola walls. Both effects tend to reduce effective area, stack permeability, and effective coke surface, resulting in lower iron temperature, retarded melting rate, lower carbon, and increased oxidation.

In addition to its cleansing effect as it descends the cupola stack, a slag blanket in the basin protects the collected metal from oxidizing gases from the tuyere areas. It insulates against temperature loss, collects the oxidation products suspended in the metal droplets, and may desulfurize or react in other ways depending on composition of the slag and cupola operating conditions.

The various regular and special fluxes are treated in Chapter 15. These fluxes are —

Limestone (calcium carbonate) $CaCO_3$
Dolomite (calcium and magnesium carbonate) $CaCO_3$ and $MgCO_3$
Soda ash (sodium carbonate) Na_2CO_3
Trona mineral (sodium sesquicarbonate)
Fluorspar (calcium fluoride) CaF_2
Carbide (calcium carbide) CaC_2
Commercial combinations

Most cupola men have experienced and recognized some of the troubles resulting from poor slag conditions, and most experienced operators have certain slag indications and appearances they prefer and associate with good operation. However, not much data on slag analysis and properties have been recorded in the literature.

ACID SLAG COMPOSITION

Table 29.1 lists acid slag contents as recorded in the American literature. Wide variations are apparent, but the desirable composition recommended by Bolton in 1921[1] agrees closely with the range recommended by Carter and Carlson in 1953.[6]

Principal slag constituents are —

Silica (SiO_2) is acid in behavior and is the largest single constituent, ranging usually from 40 to 50 per cent in an acid slag. Silica comes from coke ash, refractory lining, oxidation of silicon from the metal, and extraneous dirt.

Alumina (Al_2O_3) is classed by Carter as a neutral constituent, for the sake of simplicity, because of its amphoteric ability to act as a basic constituent in an acid slag and as an acid constituent in a basic slag. Alumina comes chiefly from the coke ash and clay refractories, and usually ranges from 10 to 20 per cent.

Lime or calcium oxide (CaO), added as limestone, is the principal basic constituent in cupola slags and generally ranges from 25 to 35 per cent.

Magnesia (MgO) is similar to calcium oxide in its behavior and may substitute for it. When dolomite or dolomitic limestone is used, MgO content might run as high as 5 to 20 per cent along with 10-25 per cent CaO. When straight limestone is used, magnesia content from all sources usually runs less than 5 per cent.[4]

Iron oxides (principally FeO with some Fe_2O_3) are usually present in the proportions of 1 to 8 per cent. Iron oxide in the slag is dependent primarily on the net balance between oxidizing and reducing influences inside the cupola. Hard blowing, low amounts of coke, uneven charge distribution, smaller cupolas, poor coke, higher percentages of steel, thin rusty steel, bad bridging, etc., are factors inclined to produce higher FeO contents. However, with good materials and smooth operation, slag FeO content generally is in the lower range of 1 to 4 per cent.

TABLE 29.1. ACID SLAG COMPOSITIONS IN THE LITERATURE

	Acid Constituent	Neutral	Basic Constituents		
	SiO_2	Al_2O_3	CaO+ MgO	MnO	FeO
Bolton—Experimental range (1921) [1]	37.9/ 52.2	6.2/ 22.9	19.8/ 44.3	1.7/ 3.6	5.0/ 15.6
Bolton—Recommended range	35/ 45	5/ 26	30/ 40	1.3/ 4.0	5/ 8
Dyar— (1921) [2]	32.0	15.0	38.0	2.5	8.0
Walls— (1934) [3]	44.2	13.4	36.5	5.8	
Somers & Gunther—range (1947) [5]	41.1/ 51.7		18.3/ 36.8		0.4/ 10.8
Carter & Carlson—Experimental range (1953) [6]	37.0/ 65.0	9.7/ 23.4	7.7/ 40.7	1.0/ 23.4	0.9/ 44.4
Carter & Carlson—Recommended range	40/ 50	10/ 20	25/ 38	1/ 5	1/ 8

TABLE 29.2. SOME TYPICAL VARIATIONS IN ACID CUPOLA SLAGS
(from Carter and Carlson[6])

Description	Cupola Size, in,	Steel, %	Coke, %	Flux %	Slag Composition % SiO_2	Al_2O_3	FeO*	MnO	CaO	MgO
Average fluidity	84	33	7.5	1.9 Lst	47.1	12.1	6.9	4.6	22.0	1.6
Average fluidity	48	22	12.8	3.0 Lst	46.2	11.0	1.1	1.4	37.2	1.0
Viscous slag	48	22	12.8	2.2 Lst	52.1	12.4	1.5	1.9	29.2	0.9
Fluid & corrosive	84	14	11.0	3.5 Lst	39.6	10.1	3.8	2.9	38.8	2.9
Overblown Cupola (490 cfm/sq ft)	21	50	14.0	5.0 Lst	45.6	18.3	16.1	2.8	15.4	1.0

*Total Iron as FeO including small portion of Fe_2O_3.

Lst — Limestone

TABLE 29.3. SOME COKE ASH ANALYSES
(from Carter & Carlson[6])

	Ash Content, %	Ash Soft. Temp., F.	Ash Analysis, % SiO_2	Al_2O_3	Fe_2O_3	MnO	CaO	MgO
Regular Foundry Cokes								
A-2	9.5	2631	54.8	29.7	7.0	0.15	1.2	2.2
E-2	7.7	2658	50.9	34.4	8.1	0.02	0.5	2.1
S	8.5	2782	48.3	36.0	9.9	0.04		1.8
Malleable Low C Coke								
M	12.9	2497	51.8	32.5	7.6	0.03	1.4	3.0

(1.0-1.5% TiO_2 in samples analyzed)

Manganese oxide (MnO) comes from the manganese oxidized from the metal, and is usually under 5 per cent. It supplements the lime as a base but is of little importance because of its low concentration.

Sodium oxide (Na_2O) may be present up to 5 per cent when soda fluxes are used. Na_2O is more strongly basic and has more effect on fluidity than equivalent weights of limestone. Higher final concentrations are difficult to attain because Na_2O sublimes at a relatively low temperature (approximately 2327 F, 1275 C).

In slag these various oxide constituents are combined into solutions of silicates, and possibly aluminates, of calcium, magnesium, manganese and iron; however, the various constituents are usually considered and determined as oxides.

Table 29.2 shows five slags representative of the usual variations in acid slags. The first two are typically average and within the range of most acid cupola slags.

The third slag (Table 29.2) is too viscous for good front slagging and smooth cupola operation. Silica content of 52.1 per cent is high, indicating insufficient limestone. The fourth slag is fluid and corrosive to refractories. Silica content of 39.6 per cent is lower than usual and especially in proportion to the higher CaO of 38.8 per cent. This slag is almost mildly basic as a result of high lime content.

Of the last slag (Table 29.2) the unusual feature is the high FeO content of 16.1 per cent. This was obtained on an experimental heat deliberately blown too hard and with a 50 per cent steel mix. Under poor conditions high FeO slags accompany oxidized metal and high oxidation losses.

TABLE 29.4. ANALYSES OF SOME TYPICAL CLAY REFRACTORIES

	SiO_2	TiO_2	Al_2O_3	Fe_2O_3	MgO	Na_2O
Clay Bricks						
L-1	62.1		32.6	1.7	1.2	1.4
K-2	58.6	2.0	31.9	3.2	1.3	2.4
Ganister—Clay Gun Mixes						
H	62.8	1.0	24.0	2.3	1.9	0.6
C	73.1	0.8	15.8	2.3	1.8	1.5

ANALYSIS OF SOURCES OF SLAG

Before going further it might be well to review quantitatively some of the sources of cupola slag in order to determine the necessary compensation for their variations.

One of the inevitable and sometimes the largest source of slag is the ash of the coke. Table 29.3 contains ash analyses of four typical cokes. Silica is the predominant constituent in all the ashes ranging roughly from 50 to 55 per cent by weight. Alumina contents generally range from 30 to 35 per cent and iron oxide contents 6 to 10 per cent. Calcium, magnesium, manganese and titanium oxides are present in small percentages.

The refractory lining consumed or fluxed away during the day's melt is another slag source as great as, frequently greater than, the coke ash. The contribution of the lining to the slag varies with cupola size and design. In many smaller cupolas, the lining consumption makes the greatest contribution to the slag, while on larger cupolas this contribution is considerably less.

Cupolas operating with projecting tuyeres show less refractory use than those with flush tuyeres operating under similar conditions. Obviously there is practically no contribution of refractory to the slag on many cupolas operating without a lining and with water cooling.

Table 29.4 shows the composition of two clay brick mixes and two gun mixes. Each is predominately silica and alumina.

Substituting a basic lining and simply changing this consumed refractory from acid material to basic material has been sufficient in most cases to change the slag from one of acid predominance to a slag with the basic constituents predominant.

TABLE 29.5. THEORETICAL CALCULATIONS OF SLAG SOURCES & FINAL COMPOSITION
(48-in. Cupola) (Charge 25% Steel, 20% Return, 55% Pig)

	Total Slag lb/100	Slag Constituents lb/100 lb Metal					
		SiO_2	Al_2O_3	FeO	MnO	CaO	MgO
Lining Cons., (1.5% of Melt)	1.50	0.95	0.36	0.03			0.03
Coke Ash (12.5% Coke, 9.2% Ash)	1.15	0.60	0.37	0.10		0.02	0.03
Si Loss, (10% of 2.20%)	0.47	0.47					
Dirt & Sand on Scrap (Est.)	0.10	0.10					
Oxidation of Iron	?			?			
Mn Loss (10% of 0.70% Mn)	0.09				0.09		
Inevitable Slag, lb	3.31						
3% Limestone to Flux	1.50					1.50	
Final Slag, lb	4.81	2.12	0.73	0.13	0.09	1.52	0.06
Calculated Composition, %		44.2	15.0	2.7±	1.9	31.7	1.2
Actual Analysis, %		43.2	16.1	3.2	1.8	30.8	1.4

Table 29.5 theoretically calculates slag composition from its sources. In this 48 in. cupola, the lining consumption provides slag equivalent to 1½ per cent of the melt. The coke ash figures 1.15 per cent of the melt.

From 0.22 per cent silicon lost in melting, the silica formed was calculated to 0.47 lb. In like manner the basic MnO can be determined from the manganese lost from the charge. Iron oxide is more difficult to calculate. The final FeO content of the slag depends largely on the net effect of the oxidizing and reducing zones.

One unintentional source of slag is dirt and sand on scrap. This was estimated as 0.10 per cent, or 2 lb per ton on a very clean charge. Under favorable conditions of dry weather, cleaned foundry return, high proportions of pig iron, etc., this source of slag is negligible. However, with the use of much purchased scrap, the use of uncleaned foundry return with adhering sand, etc., this source of slag can be several times this amount.

The effect on slag composition is obvious, and such sources of dirt may be quite variable and difficult to compensate for. In damp weather more of the dirt adheres to the scrap and is carried into the cupola than in dry weather. This has caused much undetected variation and some serious cupola troubles.

All these inherent sources of slag totaled 3.31 lb per 100 lb of melt, and are predominantly acid. In order to fluidize this primary slag, 3 per cent limestone was added. After allowance for impurities and evolved CO_2, 3 lb of stone should yield about 1½ lb CaO. This gives a total quantity of slag equal to 4.81 per cent of the melt. Theoretical calculations of the various constituents indicate the calculated composition as shown. Actual analysis was very similar to the theoretical calculation, almost within the precision of analytical methods.

EFFECT OF MELTING VARIABLES

The effect of cupola size on refractory consumption and necessary flux is shown in Table 29.6, listing four different size cupolas in the same plant. On heat No. 1 the lining consumption from the 84 in. cupola operated for 18 hr was hardly 0.5 per cent of the melt. With only 9 per cent coke and a reasonably clean charge, only 1.9 per cent flux, based on weight of metal charge, was necessary for a reasonably fluid slag.

On heat No. 2 on the 48 in. cupola operated for 11 hr, the refractory consumption was 1.5 per cent of the melt, or three times that of the larger cupola. (The higher proportion of coke and slightly higher silicon consumption obviously require some further flux increase.) A 3½ per cent limestone addition to this furnace produced a slag very similar to that resulting from 1.9 per cent limestone in the larger cupola.

On the still smaller 36 in. cupola the lining consumption increased to 3 per cent, and limestone flux found necessary was 5.5 per cent of the metal charge. The resulting slag is similar to the slags above it where less flux was used (Table 29.6).

On the 24 in. cupola final silicon is considerably different from the other heats. The lining consumption continued to increase to 6 per cent, and the necessary limestone to obtain equal slag chemistry and fluidity increased to 7 per cent or more. On this cupola refractory consumption was cut in half by the use of water cooling which permitted a reduction of flux to about 5 per cent.

TABLE 29.6. EFFECT OF CUPOLA SIZE & LINING CONSUMPTION

Cupola		Lining Used,	Flux,	Coke,	Steel,	Slag Composition, %		
I. D., in.	T/Hr	% of Melt	%	%	%	SiO_2	FeO	CaO + MgO
84	40	0.5%	1.9	9	13	47.9	3.6	31.5
48	12	1.5%	3.5	12	20	43.2	3.2	32.2
36	5	3.0%	5.5	18	25	42.7	3.6	29.0
24*	1½	6.0%	7.0	20	60	45.0	2.9	32.0

(Al_2O_3 contents 12.0/21.1, MnO 1.6/3.5%)
*Unusual high Si, low C iron.

TABLE 29.7. CALCULATED EFFECT ON SLAG SOURCES OF CUPOLA SIZE & MIXES

Sources of Slag	84-in. Cup. 13% Steel 7.8% Coke 1.30% Si.	48-in. Cup. 25% Steel 12.5% Coke 2.00% Si	24-in. Cup. 60% Steel 24% Coke 3.00% Si
Lining Consumption, lb/100 lb Melt	0.50	1.50	6.00
Coke Ash	0.72	1.15	2.20
Si Oxidation	0.32	0.47	1.29
Dirt on Scrap	0.10	0.10	0.10
Mn Oxidation	0.12	0.09	0.18
Inevitable Slag, % of Melt	1.76	3.31	9.77
Limestone	(1.4%)	(3%)	(8%)
CaO from Limestone	0.70	1.50	4.00
Total Slag, % of Melt	2.46	4.81	13.77

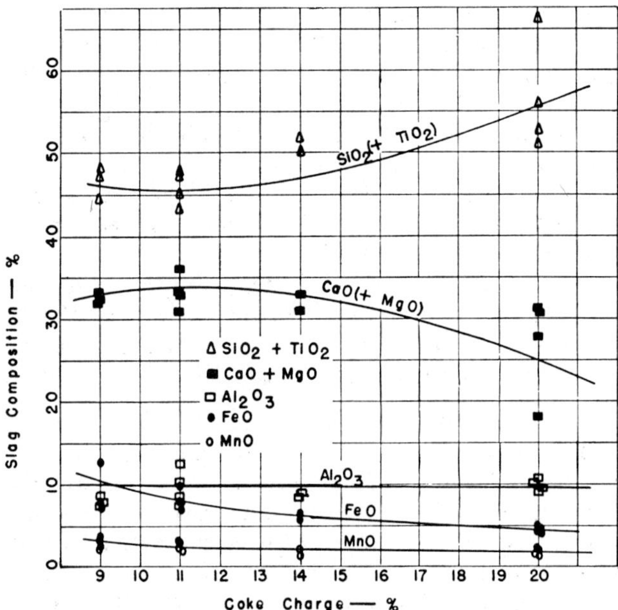

Fig. 29.1. Slag composition is plotted against coke ratio.

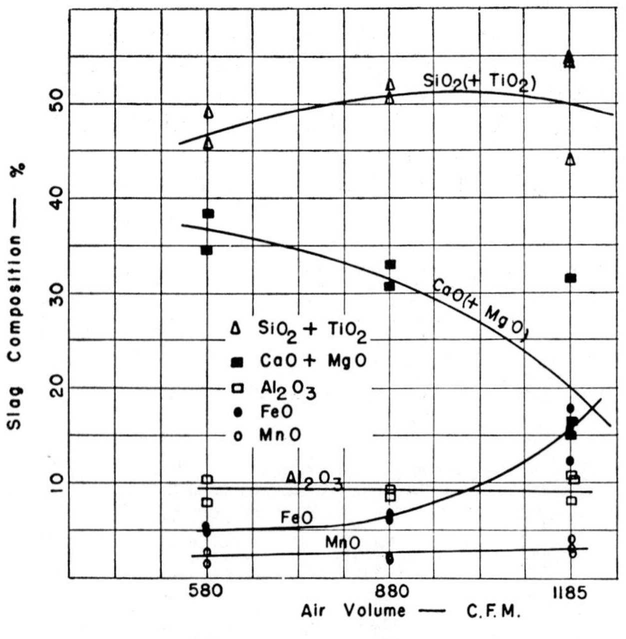

Fig. 29.2. Effect of cupola air volume on slag composition.

These differences indicate the importance of considering cupola size in comparing experiences on various cupolas and the necessity of considering refractory consumption in establishment of the correct amount of flux.

Table 29.7 totals the sources of slag in 84 in., 48 in. and 24 in. cupolas melting different mixes and showing why one cupola needed only 1.4 per cent limestone while the other cupolas required 3 per cent and 8 per cent limestone additions.

The effect of coke ratio is shown graphically in Fig. 29.1. Experimental heats were run in a 21 in. cupola at four different coke ratios.[6] As the amount of coke increased from 9 per cent to 20 per cent the SiO_2 content increased and CaO content decreased, due to more coke ash and more refractory consumption. Alumina showed only a slight increase and MnO practically no change. FeO content was higher with the lowest percentage of coke and decreased as coke increased.

The effect of air volume is shown in Fig. 29.2. One heat was blown very soft (241 cfm/sq ft of cupola area), one at an average blast rate and one decidedly "overblown" beyond any accepted standards (with 492 cfm/sq ft of cupola area). As the blast increased SiO_2 increased and CaO decreased, due to increased refractory consumption and silicon oxidation. Alumina and MnO were not appreciably affected percentagewise after dilution by the increased slag volume. Slag FeO showed a sharp increase with an excessive blast rate. This confirms the well-known dangers of blowing a cupola too hard.

Figure 29.6 shows slag results obtained by varying coke size from 5 per cent to 25 per cent of the cupola diameter on a 21 in. experimental cupola. The best slag composition was obtained with an optimum coke size averaging around 8 per cent to 15 per cent of the cupola diameter. The best cupola performance and metal composition were also obtained in this range. As the coke gets too small SiO_2 goes up, CaO comes down by dilution, and slag FeO and metal oxidation go up, due to insufficient stack permeability.

Likewise, when the coke gets too large, SiO_2 goes up, CaO comes down and slag FeO and metal oxidation go up, due to excessive interstitial space, excessive air velocity and insufficient coke surface. The danger of too large coke is not very great except on the smaller cupolas. A more likely trouble is the use of too small coke on the larger cupolas.

Preheated blast has been shown to lower iron oxide content of the slag as it reduces metal oxidation. Likewise, good even charging has been found to give lower FeO contents than irregular charging methods.

SLAG DISTINCTIONS—ACID AND BASIC

If the lime content (along with magnesia and the other basic constituents) can be increased to a point of sufficient excess over the acid silica, a slag of entirely different nature and properties results. Maintenance of such a slag with a predominance of basic constituents is not practical in contact with acid refractories, but requires neutral or basic refractories. These basic slags then have a refining capacity in addition to the usual physical benefits of slag.

Under reducing conditions (reasonably low iron oxide content) basic slags can remove a considerable proportion of the sulfur in the metal and thereby give relief from the inevitable sulfur absorption expected from the coke as well as the high sulfur contents of some raw materials. Basic oxidizing slags (high iron oxide content) are capable of removing some phosphorus under a limited set of conditions. Desulfurizing effectiveness decreases with higher FeO slags.

To facilitate comparison, Table 29.8 lists chemical ranges of acid slags, basic desulfurizing slags, and the less frequent basic oxidizing slags. The principal difference in basic slags is the lower SiO_2 and higher ($CaO + MgO$) contents. Whereas in acid slags the ratio of ($CaO + MgO$) to SiO_2 is usually 0.5 to 0.9, this basicity ratio is usually 1.0 to 3.5 on basic slags.

The higher basicity ratio generally indicates a slag composition more effective in removing sulfur from the iron. Iron melted under this slag is generally of higher carbon content. Because the constituents of the slag may have higher melting points, reactivity of the slag may be adversely affected under certain conditions and low sulfur irons will not necessarily be produced.

Another difference is the sulfur content. Normal acid slags by virtue of their composition retain no more than 0.05 to 0.4 per cent sulfur, which is not enough to consider as actual desulfurization of the metal. On the other hand, basic slags may absorb sulfur to a concentration of 0.50 to 2.50 per cent. This accounts for the desulfurizing potential of a basic slag.

Considerable differences in alloy recoveries can be expected from the different slags. The slag and metal attempt to reach an equilibrium as the droplets descend together and remain in contact with each other for a short period in the cupola basin. Time does not permit complete equilibrium but the tendencies explain many experiences.

In the oxidation of Si the reaction tends

$$Si_m + 2\,FeO_{m+s} \rightleftarrows SiO_{2_s} + 2\,Fe_m$$

to go forward in proportion to the concentration of silicon in the metal and the iron oxide in the metal and slag. Higher iron oxide contents mean further progress of the forward reaction, as the product goes

TABLE 29.8. GENERAL TYPES OF CUPOLA SLAGS

	Acid Constituent SiO_2	Neutral Al_2O_3	Basic Constituents: $CaO + MgO$	MnO	FeO	S	Ratio $\frac{CaO + MgO}{SiO_2}$
Acid	40/ 50	10/ 20	25/ 38	1/ 5	1/ 8	0.05/ 0.40	0.5/ 0.9
Basic reducing (desulfurizing)	15/ 35	8/ 15	40/ 65	0.5/ 4.0	0.5/ 5.0	0.50/ 2.50	1.0/ 3.5
Basic oxidizing (phosphorus removal)	15/ 35	5/ 10	35/ 45	1.0/ 8.0	15/ 40	0.02/ 0.50	1.0/ 3.0

into the slag. As the concentration of the reaction product, SiO_2, builds up in the slag it tends to stop the forward reaction before all FeO is consumed.

In an acid slag where SiO_2 is high, this reaction cannot proceed as far as on a basic slag where the SiO_2 content is lower.

For that reason silicon losses are higher on a basic slag for the same degree of oxidation.

On the other hand elements that form basic oxides like manganese experience lower losses under a basic slag than under an acid slag.

Because of slag-metal equilibrium principles the basic dephosphorizing slags require a low metal silicon content in order that the necessary high basicity and high FeO content can be maintained in the slag.

Basic Desulfurizing Slags

The usual basic cupola slag is employed for the purpose of sulfur elimination and control. By increasing the volume of slag and improving the slag composition through flux adjustment, sulfur can be lowered in the melting process to almost any desired level. Sulfurs as low as 0.04 per cent are not too difficult. With special practices and increased effort sulfurs as low as 0.005 per cent have been produced from the cupola with the use of special fluxes such as carbide (CaC_2).

By changing the lining from acid materials to basic materials such as magnesite or dolomite, the approximately 1 to 2 per cent refractory contribution is changed from acid to basic. This within itself is usually enough to convert the slag to a basic slag while using the usual amounts of limestone (2 to 4

TABLE 29.9. COMPOSITIONS OF VARIOUS BASIC CUPOLA SLAGS

	SiO_2	Al_2O_3	CaO	MgO	MnO	FeO	S	CaF_2
Renshaw, (1951) [7]	30/35	8/10	42/47	9/11	1.5	1.5	1.0	2.0
Carter, (1950 & 52) [8, 9]	33.4	13.3	34.3	12.7	2.7	1.5	0.99	0.6
	28.6	6.5	41.2	19.6	1.2	1.8	0.56	—
	32.4	11.7	39.0	15.1	0.6	1.2	0.62	—
	30.6	7.8	42.3	15.2	0.8	0.7	0.70	—
	21.0	—	54.1	9.5	0.3	1.3	1.07	1.0
	21.4	22.3	47.6	8.5	0.4	0.3	2.20	1.1
	28.1	7.1	45.1	16.0	—	0.8	0.81	
Flinn & Kraft, (1951) [10]	22.6	5.2	48.8	18.6	—	1.2	0.54	
	37.0	12.7	28.8	17.7	—	1.1	0.31	
	27.7	7.4	25.4	31.9	—	3.9	0.30	
Levi, (1952) [11]	28.3	6.0	50.0	8.7	—	0.6	1.36	
	27.7	7.9	43.6	15.1	—	0.4	1.45	
	27.6	11.4	37.2	20.4	—	0.4	2.01	
	28.0	9.6	41.8	14.6	—	1.1	—	

per cent of the metal charge). If lower sulfurs are desired more limestone may be added. This increases the slag basicity as well as the slag volume, both having the effect of removing more sulfur.

If very low sulfurs are needed more reducing conditions are favorable in order to decrease slag FeO and increase its solubility for sulfur. Preheated blast improves reducing conditions as well as deoxidizing fluxes like carbide.

In Table 29.9 are the compositions of some basic slags treated in the literature.

The ranges given by Renshaw[7] represent an operation of a 42 in. basic cupola in a duplex system. Sulfur content of the basic cupola metal usually ranged from 0.03 to 0.07 per cent from a charge that ran 0.12 to 0.16 per cent from an acid cupola.

The first four slags from Carter[8,9] are of only moderate basicity on a 36-in. cupola melting gray iron at a sulfur level of 0.04 to 0.07 per cent. Flux charges were 2 to 4 per cent limestone. The last two are of higher basicity where 0.01 to 0.03 per cent sulfur levels were obtained for "nodular" or "ductile" iron treatment. Flux charges contained carbide and fluorspar in addition to the regular limestone in order to obtain such a favorable excess of CaO and such a low FeO content.

The slags from Flinn and Kraft[10] are likewise from a nodular iron melted in a 32-in. cupola. Carbide and fluorspar were used with limestone to produce metal sulfurs in the very low range of 0.01 to 0.03 per cent.

The Levi slags[11] were collected from a 72 in. water-cooled basic cupola operated with blast preheated to 950 F. Sulfurs of 0.01 to 0.05 per cent were obtained with various combinations of limestone, dolomite, carbide, and fluorspar. FeO contents are low and lime to silica ratios high.

Another characteristic result of basic slags is the tendency toward higher carbon contents in the iron. The more basic slags clean the coke more freely and leave a more reactive surface, accounting for higher carbon pick-up. Lower sulfur iron along with lower oxygen has a higher carbon solubility, accounting for higher maximum carbons.

Carter has emphasized the differences in basicity level that may be employed to obtain the various advantages of basic slags. For melting gray iron where the objective is simply relief from very high sulfur and a slight increase in carbon pick-up, the mildly basic slags with only a moderate excess of lime are sufficient. Such a slag requires only a normal flux addition, is very fluid, and requires little attention in front slagging or back slagging.

To produce the very low sulfurs, slags of higher basicity are required. Since the more basic slags chill more readily they require more attention at the slag trough in addition to better flux control.

As an evaluation of basicity several formulae have been used. Carter prefers the simple ratio,

$$\frac{CaO + MgO}{SiO_2}$$

omitting Al_2O_3 from the denominator as used by some others. In a basic slag Al_2O_3 improves fluidity but does not retard desulfurization like SiO_2. No doubt, MgO is not exactly equivalent to CaO in all respects, but with MgO contents relatively low the foregoing formula seems to be accurate enough for practical purposes and within our present state of knowledge.

Table 29.10 shows typical slag compositions representative of several degrees of basicity. These have been arbitrarily grouped into mild basicity with

TABLE 29.10. TYPICAL BASIC CUPOLA SLAGS WITH VARYING DEGREES OF BASICITY
(from Carter)[9]

Flux Charge	Metal Charge	Metal Sulfur, %	Slag Composition, %: SiO_2	Al_2O_3	FeO^2	MnO	CaO^3	MgO	F	$CaC_2{}^4$	S^5	Basicity Ratio[1]	Slag Appearance
Mild Basicity													
1. First Ladle, 5% L'st, 1% Sp.	50% Steel	.079	36.5	11.5	13.4	2.6	26.1	5.7	0.5	—	0.04	0.87	Glassy, black
2. No Flux	35% Steel	.074	37.5	12.8	3.1	1.8	23.2	20.1	—	—	0.28	1.15	Resinous, dark black
3. 1% Limestone	40% Steel	.061	34.3	9.4	1.7	1.7	30.5	22.0	—	—	0.39	1.53	Dull, black
4. 2% Limestone	50% Steel	.064	35.1	7.8	2.2	1.7	35.0	16.8	—	—	0.46	1.47	Dull, brownish
Medium Basicity													
5. 4% L'st, ½% Spar	65% Steel	.047	28.6	6.5	1.8	1.2	41.2	19.6	—	—	0.56	2.12	Dull, brownish gray
6. 4% L'st, Hot Blast[6]	80% Steel	.030	26.0	9.2	2.9	0.6	32.5	28.6	1.0	(0.2)	1.26	2.35	Dull, dark gray
7. 1% CaC_2, 4% L'st, 1% Spar	80% Steel	.032	25.8	6.5	2.0	0.6	40.3	23.2	0.9	(0.4)	3.08	2.46	Dull, brownish gray
High Basicity													
8. 4% CaC_2, 4% L'st, 2% Sp.	50% Steel	.010	18.8	12.5	0.4	0.6	62.4	9.0	2.5	(2.5)	2.50	3.80	Powder, grayish white
9. 5% CaC_2, 5% L'st, 3% Sp.	All pig	.005	15.8	15.2	0.2	0.1	59.3	8.6	1.6	(4.9)	—	4.29	Powder, grayish white
100% Scrap Charges with Increasing Basicity													
10. 3% Limestone	100% Return	.069	35.4	10.1	1.9	1.9	34.1	16.2	—	—	0.46	1.42	Dull, brownish black
11. 4% L'st, ½% Spar	100% Return	.051	32.4	11.7	1.2	0.6	39.0	15.1	—	—	0.62	1.67	Dull, medium brown
12. 6% L'st, 2% Spar	100% Return	.022	30.6	7.8	0.7	0.8	42.3	15.2	—	—	0.70	1.88	Dull, light brown

[1] Basicity ratio: $\frac{\text{Total } CaO + MgO}{SiO_2}$

[2] Total Fe_2O_3 and FeO determined as FeO.

[3] Total calcium determined as CaO.

[4] Calcium in CaC_2 content not subtracted from total calcium as CaO because of less reliable analysis.

[5] Total sulfur determined by gravimetric precipitation as $BaSO_4$.

[6] 450 F preheated air.

basicity ratios 1.0 to 2.0, moderate basicity with ratios 2.0 to 3.0, and high basicity above 3.0.

Slag pancake samples taken at intervals have given reasonably good indications of basicity range. Some degree of slag control has been accomplished by examination of color and surface luster of slag samples. The mildly basic slags are generally dull black tending toward brown as basicity goes up and FeO comes down. As the basicity drops near or below 1.0 and the FeO goes high, the slag approaches a glassy luster characteristic of acid slags.

In the medium basicity range the slags become dark gray or brownish gray. In the high basicity, very low FeO ranges, the slags become lighter gray. In the highest CaO/FeO ratios the slags disintegrate upon cooling into a white powder, and small quantities of calcium carbide are found in the slag analysis.

Since most reactions in the basic cupola depend upon slag chemistry, factors affecting slag chemistry require better control. The flux must be calculated, weighed, and charged with as much accuracy as any ingredient. Consistent refractory consumption, uniform charging, and constant quantities of dirt on the scrap are necessary for consistent slag control because of their indirect contributions to slag chemistry. Flux adjustments have been found necessary to compensate for changes in the physical condition and cleanliness of steel and cast scrap.

Slag Desulfurizing Reactions

The relatively small surfur content in acid slags and mildly basic slags with high FeO contents exists principally as iron and manganese sulfides (Fe,Mn) S. Sulfur removal from the metal is limited and depends on a simple distribution of metal sulfides between the metal and the slag, and the ratio of sulfur in the slag to sulfur in metal is relatively low. Any appreciable desulfurization requires a large volume of slag. In basic open-hearth steelmaking a basic oxidizing slag accomplishes desulfurization with such a large volume of slag with a low sulfur capacity.

Basic slags with low iron oxide contents are better desulfurizing slags. In basic cupola slags, like blast furnace slags and reducing slags of the basic electric process, much sulfur can be retained in the slag as calcium sulfide (CaS).

This reaction appears as

I) $(Fe,Mn)S + CaO \rightleftarrows CaS + MnO,FeO$

The reaction is reversible and its equilibrium point depends on the concentrations of both the reactants and the reaction products. The forward reaction proceeds further as the sulfide content of metal and the CaO content of the slag increases, and the reaction is retarded and limited by the iron and manganese oxides present. Increased oxides can actually reverse the reaction and resulfurize the metal. Decreased iron oxide content obtained by reducing conditions or deoxidizing agents facilitates the forward or desulfurizing reaction.

In the cupola the high carbon content of cast iron and reducing conditions in the cupola can assist the desulfurizing reaction considerably by reducing the FeO by Reaction II.

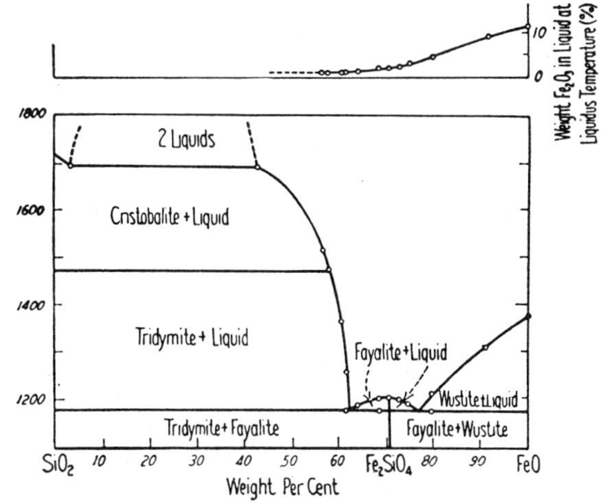

Fig. 29.3. Diagram for system FeO-SiO$_2$ (Hall and Insley, *Journal of the American Ceramic Soc.*).

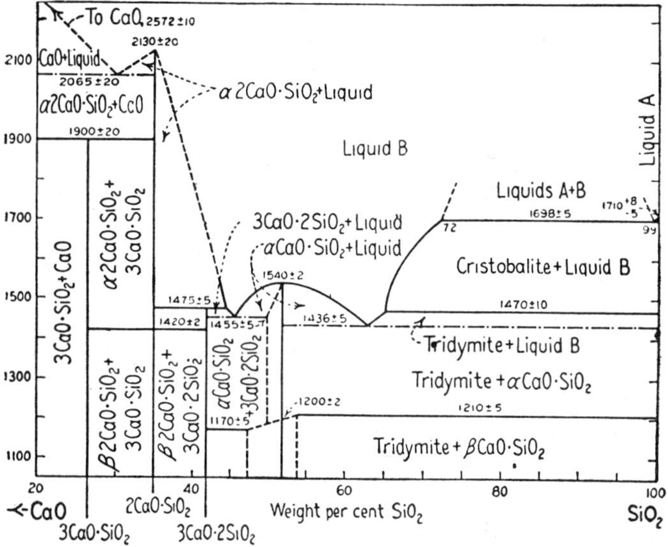

Fig. 29.4. **Equilibrium diagram for CaO-SiO2 system (Hall and Insley, *J. Am. Ceram. Soc.*).**

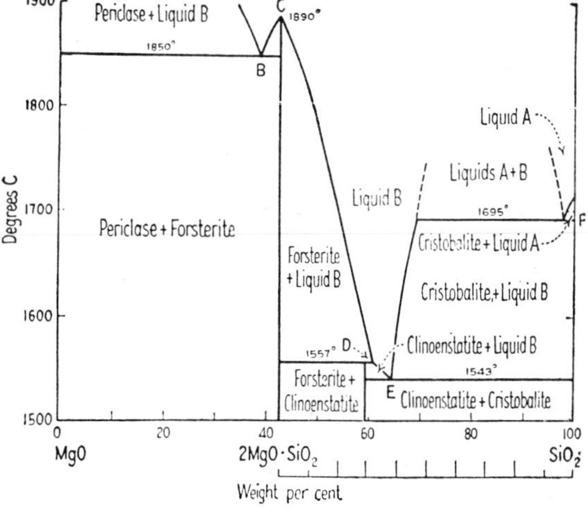

Fig. 29.5. **Equilibrium diagram for MgO-SiO2 system (Hall and Insley, *J. Am. Ceram. Soc.*).**

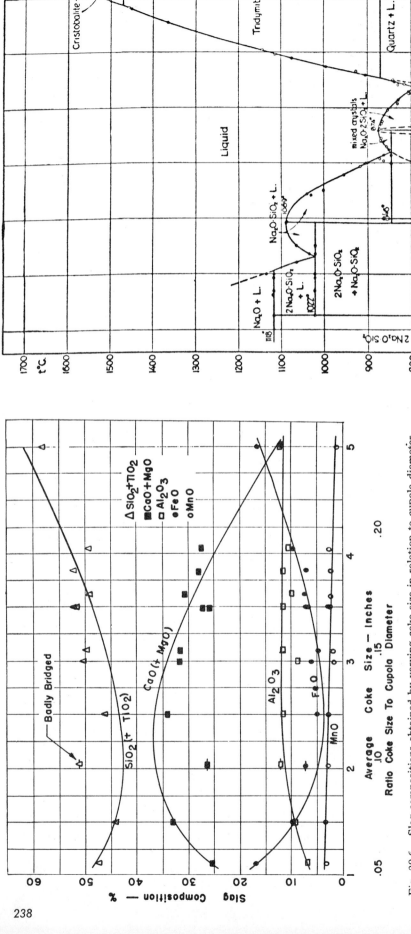

Fig. 29.6. Slag compositions obtained by varying coke size in relation to cupola diameter.

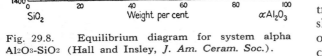

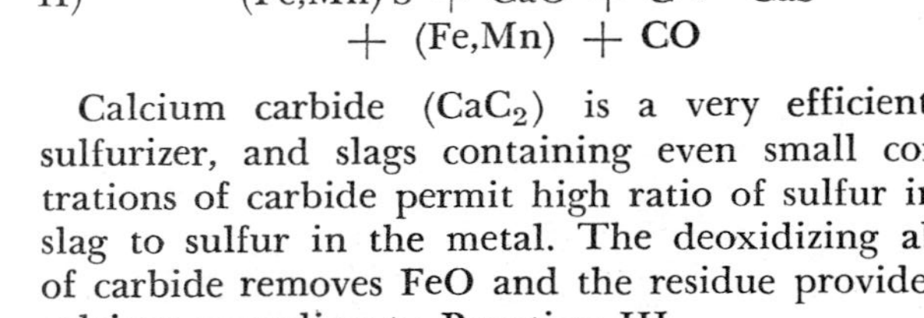

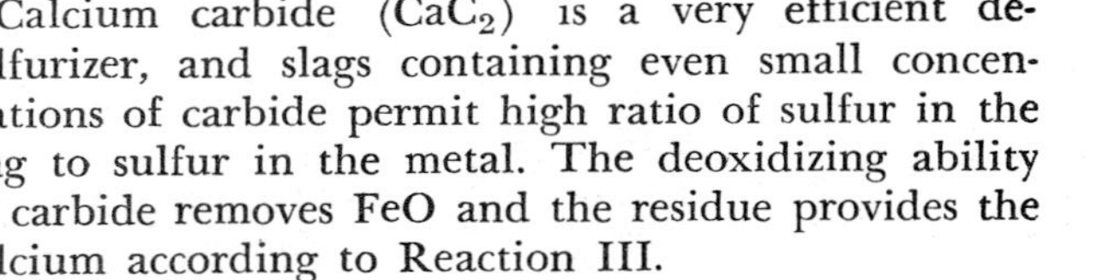

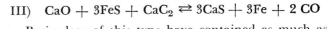

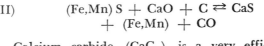

Fig. 29.7. Equilibrium diagram for system Na_2O-SiO_2 (right). (F. C. Kracek, *J. Phys. Chem.*)

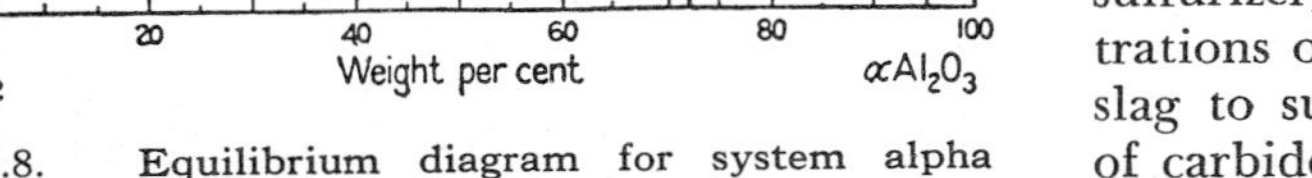

Fig. 29.8. Equilibrium diagram for system alpha Al_2O_3-SiO_2 (Hall and Insley, *J. Am. Ceram. Soc.*).

II) $$(Fe,Mn)S + CaO + C \rightleftarrows CaS + (Fe,Mn) + CO$$

Calcium carbide (CaC_2) is a very efficient desulfurizer, and slags containing even small concentrations of carbide permit high ratio of sulfur in the slag to sulfur in the metal. The deoxidizing ability of carbide removes FeO and the residue provides the calcium according to Reaction III.

III) $$CaO + 3FeS + CaC_2 \rightleftarrows 3CaS + 3Fe + 2\,CO$$

Basic slags of this type have contained as much as 2.0 to 3.0 per cent sulfur which represents 4.5 to 6.7 per cent calcium sulfide (CaS).

Cupola Slag Systems

Phase diagrams explain many slag experiences and give direction to efforts toward improved slag performance. These diagrams indicate the compositions having the lowest fusion point which generally means the best fluidity.

Although some other properties are important it appears necessary to have a slag which will have more than 100 to 200 F superheat above its fusion point at the temperatures prevalent inside the cupola. A slag with a fusion point above 2550 F (1400 C) can hardly have desirable fluidity at normal cupola temperatures. A melting point below 2370 F (1300 C) is preferable to accomplish its cleaning function, pass freely by the colder tuyere zones, and flow smoothly from the furnace.

CaO and SiO_2 are the two major slag constituents. Assuming that other constituents are absent, a pure CaO-SiO_2 system is diagramed in Fig. 29.4. Whereas pure lime melts at 4658 F (2570 C) and pure SiO_2 at 3112 F (1713 C) equal mixtures of the two melt as low as 2804 F (1540 C) as combinations of the various calcium silicates are formed. The composition with the lowest melting point of 2617 F (1436 C) is about 37 per cent CaO and 63 per cent SiO_2. Another valley occurs at 55 per cent CaO and 45 per cent SiO_2 which melts at 2687 F (1475 C).

Illustrated in Fig. 29.5, a 2-phase system of magnesia and silica behaves in a similar way, although slightly more refractory than the CaO-SiO_2 system. Lowest melting slag results at 2809 F (1543 C) from a 35 per cent MgO-65 per cent SiO_2 composition.

As seen in the FeO-SiO_2 system in Fig. 29.3, iron also forms silicates; but since minimum oxidation and low iron oxide contents are desired in most cupola slags, iron oxide seldom reaches sufficient proportions to be a significant part of the slag system.

The Na_2O-SiO_2 diagram in Fig. 29.7 explains the powerful fluidizing effect of soda compounds on acid slags. Only 10 per cent Na_2O drops the melting point of SiO_2 from 3112 F (1713 C) to 2678 F (1460 C). From 20 per cent to 40 per cent Na_2O, very low melting combinations of sodium silicates result with fusion points as low as 1472-1652 F (800 to 900 C).

Because of volatilization and attack on refractories it is difficult to obtain such high proportions of Na_2O at the slag trough. However, such very low melting combinations may be formed temporarily when the soda flux first contacts a high-silica mass high in the cupola stack. This explains why soda so readily fluxes away bridges, and fluidizes viscous slag conditions.

Figures 29.8 and 29.9 indicate the amphoteric nature of alumina. With SiO_2 the Al_2O_3 behaves as a base, and forms aluminum silicates. The lowest point is 2813 F (1545 C) at about 7 per cent Al_2O_3.

In Fig. 29.9 alumina acts as an acid with lime forming calcium aluminates. The lowest melting eutectics are near the 50 per cent composition.

Cupola slags contain too many constituents and are too complex to be represented by a 2-phase system.

The liquidus diagram for the 10 per cent Al_2O_3 plane of the CaO-MgO-SiO_2 ternary diagram (Fig. 29.10), illustrates the more complex slags which are

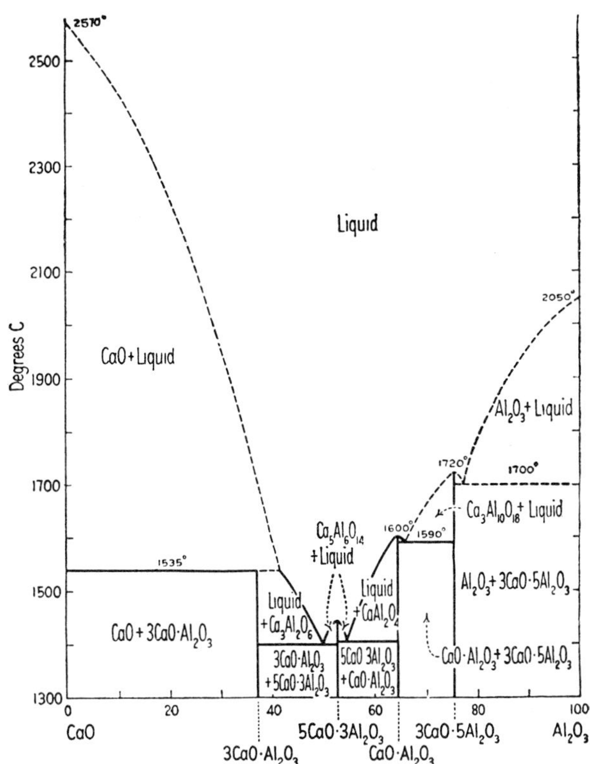

Fig. 29.9. Diagram for system CaO-Al_2O_3 (Hall and Insley, *Journal of the American Ceramic Soc.*).

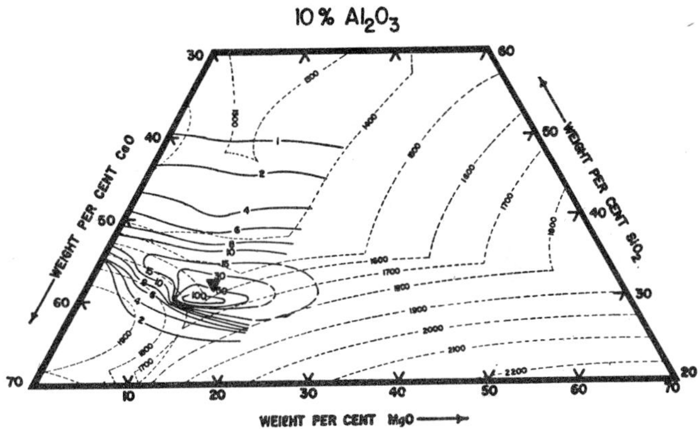

Fig. 29.10. Diagram of part of 10 per cent Al_2O_3 plane showing liquidus isotherms (dash lines, numbers indicating melting point of slag) and isodesulfurization curves (figures represent ratio of sulfur in slag to sulfur in metal at 1500 C, 2732 F).

TABLE 29.11. LIQUIDUS DATA for SLAG MIXTURE CONTAINING 10 PER CENT Al_2O_3

Basicity Ratio	Composition Weight % CaO	MgO	SiO_2	Liquidus Temp. C	F
0.64	33	2	55	1353	2468
0.64	29	6	55	1269	2316
0.64	19	16	55	1319	2406
0.91	41	2	47	1382	2520
0.91	34	9	47	1293	2359
0.91	22	21	47	1427	2601
1.43	50	3	37	1600	2912
1.43	38	15	37	1409	2568
1.43	28	25	37	1486	2706
1.81	48	10	32	1600	2912
1.81	43	15	32	1558	2835
1.81	38	20	32	1600	2912

encountered in cupola operation. The 10 per cent Al_2O_3 plane of the quaternary system represents a typical alumina (Al_2O_3) level in cupola slags.

Osborn, DeVries, Gee and Kraner, in their studies of optimum blast furnace slags,[12] developed information practical to cupola operators. Figure 29.10 and Table 29.11 are from their data. The value of Al_2O_3 and proper levels of MgO is graphically illustrated, proper amounts of each being particularly effective in lowering the liquidus temperature for any desired basicity level of the slag. Lower liquidus temperature results in increased slag reactivity and a more effective slag. This is particularly true for the more basic slags. The melting points increase rather rapidly as the slag becomes more basic, accounting for troublesome sluggishness in the highly basic slags.

The most effective slag for basic desulfurizing operations would be one which combines a low liquidus temperature with high sulfur carrying capacity.

The final test of any slag composition is its actual performance in the cupola. Furthermore, no consistent composition is maintained throughout the cupola, variations result in various stages of the descent and in various zones of the cupola. However, with the increasing flexibility of the cupola made possible by varying the composition of the slag, much profitable direction can be obtained from a study of phase diagrams and published data on oxide systems.

BIBLIOGRAPHY

1. J. W. Bolton, "How Slags Affect Cupola Operation," *The Foundry,* vol. 49, Sept. 1921.
2. Y. A. Dyar, "Characteristics of Foundry Cokes and Slags," *Iron Age,* vol. 108, Aug. 18, 1921.
3. F. J. Walls, "What Should Govern Cupola Slags?" *The Foundry,* vol. 62, May 1934.
4. C. C. Sigerfoos and H. L. Womochel, "Relative Effect of Lime and Dolomite Fluxes on Cupola Irons," AMERICAN FOUNDRYMAN, vol 8, Oct. 1945.
5. E. V. Somers and D. W Gunther, "Cupola Melting Phenomena," AFS TRANSACTIONS, vol. 55, 1947.
6. S. F. Carter and Ralph Carlson, "Acid Cupola Slags and Some Relationships with Melting Conditions," AFS TRANSACTIONS, 1953.
7. E. S. Renshaw, "Basic Cupola Melting and Its Possibilities," AFS TRANSACTIONS," 1951.
8. Sam F. Carter, "Basic Lined Cupola For Iron Melting," AFS TRANSACTIONS, 1950.
9. Sam F. Carter, "Production Experiences with a Basic Cupola," AFS TRANSACTIONS, 1951.
10. R. A. Flinn and R. W. Kraft, "The Importance of Slag Control in Basic Cupola Operation," AFS TRANSACTIONS, 1951.
11. Wally Levi, "Melting Iron in a Basic Lined Water Cooled Cupola," AFS TRANSACTIONS, 1952.
12. E. F. Osborn, R. C. DeVries, K. H. Gee and H. M. Kraner, "Optimum Composition of Blast Furnace Slag" as deduced from liquidus data for the quaternary system CaO-MgO-Al_2O_3-SiO_2, A.I.M.E. Transactions, 1954.

CHAPTER 30

Problems
Techniques

Quality workmanship and careful attention to operating details will prevent problems and aid the successful operation of a cupola.

There are, however, methods to help the operator solve problems when they do develop.

TAPPING AND SLAGGING

The proper arrangements for getting molten iron out of the cupola will go a long way toward a smooth heat. The practice of ramming the breast to form the taphole is still used, but many operators are finding the preformed refractory block much more suitable to present day needs. This preformed breast is placed from within the cupola, and lends itself to either continuous or intermittent tapping. The cupola may be started with the taphole closed or open.

Starting with the taphole open allows considerable loss of air, and the first iron is accompanied by considerable blowing, oxidation and spattering. The closed taphole will avoid these conditions and is generally preferred.

The taphole may be closed off by several methods including rammed damp blacking, regular botting clay mixture, dry blacking held in place with a clay bot, or a small refractory plug held in place by mechanical means. A typical botting clay mixture is one part fireclay and one part ganister.

Figure 28.2 shows a bot stick and two types of bot pick which may be bent for easier use. When sufficient iron has melted to safely cover the top level of the taphole, or when a "high ball" is attained, the bot may be chiseled or cut off by the flat pick and the remaining plug then removed by insertion of the sharp pick.

The ferrostatic head of metal will quickly force metal out of the cupola to the receiver. With the continuous tap cupola, the main requirement for the duration of the heat is to keep the taphole clear of obstructions with a rod.

If intermittent tapping is desired, sufficient time must be allowed during the cycle for enough metal to be accumulated in the well to bring the slag level above the slag hole. In each cycle the taphole may remain open until all the iron has been tapped, or the metal may be taken in successive short taps as required. A practice should be adopted that will produce consistent analyses of the metal.

Tapping schedules in intermittent tapping are important, and must be rigidly followed to achieve consistent analyses. It is common knowledge that frequent taps will produce lower carbon irons, while holding the metal in the well for longer periods of time will give higher carbons. This knowledge used in conjunction with a chill test will allow the operator to make some compensation for other variables by changing his tapping schedule.

Continuous tapping, through a dam arrangement, allows the taphole to remain open, and iron flows continually into a large receiving ladle for distribution to the producing units. In this process, the size of the taphole should always be adequate for the highest melting rate anticipated. Generally speaking, a 1 — 1¼-in. taphole will deliver up to 25 tons/hr, and a larger hole should be provided for high tonnage shops. Taphole blocks with 2½-in. holes have delivered over 50 tons/hr of iron. The taphole may be widened but the height should be kept relative to the dam height and other variables.

FROZEN TAPHOLES OR SLAG HOLES

Plugged or frozen tap and slag holes generally indicate the need for improvements in operating procedures or techniques. For instance the refractory around the taphole may be cold and should be heated with a torch or by blowing the bed softly for a few minutes with the taphole open prior to starting the melt. A taphole may become plugged because the bot was not secure and allowed some molten metal to flow into the hole and freeze before attempting to tapout the cupola. The practice of using a fast melt rate from wind-on to tapout is good practice to minimize loss of temperature from the metal while in the cupola well. Tapping out before sufficient head of metal is melted can cause problems in tapping the cupola properly.

A frozen tap or slag hole may be opened with a poke bar. More troublesome occasions may require a rod and sledge hammer but care should be exercised to avoid loosening the breast or brick work in the cupola. An oxygen lance is invaluable in such an emergency. This lance consists of a length of ⅛-in. pipe not less than 6 ft long, connected by a convenient length of rubber hose which is attached to a regulator on the oxygen source. The pipe is long to prevent igniting the rubber connecting hose and causing burns to the operator.

The oxygen is turned on and the iron pipe held against the obstructing plug of metal or slag, which needs to be sufficiently hot to cause the pipe to ignite and burn. The heat thus generated will melt the plug.

TABLE 30.1. CALCULATED AIR LOSS THROUGH OPEN TAP AND SLAG HOLES*

Wind Box Pressure, oz	Cubic Feet per Minute Lost† — Diameter of Tap or Slag Hole, in.			
	½	1	2	3
	Cupola Well at 2400 F			
4	4	15	59	132
8	5	21	83	187
12	6	25	101	228
16	7	29	117	263
20	8	33	131	294
	Cupola Well at 2800 F			
4	3	14	55	124
8	5	19	78	175
12	6	24	95	214
16	7	27	110	247
20	8	31	123	276

† Cubic feet of air per minute passing through the open slag or tap hole at 2400 and 2800 F inside cupola, referred to 14.7 psi and 60 F.

* Using formula of Moss, A. S., "Measurement of Flow of Air and Gas with Nozzles." *Transactions,* American Society of Mechanical Engineers, Applied Mechanics Section, vol. 50. no. 2, January-April, 1928, p. 1-15.

If the obstruction is too cold to ignite the pipe, the lance with the oxygen turned on may be dipped into a ladle of molten iron or inserted into the incandescent coke bed through a tuyere for ignition, and then moved back against the obstruction.

Care should be exercised in using the lance to prevent the end of the pipe from blocking off or melting shut as this may cause hose or pipe failure. The angle at which the lance enters the taphole should be regulated by bending the pipe so it is directed against the metal or slag and not against the refractories as much damage can be done in a short period of time.

Prompt action is essential when a taphole becomes blocked. Oxygen equipment should be ready for use, requiring only manipulation of the valve to swing the lance into action. The lance finds other useful applications such as cleaning a blockage under the slag knife, opening a teapot ladle or forehearth spout or removing slag buildup in critical situations.

Opening a frozen taphole may cause excessive damage to the breast or slag hole and necessitate shutting down, possibly draining, the cupola for repairs.

A new breast or slag hole may be built or rammed. Be sure the repair is securely anchored to the surrounding refractory by using a plastic type of patch which will stick to hot surfaces without excessive spalling or cracking. A typical plastic patch mixture contains one part clay, one part graphite and one part ground firebrick.

FRONT SLAGGING

Slagging the cupola through a combined tapping and slagging spout placed in front of the cupola has gained general acceptance. This spout differs from the intermittent tap type in that the outer end is higher than the taphole as shown in Fig. 2.7 *(page 21)*.

A refractory slag knife or skimmer brick is placed in the spout so as to divert the slag to flow through an opening or slag notch in the side of the spout between it and the taphole. The depth of metal at this location should be at least 10 in. for positive separation of slag and metal.

Cupolas melting 2 tons/hr or less, as well as the higher tonnage units, may be operated with this continuous tap arrangement. Advantages are less effort in tapping, better control of analyses by the constant tapping procedure and by maintaining a constant slag level in the cupola; less trouble with slag elimination as the slag comes through the taphole with the hot metal, and better control of low carbon irons due to the small amount of iron in the well.

In basic melting, where the slag has a greater effect on iron chemistry, front slagging produces more consistent iron.

Where the vertical distance from floor to spout is inadequate the dam will allow the end of the spout to be raised several inches. This can be an asset in the use of larger ladles, ladle cars, larger forehearth or other conditions requiring more distance from floor level to spout.

A properly designed spout has the slag-metal interface in the upper portion of the taphole with sufficient head of metal and slag to seal the taphole from air currents. A rough method of calculating dam height is to divide the wind box pressure in ounces by four and add ½-in. For example, a wind box pressure of 16 oz would require a dam height of 4½-in. It should be remembered that this distance is measured from the top of the taphole and it is wise to occasionally check this dimension with a carpenter's level and with a bar inserted in the taphole of approximately the same size as the taphole. Chapter 28 describes and explains the front slagging spout in detail.

Occasionally the cupola will not slag properly or on schedule because of miscalculation of dam height or by careless workmanship in placing refractory materials in the spout. After checking to see that the taphole is open, wind pressure is normal, etc., it may be determined that the dam is too high. Many operators use part of a brick or monolithic material or combination of both on the top portion of the dam, which may be removed during a brief shutdown of the cupola to obtain proper balance. Increasing wind volume may help such a condition but if the production rate is exceeded, the cupola must alternately be shut down and blown hard or the excess iron must be disposed of, which is not conducive to good cupola practice.

When effective dam height is not adequate due to erosion of the taphole or to an error in dam construction, the taphole may blow, causing leakage of air and considerable spattering of hot material in the vicinity. This condition can rapidly destroy the breast. It should be corrected quickly. Wind volume should be reduced and in some cases, this is sufficient to complete the shift. If not, the cupola should be operated at reduced wind volume until materials are obtained with which to increase the dam height as much as necessary to seal the taphole for normal operating conditions.

SLAG HOLE PRACTICE

A slag hole is desirable in the cupola even though it is designed for front slagging or if the cupola will not run long enough to require slagging. One emergency such as a frozen taphole can make the slag hole worthwhile.

Slag holes are still hand rammed, but for uniformity the trend is toward a preformed block. Many slag hole blocks have multiple holes, allowing the operator to plug one hole after it has become enlarged, and use another of original dimensions.

Maintaining a constant size slag hole throughout the heat promotes uniform blast. Blast variations may be as much as 5 to 10 per cent depending on the amount of air blown through the slag hole (Table 30.1) and air is as critical a raw material as the metal charge.

Slag holes should be small, generally ranging from ¾-in. on small cupolas to 2 in. diameter on larger units. If slag will not run through a relatively small hole, it is too cold or sticky and may need an adjustment in chemistry for better fluidity. If the slag hole becomes so enlarged that chunks of coke are blown out, corrective measures should be taken.

The location of the slag hole is of utmost importance. It should be as far away from any tuyere as practical to avoid the effect of cold air on slag temperature. Hot blast cupolas minimize this effect of blast, but it should be remembered that hot blast temperatures of 350 to 900 F (177-482 C) are still cool to a 2300 F (1260 C) slag. If the slag hole is low, (more than 8 in. below the tuyere), the metal level may be too low to heat the slag in the tuyere area thus permitting a bridge to form.

It is good practice to have the slag hole horizontal or with a downward slant toward the outside of the cupola.

THE CUPOLA BOTTOM

Proper selection of materials and quality workmanship will assure a minimum amount of trouble with a cupola bottom. Bottom runout should be a rare occasion in a well supervised shop.

The bottom door or doors should close tightly against the mantle. When doors become warped or out of shape, they should be replaced or reworked to give a good closure. Props or latches should be in good condition and provide a solid closure. Fig. 2.5 shows an effective way to raise and close bottom doors.

More common causes of cupola runouts include improper chipping of slag from the side walls, weak sand, foreign material in the sand, improper ramming techniques and improper placement of kindling or charge materials.

Accumulations of slag on the side walls should be removed by chipping before the new sand bottom is rammed. If this slag remains in the area adjacent to the sand bottom, it can readily melt out providing a perfect avenue for the flow of molten iron along the wall.

Most shops find molding sand quite suitable for ramming the cupola bottom. If the bottom does not drop freely, the strength of the sand may be reduced by mixing with new sand, taking care that roots, sticks and lumps are not present. Sand mixed in a mechanical mixer is usually more uniform than sand mixed by turning with a shovel. The combination of tempering and hand mixing can result in wet or weak spots if not properly done. Molding sand should preferably be used as prepared for the molding floor. Waste sand should be carefully checked for the presence of fins and tramp iron.

The ramming operation should require careful attention. The sand should be properly distributed over the bottom and heeled around the edge at the refractory wall.

The operator will do a better job with a pneumatic rammer, especially when the bottom is rammed late in the shift after picking up bottom drop, chipping, and lining. Sloping the sand toward the taphole will result in better drainage and less pressure on the bottom caused by a pool of contained metal in a depression in the bottom sand.

Kindling and coke should be placed on the bottom sand with care. Rough handling may cause penetration into the sand and weak areas may result. If kindling is placed in the conventional inverted cone shape, the lower ends should be placed on a flat board resting on the sand bottom.

When a bottom runout does occur, the blast should immediately be cut off and the cupola drained completely of iron and slag. Air or water should be used to chill the area where the runout occurred. In some cases where the run-out is not too severe, and the shift is near completion, the runout may be stopped by immediately applying water and keeping the metal frozen until the end of the shift. More frequently the cupola must be drained and a patch applied.

A jury rig or patch may be prepared by placing a refractory brick flush with the bottom door and over the runout area, with a liberal application of mud. This patch may be held in place by a prop from the ground, by a plank with a ladder rung used as a fulcrum point so that constant pressure may be applied to the patch, or by any other expedient. When the runout has been stopped and the patch applied, the drainhole should be closed and melting resumed.

BRIDGING : TUYERE PRACTICE

Bridging is generally caused or accentuated by cold air entering through the tuyeres, and another variable. For instance a slag which should normally drip past the tuyeres may be of such composition that it would freeze at a higher temperature than normal and start a buildup in the tuyere area. Improper distribution of flux, undesirable charge materials, operating conditions causing high iron oxide slags, highly basic light slags or foamy slags, poor stack permeability, etc., may contribute to bridging.

When not too severe, bridging in the tuyere area may be controlled by poking, taking care to pull out the dislodged material through the tuyere opening. Closing one tuyere off at a time, using a valve in the downcomer, will allow the heat from the coke bed to melt the frozen slag in that area. The primary cause should be determined as soon as possible and corrective measures taken. Use of fluorspar in the charge, or sodium fluxes placed through tuyeres, produces easily handled fluid slags.

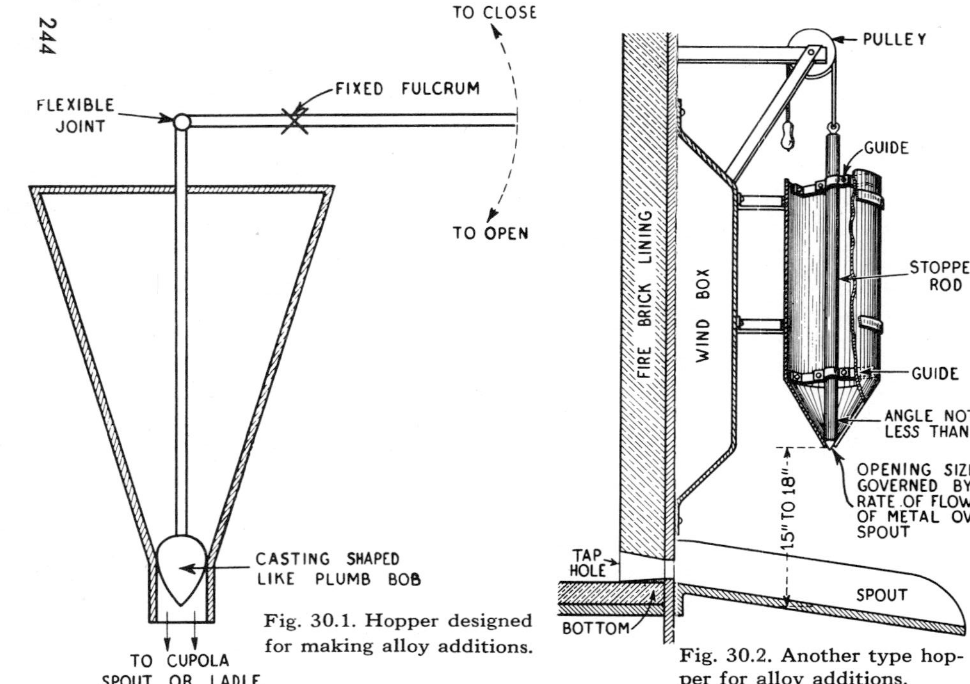

Fig. 30.1. Hopper designed for making alloy additions.

Fig. 30.2. Another type hopper for alloy additions.

Fig. 30.3. Low pressure type (oil or gas fired) heater for drying large ladles.

Bridging may occur above the melt zone and is usually associated with poor sizing of raw materials, or size plus one of the variables. Charge materials generally should not be longer than ⅓ cupola diameter.

RUNNING MORE THAN ONE IRON MIX

A good operator can make the cupola a versatile tool in which more than one type of iron may be melted.

The change from one mix to another may not be drastic. Progress of the melt can be observed by chill tests. When the proper chill is obtained, the receiver should be emptied to receive the new mix.

Extreme changes in chemistry may require that the cupola be melted clean, the bed adjusted and the new charge started as when beginning a new campaign. Wash iron or iron from both mixes should be carefully disposed of, used with care, or pigged if not suitable for the castings concerned.

Chemical requirements may permit an extra coke split between changes of mix so a reduction in melting rate will indicate the change. There is added risk of off analysis if a mix change is based solely on a time schedule, as cupola volume and charge density can vary considerably.

If metal is needed for widely separated periods, after the first campaign the cupola may be melted clean, all slag and metal drained leaving only coke in the stack. When the second melt is begun, the drain hole should be closed, taphole prepared, cupola filled up and melting started as usual. The procedure of banking a cupola involves economic factors which should be weighed against alternate methods.

Oxygen Enrichment and Hot Blast *Problems and Techniques* are treated in Combustion Chapter 33, *page 280.*

ADDITION OF ALLOYS AND INOCULANTS

Alloys and inoculants may be used to control the chilling characteristics of an iron within limits. Wide variations in chemistry or chill behavior should start a search for fundamental causes of the erratic performance.

Conventional chill control generally uses a graphitizer such as ferrosilicon (sized to ⅜-in. and retained on 12 mesh) or graphite to decrease chill, and a carbide stabilizer such as ferrochromium to increase chill. Silicon alloys containing over 75 per cent silicon are practical where temperature loss must be held to a minimum. Calcium is a very potent inoculant. Silicon alloys containing small amounts of calcium are used for extra inoculation.

Several good electrical and mechanical feeders, with variable flow rates for making alloy additions, are on the market. For small operations either of the devices shown in Figs. 30.1 and 30.2 can be used.

These feeding methods should direct the material into the stream of iron flowing from the cupola spout or holding ladle. Inoculants should be added just prior to pouring the casting to avoid fading. While inoculation effect may last more than 15 to 20 min,

Fig. 30.4. Heating units with capacity for drying or preheating several large ladles.

the effect is much more pronounced if made just prior to pouring.

Small envelopes or containers of previously weighed alloying agents may be used when these methods are not practical or expedient. The alloy should be added during pouring near the bottom of the ladle at a point where the stream of iron impinges in order to obtain maximum turbulence and mixing.

Alloys placed on the bottom of a ladle may not go in solution. Alloys should be carefully weighed on accurate scales which for convenience may be graduated in decimals of a pound rather than ounces. The calculation, weighing and adding of alloys should be under the direct control of the cupola foreman.

Highly reactive alloys such as magnesium used in the production of ductile iron may require special hoods, shields, eye protection or other safety equipment for the safety of the operator (Chapter 18).

Recovery is generally poor in this type alloy. Various techniques and devices are used to prevent loss of magnesium. Proprietary magnesium alloys can be placed on the bottom of the ladle and metal tapped rapidly on top of the ladle. Tapping slowly will cause the alloy to burn on top of the iron and recovery will be very poor.

Ladles are sometimes lined with a refractory shelf on the side of the ladle under which the alloy is placed before iron is tapped into the ladle. This allows a head of metal to be developed before the magnesium reaction has progressed. Magnesium vapor then feeds out from under the shelf and bubbles through the iron, improving recovery.

Another variation of this same principle is to recess the bottom of the ladle or build a partition in the ladle to form a recess, then place the alloy in the recess and cover with clean pieces of scrap iron or steel. Some work with refractory materials as a cover to retard the reaction of the alloy has been reported. Temperature of the metal must be adequate for heating or melting these added materials.

Still another method of adding magnesium alloys is the use of the immersion bell in which the alloy is placed in a refractory bell and submerged in the iron by a heavy weight or by an air or hydraulic cylinder. This is effective in improving recovery as the magnesium does not change to a gas until it is covered by iron. The vapor bubbles through considerable iron before it can escape into the atmosphere.

Fig. 30.5. Oven designed for drying hand ladles.

PRE-HEATING LADLES

Ladles may be lined with brick or plastic mixes or combinations of these materials. The least amount of moisture that can be used and still maintain good workability is desirable. Excessive moisture tends to form shrinkage cracks.

Low heat should first be used on a newly lined ladle since high temperatures will drive off free moisture too fast, cause excessive shrinkage and cracking. The type of heat is not especially important, but the ladle should be thoroughly dry. Ladle-drying equipment is shown in Figs. 30.3, 30.4 and 30.5.

When the lining cracks even with slow drying, the cracks should be filled with a heavy clay slurry and the slow drying operation repeated until no cracks are visible after drying. The temperature of the ladle should then be raised, the lining heated to a dull red color and maintained at this temperature until no steam or condensate is visible. The dry ladle may be stored in a dry place but should be thoroughly reheated prior to use.

Dry slowly or heat with a flame described as slow, yellow, or rich. High heat can be achieved with best economy by using an air inspirated burner or by using compressed air from a fan, blower or compressor. The air should be adjusted to a blue flame with only a tinge of yellow visible.

EXCESS OR WASTE IRON

Quantities of iron may become cold, for some reason more iron is melted than can be used during the heat, excess iron may be on hand at the end of a shift from back iron, cupola drainings, overmelt, etc. This iron should be pigged into a readily usable form for remelting.

Small metal molds that will hold 20 to 50 lb are used for smaller quantities of iron. These molds should have plenty of draft to avoid sticking, and be coated with a refractory slurry or parting agent prior to use. They must be thoroughly dried.

Large quantities of excess melt can be poured into previously prepared sand pig beds in the cupola area. When the pigging of large quantities of iron becomes the rule rather than the exception, a pigging machine should be considered.

FINISHING A HEAT

After the last charge is in the stack, melting proceeds about as before except as the stock line descends the back pressure decreases, lowering the wind box pressure. With fan type blowers, the increase in air volume due to reduced pressure can be significant. This period of operation should be closely supervised. Inattention may result in oxidized iron, excessive damage to the lining, and possible damage to fixtures such as tuyeres, wishbone, or charging door components. As the wind box pressure decreases, air volume should be kept constant, or reduced by progressively closing the blast gate or by reducing air volume at the source.

The automatic air weight controls described in Chapter 6 maintain a constant air volume as the wind box pressure decreases. With manual control the volume gage should be watched, and required adjustments of the blast gate made promptly. A volume gage is most helpful, but, if none is provided, the blast gate should be progressively closed as the liquid column of the pressure gage descends.

Excessive air disturbs the combustion balance. Free oxygen in the melting zone can oxidize the iron and lower carbon to such an extent that the castings may be scrapped. If the bed is allowed to burn down to the level of the tuyeres, the tuyere castings may be heated so they will sag, resulting in damage to the cupola lining.

Melting the last charge in the cupola is generally not considered good practice. By dropping one or two charges through the cupola, the lining is protected and oxidation avoided. The unmelted iron can be reclaimed and all but a portion of the coke can be recovered.

Another practice is to add an extra charge or two of coke after the last metal charge to assure enough coke in the bed to consume the oxygen of the blast. Drop coke may be used for this purpose.

DROPPING BOTTOM

A bed of loose dry sand should be maintained under the cupola to receive the drop. Good permeability prevents the accumulation of steam, and may prevent an explosion. Slag may be allowed to run into this area for drying purposes.

In some foundries, all props except the key bottom door prop are removed as soon as the melt is completed. While this work is in progress, metal and slag should be drained through the taphole in the intermittent tap type cupola, or through the drain hole provided in the continuous tap cupola.

At a signal for all personnel to stand clear, final preparations to drop the bottom should be made. The key prop is coupled to a chain or a long bar by which it can be rapidly pulled or knocked out of place. A much safer method may be accomplished by attaching a chain or cable and hooks to all props, and pulling all at one time from a safe distance by the use of a winch, crane, air cylinder, tractor or truck.

Prompt cooling of the cupola drop may be achieved by flooding with water. Directing water against the bottom doors can prevent warpage as the bare metal is now exposed to the hot drop on one side and cooler air on the other. If physically practical, the drop may be pulled from under the cupola for faster cooling and to expedite patching the cupola for another heat.

Figure 9.11 shows a convenient drag arrangement. A chain sling from a winch is hooked around the key prop with a slack loop of the chain hooked to the drag so that as the winch is actuated, tension is first applied to knock out the prop, and then to pull the drag and drop out from under the cupola.

BANKING THE CUPOLA

The cupola must frequently be shut down for prolonged periods during a heat. The occasion may be a lunch period, a meeting or other interruption in pouring schedules. Such delays can be handled without risk if the shut down is anticipated. Extra coke should be added which will arrive at the coke bed level at the time of shut down. Extra coke should vary in quantity with the length of time the cupola will be down, and usually reduces the melt rate as it reaches the bed level.

Proper ventilation for the blast piping system should be provided when the cupola is shut down to avoid accumulations of explosive CO gas mixtures. This may be done by opening tuyere covers or by automatic safety valves provided by some cupola manufacturers and equipment suppliers.

Shut downs that last for long periods of time may require that the cupola be blown periodically, and a small portion of metal melted and pigged in order to maintain temperature of the refractories and to keep the tap hole open. When banking overnight, it is necessary to completely drain the cupola of both metal and slag. Sufficient fuel must be provided to offset the amount consumed by natural draft during the shut down period. The cupola can then be started up as a newly lined cupola. It should be remembered that the ash accumulated from prolonged burning of the bed coke should be removed by blowing the bed prior to charging, or compensated for by adding extra flux.

CHAPTER 31

Chemical and Physical Controls

Knowing what to do and when to do it are qualifications necessary for efficient and successful cupola operation. However, because of the many variables in cupola operation, there must also be some means of verifying and regulating what is being done in order to apply this knowledge intelligently.

The methods of control generally used may be divided into two representative classes—foundry tests and laboratory tests. The extent to which these controls are used is primarily a matter of economics, whether applied to a large or small foundry. It is necessary to produce good castings to stay in business, and the percentage of good castings is dependent on the control exercised. Therefore, it can be seen that it is good economics to employ accurate control tests at adequate frequencies. The controls must be accurate to be of value. If they are not accurate there is misdirection instead of control, and misdirection can do more damage than lack of control.

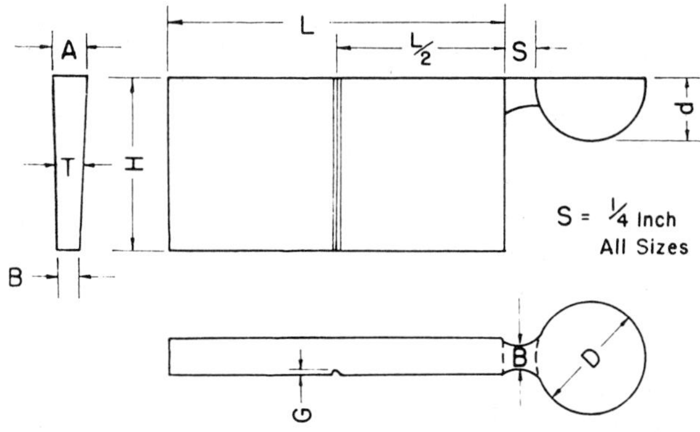

Recommended Dimensions - Inches

Chill Test No.	T	A	B	H	L	D	d	G	Recommended Chill Depth Range 32nd"*
1 C	3/16	1/4	1/8	1 1/4	2 1/2	3/4	1/2	1/32	3 - 12
2 C	1/4	5/16	3/16	1 1/2	3	7/8	1/2	1/32	4 - 16
3 C	3/8	7/16	5/16	1 3/4	3 1/2	7/8	1/2	1/16	6 - 24
4 C	1/2	9/16	7/16	2	4	1	5/8	1/16	8 - 32
5 C	3/4	13/16	11/16	2 1/2	5	1	5/8	3/32	12 - 48

*T/2 to 2T

Casting to be made in dry sand core.

Allow 3/4 inch of sand on all sides.

Fig. 31.1. Recommended dimensions for chill test specimens. A.S.T.M. Designation *A367-58*.

FOUNDRY TESTS

Chill Tests

The value of chill and wedge tests as an aid in controlling quality of cast iron has long been recognized by most foundrymen. The necessary equipment is relatively simple and inexpensive, manipulative skill is readily acquired, and the test itself is rapidly made. However, the interpretation of the information yielded by the chill test requires judgment and experience. The importance of chill test control is frequently under-rated. Real quality control is practically impossible in the absence of a sustained chill-test program. Use of the chill tests gives the operator a means of detecting changes in the condition of the metal which reflect changes in the performance of the cupola.

A chill test is made by pouring a small casting so designed that it will have white iron in its fastest freezing part, gray iron in its slowest, and mottled iron between the two. Such a casting can be obtained by a chill test design which either 1) allows one face of the casting to freeze in contact with a metal plate, or 2) the use of wedge type of mold in

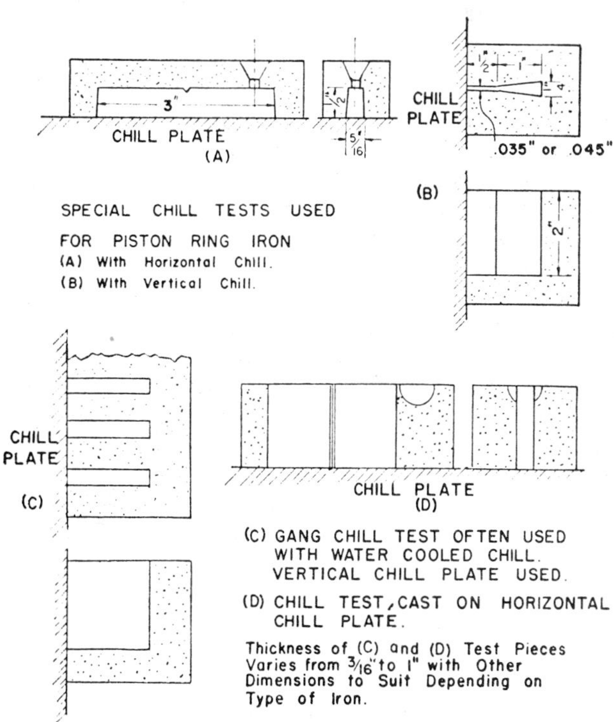

Fig. 31.2. Representative types of chill tests used by gray iron foundries.[1]

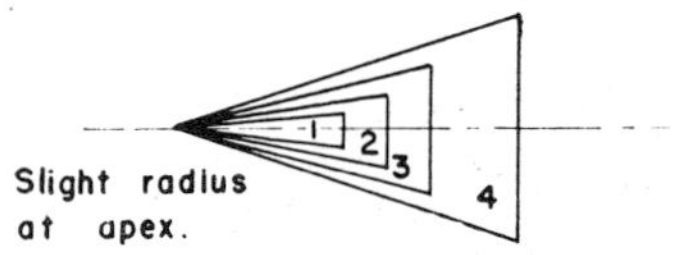

Cross Section of 4 Wedges

Wedge Dimensions – Inches

Wedge No.	B	H	∠A	Length
W 1	0.20	1.00	11.5°	4
W 2	0.40	1.25	18°	4
W 3	0.75	1.50	28°	4
W 4	1.25	2.00	34.5°	6

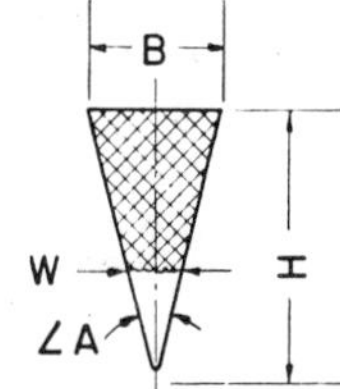

Measurement of chill expressed in 32nds of an inch.
W should not exceed B/2.

Fig. 31.3. Recommended dimensions for test wedges. A.S.T.M. Designation *A367-58.*

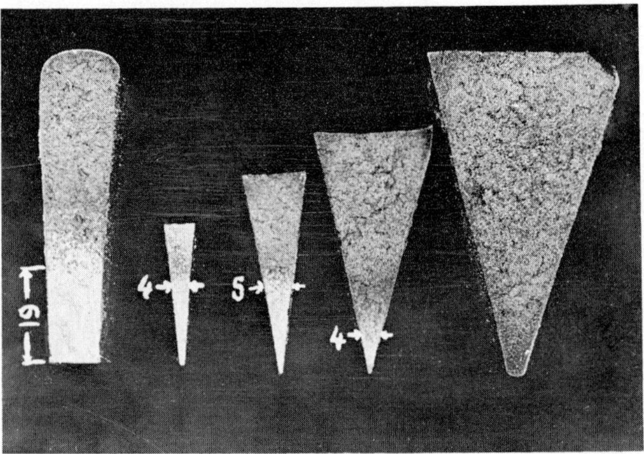

Fig. 31.4. Fractures of test wedges showing depth and width of chill. Whole numbers represent 1/32 in.[1]

which the narrow end of the wedge is sufficiently thin to freeze white. In the latter case, by properly selecting the chill mold, any cast iron can be made to form a chill, thinner metal selections being applicable to the softer irons that are higher in silicon and total carbon, and thicker sections being applicable to the harder irons.

It may be necessary for the cupola operator to experiment with chill molds and their design in order to determine the test block or blocks which correlate best with the castings, and which also satisfy the requirements as to rapidity of test. Figure 31.1 shows typical chill test specimens following the recommended practice for standardization.

Figure 31.2 shows suggested methods for making chill tests. Figure 31.3 shows various test wedges and suggested methods for casting these wedges. Figure 31.4 shows that depth of chill and the width of chill on a wedge are measured in whole numbers representing the depth and width in 32nds of an inch.

The mold for pouring the chill test specimens generally is made from oil-bonded sand, and can be designed as a gang core or as an individual core. The outside of the core should extend ¾ to 1 in. beyond the sides and ends of the test block cavity. Where the test block is cast against a chill plate, the oil binder forms a gummy film over the chill plate which must be cleaned from the chill plate after each test. Using glutrin rather than an oil binder will mitigate this condition.

The chill plate against which the blocks are poured can be made from gray iron, steel, water cooled copper or graphite, and should be machined or ground to a smooth finish. It should have enough mass compared with the chill test specimen to insure rapid chilling. It can be made as one large plate or as an individual plate, the latter having the advantage of requiring less space for the test. Although individual plates heat more rapidly, they can be interchanged with spare plates to allow them to cool prior to the next use.

When using the plate method, probably the greatest cause of error is the failure to keep the chill plate in proper condition. The depth of chill in the test specimen will not be significantly affected until the plate temperature reaches approximately 500 F, but the tendency for the casting to burn on the chill plate increases with increase in plate temperature. Therefore, chills should be rotated frequently.

The surface of the chill plate must be kept clean. Condensed core oil can be removed with coarse steel wool, or by rubbing the test block core across the face of the plate. The plates should be refinished when the surface shows signs of pitting or heat checking.

Metal sampling and casting quenching procedures are also possible sources of error. A small, blackened cup-like ladle is generally used to obtain the sample. An error can be caused from obtaining a sample containing high concentrations of late ladle additions, and excessive or damp blacking on the sample spoon.

Sampling from the stream should be done only when tapping from a full well. The temperature of the metal when pouring the test block should be held uniform. The cast specimen should not be quenched at too high a temperature and all blocks should be quenched at approximately the same temperature. Quenching hot (1700-1800 F) will not affect the chill depth, but will affect the appearance of the gray portion of the block. For normal practice blocks should be quenched at a temperature below 1400 F.

Chill tests are not a substitute for chemical analysis, but rather offer a rapid method of integrating the combined effects of carbon and silicon and correlating this with the expected properties of the castings, provided the factors affecting the appearance of the chill fracture are understood and interpreted.

Although the amount of chill in the test piece is the part most easily measured, the gray portion of the fracture also gives indication of the properties of the metal, and in many cases is quite important. Carbon content and physical properties are more readily estimated from this portion of the block, particularly in inoculated irons. High carbon irons develop a dark, coarse grained structure with a dull fracture, while lower carbon irons develop a lighter, closer grained structure.

The chill portion of the test block primarily reflects the carbide-forming tendency and the carbide stability of the iron. Chill depth is increased by melting under more oxidizing conditions, by superheating the iron, decreased silicon and decreased carbon, and addition of various carbide-forming alloys. Since the composition is only one of the factors which influences the carbide stability of the iron, the relationship between the amount of chill and the composition may vary.

Normally the cupola operator is most concerned with the control of the carbon and silicon contents of the iron through the use of chill tests, but other elements do affect the chilling tendency of gray iron. Elements which reduce depth of chill are: silicon, nickel, copper, aluminum, titanium, phosphorus and zirconium. Elements which increase depth of chill are: tellurium, chromium, molybdenum, antimony, bismuth, tin, sulfur,* manganese,* tungsten and vanadium.

Any deviation in appearance from a standard chill depth indicates a change in the iron. This change may be affected by a change in chemistry or the effect on chemistry by such influences as oxidation during melting, high moisture content in the blast, or a marked melting temperature change. Late ladle additions which correct the appearance of the chill will not produce an iron of identical properties, but will tend to bring the properties closer. Irons having a portion of their silicon introduced as a ladle addition will show a lower chill than the iron which has an identical silicon content as melted.

Fluidity Test

Saeger and Krynitsky of the National Bureau of Standards devised a fluidity test that embodies most of the principles now accepted for general use.

Figure 31.5 shows test spiral and castings. Complete details of the test were reported by Porter and Rosenthal.[2] The mold is usually in oil sand, but may be made in any molding sand, the index of fluidity being the length of the spiral in inches.

This test is used to help determine the cause of misruns and minimum pouring temperatures. Many foundries pouring thin-section castings require a minimum length of spiral in the fluidity test as a prerequisite to pouring off the castings. If the metal does not meet this minimum length it is used elsewhere. There are some disadvantages to the test because of its sensitivity to variations which may occur in the procedure. Fluidity is affected by the pouring temperature more specifically, or by the amount of superheat. Results of the test vary according to the mold temperature, hardness, permeability, gas content, variation from the horizontal, etc. With reasonable care in preparing and pouring the mold, reproducible results can be obtained.

Temperature

Temperature control is of sufficient importance that all foundries should establish a minimum and maximum pouring temperature for the class and type of casting they produce. From the quality standpoint it is necessary to adhere to these temperature limitations as they can govern the difference between a salable casting or a lost casting. Experience indicates that judging the temperature of the metal by its color may lead to haphazard results. Real accuracy can be obtained only by the use of a pyrometer. Several optical, radiation and immersion type pyrometers are described in detail in Chapter 8.

*Variation in the sulfur-manganese ratio may result in either increase or decrease of chill depth, since only the manganese in excess of the amount required to form manganese sulfide acts to increase chill depth.

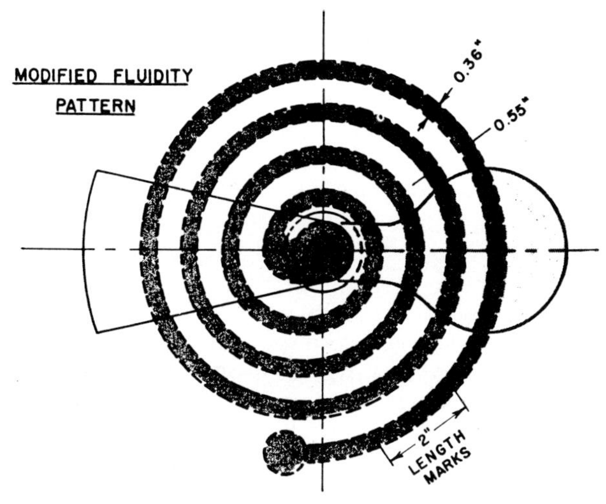

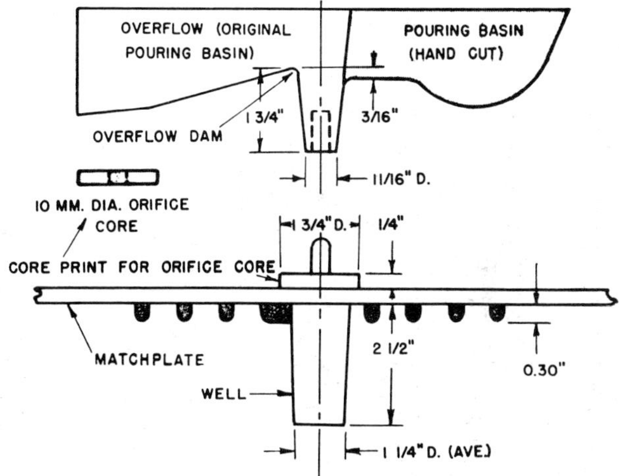

Fig. 31.5. Scale drawing of the modified fluidity pattern, and photographs of test castings poured in original Saeger and Krynitsky fluidity spiral (left), and fluidity spiral as modified (right).[2]

Determining Carbon At The Cupola

Control of the carbon and silicon contents of iron through the use of chill blocks is rapid, but should be confirmed by other test methods.

The *Eutectometer,* a device for rapid determination of carbon (carbon equivalent) at the cupola, has proved accurate for carbon control under normal production conditions. Details of the test have been reported.[3,4]

Requiring about one minute, the test involves only a core sand mold, thermocouple and temperature recorder. The carbon equivalent is obtained by making use of the relationship of carbon content to liquidus, as shown by the iron carbon phase diagram. With a reasonably constant silicon range, i.e., not exceeding 0.20 per cent, the total carbon versus liquidus temperature calibration is easily achieved. Silicon content and alloys will of course effect the arrest point, but metal at the cupola spout is normally reasonably constant in residual alloys and per cent silicon. Abnormal variation in silicon can be estimated from the fracture of the chill test specimen and a rough correction made on the basis of one point of carbon being equal to 4 points of silicon in their relation to the temperature of the liquidus arrest. Reproducibility should be within ± 0.04 per cent, which is better than typical chemical analyses subject to sampling, equipment standardization and operator skill variables.

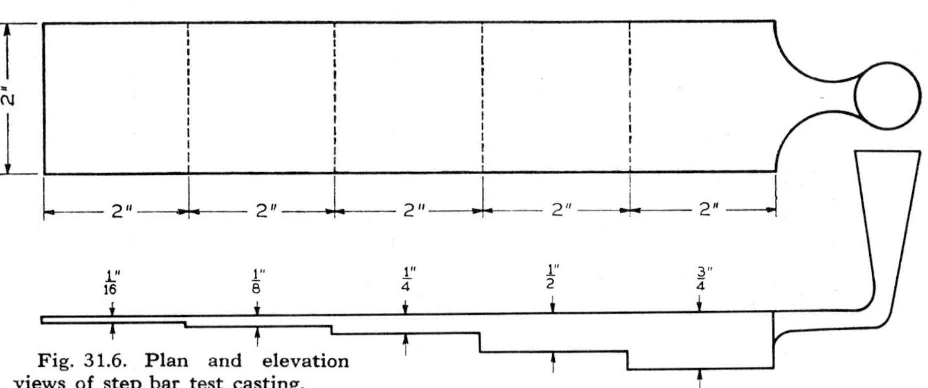

Fig. 31.6. Plan and elevation views of step bar test casting.

Figure 31.7 (photograph and scale drawing) illustrates a typical test casting for cupola carbon control. An appreciable amount of metal is flowed through the thermocouple cavity into a flowoff reservoir to preheat the thermocouple assembly for fast response; it also reduces thermal gradients and undercooling.

Approximately 6 lb of cupola spout metal is necessary to pour the test mold. Twenty gage matched chromel-alumel thermocouples in 1/4-in. OD insulators containing two 1/16-in. holes are utilized. The wires must be sealed in the insulators by filling the holes with a high temperature cement, which is then oven dried. A one sec response temperature recorder having a chart speed of one inch/22 sec and a chart temperature range of 1800 F to 2400 F (982-1316 C) with a temperature scale of 2 in./100 F (38 C) is recommended.

Although the carbon content of the iron is indicated by the liquidus arrest temperature, it is best to calibrate the equipment on the basis of the difference in temperature between the liquidus and solidus arrest points. This will compensate for any errors of the system in recording the true liquidus and solidus temperatures.

LABORATORY TESTS

With emphasis being placed on quality castings that must be made to definite specifications, with economics dictating the use of questionable or poorer class raw materials, it becomes increasingly necessary that supplemental laboratory tests be performed. Laboratory tests may be divided into two categories—chemical and physical. There is no question about the importance of a plant laboratory, but its establishment is strictly a matter of economics. There are a number of commercial laboratories located close enough to most foundries so that results of chemical analyses can be reported promptly by phone or telegraph.

Chemical Tests

Control by chemical analysis should include sampling of the iron at the cupola spout, in the ladle after ladle additions, and all materials entering into the make-up of the iron until the time it is poured into the mold.

Selection of the proper sample is important. A special sample may be poured for chemical analysis, or one of the halves of a transverse test bar or a heavy chill block is an excellent source of drillings. Specimens should be cleaned thoroughly to remove adhering sand, and drilled with a clean 1/8- to 1/2-in. drill, rejecting the drillings that contain any casting scale. Using the 1/8-in. drill, a hole should be drilled to the exact center of the bar, or through the bar, but not through the casting scale on the opposite side, to sample all zones of carbon, especially when combined carbon is required.

Drillings should be received on a clean piece of metal foil formed for the purpose, or on clean heavy paper. All powdery drillings must be included in the sample as they are chiefly graphite. When the chemical analyses are to be made by a commercial laboratory, it is recommended that the solid specimen be submitted because of the possibility of error through loss of graphite from the drillings. Samples which have all the carbon in the combined form are preferred for accurate total carbon determination. These can be produced by pouring droplets of iron into water, by pouring into a cast metal specimen mold, which produces chilled pins, or similar methods which will freeze the metal rapidly enough to produce white iron.

Pieces of chilled pins may be used for total carbon analysis. Drills of 1/4- to 1/2-in. size should be used for drillings for the determination of silicon, sulfur, manganese, phosphorous and tramp elements such as aluminum, chromium, tellurium and bearing

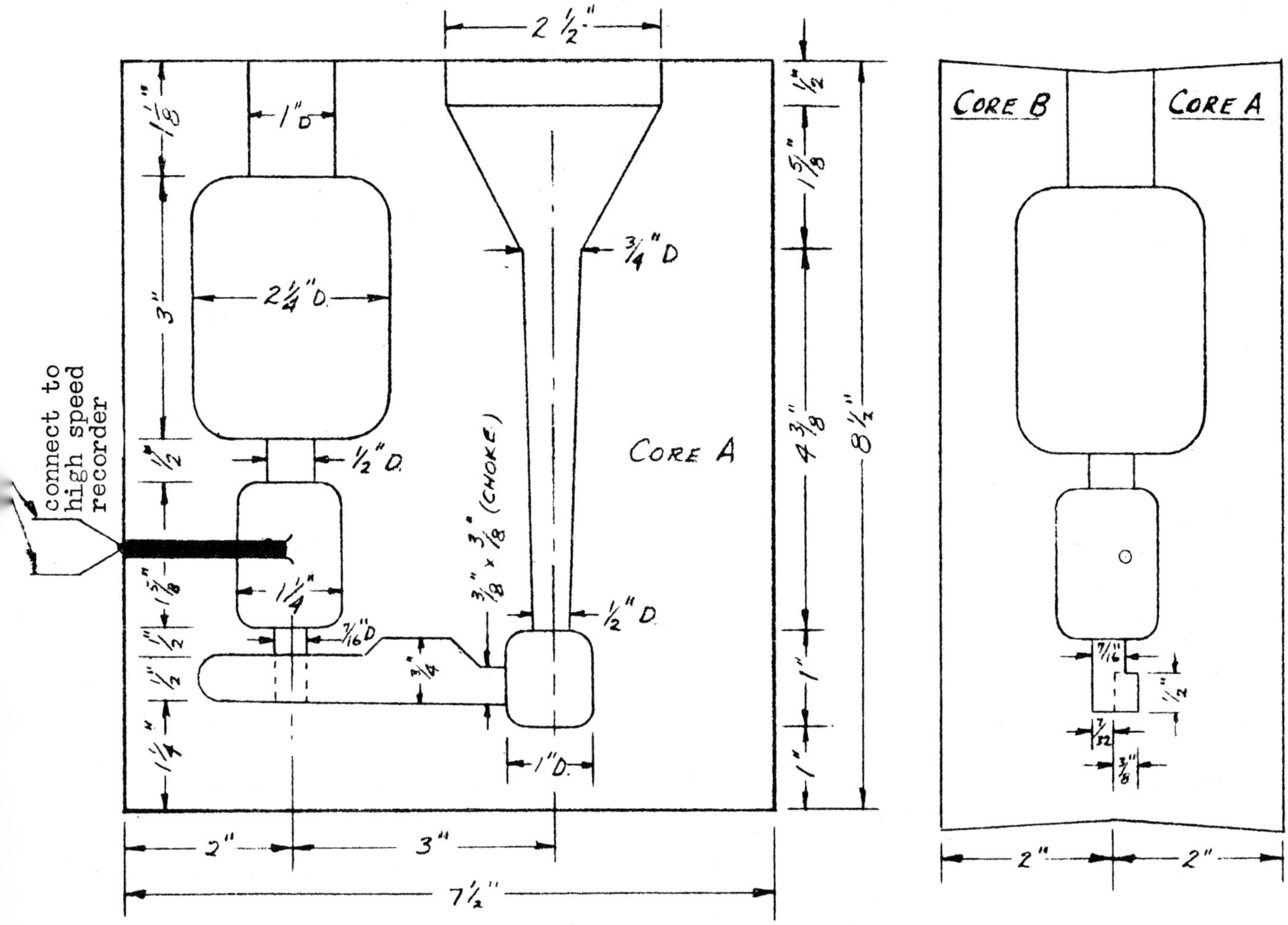

connect to high speed recorder

CORE A

CORE B

CORE A

Fig. 31.7. Detailed drawing of core box and . . .

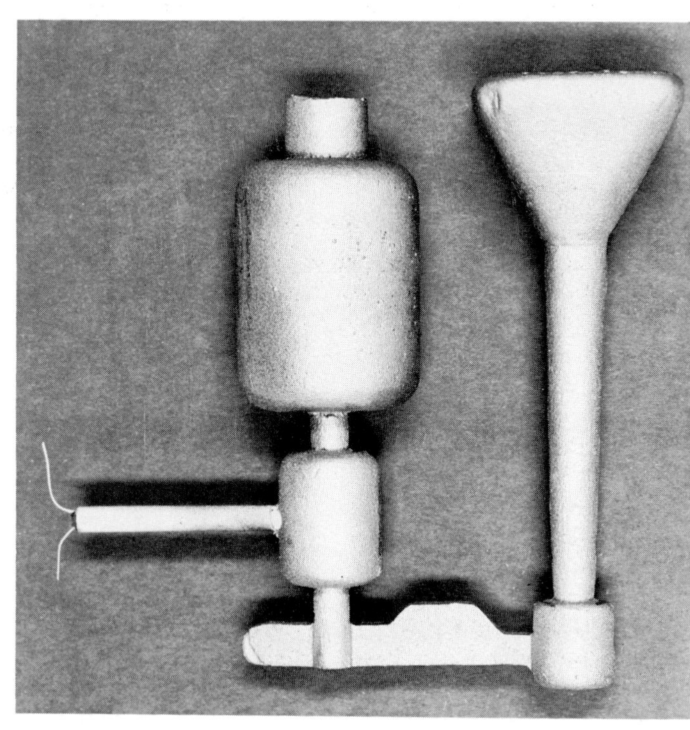

typical test casting for cupola carbon control.

metals. These tramp elements are usually introduced by the scrap used in the charge.

Assuming that good cupola practice prevails, the number of chemical determinations necessary for adequate control depends on the nature of the product. Many foundries require a large number of tests depending on the size and class of product. When working to close specification, when adding expensive alloys, or when making high strength irons, frequent chemical determinations should be made. Phosphorus changes so little in melting that it need be taken at less frequent intervals. Sometimes the characteristics of the product and the scrap may require frequent analysis, as often as every ½-hr. Experience has shown that the vendor's analysis of pig iron and alloys can be relied upon, but for best results periodic checks should be made to verify the results.

In many production foundries the iron is tested chemically every ½-hr or oftener, and in some the spectroscope is used for frequent rapid analytical results. Any chemical determination is worthless unless it is promptly reported and interpreted.

Physical Tests

The prime purpose of physical testing is to determine whether the castings are being produced to meet the requirements necessary to conform with the customer's specifications. The physical tests themselves are inexpensive and, when made in conjunc-

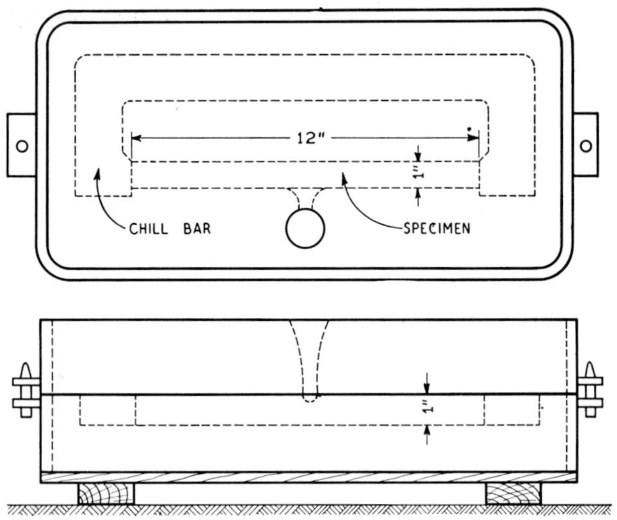

Fig. 31.8. Method for testing shrinkage properties of a cast iron. Final length of bar is compared with original 12 in. gap.

tion with frequent chill tests and chemical analyses, give a comprehensive picture of each heat. Normal intervals for physical testing are every 3 hr during a heat involving but one iron mixture. Added iron mixtures require more frequent tests. All test results should be systematically recorded.

The transverse test usually is performed on the 1.2 in. ASTM bar, recording the breaking load in pounds and the deflection in hundredths of an inch. One half of the bar may be drilled for chemical analysis and used for the tensile test. Pairs of bars should be cast during the first ½ hr of the heat, and at 3-hr intervals with the last bars during the last hour of the heat. Casting imperfections make the results worthless, so exceptional care should be taken when pouring the test bars.

Tensile tests can be made from one half of the broken transverse bar. Occasional tensile tests are desirable and in many cases necessary, although they are more expensive because of the machine work required. A well-organized routine of transverse and hardness tests are required to give sufficient control.

Hardness tests may be performed on the transverse bars or on each step of the step-bar casting shown in Fig. 98. Readings from each step give a good idea of the hardness of the corresponding metal section of castings. The frequency and importance of hardness tests depends on the nature and class of castings produced. If the castings are to be subsequently machined, the customer usually has definite limits within which he will accept.

It has been shown that there is a rough correlation between hardness and tensile strength, and many castings will have certain specified hardness ranges because of this relationship. There are many and various hardness tests that may be performed. The most common are the Brinell and Rockwell types. The spot to be tested must be ground flat and be beneath the cast surface skin. The specimen must be solidly mounted during the hardness test.

SPECIAL TESTS

Step Bars

Figure 31.6 shows a step bar casting that is useful for studying the influence of section size and chilling tendencies of any iron. This test serves as a daily control test specimen for hardness. The step bar can be broken longitudinally to observe the chilling effect and structure of the metal sections. This test is quite useful where castings are being made for pressure soundness.

Contraction Test

Figure 31.8 shows a useful means of estimating the shrinkage properties of any iron for use in making patterns. The final length of the bar is compared with the original 12 in. gap.

X-Ray

X-ray tests may be made either with an x-ray machine or a radioactive source of energy. This test is most useful in determining porosity or internal faults in high strength and pressure-tight castings, and in developing adequate gating and risering for various types of castings.

Microstructure

A microscope is useful for routine inspection of the structures obtained, and practically a necessity for the understanding of the basic relationships between chemical composition, rate of freezing, and attendant mechanical properties. For these purposes, special training is required.

REFERENCES

1. Krause, D. E., "Chill Tests and the Metallurgy of Gray Iron," AFS Transactions, vol. 59, p. 79-91 (1951).

2. Porter, L. F., and Rosenthal, P. C., "Fluidity of Cast Iron," AFS Transactions, vol. 60, p. 725-739 (1952).

3. Redshaw, H. S., Payne, C. A. and Hoskins, H. A., "Gray Iron Control by Cooling Curve Techniques," (Modern Castings February 1962) AFS Transactions, vol. 70 (1962).

4. Schaum, Jack H., "Carbon Equivalent in 60 Seconds," Modern Castings, vol. 41, no. 3, p. 37 (March 1962).

CHAPTER 32

Economics

The contents of this chapter are not presented in an attempt to prescribe, but rather to suggest possible improvements and savings that might be adopted or adapted.

The primary purpose of a melting unit is to produce, at the required volume and rate, molten metal having satisfactory chemical and physical properties.

The cupola melting unit is the most economical of all melting units for cast irons. The same holds true for melting duplex malleable iron, triplexing steel, and for certain nonferrous metals. Because the cupola provides one of the easiest methods of melting, close consideration, attention and control are not always given to the cupola operation. Therefore, quality and costs can usually be improved by careful study of all the factors.

CONSIDERATION OF INITIAL INVESTMENT

A cupola is a comparatively simple and inexpensive piece of equipment to purchase and install if its life, in tons melted, is considered. The following factors should influence the selection of a new cupola.

Usually, two cupolas operated on alternate days are preferable to a single unit. Being able to patch in the daytime and in a cool cupola makes for economy. There is also a safety factor in having the other cupola ready to go into service fairly early in the day if necessary. The dual installation will pay for itself within a short time.

The cupola size should be somewhat larger than necessary for the anticipated demand. Then the lining in the cupola can be adjusted to accommodate the melting demand.

The height of the cupola stack from the tuyeres to the charging door should be between 18-22 ft. Lack of height reduces the thermal efficiency. Excessive height does not increase efficiency and has the disadvantages of 1) subjecting the coke charges to excessive shock in charging, and 2) too many charges in the cupola prevent quick changes in the charges should this become necessary.

The height from the floor to the bottom doors should be sufficient to allow the cleanup men and patchers to stand erect under the cupola for better efficiency. If a mixing or receiving ladle is contemplated, either now or in the future, the height of the cupola bottom from the floor is important.

Most cupolas are supplied, originally, with upper tuyeres, but these can be eliminated at the plant if not desired. Except for unusual cases, the use of upper tuyeres increases operating costs unnecessarily because a higher bed of coke is required.

The location of the cupolas merits very careful study, because poor location can cause a constant recurring expense. Whether hand or mechanically charged, labor is involved and the closer the cupolas can be located to the piles or bins of melting stock, the less charging time (and money) is involved. The location of the cupolas in regard to the pouring areas must also be considered. This is usually less important, because the molten iron in ladles is transported by crane or truck and a few feet more or less makes little difference.

The cupola blower can be any one of the various types, as desired. Care should be taken that its range of volume is wide enough to take care of anticipated melting rates and still be controlled. The blower should be able to operate at high pressures if necessary because the quality of coke or melting stock may fluctuate, and with a more dense charge more blast pressure is needed.

Automatic blast controls are a necessity for uniform operations, but they are not a substitute for a conscientious cupola operator. The importance of using the correct amount of air is emphasized, when it is realized that the weight of air put through the cupola is approximately equal to the weight of the metal charges.

The blower should be located so that the amount of friction is minimized by short blast pipes and the absence of unnecessary bends and obstructions.

A good weighting system for cupola charges, with constant checking of the scales, is an absolute necessity. This gives control of what goes into the cupola. Economically, the correct amount (not too much nor too little) is required in each charge, since the quality of melting as well as the quality of the melted iron is affected.

Mechanical charging eliminates hard work and reduces labor costs. The type of charger equipment is somewhat dictated by the location of the bins and the cupola. The tonnage melted is also a factor, but with rising labor costs mechanical charging is becoming economical for much smaller heats than formerly and should be seriously considered.

A yard crane and magnet, either bridge or crawler

type, is usually a paying investment. It can be used for unloading scrap and pig iron, and also to load the charges into a weigh hopper, thus reducing labor costs. It is a paying investment even if mechanical charging equipment is not available.

The satisfactory handling of coke is always a problem. It is expensive to handle and has the undesirable property of breaking up easily. In certain localities coke can be secured on a schedule in drop-bottom containers. These can be lifted off the car and the coke dropped on the charging deck or near the weigh hopper. Belt conveyors are extensively used.

One system uses a portable horizontal belt laid across the tracks and under the hopper car with an inclined belt to convey the coke to a pile or bin. Another system has a pit under the track; the coke drops from the hopper car into the pit, and then is conveyed by belt or bucket conveyor to the bin or pile. Some foundries use a clamshell bucket for handling the coke but, while fast, it tends to break the coke excessively. A number of foundries have found that it pays to screen out the coke under 2 in. in size and either discard or sell it as heating coke. "Coke breeze" is sometimes used to pave the bottom of coke and scrap bins to eliminate picking up dirt when the bins are unloaded by magnet, etc.

Hot blast equipment is available according to various methods, such as 1) the waste gas system, 2) the waste heat system, and 3) the independently-fired system. Each has its advantages and disadvantages, and comes in a range of prices. Generally speaking, this equipment should be considered from an economic standpoint (saving in coke) if the heat is above 75 tons melt.

Blast humidity control is accomplished by various systems, all of which are comparatively expensive. Therefore, they are installed only when certain circumstances require it, such as very uniform melting conditions or special quality irons.

Devices to reduce the cupola smoke and emissions are becoming more evident, not from an economic angle, but from the standpoint of being a "good neighbor" to the surrounding area. Communities are establishing codes of varying stringency, so it is well to be aware of the costs and limitations of the available kinds of equipment. There are five fairly distinct types of devices; 1) spark arrestors; 2) plain washers; 3) burners at the charging door; 4) bag types; and 5) electrostatic precipitators. Improvements are constantly being made on these types of equipment.

Mixing ladles and forehearths are generally used for 1) leveling out the variations in composition of the iron and 2) desulfurization or other treatment. The leveling out factor is lost if the mixing ladle is not kept reasonably full. Externally heated mixing ladles may be desirable in order to obtain proper temperatures.

The extra cost of refractories and the loss in metal temperature should be balanced against the benefits of a mixing ladle or forehearth.

OPERATING EXPENSES

Fire brick are normally used for the original lining of the cupola. These fire brick, in the shape of blocks, are replaced only at long intervals and should be of a good grade. The fire brick in the melting zone are replaced after every heat (patching), so their quality is not so important. In fact, some foundries find it economical to use "seconds" or used fire brick from dismantled furnaces, etc. A material called firestone is sometimes used advantageously. The monolithic lining, blown in with a gun, is showing up very well in a number of operations. Hollow cast iron blocks are used for a few rows below the charging door, which eliminates the breaking up of ceramic fire brick from the impact and abrasion of the metal charges. An acid lining and patching material (fire brick, firestone or monolithic) is normally used.

A basic lining, which is more expensive, is used under certain conditions when low sulfur and higher total carbons are needed for special irons. As lower carbon materials can be used in the charge of a basic-lined cupola, the possible over-all savings should be investigated. Some foundries find it economical to change from an acid lining to a basic lining when the price ratio of pig iron vs. cast scrap or steel scrap widens. In other words, the savings in the all-steel or cast scrap mix can more than compensate for the increased cost of the basic lining.

Where severe erosion is involved, water cooling can be used to reduce refractory consumption. The availability and price of water is a determining factor.

BANKING CUPOLA BED

Methods of lining the cupola and banking the bed have been developed in certain foundries so that considerable savings have resulted. Cupolas are being run continuously for 16-24 hr on regular schedule. Other cupolas are being operated for six heats of 8-hr duration each without dropping the bottom, but banking the bed between heats. This possible savings should not be overlooked where melting conditions are applicable.

By far the greatest number of tap and slag holes are still rammed in, but shapes made of ceramic and other materials merit serious consideration from a labor-saving standpoint, especially for long heats.

In too many cases excess labor costs are overlooked. Delays, breakdowns, avoidable emergencies, last-minute changes, poorly trained and undependable personnel all contribute to slow, high-cost cupola operations. The other foundry units also suffer in waiting for metal. The cupola melting department can more than justify well-trained and dependable men—spare men are not only costly to carry but usually are not sufficiently well trained. The methods of cupola operation should be standardized and written up in detail. Daily records of each heat should be kept on printed forms, and someone should check them every day. Melting and pouring schedules can and should be set up in advance so that the operations move through the heat in an orderly and timesaving manner. Any delays, breakdowns or emergencies in the previous heat should be listed, investigated, and taken up with the proper person to obviate a recurrence.

Almost everyone uses too much coke, and closer attention to not only the daily but the hourly melting can effect worthwhile economies. However, the metal requirements (temperature and carbon), quality of coke and melting stock, and the rate of melting are not the same for all cupola operations, so there cannot be any over-all target. Also, it is poor economy to reduce the consumption of coke so much that the quality of the iron suffers. A little coke will pay for a lot of scrap castings.

It is good economy to use the best available coke. Usually it is safer to have more than one source of supply. But once having standardized, further changing should be minimized, since each coke has slightly different characteristics and changing around makes for poor and sometimes lost heats.

A good grade and size of either limestone or dolomite stone is needed as a flux. Local sources should be checked, as sometimes the distant source is no better and costs more.

Just as there is no one best cupola charge or mix to produce a certain iron, no one mix will remain the best at all times. In general, the mix is controlled by 1) materials available; 2) costs; and 3) product desired. But any of these factors can change so they should be continually reviewed. The purchasing agent, accounting department and the metallurgist should work very closely with the melting department. Too often, habit prevents an advantageous change. New and more economical products become available, but are at times overlooked. At least once a month the Melting Department should have an up-to-date list showing the *delivered* prices of all raw materials such as melting stock, coke, lining materials, etc. Freight rates and handling charges sometimes change the cost considerably.

It is worthwhile to calculate the cost of a cupola mix when the charge is figured. Knowledge of costs is the first step in controlling them (Table 32.1).

In this way everyone is kept aware of the possibilities of saving money by using economical mixes. Of course, the type of castings being produced has the first consideration in determining the melting stock. But it is just as big a mistake to use higher than necessary quality or price materials if the type of castings does not require it.

Pig iron usually is the highest priced melting stock. For most castings 10-30 per cent pig iron is used.

Melting practice control can reduce the amount of pig iron in a mix and allow substitution of lower priced materials, with compensating additions of silicon and manganese, and result in savings. Pig irons are priced in accordance with various silicon, manganese and phosphorus ranges. There is a saving and often other benefits in selecting the suitable grade or type of pig iron.

Steel scrap is usually the cheapest melting stock, so it is economically desirable to use as much as possible in the mix. But there are definite limitations due to its low carbon content, etc. Also, some types of steel scrap should be used with caution. Thin sheets oxidize excessively unless in dense bundles. Steel turnings should be briquetted and even then are not too satisfactory unless clean and dense. Some steel scrap contains appreciable amounts of alloys, and these should be considered in the mixture composition.

Cast scrap is the backbone of most cupola charges. There are inumerable grades, types, and qualities covered by the name "cast iron scrap." Objectionable inclusions are aluminum pistons, bearing metal, burned grate bars, enameled ware, steel, etc. It is worthwhile to buy from reputable dealers and inspect shipments continually.

Return scrap is actually more desirable than purchased cast scrap as its composition is known. For various reasons it should be consumed as fast as it is produced, and not allowed to accumulate.

INCLUSIONS IN CAST SCRAP

Clean, segregated chips of cast iron borings can be used economically if they are made in briquets that are at least 80 per cent of the density of solid cast iron. If the melting practice is controlled closely, these briquets can be used in quantities up to 50 per cent of the mix.

The adjustment of silicon in the mix can be done by using various materials such as silvery iron, lump ferrosilicon, and ferrosilicon briquettes. Each has its advantages, which should be considered as well as cost. The competitive economic position of these materials is not entirely controlled by their quoted price per pound of contained silicon. As they are all used for the introduction of silicon, but vary in concen-

TABLE 32.1. DAILY CUPOLA CHARGE MIXTURE

Cupola No.				Heat No.								Date:			
Material	Pounds per Charge	Silicon %	Silicon lb	Manganese %	Manganese lb	Phosphorus %	Phosphorus lb	Sulfur %	Sulfur lb	Total Carbon %	Total Carbon lb	%	lb	Costs $ lb	Costs $ Charge
Pig Iron, Bin 4	300	2.7	8.1	1.0	3.0	0.11	0.33	0.04	0.12	3.7	11.1			0.03	9.00
Pig Iron, Bin 8	200	2.5	5.0	1.0	2.0	0.20	0.40	0.03	0.06	3.9	7.8			0.03	6.00
Steel Scrap, Bin 1	400	0.2	0.8	0.60	2.4	0.03	0.12	0.03	0.12	0.3	1.2			0.018	7.20
Cast Scrap, Bin 3	525	2.0	10.5	0.70	3.7	0.25	1.31	0.12	0.63	3.2	16.8			0.02	10.50
Returns, Bin 2	500	2.1	10.5	0.75	3.7	0.12	0.60	0.10	0.50	3.2	16.0			0.02	10.00
Fe Si	75	16.0	12.0											0.063	4.73
Mn Briq.	2				4.0									0.221	0.88
Total	2000		45.9		18.8		2.76		1.43		52.9				$48.31
Anal. Charged		2.30		0.94		0.14		0.07		2.65					
Melting Change		0.23		0.14				0.05		0.55					
Est. Anal.		2.07		0.80		0.14		0.12		3.20					

Signed: ______________

tration of this element, their competitive position will vary with the cost of make-up iron. If 16 per cent silvery is considered as steel plus silicon (a valid assumption in view of its low carbon content), then a gross ton might be considered as 358 lb of silicon and 1882 lb of steel scrap. For comparison, 895 lb of ferro-silicon briquettes (containing 716 lb of 50 per cent ferro-silicon, or 358 lb of silicon plus 358 lb of iron) plus 1524 lb of steel scrap, will yield amounts of iron and silicon equivalent to a gross ton of silvery. The economic position of these two materials would obviously depend as much on the price of steel scrap under given market conditions as on the actual selling price of the two sources of silicon.

The cheapest source of manganese in the mix is in the pig iron, but this is limited to about 1 per cent maximum. Lump ferro-manganese is the next cheapest, but is somewhat difficult to handle and is very concentrated for cupola melting. Ferro-manganese briquettes are the highest priced of the three, but are easy to handle.

Other alloys such as nickel, copper, chromium, molybdenum, vanadium, etc., are sometimes put in the cupola charge advantageously, but are more often ladle additions. Careful consideration will determine the most economical and satisfactory method of adding these alloys. The segregation and careful charging into the cupola of returns containing alloys is a must from economic as well as metallurgical aspects.

Control of inventories of melting stock (pig iron, scrap, alloys and coke) is very desirable, not only to keep costs in line but to maintain quality. Inventory records should be checked regularly by visual or physical tests. Bins of material should be exhausted in rotation and inventory corrections made often.

The foundry that recognizes the interdependence of factors caused by variations in product desired, materials available, fluctuations in prices, etc. can realize large savings and still maintain the desired quality. The interrelated economic factors infuencing the choice of melting materials and type of operations under given conditions are not always used to advantage as well as they might be.

The cost of the melting stock, alloys, coke, flux, lining materials and labor required to produce a ton of iron can readily be obtained, and should be gone over with the melting department at frequent intervals. Realization of actual costs is the first step in control. The foundry that controls its cost is the one that stays in business.

Combustion

The primary objective in cupola operation is to produce iron of the desired composition and temperature at a definite rate in the most economical manner. In addition, the metal should be melted in contact with gases having a definite CO_2/CO ratio so that, subsequently, it will exhibit a normal behavior.

It seems certain that the properties of the metal are not defined by actual chemical composition alone, but also are affected by the gaseous atmosphere in contact with the molten metal in the cupola, be it oxidizing or reducing in character. It is becoming a well-recognized fact that it is necessary to exert a close control over combustion processes in the cupola if uniformly high quality castings are to be produced.

Although the combustion of fuel in a cupola, in which a deep bed of ignited fuel burns in a blast of air, appears to be one of the simplest of operations, there are a number of important variables that influence the overall results. Among these are the chemical composition, size, size consist and reactivity of the fuel, the physical make-up of the bed and the charges, and the velocity and humidity of the air. Numerous studies of both theoretical and practical character have developed information from which a reasonably sound understanding of the entire process can be evolved.

CHEMICAL REACTIONS

The major chemical reactions between fuel and the reactive constituents present in the gaseous atmosphere within a cupola, in their probable order of importance, are:

I. $C_{(coke)} + O_{2(g)} \rightleftarrows CO_{2(g)}$

$\Delta H_{77\,F} = +174{,}600$ Btu/lb mole

$\Delta H_{2900\,F} = +175{,}900$ Btu/lb mole

II. $C_{(coke)} + CO_{2(g)} \rightleftarrows 2CO_{(g)}$

$\Delta H_{77\,F} = -72{,}900$ Btu/lb mole

$\Delta H_{2240\,F} = -69{,}700$ Btu/lb mole

III. $C_{(coke)} + H_2O_{(g)} \rightleftarrows CO_{(g)} + H_{2(g)}$

$\Delta H_{77\,F} = 55{,}200$ Btu/lb mole

$\Delta H_{2240\,F} = 57{,}800$ Btu/lb mole

Reaction I. This is the heat producing reaction of the process. Even at the maximum temperatures occurring in the cupola the equilibrium constant is such that at equilibrium the reaction is essentially complete in the forward direction as written. The rate of the reaction is immeasurably fast at the temperatures existing in the cupola, and is controlled only by rate of mass transfer of oxygen from the gas stream to the external or aerodynamic fuel surface.

In reality, Reaction I is not a single reaction but the summation of two successive reactions as follows:

Ia. $C_{(coke)} + \frac{1}{2}O_{2(g)} \rightarrow CO_{(g)}$

$\Delta H_{2900\,F} = 53{,}800$ Btu/lb mole

Ib. $CO_{(g)} + \frac{1}{2}O_{2(g)} \rightarrow CO_{2(g)}$

$\Delta H_{2900\,F} = +122{,}100$ Btu/lb mole

Available data indicate that Reaction Ib is the slower of the two,[1,2] but as the flame speed of this reaction at these temperatures is of the order of 3000 ft/min, for all practical purposes the two successive reactions may be considered as the overall Reaction I.

Reaction II. This is a heat absorbing reaction and extracts heat from the cupola. At the temperatures existing in the bed, the equilibrium constant is such that at equilibrium the reaction is essentially complete in the forward direction as written. At lower temperature, however, reversal of the reaction is favored and carbon deposition can occur.

The rate of this reaction is strongly temperature dependent, and the mechanism changes from mass transfer at temperatures above about 2700 F to chemical control below about 2000 F. In the transition range from about 2700 to about 2000 F the rate is probably controlled by the rate of diffusion of reactant into and products out of the capillary system of the fuel.

Reaction III. This is a heat absorbing reaction but is important in cupola operation only in proportion to the amount of water vapor carried into the cupola with the air stream. The equilibrium constant and rate are of similar order of magnitude to Reaction II, and the rate controlling mechanism similar.

ZONES IN THE CUPOLA

The gases in the cupola at various levels consist

principally of CO_2, CO, O_2 and N_2 with varying amounts of H_2O and H_2, depending upon the humidity of the blast air. Carbon dioxide, oxygen and water vapor are oxidizing gases, while carbon monoxide and hydrogen are reducing gases. Nitrogen is an inert and its principal role is that of a heat transfer medium.

Although the actual zones in a cupola vary in shape and location according to various factors which will be discussed later in this section, it is desirable for a preliminary consideration to assume an idealized bed such as depicted in Fig. 33.1, where the assumptions are made that the air is distributed uniformly across the entire cross section of the cupola at tuyere level, and that its upward passage meets a uniform resistance across the entire bed.

In such an idealized fuel bed, the oxygen in the blast air introduced at the tuyere level will react with the incandescent fuel. The oxygen content will diminish rapidly with simultaneous production of CO_2, which in turn reacts with the fuel to form CO. Any water vapor present will simultaneously react with fuel to produce CO and H_2.

The reactions occurring are such as to produce rather well defined zones in the cupola, the control of which are of utmost importance to satisfactory and efficient cupola operation. These zones are the combustion and reduction zone of the bed and the reduction zone in the preheat section. The conditions in each and the factors controlling each will be discussed individually.

Oxidation or Combustion Zone

In this zone the principal reaction is the combination of oxygen with the fuel. Its physical limits are the point of entry of the air and the level where the oxygen concentration is reduced to one per cent or less. The latter is the approximate level at which the CO_2 concentration reaches a maximum (usually 14 to 18 per cent) and also the level of the maximum temperature in the cupola (normally between 2800 and 3400 F). Reaction II begins in this zone as indicated in Fig. 33.1; it cannot attain significant proportions until the oxygen concentration is reduced to relatively low value.

The rates of all reactions in this zone are controlled primarily by mass transport and are, therefore, essentially *independent* of the reactivity, combustibility, internal surface or ignitability of the fuel, and above 2000 F only slightly dependent on temperature. The rates are dependent upon the aerodynamic surface area of the fuel, which is approximately proportional to the average lump diameter and to the concentration of the reactants in the gas stream.

For normally packed, irregularly shaped lumps such as coke, the oxygen will be almost completely consumed in passing 3 to 5 lump diameters of fuel[3,4,5] at the temperatures and blast rates normally employed in the cupola. For fuel of more regular shape and smoother surface, such as anthracite or briquettes, it may require up to 6 or 7 lump diameters.[6]

It has been shown[5,6] that for the same blast rate the maximum temperature will decrease slightly with increase in fuel size (about 150 F for a change from 2- to 3-in. coke). For the same size fuel the maximum temperature will increase slightly with increase in blast rate (about 200 F for a change from 100 to 300 cfm/sq ft). Also, the depth of this zone will decrease slightly with increase in blast rate.[5,7,8,9] In this zone, the consumption of carbon is essentially from the external surface of the individual lumps.

Reduction Zone of Bed

In this zone, the physical limits of which are the top of the combustion zone (maximum temperature about 2800 to 3400 F) and the melting zone (temperature 2140 F or higher, depending upon metal composition), the principal reaction is the combination of CO_2 with the fuel to form CO. Most of the water vapor present in the blast air also reacts in this zone to yield CO and H_2.

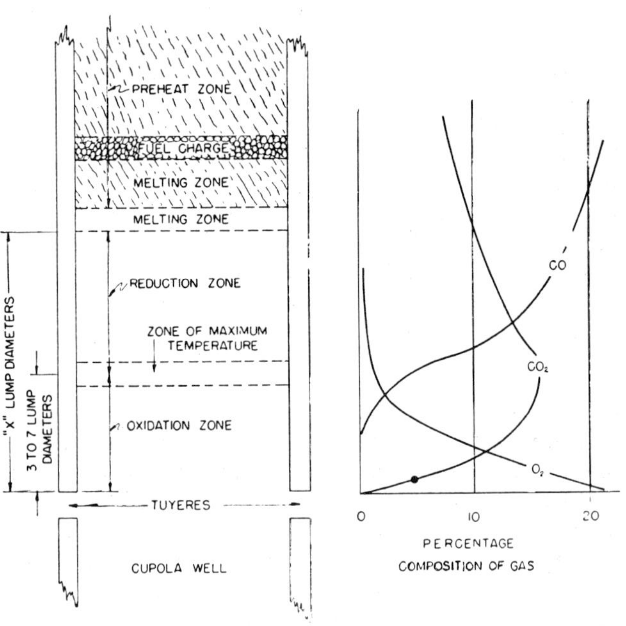

Fig. 33.1. Idealized diagram representing conditions in cupola fuel bed.

In the lower portion of this zone (temperature above about 2700 F) the reaction rate is controlled by mass transport. It is, therefore, independent of fuel reactivity and only mildly dependent (proportional to approximately the 0.4 power of the absolute temperature) upon temperature and blast rate. It is dependent upon the aerodynamic surface of the fuel and the concentration of the carbon dioxide in the gas stream. As in the oxidation zone, reaction in this portion is primarily on the external surface with resulting size diminution of the fuel.

In the upper portion of the bed (between the temperature limits of about 2700 F and the melting temperature of the metal) the reaction rate appears to be controlled primarily by the rate of diffusion of reactant gas and products through the capillary system of the fuel. At the highest temperature the diffusion rate is extremely fast and approaches the rate of mass transfer to the aerodynamic surface. At the lowest temperature it is relatively slow and approaches the rate of the chemical reactivity of the fuel itself.

The depth within the lump to which reactant penetrates is, therefore, a function of the temperature and of the character of the capillary system of the fuel. At the highest temperature reaction occurs near the external surface, while at the lowest temperature it occurs throughout most if not all the capillary system of the fuel.

In this portion of the bed, therefore, size reduction of the fuel will be slight because the reaction is principally internal rather than external. The size reduction that does occur is primarily due to increased abrasion losses resulting from weakening of the fuel structure as a result of the internal reaction removing part of the carbon.

Based upon consideration of the heat extraction from the bed, due solely to the reduction reactions, data for deep fuel beds would suggest that the reduction zone should be up to 20 times as deep as the oxidation zone for the blast conditions and type of fuel normally encountered in cupola operation. That this is not so is due in part to non-equilibrium temperature conditions between gas and fuel, and in part to two other heat extracting operations—the superheating of molten metal produced in the melting zone and the melting and superheating of slag-forming constituents. Quantitative data on these latter effects are discussed in Chapter 34 "Thermochemical Principles."

Heat Transfer

A major factor influencing the depth of the bed reduction zone is rate of heat transfer between gases and fuel in this zone. The gases leaving the oxidation zone are in substantial temperature equilibrium with the fuel, but above this zone a temperature differential between gas and fuel is the driving force that permits the transfer of heat from the gas stream to the fuel, where it is subsequently extracted by the reduction reaction.

For an equivalent driving force, heat transfer is directly proportional to surface area of the fuel and to time of contact between gas and fuel. With the time of contact between gas and fuel only a small fraction of a second (normal range of velocities about 40 to 80 ft/sec for blast rates in the range of 200 to 400 cfm/sq ft of bed area) rather wide temperature differentials can exist. Higher blast rates will result in lower contact times, hence poorer heat transfer (despite a probable thinning of the gas film surrounding each lump) and, therefore, a decrease in depth of the reduction zone.

The heat extracted in superheating metal from its melting temperature, up to the maximum temperature of 2800 F or higher, depends on the amount of superheat imparted to the metal and on the metal to carbon ratio employed in a given operation. For a metal to fuel ratio of 10/1 and a superheat of 600 F the heat extracted will be approximately 15,000 Btu per mole of carbon consumed.

For lower metal to fuel ratios the heat extraction is proportionately lower, and for higher superheats proportionately higher. In any event it is a very significant factor in decreasing the temperature of the reduction zone, hence in decreasing the depth of this zone in the cupola.

Similarly, the phase change of slag formation and subsequent superheating of the slag extracts heat from this zone. Although the heat extracted per pound of slag is relatively high (normally of the order of magnitude of 550 Btu/lb of slag) the heat extracted in terms of moles of carbon consumed is small relative to that extracted in superheating the metal. It does, however, increase as the volume of slag increases and tends to lower reduction zone temperature, hence the depth of this zone.

From the foregoing discussion it is obvious that generalization regarding depth of the bed reduction zone must of necessity be extremely qualitative due to the several variables involved. However, the approximate effect of changes in various factors, *assuming other factors remain constant,* can be predicted as follows:

1) Increase in fuel size will increase the depth of the zone to an extent somewhat less than the direct ratio of lump diameters.
2) Decrease in surface area per lump will increase the depth of the zone.
3) Increase in internal surface of the fuel (approximately a function of reactivity) will decrease the depth of the zone.
4) Increase in the metal to fuel ratio will decrease the depth of the zone.
5) Increase in the slag volume will decrease the depth of the zone.
6) Increase in blast rate will increase the depth of the zone due to increase in the lower temperature limit of the zone, but will result in more metal to superheat and poorer heat transfer which in part counterbalance the increase.

Interpretation of data from various studies on bed depth suggest that for "normal" operation the reduction zone is probably in the general range of 8 to 12 lump diameters deep. With highly reactive fuel it may be substantially less than this, and for abnormally high blast rates somewhat deeper. For charges containing high percentages of steel or other high melting scrap the depth will be considerably less due to the higher upper temperature limit of the zone.

Melting Zone

When the metal reaches the melting zone, it should have been preheated to substantially melting temperature. The principal reaction here is, therefore, the phase change from solid to molten metal. This extracts additional heat, the exact amount being a function of the heat of fusion of the metal melted (84.6, 41.4 and 181 Btu/lb for pig iron, gray cast iron and steel scrap, respectively) and on the metal to fuel ratio employed. Evidence[10,11] indicates that a significant part of the carbon pick-up by metals deficient in carbon also occurs in this zone. The reaction is probably

$$3\,Fe + 2\,CO \rightarrow Fe_3C + CO_2$$
$$H_{770F} = +79{,}560 \text{ Btu/lb mole}$$

Preheating Zone

The principal function of this section of the cupola, which lies above the melting zone, is to serve as a heat exchanger wherein waste heat is recovered by direct heat exchange between upward flowing gases and downward flowing charges and fuel. In addition to heat exchange, however, chemical reactions occur which are not necessarily beneficial.

Between the melting zone temperature and some lower limit of temperature which is a function of the reactivity of the fuel, Reaction II continues. In this temperature range the rate is chemically controlled, occurring almost entirely on internal surfaces of the fuel. It is, therefore, a direct function of the reactivity of the fuel and of the CO_2 concentration, and an exponential function of temperature. For low reactivity fuel the rate becomes negligibly slow at about 1600 F, but for highly reactive fuels it may still be significant down to temperature of 1200 F.

The reaction is undesirable in this portion of the cupola since it not only extracts heat that would otherwise be usefully employed to preheat the charges, but it also consumes carbon and increases the carbon consumption per pound of metal melted and superheated. Highly reactive fuels are, therefore, to be avoided.

In the preheat zone two other reactions also occur. One is the catalytic decomposition of carbon monoxide to deposit carbon due to a reversal of Reaction II. The rate of this reaction is negligible below 900 F, and above about 1200 F the equilibrium is unfavorable. At about 1000 F, however, the reaction is quite rapid in the presence of catalytic surface such as carbon or oxides of iron.

The form of carbon deposited is relatively reactive and the principal effect of this reaction is to change the relative CO/CO_2 ratio of the effluent gas and increase slightly the exit temperature of the gas. In effect, carbon is cycled within the preheat zone by deposition at the lower temperatures and CO formation at higher temperatures nearer the melting zone.

Another reaction which is believed to occur in the preheat zone is the pick-up of sulfur by the solid metal from the sulfur compounds present in the gas. The exact chemistry of the reaction is somewhat in doubt as little information is available on the nature and distribution of sulfur-containing gases at different levels in the cupola.

It has been observed,[5,11] however, that steel picks up sulfur shortly after its introduction into the cupola but loses some of it as the temperature increases as the metal approaches the melting zone. Cast iron, on the other hand,[11] showed the greatest pick-up just before melting occurred.

PHYSICAL FACTORS INFLUENCING ZONES IN CUPOLA

In addition to the factors discussed in the preceding section there are certain physical limitations that cause the zones in an actual cupola to look a lot different from those depicted for the idealized bed in Fig. 33.1, and influence actual operating results. Important limiting factors are treated here –

Blast Penetration

In actual practice, the blast is introduced through a number of tuyeres located around the periphery of the cupola. Since the oxygen is consumed in passing about 3 to 7 lump diameters, and this corresponds to the region of maximum temperature, it follows that a reduction zone with progressively decreasing tempeatures exists toward the center of the cupola at tuyere level. Fortunately, the actual blast velocity in the horizontal direction approaches zero as the gases penetrate toward the center, and the heat extraction is not too great if the reduction zone is not permitted to extend beyond a few lump diameters.

Nevertheless, an optimum relationship exists between fuel diameter and cupola diameter, and for practical operation it appears to be between $\frac{1}{10}$ and $\frac{1}{12}$ for normal types of coke. With ratios significantly greater than this, sufficient gas flow will occur to cause a cold center with adverse effects upon the superheating of metal. With ratios significantly less than $\frac{1}{10}$, free oxygen penetrates to the center of the cupola where it can react readily with molten metal.

It is, of course, apparent that if the oxidation zone surrounds each tuyere and the blast direction at tuyere level is essentially upward, the shape of the oxidation zone is not a plane across the cupola at some given level but is rather that of an inverted cone. If the oxidation zone ends before reaching the center of the cupola the effect is to produce a zone resembling a truncated cone.

In view of the fact that the zones above this level are primarily functions of the lump diameters of the fuel, it is apparent that the shape of the oxidation zone establishes the basic shape of the melting zone. As discussed later, wall effect has an additional influence on dishing the zones.

Blast Preheat

Blast preheat increases the temperature of the oxidation zone in direct proportion to the sensible heat supplied in the air while at the same time decreasing slightly the depth of this zone. The reduction zone is increased in depth by an amount equal to the decrease in the depth of oxidation zone, but the change has little influence upon the height of the melting zone. In overall effect, therefore, blast preheat results in a greater volume of the bottom portion of the bed being at a significantly higher temperature and less of this volume being an oxidizing atmosphere.

Balanced Blast

Air admitted above the normal tuyere level reacts with carbon monoxide in the reduction zone according to Reaction Ib, or with carbon of the fuel according to Reaction I. Undoubtedly both reactions occur, since the quantity of CO adjacent to the auxiliary tuyeres is unlikely to be sufficient to consume all the oxygen before it can react with the solid fuel.

Irrespective of mechanism, the net effect is the same. The temperature is increased in the reduction zone around the auxiliary tuyeres in proportion to the amount of air admitted, resulting thereby in an increase in the depth of the reduction or superheat zone. This can be especially beneficial with the more reactive fuels, which otherwise tend to give shallow reduction zones.

The effect upon the shape of the zones in the

cupola of blast introduction through auxiliary tuyeres in the reduction zone will in general be to accentuate the dishing of the zones. The higher the relative surface area of the fuel and smaller the fuel to cupola diameter ratio the more pronounced the effect.

Fuel Bed Resistance

Fuel bed resistance is frequently an important factor in cupola operation. Attempts to operate the cupola at appreciably higher than designed capacities, or to use smaller sized fuel, frequently result in pressures against which the commonly used centrifugal blower is incapable of delivering the required volume of air.

Poor quality fuels that break down appreciably in size due to thermal or mechanical shock also produce increased fuel bed resistance which may result in pressure problems, as may also the use of fuel containing appreciable quantities of small sized material. Unusually dirty scrap is another source of fuel bed resistance.

The resistance to gas flow in the cupola (roughly proportional to windbox pressure) is determined primarily by the resistance of the bed, which in turn is a function of the size consist of the fuel, and of the gas velocity. Usually the metal charged is appreciably larger than the fuel, and the stock column above the melting zone influences total resistance but slightly, except in cases where it tends to compact the fuel bed due to its weight.

Under any specific set of conditions the pressure drop through a fuel bed can be calculated with a fair degree of accuracy knowing the size of all the materials, the percentage of voids, the temperature and composition of all the gases passing through the bed and their velocity. For practical operation of the cupola, however, such involved calculations are unnecessary since it is usually sufficient to know what factors influence fuel bed resistance and how they can be modified.

As a rough approximation, for closely sized fuels in the range normally employed in cupolas, and at constant blast volume, the pressure drop through the bed is inversely proportional to the square of the average diameter of the fuel and inversely proportional to the fourth power of the voids. For a given cupola fuel the percentage of voids in the bed will remain essentially constant with change in size for fuel sized between reasonably close limits.

Different fuels, however, will pack to different degrees depending on shape and surface roughness, ana therefore produce different percentages of voids; thus anthracite packs to a denser bed than coke and exhibits only 45-47 per cent voids as compared to 53-55 per cent voids for by-product coke. Hence, other conditions being constant, a given size of anthracite may be expected to exhibit nearly twice the fuel bed resistance of coke. Similarly, changing the size of the same fuel from an average of 4 in. to an average of 3 in. will approximately double the fuel bed resistance, other conditions remaining constant.

Although no general relationship can be offered for estimating the increase in fuel bed resistance resulting from the use of fuel containing or producing appreciable quantities of size degradation products, the increase may be appreciable. For example, as a result of rough handling, a fuel originally sized to 4 in. x 3 in. had the following screen analysis:

4 in. x 3 in.	82.5%
3 in. x 2 in.	5.5%
2 in. x 1 in.	5.8%
1 in. x ½ in.	2.7%
Minus ½ in.	3.5%

This composite fuel showed an increase in fuel bed resistance (in a non-ignited bed) of approximately 50 per cent at a blast rate of 200 cfm/sq ft of bed area. In a burning fuel bed, the increase in resistances would probably be even greater since pressure drop is approximately proportional to the square of the gas velocity, and gas velocity would increase with increase in gas temperature for a fixed volume of blast.

Some of the fines would undoubtedly be consumed before reaching the bed, however, and the increase in pressure would not be directly proportional to the temperature rise. In the foregoing example, removal of the minus one-inch material reduced the increase to negligible proportions – less than 5 per cent.

For a given size and type of fuel, the fuel bed resistance is approximately proportional to the square of the gas velocity through the bed, which for a given cupola is also proportional to the blast volume. A decrease in blast volume of only 30 per cent is sufficient to decrease pressure drop through the bed to about one-half the original value.

It is thus apparent that if lack of air volume due to high windbox pressures is causing difficulty, there are several possible solutions. By forking or screening the fuel, the minus one-inch material will be reduced to negligible proportions and, if an appreciable quantity of this material was originally present, pressure will be reduced materially.

A larger size fuel may be used within the limits discussed in the section on wall effect. The velocity of the gases through the cupola may be reduced by increasing the inside diameter–a one or two inch change in diameter makes a significant difference in small cupolas. (With the same air volume, increasing a 30 in. lining to a 31 in. cuts the pressure drop by about 14 per cent.)

Wall Effect

Because of the relationship between shape of fuel and contour of the wall of the cupola, the fuel within one or two layers next to the wall cannot pack in the normal manner and the void volume in this peripheral region is therefore greater than in the main body of the cupola. This increase in void volume causes lower resistance to gas flow, hence a tendency for the gases to channel.

Any oxygen appearing in the gas above the melting zone is undoubtedly due to this channelling effect unless there are actual channels developed within the bed itself due to other causes. This phenomenon is usually expressed as "wall effect factor" defined as "that fraction of the resistance of a bed of infinite diameter, exhibited by the actual bed under study." The "wall effect factor" is a function of the ratio of average lump diameter to container diameter.[12]

For a ratio of 1 to 12 the factor is 0.7, and for a ratio of 1 to 6 it is 0.6. Thus as the ratio of fuel size to cupola diameter is reduced, a greater percentage of the gases should pass upward through the bed in sections adjacent to the walls. The effect, of course, would be noticable primarily in the bed. Above the bed the stock column is usually so open as to offer negligible resistance to gas travel, and the velocities tend to equalize across the whole area.

In this connection it should be pointed out that measurements reported by Piwowarsky *et al*[5] indicate no significant differences in blast velocity across the bed of an experimental cupola. Such measurements are, however, unreliable because the values obtained depend on local conditions at the point of measurement, and it is possible by having the inlet to the measuring tube in the slip stream behind a given lump to actually record negative velocities.

The most important influence of wall effect, however, is not so much velocity changes as it is change in the quantity of fuel per unit volume, hence change in surface area per unit volume. In the region up to about 3 lump diameters from the walls, there is considerably less fuel surface per unit volume, hence all the zones of the bed are spread out in this section of the cupola and in part account for the pronounced dishing toward the center of the cupola.

INFLUENCE OF ZONES ON METAL PRODUCED

In the foregoing discussion little mention is made of the influence of the zones on metal temperature and composition. From a consideration of the chemical and physical factors controlling the depth, temperature and atmosphere in the zones it is now possible to consider the probable effects upon the metal, which is actually the primary reason a knowledge of the control factors is of interest.

Superheat

The superheat zone is the entire region of the cupola from melting zone to that level, somewhere in the oxidation zone, where the metal temperature exceeds the fuel temperature. For all practical purposes this is essentially tuyere level. The degree of superheat imparted to the metal will be a function of the temperatures to which it is exposed and to the time of residence at these temperatures.

Purely from the viewpoint of superheat, therefore, the deeper the zone and the higher the maximum temperature, the higher the degree of superheat. It must be pointed out, however, that even though the molten metal is in contact with the gaseous atmosphere at all times the temperature attained will be primarily that of the fuel rather than that of the gas stream, since radiation and conduction are more effective than convection at the temperatures involved.

Since the maximum temperature of the fuel does not normally vary over a very wide range unless radical changes in fuel size or blast rate are made, it follows that time of contact in the higher temperature region of the bed is the principal controlling factor in superheat. Thus, shallow or low temperature zones are detrimental and deep high temperature zones beneficial.

At a constant blast rate the latter results from an increase in fuel size, although the increase in fuel size also results in a slight decrease in maximum temperature. For constant fuel size, increase in temperature and depth of the higher temperature zone results from increase in blast rate. This effect is well illustrated in Figs. 33.3-33.7 by following the rise in metal temperature with increase in blast rate at any given carbon to metal ratio, despite the increase in melting rate.

For two fuels of markedly different reactivity the observed effect of lower metal temperatures for equivalent blast rate and size is not due to lack of bed temperature or depth of zone, but is due to the fact that less fuel actually reaches the melting zone so that the fuel to metal ratio is actually less in the case of the more reactive fuel despite the fact that the same ratio is being charged.

Metal Losses

Metal losses are a function of the oxidizing character of the atmosphere to which the molten metal is exposed. By far the most effective oxidizing agent is, of course, free oxygen. However, water vapor and carbon dioxide are also mild oxidizing agents. Fortunately, oxygen is consumed very rapidly and is present in only low concentrations in the major portion of the bed. Increase in fuel size will increase the distance penetrated by the oxygen in almost direct proportion to average lump diameter for fuel of comparable surface area.

Similarly, the percentage of the cross-sectional area having significant concentrations of oxygen increases as the ratio of fuel to cupola diameter increases. The percentage also increases as the surface area per lump decreases for equivalent size material. Any one of these effects can be expected to increase metal losses due to exposure to oxygen. Exposure to high concentrations of the mild oxidizing gases CO_2 and H_2O occurs principally in the reduction zone of the bed. The relative extent depends on fuel size and blast rate as in the oxidation zone.

At constant blast rate, increase in fuel size increases the depth of the zone and the time the molten metal is in contact with these oxidizing gases. Increase in blast rate at constant fuel size spreads the reduction zone only slightly, but does increase the concentration of CO_2 and H_2O at any given level due to factors discussed in the section on "Reduction Zone." It is for this reason that "stage of combustion" discussed in a later section offers a means of control of metal losses.

THE MELTING PROCESS

In the operation of a cupola, metal and fuel in fixed proportions are charged into the cupola. In passing down the shaft to the melting zone, the charges are preheated by the hot upward flowing reaction gases so that by the time they arrive at the melting zone fuel and metal are at substantially the temperature of this zone.

In the melting zone, a phase change occurs which extracts heat from the cupola, the amount extracted depending principally upon the composition of the metal charge. The molten iron trickles down through the incandescent fuel and acquires superheat. In the superheat zone, another phase change—the formation of slag—occurs, which extracts additional heat from the bed.

Although major variations in the composition of the metal and in the nature of the slag forming material cause changes in the overall results, definite relationships exist between melting rate, metal temperature, blast rate and the metal to fuel ratio for any given set of conditions. No matter what the ratio of metal to fuel introduced into the cupola, it is obvious from the discussion under chemical reactions that in any given cupola a stabilized condition will establish itself depending upon the rate of air supply.

It is also apparent that the fuel introduced with the metal charges will be consumed in melting and superheating these charges or in losses such as sensible or latent heat in the stack gases and slag. If the bed height of the original fuel is not that which conforms to the air rate for the size and reactivity of the fuel used, the bed will either burn down or build up to the correct level over a period of time during which the melting rate or metal temperature will continuously change until the stablized condition is attained.

Thus under stable conditions in a given cupola and at a fixed blast rate and metal to fuel ratio, there is one and only one melting rate and metal temperature for any particular fuel. It is also obvious that if either blast rate or fuel ratio is changed during the operation, a new set of conditions will be established.

Graphical Representation of Cupola Operation

Much work has been done in several countries throughout the last few decades which serves as a basis for the development of charts relating metal temperature, melting rate, blast rate and iron to fuel ratios. Jungbluth and his co-workers, especially Korschan,[13] are responsible for research which led to a mathematical representation of the various factors involved. These investigators used standard quality foundry coke in a 21.5 in. experimental cupola under carefully controlled test conditions. Their results, converted to English units,[14] are shown graphically in Fig. 33.2.

This simple plot was subjected to a progressive method of interpolation by Massari and Lindsay[14] and the data converted to a basis suitable for use with a 72 in. diameter cupola. The original conversion chart was checked during an entire year's operation on a 72 in. cupola where the iron-carbon ratio varied from 6.75 to 8.50, and was found to be slightly in error in that metal temperatures were about 50 F higher than predicted. This observation led to the construction of a new chart for the 72 in. cupola in which the temperatures were set 50 F higher.

A consideration of the dimensions of the two cupolas results in the realization that the 72 in. cupola has 3.35 times as much wall area, through which heat may be lost, as the 21.5 in. cupola. On the other hand, for corresponding conditions of operation, 11.25 times as much iron is melted in the 72 in. cupola. It may also be said that the total heat developed is 11.25 times as great in the 72 in. cupola. Naturally, if the heat developed is 11.25 times as much per unit time and the wall area is only 3.35 times as much, less heat proportionately will be lost through the walls of the large cupola.

Coincidentally the difference in temperature of the iron in degrees Fahrenheit is the same as the difference in diameters in inches. A 72 in. cupola then may be expected to yield iron some 36 F hotter than a 36 in. cupola operating under corresponding conditions. It was on this basis that all of the charts presented in Figs. 33.3 through 33.9 were developed, using the 72 in. cupola chart as a master.

It is important to note that the data contained in these charts represent cupola operations after melting equilibrium has been attained some time after the beginning of the heat and up to the time charging is stopped. If the bed height is incorrect for the conditions of operation, melting equilibrium may not be attained for some time after the heat is started and the charts will not apply to this period. Similarly, fuel of markedly different reactivity will alter the heat balance so that in effect the metal to fuel ratio reaching the melting zone is altered, in which case results will be displaced on the chart.

Attention should be called to the fact that the air-volume is given in cu ft per min (cfm) measures at standard conditions (32 F and a pressure of 29.92 in. of mercury). Actually, however, the air in the foundry is seldom at exactly this temperature or pressure, and therefore it becomes necessary to make a conversion of the volume to these standard conditions. These adjustments can be made by multiplying by the proper factors. Some of the factors are shown in Table 33.1.

The measuring instruments account for the air which passes the point of measurement in the entrance duct. Some of this air, however, does not actually go through the cupola but manages to escape as leakage before reaching the tuyeres. It has been estimated by various authorities that this leakage may be, in some cases, as much as 15 per cent.

Corrected to standard conditions, air volumes in Figs. 33.3-33.9 signify the air which goes through the

TABLE 33.1. FACTORS FOR CONVERSION TO STANDARD CONDITIONS (32F AND 29.92 IN. Hg PRESSURE FROM ACTUAL BLAST CONDITIONS

Temp. (°F)	Factor	Temp. (°F)	Factor
0	1.070	50	0.965
5	1.058	55	0.955
10	1.047	60	0.946
15	1.036	65	0.937
20	1.025	70	0.928
25	1.014	75	0.920
30	1.004	80	0.911
35	0.994	85	0.903
40	0.984	90	0.895
45	0.974	95	0.886
Pressure	**Factor**	**Pressure**	**Factor**
29.0	0.969	29.6	0.989
29.1	0.973	29.7	0.993
29.2	0.976	29.8	0.996
29.3	0.979	29.9	0.999
29.4	0.983	30.0	1.003
29.5	0.986	30.1	1.006

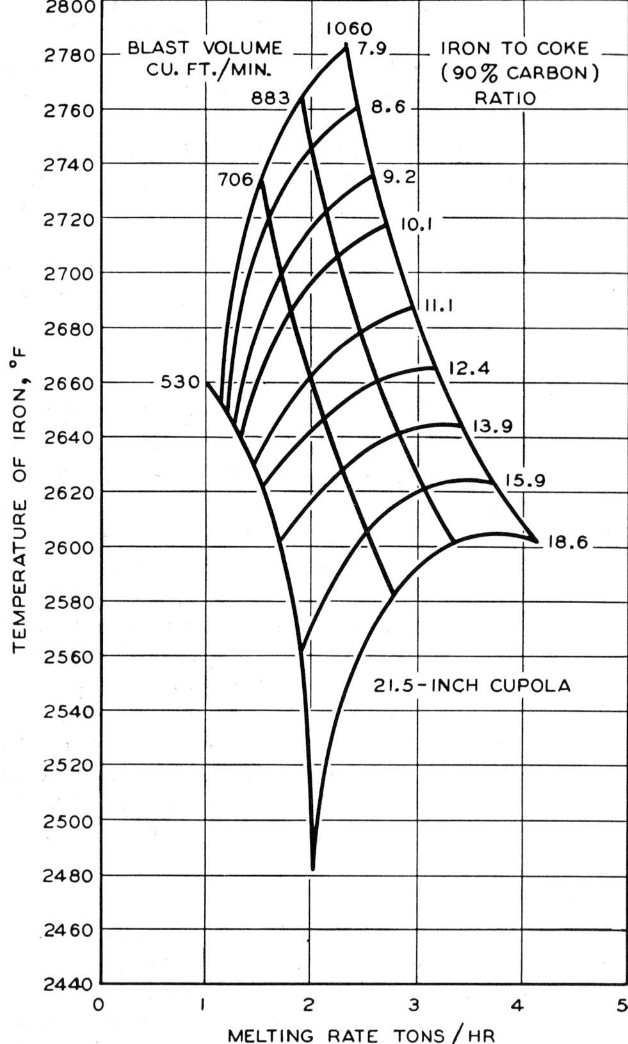

Fig. 33.2. Operating conditions for a 21.5 diameter cupola—relation between iron temperature and iron-carbon ratio, blast volume and melting rate.

cupola. The charts can be used to determine the air leakage that prevails if there is an independent measure of the air volume at some point in the air duct.

Use of Charts

To illustrate how the charts may be used, take a condition in which a 54 in. diameter cupola is operated with an air volume of 5600 cfm at 80 F and 29.6 in. of mercury with a leakage of 10 per cent and an iron-carbon ratio of 9 to 1.

Referring to the data of Table 33.1, note that 5600 must be multiplied by the factor 0.911 for the temperature correction and this result, in turn, multiplied by 0.989 for the pressure correction. By these multiplications it will be found that approximately 5100 cfm (S.T.P.*) is passing the point of measurement.

If there is a leakage of 10 per cent, only 4600 cfm will enter and go through the cupola. On turning to the chart for the 54 in. cupola, it will be found that the iron-carbon ratio line 9.0 intersects the 4600 air-volume line at a point corresponding to 2719 F and a melting rate of 11.45 tons/hr.

Inasmuch as the air leakage cannot be estimated closely, it is far better not to employ the air volume as one of the independent variables in using the charts. Of the four variables, it is only necessary to know two to fix the other two. If a cupola has been operated for as much as an hour the active iron-carbon ratio should be identical with the ratio in the charge additions and, therefore, rather precisely known.

The temperature also can be measured with considerable ease with an optical pyrometer. Some skill is required in the proper use of this instrument; quite unreasonable values have been obtained in the past by operators who had not yet developed the proper proficiency. Knowing the temperature and the iron-carbon ratio, one can get the values for the other two variables from the charts. It is often convenient to use the melting rate with the iron-carbon ratio to fix the temperature and air volume.

It should be pointed out that the iron-carbon ratio is used in preference to the iron-coke ratio because it implies a more uniform composition. The iron-carbon ratio can be obtained by dividing the iron-coke ratio by the percentage of carbon in the coke and multiplying by 100. It is often assumed that the carbon content of by-product coke is 90 per cent, in which case the iron-carbon ratio is 1.11 times the iron-coke ratio.

It also should be pointed out that the iron-carbon ratio can be constant only after the cupola has settled down to equilibrium operating conditions in spite of the fact that the same charges are made time after time. There must be changes, for possibly an hour or more, in the coke bed height and in temperatures throughout the cupola as equilibrium is attained. A change of blast volume, even late in the heat, will upset the equilibrium and time will be required for it to be attained again at the new setting.

In attempting to make use of the charts, one must keep in mind the necessity of considering the conditions of equilibrium. Herein it is assumed that equilibrium exists if the air volume and other materials of the charge are added in constant amounts, and that dropping of the bottom of the cupola, just after it is charged to a given level, will reveal the same amounts of each material as would be found were the bottom dropped sometime later.

An examination of the charts indicates that the iron-carbon ratio lines run from the lower left to the upper right. Therefore, if the iron-carbon ratio is held constant and the air volume is increased, the changing condition is represented by a point traveling along the constant iron-carbon ratio line.

Suppose a 36 in. cupola is operating with 1650 cfm (S.T.P.) and an iron-carbon ratio of 8.5 to 1 and it is desired to find just how the melting rate and temperature will be changed if the iron-carbon ratio is held constant and the air volume is changed to 2000 cfm. The original condition is represented by the intersection of the 8.5 iron-carbon ratio line and the 1650 air volume line. Here it is found that the

*S.T.P.—Standard Conditions of Temperature and Pressure, 32° F and 29.92-in. Hg pressure.

melting rate is 3.97 tons/hr and the temperature is 2676 F.

The new condition can be determined by moving out the 8.5 iron-carbon ratio line to the 2000 air-volume line. Now it will be found that the melting rate has been increased to 4.81 tons per hour and the temperature to 2709 F.

Increasing the air-volume increases the melting rate and raises the temperature. Faster melting is obtained because more coke is burned thereby supplying more heat which melts more metal. The temperature is raised because the loss of heat through the cupola walls is practically the same for identical time periods regardless of the melting rate. The proportion of the total heat lost through the walls is less with fast melting and, therefore, the iron must be hotter. Not only the iron, but the slag and effluent gas also will be hotter.

The air volume lines run from lower right to upper left with decreasing iron-carbon ratios. For illustration, a point is taken representing the operation of a 48 in. cupola where the air volume is 4000 cfm and the iron-carbon ratio is 10 to 1. Here the melting rate is 10.8 tons/hr and the temperature is 2699 F.

Air Volume

While holding the air volume constant and changing the iron-carbon ratio to 7 to 1, it will be found that the intersection point moves out along the 4000 air-volume line toward the upper left to the 7.0 iron-carbon ratio line. It will be found that the melting rate has decreased from 10.80 to 8.32 tons/hr and the temperature has increased from 2699 to 2783 F. A decrease in the iron-carbon ratio means an increase in the relative amount of coke.

Therefore, the melting rate decreases with constant air-volume and decreasing iron-carbon ratio because there is more coke to burn out from under the iron before it can be lowered into the melting zone. The temperature increases with a decrease in the ratio because although the same total heat is developed, more heat units are developed per pound of metal.

On examining any of the charts, one finds that the air-volume can be increased or decreased with either an increase or decrease in the iron-carbon ratio. These variables are completely independent of each other. In spite of this, however, the misconception often is encountered that the coke must be increased if the air volume is increased. The thought prompting this erroneous conclusion is that it takes more air to burn more coke—a perfectly logical deduction if one considers only what happens in the oxidation zone.

The misconception arises because of the changes in connotation of the phrase "cut the air." "Cutting the air," as referred to in the foundry, has nothing to do with reducing the amount of air relative to the coke. It merely signifies the reduction of air with respect to time. Cutting the air then means a reduction in rate.

On the contrary, a "cut in coke" has nothing to do with a rate but is a reduction in coke relative to iron. The coke reacts with air only after the air reaches the zone of combustion, and furthermore reacts just as fast or just as slowly as the air gets there. Consequenty, when the air volume, which is a rate, is reduced, the burning rate of coke is automatically reduced and the cupola charges tend to replace the coke faster than before the air volume reduction.

Many cupolas are operated with inappropriate air volumes. In making thin, cored castings especially, one finds that further and further reductions in air volume so as to get lower and lower melting rates lead to higher and higher foundry reject losses. This is particularly true if the inside diameter of the cupola is held constant while making the air volume reductions.

Rather than operate a 66 in. diameter cupola with an iron-carbon ratio of 7.0 and an air volume of 5200 cfm (S.T.P.) to get a temperature of 2714 F and a melting rate of 11.4 tons/hr, it is preferable to line the cupola down to 60 in. where a melting rate of 11.4 tons/hr can be maintained with an air volume at 5500 cfm and an iron-carbon ratio of 7.0 with a temperature of 2775 F.

Not only is the iron hotter for a constant melting rate, but the faster melting rate per sq ft of cross section means that the iron is not in the cupola so long and consequently less oxidation takes place in the smaller cupola. Too few cupolas are operated with the proper air volume. As stressed above, it is better to operate a smaller cupola with a sufficient blast than a larger one with a low blast to get a specific melting rate.

Melting Rates

Owing to the standardization of the graph background, it has been impossible to show comparable ranges of melting rates for all cupola sizes. It happens that the chart for a 42 in. cupola covers a wider range than any of the others. If the conditions of operation for one of the other cupolas is represented by a point completely off a chart, it is possible to make conversions, by using the 42 in. cupola chart, and reconverting the answers to apply to the cupola in question.

In order to show the method by which these conversions may be made, the case of a 60 in. cupola operating with an air volume of 5800 cfm (S.T.P.) and an iron-carbon ratio of 12.0 may be taken as an example. A glance at the 60 in. cupola chart will suffice to show that the point is completely off the graph.

A corresponding point, however, will be found on the 42 in. cupola chart if it is on any of them. To find the temperature and melting rate, it first is expedient to find comparable values for corresponding conditions in a 42 in. cupola. In the first place, it may be said that the iron-carbon ratio is the same for both cupolas operated under corresponding conditions. The air volume, however, for the 42 in. cupola may be found as

$$5800 \times \frac{42^2}{60^2} = 2840 \text{ cfm}$$

Referring to the chart for the 42 in. cupola, it is found that the melting rate, when the iron-carbon ratio is 12.0 and the air volume is 2840 cfm is 8.75 tons/hr and the temperature is 2658 F. These values now should be changed to corresponding values for the 60-in. cupola. The melting rate is

$$8.75 \text{ x} \frac{60^2}{42^2} \text{ or } 17.85 \text{ tons/hr}$$

The temperature is

$$2658 + (60 - 42) \text{ or } 2676 \text{ F}$$

In general, it may be said that both the melting rate and the air volume for one cupola may be found to correspond to those of a second cupola, by multiplying by the square of the diameter of the cupola to which the conversion is made and dividing by the square of the diameter of the cupola from which the conversion is made.

It must be borne in mind that cupolas differ in some details and this condition, of course, will lead to different results. A cupola tends to give hotter iron as height or wall thickness is increased provided the other variables remain constant. An increase in height, however, may result in a lower air volume unless the blower is able to deliver the required amount of air against the increased blast pressure.

Different results given by cupolas may be charged to an actual difference in air volume. The factor of proper air volume has not yet received the consideration which the industry owes it. Even though it is a general misconception that air is cheap, air delivered to the cupola is a substantial item of expense and it therefore behooves foundry management to make the most efficient use of it in operating a cupola. Due to small differences which exist among cupolas, it is suggested that the operator try to establish a precise chart for each of his cupolas based upon the more general patterns which have been presented here.

Air Requirements

The weight of air supplied to a cupola is approximately equal to the weight of metal charged, and no less attention should be given to it than is accorded the selection and apportioning of the charges of fuel, flux and metal. The combustion reactions depend upon the air supply for the oxygen which causes them to take place. The efficiency of the melting operation is based upon the admission of the correct amount of air for the melting conditions desired.

In perfect combustion, a definite weight of oxygen (32 lb) combined with a definite weight of carbon (12 lb) according to Reaction I to produce a definite weight of carbon dioxide (44 lb). Stated in other words, 378 cu ft (N.T.P.) of oxygen combines with 12 lb of carbon to produce 378 cu ft (N.T.P) of carbon dioxide measured.

Air, however, contains only 21 per cent oxygen so 1800 cu ft of air are required. The composition of the gas from complete combustion with air would, therefore, be 378 cu ft CO_2 and 1422 cu ft N_2 or

$$\frac{(378)\ (100)}{(1422 + 378)} = 21\%\ CO_2$$

In deep fuel beds, it is impossible to obtain complete conversion of O_2 to CO_2 for the reason previously explained, and varying percentages of the CO_2 are reduced to CO according to Reaction II. If all 378 cu ft of CO_2 were reduced, 2 times 378 or 756 cu ft of CO would result. The composition of the effluent gas would then be

$$\frac{(756)\ (100)}{(1422 + 756)} = 34.7\%\ CO$$

In actual practice both carbon dioxide and carbon monoxide are always present. When the carbon dioxide content of the effluent gas is known and no free oxygen is present, the carbon monoxide content can be calculated from the relation

$$\%\ CO = \left(\frac{34.7}{21.0}\right) (21 - \%\ CO_2) = (1.652)\ (21 - \%\ CO_2)$$

Similarly, the nitrogen content can be calculated from the relation

$$\%\ N_2 = 100 - (\%\ CO_2 + \%\ CO)$$

Assuming no oxygen, volatile impurities or other sources of CO and CO_2, it is possible to obtain a complete analysis of the gas if the carbon dioxide content is measured.

In actual practice, the foregoing equations are not entirely correct. The decomposition of limestone liberates CO_2, part of which may react with carbon to yield CO. When the limestone addition is equal to about 25 per cent of the carbon content of the coke the relation between CO_2 and CO is

$$\%\ CO = (1.682)\ (21.28 - \%\ CO_2)$$

Similarly, the decomposition of water vapor according to the Reaction III introduces an error since in this case only one volume of CO is produced for each volume of water vapor in the air blast. Likewise, any volatile matter in the fuel is usually released before the fuel reaches the melting zone, and these volatile products dilute the effluent gas and cause minor errors in calculation when the simplified equation is used.

However, the corrections tend to compensate each other to some extent and may generally be neglected in view of the rather low precision of most gas sampling and analysis methods employed in cupola operations. Based on the uncorrected relationship, Fig.33.10 shows graphically the effluent gas composition in terms of CO, CO_2 and N_2.

The simplest and probably the most accurate method of determining air requirements for a specific set of conditions is to utilize the appropriate chart of Figs. 33.3-33.9 together with the correction factors of Table 33.1, plus additional correction for probable losses between the air actually measured in the blast line and that actually passing up through the cupola. Several examples of such calculation have already been shown in the section titled "Use of Charts."

For any specific set of conditions, the air requirement can be estimated rapidly with the aid of the data presented in Table 33.2 which show the theoretical weight of air required for various stages of combustion. Based upon the measured composition of the effluent gases, metal to fuel ratio and melting

TABLE 33.2. THE AIR REQUIREMENTS (N.T.P.) FOR COMBUSTION

Effluent Gases			Fraction of 1 lb Carbon Burned to		Air Requirements, lb per 1 lb Carbon			Gases Produced lb per lb Carbon				Heat Developed, btu per lb Carbon			Efficiency of Combus-tion, %	lb/ lb C	cu ft/ lb C	cu ft per ton Iron 90% Coke 10:1 Ratio	54-in. Cupola M. R.12/hr cu ft/min	
CO_2 %	CO %	N_2 %	A CO_2	B CO	O_2	N_2	Air	CO_2	CO	N_2	Total	CO_2	CO	Total					theo.	+5%
0	34.7	65.3	0.000	1.000	1.33	4.44	5.77	0.00	2.33	4.44	6.77	000	4350	4350	29.9	5.77	75.4	13,600	2720	2860
1	33.0	66.0	0.029	0.971	1.37	4.57	5.94	0.11	2.26	4.57	6.94	422	4224	4646	31.9	5.94	77.7	14,000	2810	2950
2	31.4	66.6	0.060	0.940	1.41	4.70	6.11	0.22	2.19	4.70	7.11	873	4089	4962	34.1	6.11	79.9	14,400	2880	3030
3	29.7	67.3	0.092	0.908	1.45	4.85	6.30	0.34	2.11	4.85	7.30	1338	3950	5288	36.3	6.30	82.4	14,800	2960	3110
4	28.1	67.9	0.125	0.875	1.50	4.99	6.49	0.46	2.04	4.99	7.49	1819	3806	5625	38.6	6.49	84.8	15,300	3060	3220
5	26.4	68.6	0.159	0.841	1.54	5.14	6.68	0.58	1.96	5.14	7.68	2314	3658	5972	41.1	6.68	87.3	15,700	3140	3300
6	24.7	69.3	0.195	0.805	1.59	5.30	6.89	0.71	1.88	5.30	7.89	2837	3502	6339	43.5	6.89	90.0	16,200	3240	3400
7	23.1	69.9	0.232	0.768	1.64	5.47	7.11	0.85	1.79	5.47	8.11	3376	3340	6716	46.2	7.11	92.9	16,700	3340	3510
8	21.5	70.5	0.271	0.729	1.69	5.64	7.33	0.99	1.70	5.64	8.33	3943	3171	7114	48.8	7.33	95.8	17,200	3440	3620
9	19.8	71.2	0.312	0.688	1.75	5.82	7.57	1.15	1.60	5.82	8.57	4540	2993	7533	51.7	7.57	99.0	17,800	3560	3740
10	18.2	71.8	0.354	0.646	1.80	6.01	7.81	1.30	1.51	6.01	8.82	5151	2810	7961	54.7	7.81	102.1	18.400	3680	3870
11	16.5	72.5	0.400	0.600	1.87	6.21	8.08	1.47	1.40	6.21	9.08	5820	2610	8431	57.9	8.08	105.6	19,000	3800	4000
12	14.8	73.2	0.447	0.553	1.93	6.42	8.35	1.64	1.29	6.42	9.35	6504	2406	8910	61.2	8.35	109.1	19,700	3940	4140
13	13.2	73.8	0.496	0.504	1.99	6.64	8.63	1.82	1.17	6.64	9.63	7217	2192	9409	64.7	8.63	112.8	20,300	4060	4260
14	11.6	74.4	0.547	0.453	2.07	6.86	8.93	2.01	1.06	6.86	9.93	7959	1971	9930	68.3	8.93	116.8	21,000	4200	4410
15	9.9	75.1	0.602	0.398	2.13	7.11	9.24	2.21	0.92	7.11	10.24	8759	1731	10490	72.1	9.24	120.8	21,800	4360	4580
16	8.3	75.7	0.658	0.342	2.21	7.35	9.57	2.42	0.80	7.35	10.57	9576	1488	11064	76.0	9.57	125.1	22,600	4520	4750
17	6.6	76.4	0.720	0.280	2.29	7.63	9.92	2.64	0.65	7.63	10.92	10476	1218	11694	80.4	9.92	129.7	23,400	4680	4820
18	5.0	77.0	0.783	0.217	2.38	7.91	10.29	2.87	0.51	7.91	11.29	11393	944	12337	84.8	10.29	134.5	24,300	4860	5100
19	3.3	77.7	0.852	0.148	2.47	8.21	10.68	3.13	0.34	8.21	11.68	12397	644	13041	89.6	10.68	141.2	25,400	5080	5330
20	1.7	78.3	0.922	0.078	2.57	8.52	11.09	3.39	0.18	8.52	12.09	13410	339	13749	94.5	11.09	145.0	26,200	5240	5500
21	0.0	79.0	1.000	0.000	2.67	8.87	11.54	3.67	0.00	8.87	12.54	14550	000	14550	100.0	11.54	151.0	27,200	5480	5750

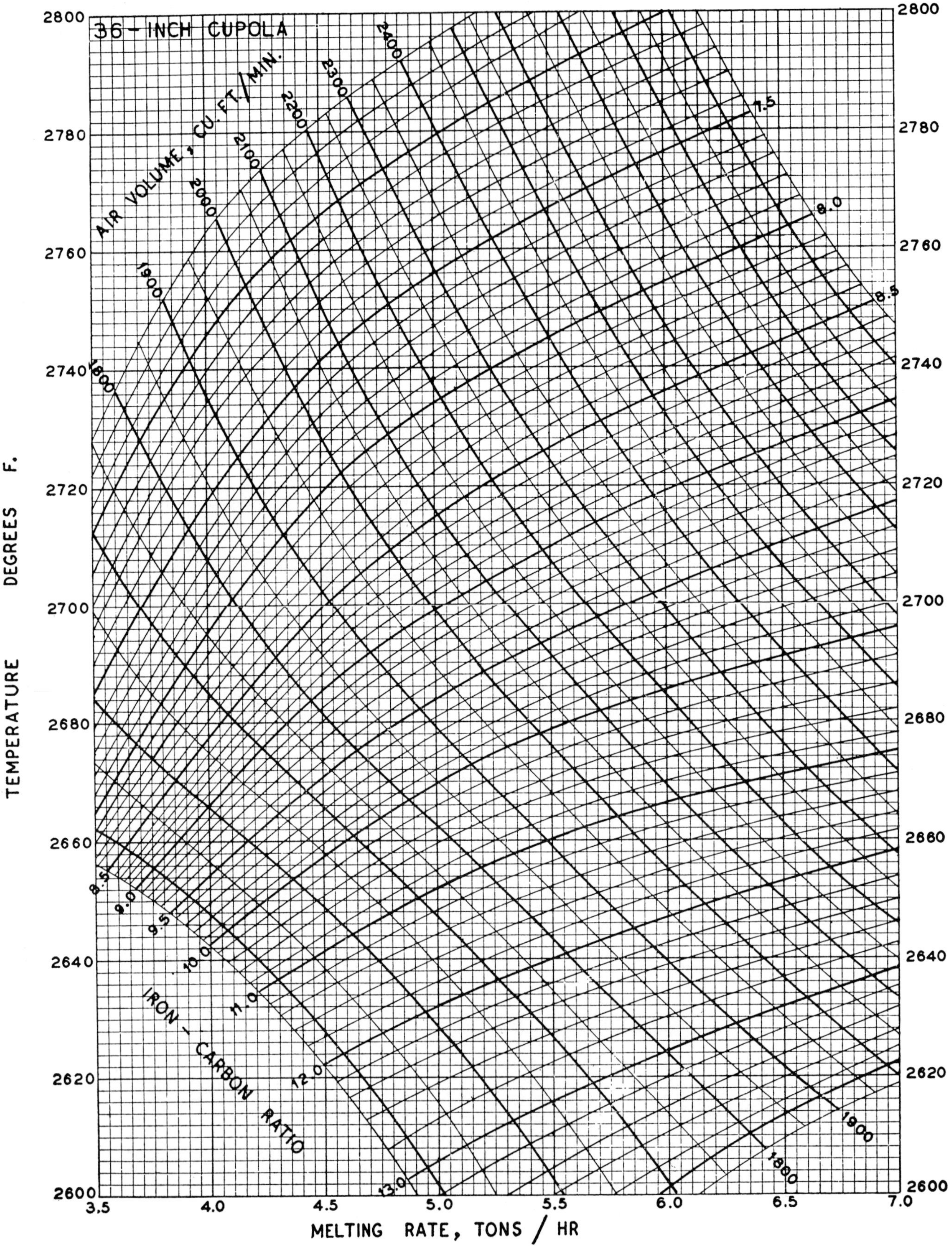

Fig. 33.3. Operating conditions for a 36 in. diameter cupola.

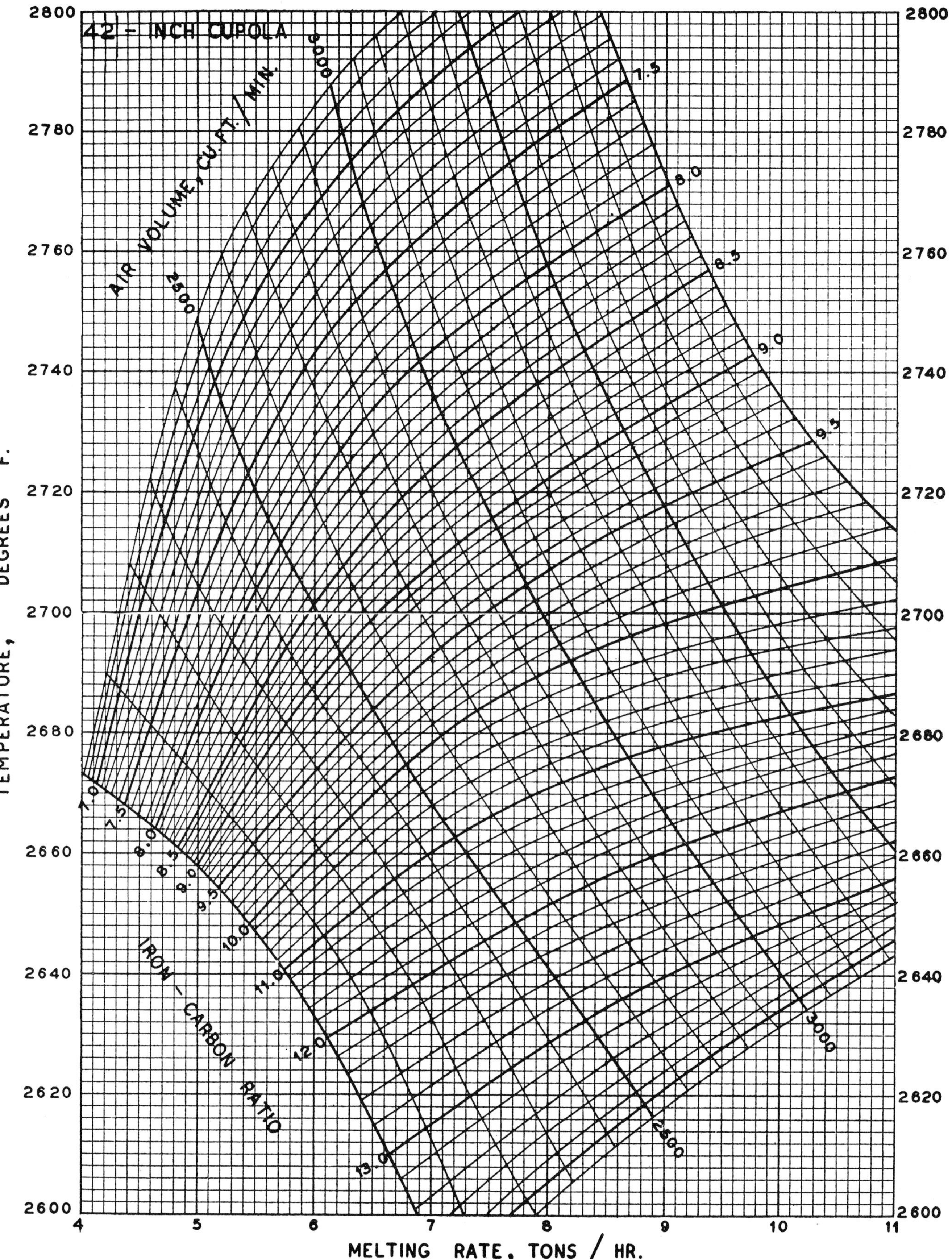

Fig. 33.4. Operating conditions for a 42 in. diameter cupola.

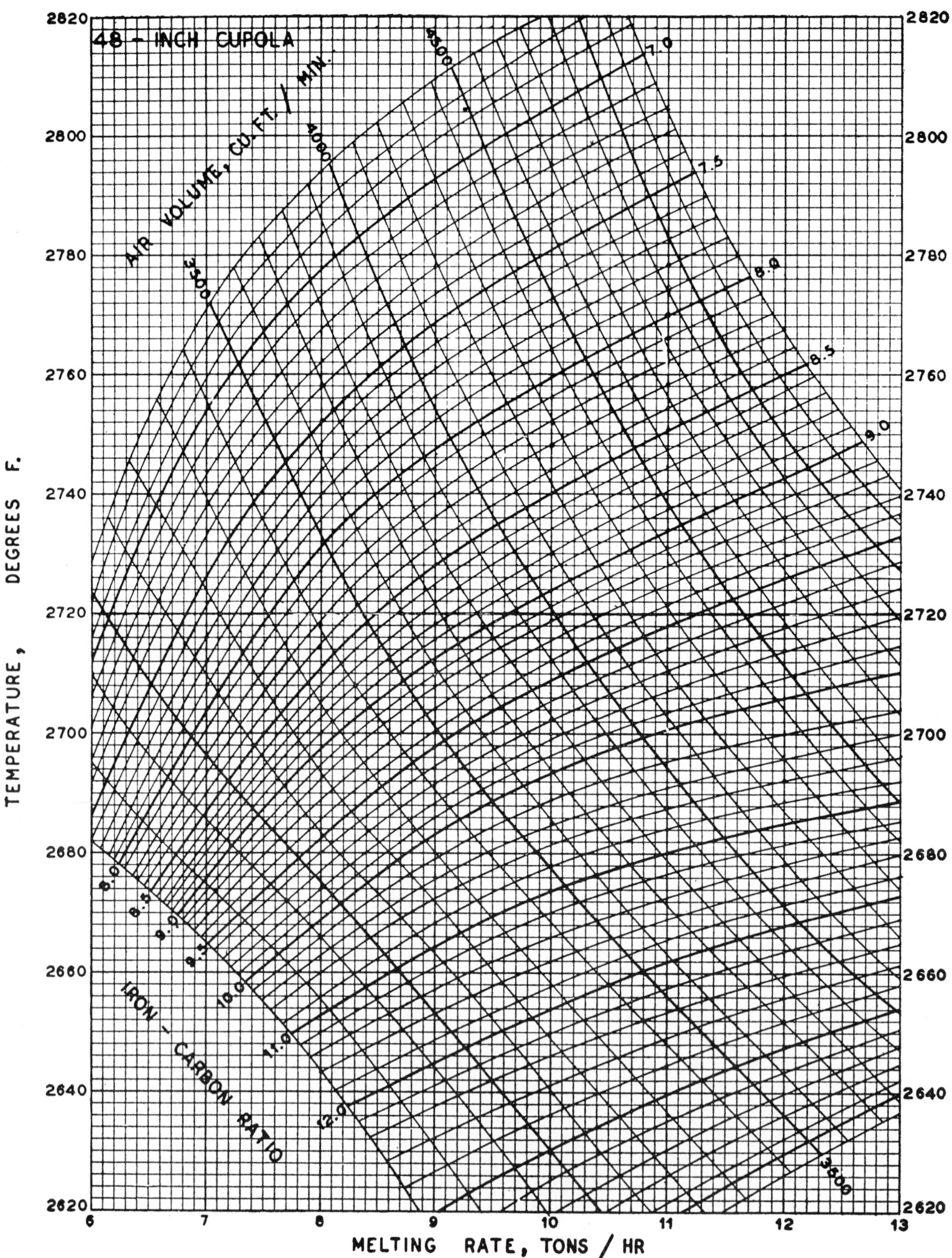

Fig. 33.5. Operating conditions for a 48 in. diameter cupola.

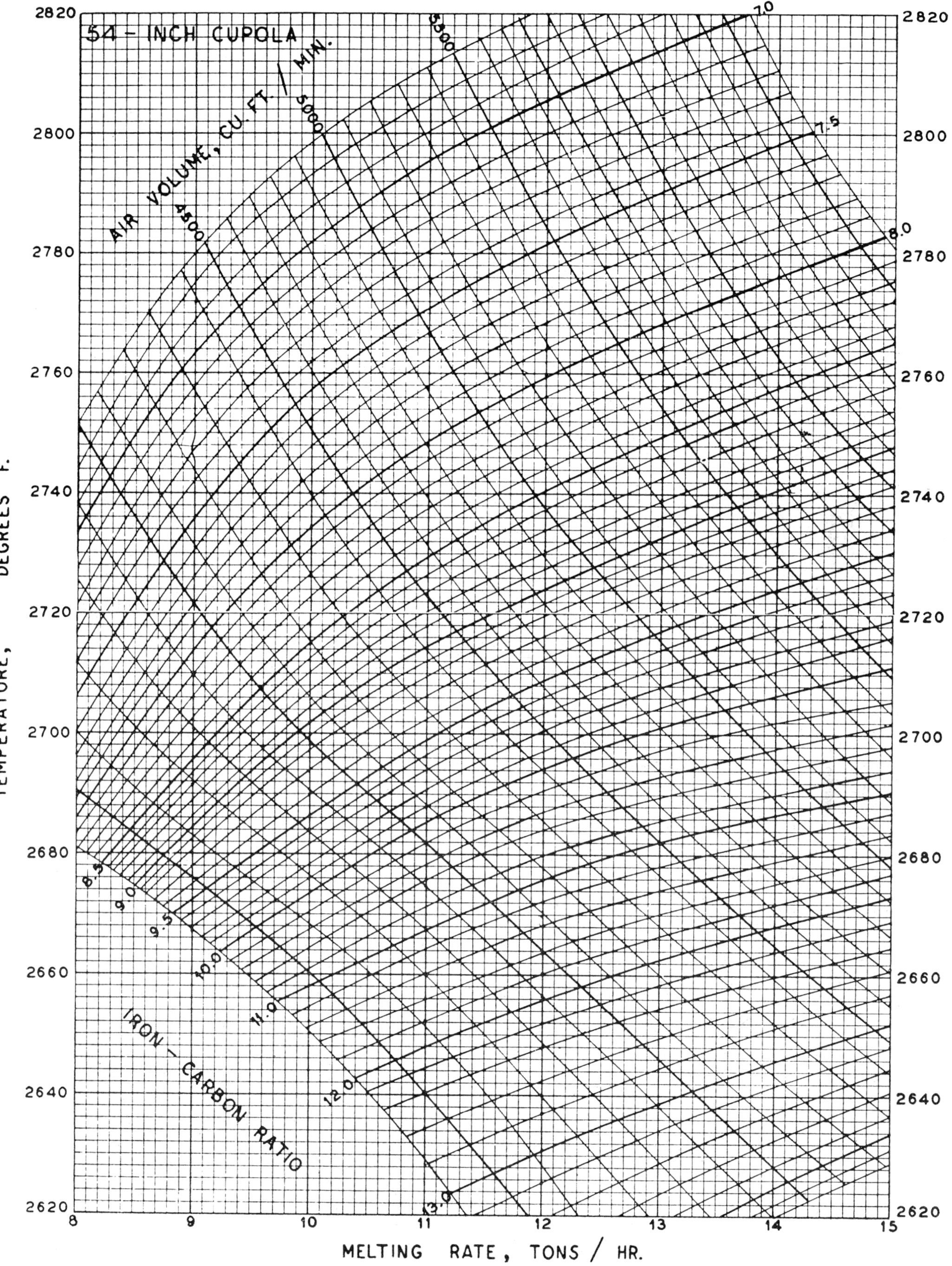

Fig. 33.6. Operating conditions for a 54 in. diameter cupola.

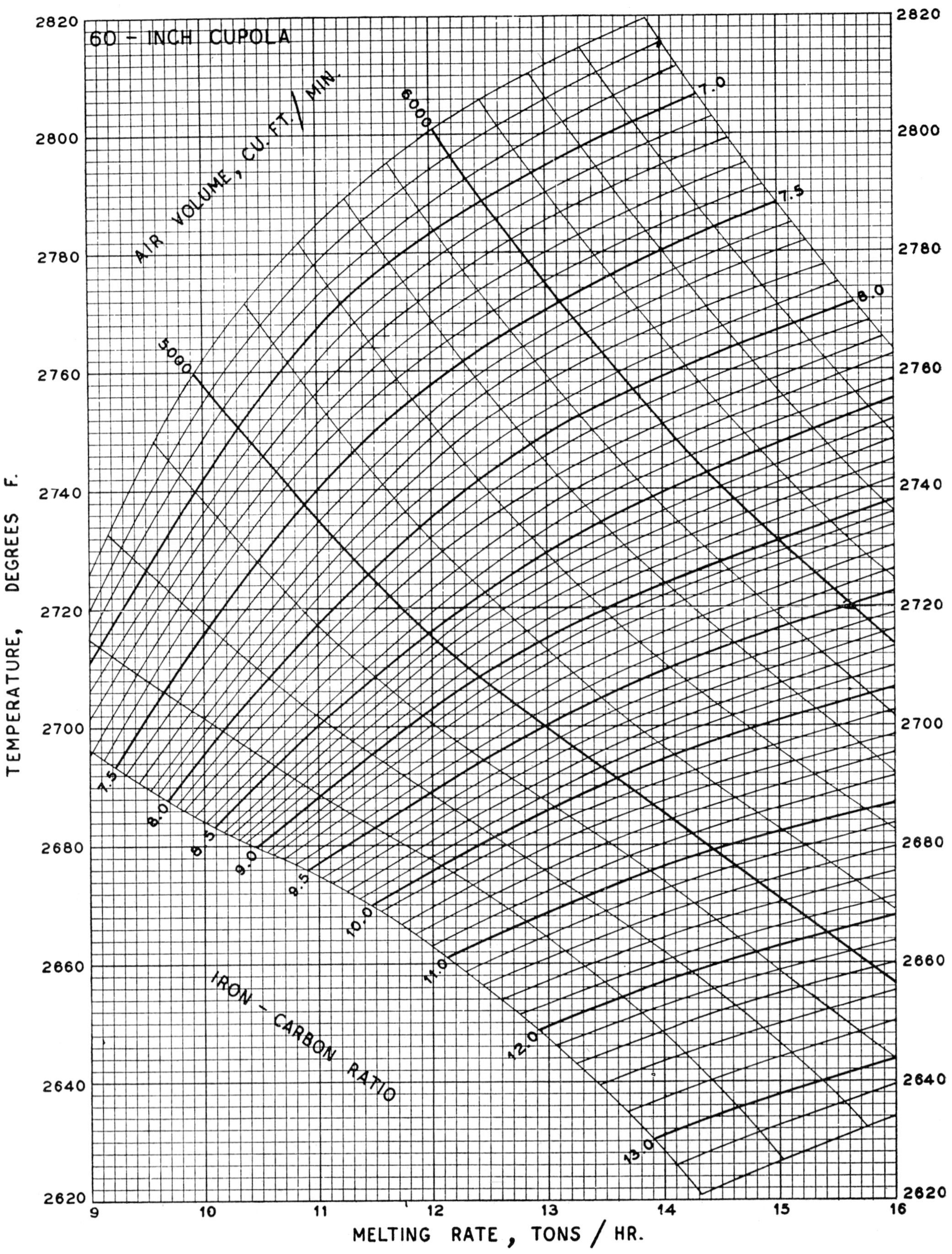

Fig. 33.7. Operating conditions for a 60 in. diameter cupola.

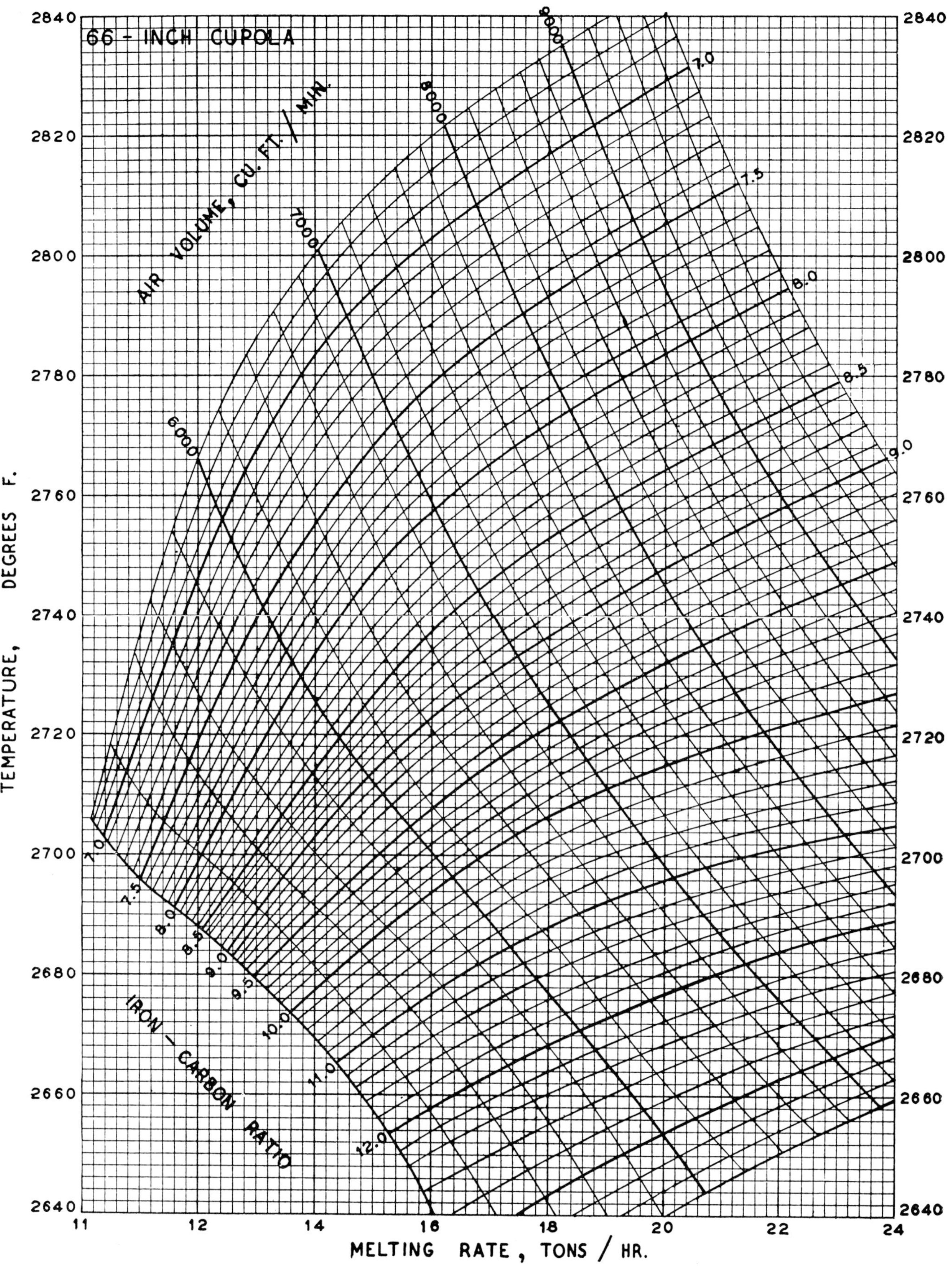

Fig. 33.8. Operating conditions for a 66 in. diameter cupola.

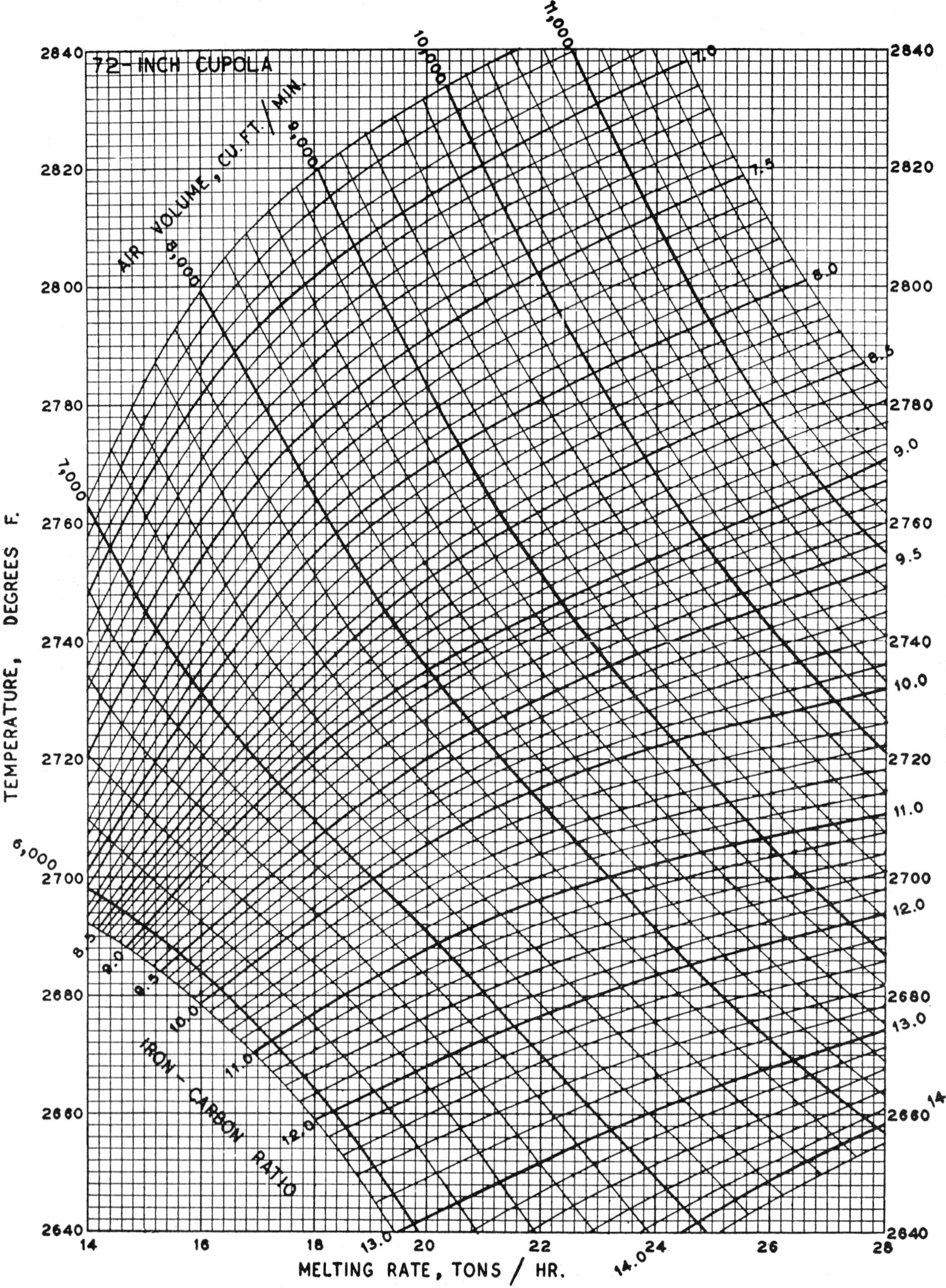

Fig. 33.9 Operating conditions for a 72 in. diameter cupola.

rate, air requirements may be calculated from these data as follows:

Air Requirements (theoretical at N.T.P.)

$$= (\text{cu ft air/lb carbon}) (\text{lb carbon/ton of iron}) (\text{tons iron/min})$$

As a specific example, suppose the effluent gas analysis shows 12 per cent CO_2, the melting rate is 12 tons/hr and the ratio is 10:1 using coke containing 90 per cent carbon. Then the air requirements (theoretical) are

$$(109.1)\ (200)\ (0.9)\ (12/60) = 3940 \text{ cu ft (N.T.P.)}$$

If an air loss between meter and tuyeres is assumed as 5 per cent, the metered air should be

$$(3940)\ (105/100) = 4140 \text{ cu ft (N.T.P.)}$$

If the actual conditions of metering are 80 F and 29.3 in. of mercury pressure, the volume metered can be calculated using the correction factors of Table 33.1 and would be

$$(4140) \left(\frac{0.946}{0.911}\right) \left(\frac{1}{0.979}\right) = 4430 \text{ cu ft at 80 F and 29.3-in. mercury pressure}$$

(Note that data of Table 33.2 are in terms of N.T.P., 60 F and 29.92 in. Hg pressure while the

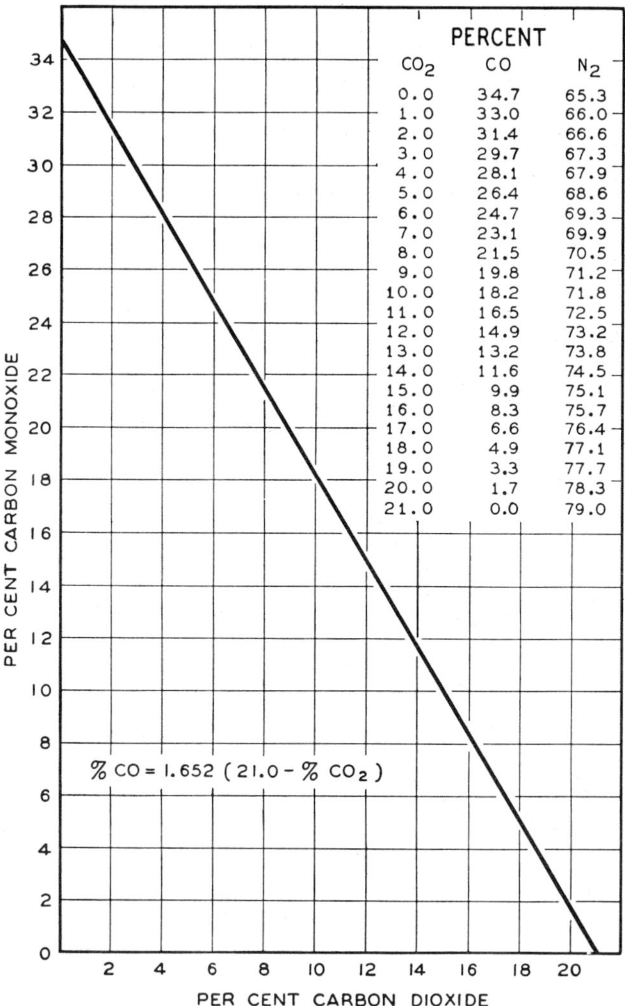

CO_2	CO	N_2
0.0	34.7	65.3
1.0	33.0	66.0
2.0	31.4	66.6
3.0	29.7	67.3
4.0	28.1	67.9
5.0	26.4	68.6
6.0	24.7	69.3
7.0	23.1	69.9
8.0	21.5	70.5
9.0	19.8	71.2
10.0	18.2	71.8
11.0	16.5	72.5
12.0	14.9	73.2
13.0	13.2	73.8
14.0	11.6	74.5
15.0	9.9	75.1
16.0	8.3	75.7
17.0	6.6	76.4
18.0	4.9	77.1
19.0	3.3	77.7
20.0	1.7	78.3
21.0	0.0	79.0

Fig. 33.10. Relationship between CO_2 and CO in effluent gases.

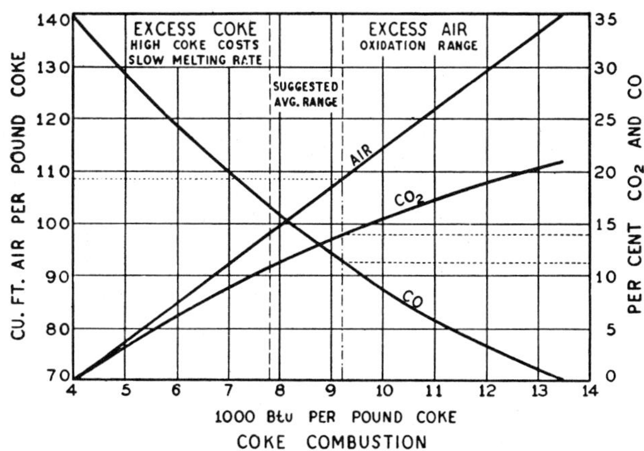

Fig. 33.11. Relationship of air and coke to combustion.

data of Table 33.1 are for conversion *to standard* conditions of 32 F and 29.92 in. Hg pressure.)

A useful graphic representation to the combustion of coke has been presented by Mulcahy[15] as shown in Fig. 33.11. The chart is based on coke of 92.5 per cent carbon content and the line for air requirement will have slightly greater or lesser slope for fuels of greater or lesser carbon content, respectively. The units of the abscissa likewise will be displaced slightly with changes in coke quality.

However, high Btu/lb is not necesarily a criterion of useful Btu in the coke, as the volatile matter shows higher Btu/lb than does the fixed carbon yet contributes little if anything to the melting operation. The exact location of the suggested range of operation with respect to Btu content applies therefore only to cokes of low volatile matter content.

COMBUSTION CONTROL

Unfortunately, it is not possible to observe directly the conditions that exist within a cupola and to detect the need for corrections in air volume or charges until conditions have deteriorated to the point where quality of the molten iron is affected. Utilizing the relationships discussed in the preceding sections, however, it is possible to obtain an early indication of impending need for correction from analyses of the effluent gases.

As previously discussed, the heat required to preheat, melt and superheat the metal is furnished by the combustion of the fuel. Part of this heat is removed from the cupola, however, as a result of carbon dioxide being reduced to carbon monoxide in the reduction zones. The lower the percentage of carbon dioxide converted, the greater the quality of heat available for effective use.

Consequently, more efficient combustion (in reality less efficient reduction of carbon dioxide) will result in more iron being melted per pound of fuel. Within certain limitations, the efficiency of combustion is directly related to the carbon dioxide content of the effluent gas. Hence, the carbon dioxide content of the effluent gas may be taken as a fairly reliable indication of conditions in the bed.

Within the same limitations, effluent gas composition also serves as a direct indication of the oxidizing or reducing character of the atmosphere to which the molten metal is being subjected. As the character of the atmosphere has a marked influence upon metal composition and properties the correct interpretation of gas analysis data can be most helpful.

It must be emphasized, however, that interpretations based on effluent gas composition from one fuel or set of operating conditions are not always directly translatable into results to be expected from another fuel or set of operating conditions. If, as is usually the case, only CO_2 analyses are made and the results converted to complete analyses using the relationship shown in Fig. 33.10, these factors, if not considered, can introduce errors in interpretation:

a) Fuel of higher than normal volatile matter content will yield volatile products that dilute the effluent gas and the CO_2 content will thereby appear to be lower than for a lower volatile fuel.
b) Higher than normal additions of limestone or other carbonates will yield additional CO_2, only part of which will be reduced to CO. The CO_2 analyses will, therefore, appear higher than normal.
c) High moisture content of the blast yield H_2 and CO, both of which dilute the effluent gas with respect to CO_2. This can be a serious factor in hot, humid weather.
d) Fuel of higher than normal reactivity will continue to reduce CO_2 in the preheat zone and will yield much lower CO_2 values which are not representative of the gas composition in or near the bed.

Despite these limitations, effluent gas analyses are valuable for control purposes, and by applying suitable modification in interpretation can be useful in comparing different fuels or the effects of altered operating conditions.

Influence on Efficiency

Although not synonymous, melting efficiency (iron to fuel ratio) and combustion efficiency (CO_2 content of effluent gas), are closely related as indicated by the Fig. 33.12 data obtained from a study of the operation of hot blast cupolas in 12 foundries.[16] It is apparent, therefore, that definite savings in fuel can be made as a result of combustion control.

Influence on Metal Composition

Silicon and Manganese. The determination of the carbon dioxide content of the effluent gases, together with the composition of the metal issuing from the cupola spout, affords a convenient means of relating the losses of silicon and manganese during the process of melting to the various stages of combustion. A correlation between gas composition and element loss can be obtained from a knowledge of the carbon dioxide concentration of the gases at the time a particular iron sample is taken for analysis.

Based upon such data, Fig. 33.13 graphically shows the relation between the stage of combustion as determined by the carbon dioxide content of the effluent gases, and the percentage loss of silicon and manganese.[16] The latter figure is obtained by deducting the net silicon and manganese from the gross silicon and manganese in the cupola charge. These curves show that, as the percentage of carbon dioxide (a moderately oxidizing gas) increases, the loss of both silicon and manganese will also increase.

Conversely, of course, the reverse situation is true. From such data it is quite apparent that efficiency of combustion is, in part, restricted by the losses of silicon and manganese when considered from a purely economic viewpoint. This will be discussed more in detail when the economic benefits to be derived from

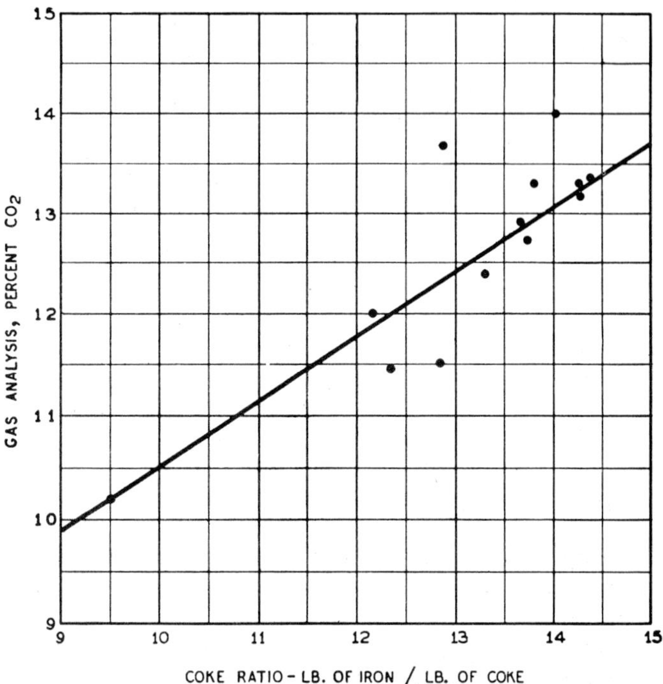

Fig. 33.12. Coke ratio vs. composition of effluent cupola gas.

controlled combustion are analyzed. It is obvious that these losses, unless definitely controlled, will have a direct effect on the internal structure and hence the physical properties of the metal.

Carbon. The mechanism of carbon pick-up in the cupola is still a somewhat debatable question. One view is that the process involves direct solution of carbon by the molten metal in contact with the fuel surfaces, the other that the process is one of carburization in which CO reacts with the metal to form the carbide.

Rambush and Taylor[10] have shown that the carbon content of steel bars increased only slightly while they were still solid but increased rapidly as they began to melt. Lownie, *et al*[11] have reported similar results and have also shown that carbon pick-up in the well, where the metal is in intimate contact with hot carbon, can account for but a small percentage of the total.

It would appear, therefore, that the carbon pick-up is principally through carburization and dependent, therefore, on the CO content of the gases in contact with the melting and molten metal, hence indirectly a function of the stage of combustion. That this concept is probably correct is indicated by the data reported by Massari[16] for a series of analyses of metal and effluent gas obtained simultaneously.

These results, shown in Fig. 33.14, indicate that carbon pickup increases with decrease in CO_2 con-

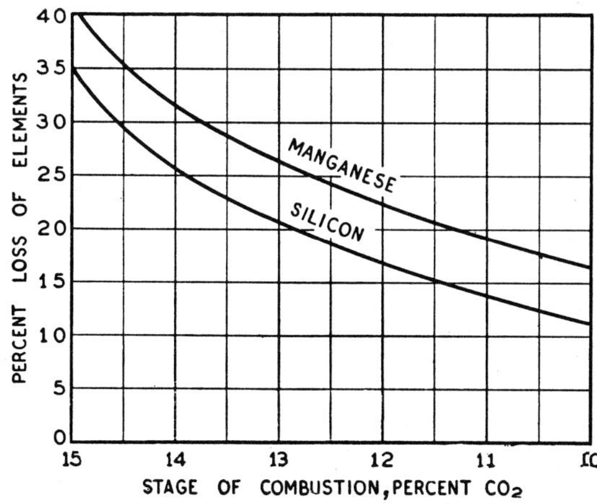

Fig. 33.13. Effect of stage of combustion on element loss in cupola.

tent (increase in CO content) of the gas. Although difficult to accomplish, these data indicate that, within certain limits, the total carbon content of the iron can be controlled if the conditions in the bed can satisfactorily be controlled. Variations in carbon pick-up with fuels of different reactivity are probably due to actual differences in the CO/CO_2 ratio in the upper portion of the bed.

Sulfur. Lownie *et al*[11] have shown that sulfur pick-up is essentially a surface phenomenon that occurs above the melting zone and is favored by low temperatures. They report that steel picks up sulfur rapidly on its surface shortly after introduction into the cupola and loses it slowly as the charge descends into the hotter portions of the cupola.

Cast iron was also found to pick up sulfur on the surface, but the maximum pick-up appeared to occur just before melting occurred. Since sulfur pick-up is a function of the chemistry of the metal and especially of the carbon content[5] no direct correlation between stage of combustion and sulfur pick-up can be expected to cover all cases.

It would appear probable, however, that such a correlation should exist for operations charging substantially a constant type of charge since stage of combustion is an indirect indication of temperature distribution and type of atmosphere within the cupola. Detailed investigations along these lines would certainly be of considerable interest as would also detailed studies on the chemical nature and quantity of the sulfur compounds at various levels in the cupola.

ECONOMIC BENEFITS

As certain metallurgical benefits result from careful control of the combustion processes of the cupola, so it will be shown that at the same time, definite economic advantages can be realized.

Cost of Coke

It has been stated that an increase in the carbon dioxide content of the effluent gases is coincidental with an increase in the quantity of iron melted per pound of coke consumed, that is to say, with a better coke ratio. A higher percentage of carbon dioxide in the effluent gases is indicative of the more complete combustion of the coke, and liberation of a greater portion of the potential heat in the fuel.

Consequently, the cost of coke per ton of iron melted will decrease with increase of carbon dioxide in the effluent gases, as Fig. 33.15 shows. Hence, solely from the standpoint of coke economy, it is evident that a definite saving will result from more complete combustion.

Cost of Elements

However, it is also shown in Fig. 33.15 that, as the efficiency of combustion increases, the losses of silicon and manganese increase. This means that, as the percentage of the carbon dioxide in the effluent gases increases, the cost due to silicon and manganese melting losses will increase. Consequently, aside from the metallurgical aspects previously discussed, maximum economy is not attained with maximum efficiency of combustion, since the saving in coke will not counterbalance the cost of the elements lost.

Cost of Coke vs. Cost of Element Loss

If the summation of the cost of coke and element loss per ton of iron melted is plotted against the stage of combustion (percentage of CO_2 in the effluent gases) as in Fig. 33.15, it will be seen that the composite curves pass through minima. These data, for a hot blast cupola, show that maximum economy is obtained when the carbon dioxide concentration of the effluent gases is held between 13 and 14 per cent in the case of the low silicon iron, and in the vicinity of 12 per cent when the metal melted contains 1.40 per cent silicon.

When these stages of combustion are achieved for the two irons considered, the most economical quantity of coke is consumed to melt a given tonnage of iron with the minimum cost of alloys. For an equivalent cold blast cupola melting operation, similar economies will result when the carbon dioxide content of the effluent gases is from 1.5 to 2.0 per cent lower.

In addition to these economies which can be accomplished by combustion control, operating losses are minimized. It is obvious that a control that insures greater uniformity of melting will reduce shop losses and rejections.

The capital invested in combustion control equipment can be amortized in a reasonably short time as a result of the various economies which can be effected.

METHODS AND APPARATUS

It now is conceded generally that is is just as essential to utilize a reliable means of controlling the quantity of air entering the cupola as it is necessary to measure the quantity of coke and iron, and to regulate the composition of the charge. However, the manner in which the air is controlled merits close consideration. Uniformly low element loss and iron tapped at consistenty high temperatures are the results of a correctly maintained stage of combustion.

For the regulation or automatic control of the blast delivered to the cupola, three principal types of equipment have been developed. These devices are described in Chapter 6.

Maintenance of a Constant Stage of Combustion

A constant weight of air entering the cupola does

not necessarily result in a constant or uniform stage of combustion in the melting zone, since the latter may vary depending upon the type, size, and chemical reactivity of the fuel, in addition to other factors.

A constant volume of air likewise does not at all times contain the same weight of oxygen with which to burn the coke, since the concentration of oxygen (wt/cu ft) will vary with barometric pressure and atmospheric temperature. Similarly, the weight of oxygen delivered will vary with the humidity of the air since any water vapor present replaces an equal volume of air. As a consequence the stage of combustion will, of necessity, vary even if the blast control equipment is designed to maintain a constant volume of air.

In view of the previous discussion relating to the metallurgical aspects and economics of melting, it appears, for optimum operating conditions, that a more satisfactory control could be obtained by keeping track of the carbon dioxide concentration in the effluent gases and adjusting the blast volume, when necessary, to maintain uniformly the most satisfactory rate of combustion.

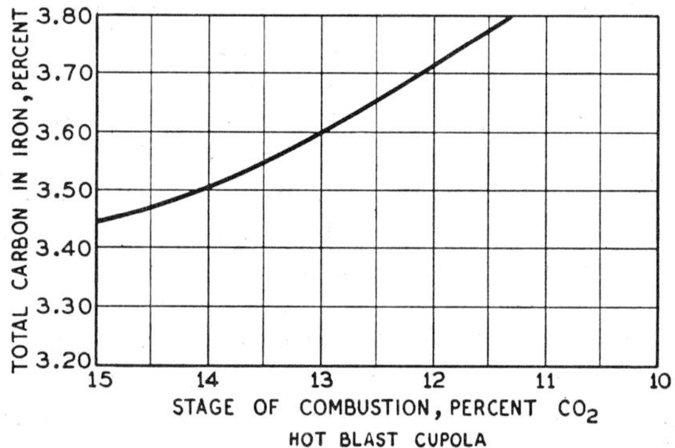

Fig. 33.14. Relationship between total carbon content of the iron and the stage of combustion within the cupola.

Method of Sampling

The one major weakness with this method of cupola control is in securing a truly representative sample under the adverse sampling conditions existing in the shaft of the cupola. In the case of exploratory analyses where an operator is present to handle the sampling equipment, fairly reliable samples can be taken with a length of 1/8-in. standard steel pipe inserted into the charge to a depth of about 3 ft.

This method makes it possible to take samples at various locations radially and with respect to the tuyeres and the entrance of the blast main into the windbox. It is possible also, by permitting the pipe to remain in the cupola, to obtain gas samples at various levels almost to the melting zone, by allowing the pipe to travel downward with the charges.

For a permanent installation to give continuous sampling, one method that has been tried with only limited success because of the sampling difficulties involved is the permanent installation of gas sampling tubes through the walls of the cupola. These tubes, four in number, and 1 in. in diameter, were located approximately 3 ft below the normal level of the charges by burning and drilling holes through the cupola shell and lining for the insertion of the tubes, which project to within 1 in. of the face of the lining.

It is important that the connecting piping be so planned that approximately equal quantities of gas be withdrawn by each tube and, after mixing, will constitute an average sample typical of the conditions within the cupola at that time. It is equally important that a gas-tight seal between lining and sampling tubes be maintained. Even with these precautions, however, this method can sample the gases only at the periphery.

Although this frequently gives a reliable sample it presupposes uniform gas composition from the wall to centerline of the cupola, which is not always true if there is any tendancy toward channelling in the bed or in the shaft.

Types of Gas Analyzers

Gas analyzers may be divided into four classes, according to their principles of operation. These methods depend upon chemical absorption, specific gravity, thermal conductivity and combustion.

Instruments for portable purposes and meters for permanent installation are available. The portable instruments are primarily for test purposes such as determining the stages of combustion that exist at

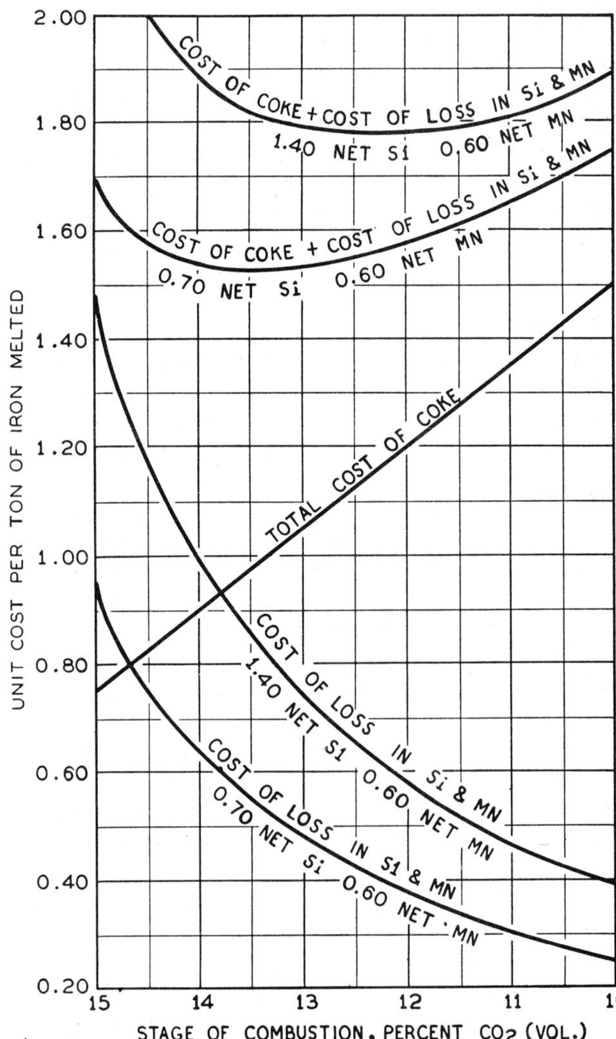

Fig. 33.15. Stage of combustion in the cupola vs. melting cost.[16]

various levels or locations throughout the cupola. The indicating type is most commonly used and is operated manually. The observed readings are recorded for further use. Permanently installed meters generally operate automatically and are of the recording type.

Certain functions are necessarily performed, regardless of the principle used; that is, a sample of the gas to be analyzed is forced into the analyzing section of the meter and the measurement of the CO_2, or other component of the gas, is obtained by one of the four principles. An indicator and scale, a record on a chart or a combination of both may be used to show the CO_2 content of the sample. The reading generally is taken in per cent by volume of the total sample.

Carbon dioxide is the one component of the effluent gases from the cupola from which a direct indication of the combustion conditions can be determined easily and quickly. The effluent gases also contain carbon monoxide (CO), nitrogen (N_2), and possibly a small amount of oxygen (O_2). The determination of all these gases can be accomplished most easily with the hand-operated Orsat type instrument.

Chemical Absorption Type

The chemical absorption method includes both manual (Orsat) and automatic devices of varying degrees of complexity.

The Orsat or manual chemical absorption type is a portable instrument in which CO_2, CO and O_2 can be determined by successive absorption of these constituents in suitable reagents. The volume of each absorbed from a given volume of gas is recorded and converted to a volume per cent basis. The volume unabsorbed is assumed to be nitrogen. Simplified units with only a single absorber for CO_2 are in common use where this is the constituent of primary interest.

The selection and care of equipment, reagents required, manipulative techniques employed and methods of calculation, are described in detail in any standard text on gas analysis[17] and should be consulted before such equipment is employed. Any other acidic gas such as H_2S or SO_2 present in the gas will be absorbed by the CO_2 absorbent and will introduce a corresponding error unless removed prior to the Orsat analysis. However, the quantity of such material present in the effluent gases from cupolas is usually too small to introduce a significant error.

Automatic analyzers based upon the principle of volumetric measurement and chemical absorption are available from a number of manufacturers. These are usually designed to analyze for CO_2 only, are equipped with temperature compensating devices, and operate at constant pressure so that errors due to volumetric change resulting from temperature and pressure changes are eliminated.

Such devices analyze a relatively small volume of gas quite rapidly and give a continuous record. Care must be taken in installing such units that the sample analyzed is taken from a flowing stream of gas that is actually representative of the gas at the point of sampling in the cupola. Frequent calibration (at least once a day) with a standard Orsat is recommended.

Specific Gravity Type

The density (weight per unit volume) of cupola gas increases in direct proportion to its CO_2 content provided the H_2 and/or volatile matter content of gas does not change. This is due to the fact that within the limits of measurement CO, N_2 and O_2 have essentially the same specific gravity, while that of CO_2 is nearly 55 per cent higher.

Hydrogen, however, has a specific gravity only 7 per cent that of nitrogen, and small changes on hydrogen content result in wide variations in specific gravity of the gas mixture. Fortunately, the hydrogen content does not normally vary greatly as it is dependent on the absolute humidity of the air which may be expected to remain reasonably constant over any given day of operation.

The principle upon which these devices operate is that of imparting a rotating motion to the gas by means of a motor driven fan. The rotating gas impinges on an impulse wheel located opposite the fan in the same chamber and produces a torque on the wheel proportional to specific gravity of the gas. The influence of changes in fan speed, temperature, humidity and pressure are eliminated by comparing the torque produced on the impulse wheel by the gas under study with that produced on a second wheel by a fan, driven by the same motor, operating in a second chamber containing air.

The two fans rotate in opposite directions and the differential torque measures the difference in specific gravity of the gas and air. Suitable mechanical coupling permits the device to operate as an indicating or recording instrument.

Thermal Conductivity Type

The thermal conductivity of CO, N_2, O_2 and air are nearly the same, while that of carbon dioxide is approximatey 40 per cent lower. Advantage is taken of this fact in the thermal conductivity type analyzer. This device is essentially a Wheatstone bridge, the resistances in two arms of which are incased in gas analyzing cells. In one of these is air and in the other the gas to be analyzed. An electrical current passes through the bridge circuit at a fixed rate and heats the wires in the two cells.

The conduction of heat away from the wires in the two cells depends upon the thermal conductivity of the gas and of the air. If the thermal conductivity of the two differ the bridge becomes unbalanced and the meter shows a deflection proportional to the difference in thermal conductivity. Suitable electrical linkage makes these instruments either indicating or recording. Since hydrogen has roughly 10 times the thermal conductivity of carbon dioxide small variations in hydrogen content of the cupola gas cause significant errors in the readings from the specific gravity type instrument.

Combustion Type

These instruments are based on the principle of measuring the heat developed in burning the CO and H_2 in the gas and thus measure CO + H_2 rather than CO_2. Since hydrogen and carbon monoxide have virtually the same heating value, variations in the ratio of the two have little effect upon the results obtained.

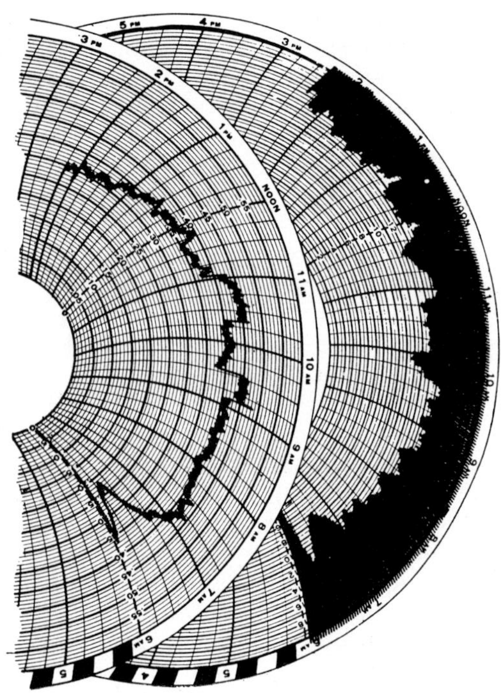

Fig. 33.16. Sample charts showing relationship of blast volume to CO_2 in effluent gas throughout a cupola heat.

In actual operation, the gas to be analyzed is mixed with a predetermined quantity of air and the mixture passed at a uniform velocity through a gas cell containing a platinum wire. This wire is heated by a constant electrical current to a temperature sufficient to ignite the combustible gas mixture, which burns catalytically along the wire, thereby raising its temperature and, therefore, its resistance.

The resistance of the wire is then compared with that of an identical wire mounted in a sealed air cell. The two cells form two arms of a Wheatstone bridge and the unbalance is proportional to the amount of combustibles in the gas sample. Suitable electrical linkage makes such instruments either indicating or recording.

The temperature rise of this wire due to even minute amounts of combustible is considerable, and is so much greater than the thermal conductivity effect that the latter does not seriously affect the result. However, because of its sensitivity, small amounts of methane which have approximately three times the heating value of CO and H_2 will introduce serious errors if present.

Normally this is not a serious factor with foundry coke, but green coke or other fuels containing hydrocarbon materials may release measurable quantities of methane which will invalidate the readings given by this type instrument.

HOT BLAST

The hot blast unit adds flexibility to a cupola. In many cases it offers better control at lower cost.

The claims for hot blast include higher temperature or less coke, better silicon and manganese recovery, more fluid slag and less bridging, lower refractory consumption, lower sulfur content because less coke is used, better slag fluidity, and improved carbon pickup over a cupola operating cold blast under similar conditions.

The term hot blast describes temperatures from warm to over 1000 F (540 C) and from simple units to the complicated recuperative systems. Initial cost, anticipated savings, cost of maintenance, cost of operation and other factors should be weighed carefully when considering the purchase of a hot blast unit.

Where substantial quantities of alloys are melted in the cupola, there are savings from a hot blast unit. Hot blast operations resulting in greater melting rates consume less coke.

The hot blast is a useful tool in controlling slag action in basic melting. When lower carbon iron is indicated by analysis, chill test, or temperature readings, an increase in hot blast temperature raises carbon content. Operators have indicated that an increase of 100 F (38 C) in blast temperature will increase carbon in the melted iron by approximately 10 points or .10 per cent.

OXYGEN ENRICHMENT

Enriching the cupola blast with oxygen may be justified under certain conditions. An increase of 4 to 5 per cent oxygen may be used to obtain hotter iron at the start of a heat. Oxygen enrichment may be used to help correct a poorly operated cupola which is melting too cold, but at the same time, extra fuel should be coming down to relieve this situation. A search should be started for the origin of the trouble. Oxygen may also be used to speed the transition from gray iron melting to a malleable mix.

Oxygen, a potent charge additive, should be used with care. Normal practice is to tap directly into the main blast line, using a calibrated orifice and pressure gage for volume control. Special precautions must be taken to keep grease, oil or organic material away from the free oxygen.

CONCLUSIONS

Combustion in the cupola can be controlled automatically by the use of an automatic CO_2 analyzer equipped with a compensating mechanism in conjunction with automatic volume control equipment. This arrangement will maintain a constant air volume regardless of charge conditions within the cupola.

Provisions are made for sampling the effluent gases which are then analyzed for CO_2 at regular intervals. It is important that the gas sample represent the average condition in the melting zone or a faulty control will result. From this instrument, a continuous and permanent record of the CO_2 analysis throughout the entire heat is obtained (Fig. 33.16).

The arrangement can be made automatic by electrically interlocking the carbon dioxide analyzer with the automatic volume control equipment which is set for the nominal blast volume that coincides with optimum operating conditions. Dependent upon whether the CO_2 is higher or lower than the desired value, the nominal control point on the automatic volume control will be shifted by the action of the CO_2 compensator electrical interlock.

Since the automatic volume control is in turn connected to a reversing motor which controls the spill gate on the cupola blower, or air intake on a centrifugal fan, this regulation of blast source is either closed or opened as a result of the shift in the nominal control point, thus admitting less or more blast and causing CO_2 to return to the nominal value. By such means, the ratio of CO_2 to CO in the effluent gases, and in turn the combustion equilibrium in the melting zone, may be regulated. The best possible control over the operation from a metallurgical and economical standpoint thus is attained.

The analysis of the effluent gases is a valuable index by which the operation of the cupola can be controlled until charging has been stopped, and the gases begin burning at the charging level. At this time, the gas sample obtained is no longer an index of the type of combustion in the melting zone, and care must be exercised in finishing the heat prior to dropping bottom.

Due to the individual peculiarities of each cupola installation, the final setting and adjustment of each of the various components of this automatic control, as well as of any other, must be accomplished after the equipment has been completely installed, and the cupola is under actual operating conditions. After the cupola has been under blast for approximately 2 hr so as to be certain that it has attained an equilibrium condition, the various adjustments are made to coordinate the automatic controls to satisfy the demands of the desired stage of combustion within the cupola.

With caution and careful observation, the automatic control should then be placed into operation, and further necessary adjustment made over a number of days of operation, continuously observing the cupola operation and the performance of the control mechanism. Each cupola is in itself an independent unit, and optimum conditions in one cupola are not necessarily so in another. Consequently, it is necessary to adjust the controls for the operating conditions of each cupola.

Automatic blast control equipment[18,19] should not be considered a cure for all cupola ills. The control cannot overcome careless and poorly supervised cupola operation. Close observation and control over the selection of raw materials, charging, and the other details of operation are still absolutely essential.

Poor distribution of charges, operation of the cupola so that it becomes necessary to melt at a rate far less than that for which it was originally designed, or intermittent stopping of the blast, are all conditions which result in irregularities in the metal produced. It can safely be said, however, that if other cupola conditions are normal, the use of automatic control equipment will result in a uniformity of operation impossible to attain by hand manipulation or observation based upon practical experience alone.

REFERENCES

1. Arthur, J. R., Bangham, D. H., and Browning, J. R., "Kinetic Aspects of the Combustion of Solid Fuels," *Third Symposium on Combustion Flame and Explosion Phenomena,* p. 466, Williams and Wilkins Co., Baltimore, Md. (1949).
2. Day, R. J., "Kinetics of the Carbon-Oxygen Reaction at High Temperatures," Ph.D. Thesis, The Pennsylvania State College (1949).
3. Kreisinger, H., Oritz, F. K., and Augustine, C. E., U. S. Bureau of Mines, TP #137 (1916) and TP #139 (1918).
4. Hiles, J., and Mott, R. A., *Fuel 23* 154 (1944).
5. Piwowarsky, E., *Gusseisen* 2nd Ed., Springer-Verlag O.H.G., Berlin, Germany (1951). Piwowarsky, E., and Kramer, K., "Fundamental Studies on an Experimental Small Cupola," *Die Neue Giesserei,* Techn.-Wissensch. Beihefte. *1* 3 (1949).
6. Wright, C. C., Unpublished work on Anthracite Combustion (1946).
7. Grodzovskii, M. K. and Chukhanov, Z. F., *Fuel 15* 321 (1936), *Fuel 18* 292 (1939).
8. Chukhanov, Z. F., *Fuel 19* 17, 49 and 64 (1940).
9. Karzhavina, N. A., *Fuel 19* 220 (1940).
10. Rambush, N. E., and Taylor, G B., *Foundry Trade Journal 77* 197, 212, 229, 253 (1945).
11. Lownie, H. W., Jr., Krause, D. E., and Greenidge, C. T., TRANSACTIONS, American Foundrymen's Society *60* 766 (1952).
12. Furnas, C. C., U. S. Bureau of Mines, Bull. 307 (1929).
13. Jungbluth, H. and Korschan, H., *Technische Mitteilungen Krupp-Forschungsberichte* No. 5 79-100 (June 1938). *Arch. Eisenhultenw 12* 167 (1938-9).
14. Massari, S. C., and Lindsay, R. W., TRANSACTIONS, American Foundrymen's Society *49* 94 (1941).
15. Mulcahy, B. P., TRANSACTIONS, American Foundrymen's Society *52* 819 (1944).
16. Massari, S. C., *The Foundry 67,* 98, 100 (1939).
17. Altieri, V. J., *Gas Analysis and Testing of Gaseous Materials* 1st Ed., American Gas Association, New York, N. Y. (1945).
18. Crawford, H. V., TRANSACTIONS, American Foundrymen's Society *36* 525 (1928).
19. Hill, D. M., *The Whiting Founder* no. 26, 6 (Spring, 1941).

CHAPTER 34

Thermochemistry Heat Balance

The main purpose of a cupola is to burn coke to provide heat for the melting of iron. However, the chemical reactions occurring in a cupola are neither so few nor so simple as the preceding sentence would suggest. Heat is developed from several sources in addition to coke; for example, from the oxidation of silicon and manganese. Also, in addition to melting iron, heat is required to calcine limestone, form and melt a slag, provide for radiation losses, and fill other requirements.

The operation of a cupola can be understood only if one is familiar with the manner in which heat is developed and used in a cupola. A good understanding of the heat requirements of a cupola can be used to make its operation more efficient and more economical.

The calculation of heat values in a cupola is based on the laws of thermochemistry and thermodynamics. Although the application of these laws can become quite complicated, their application to cupola melting can be relatively simple. In this chapter, several laws of thermochemistry are explained, and sample calculations are given to show their application to commercial cupola operations.

UNITS OF MEASUREMENT

Weight

Atomic Weights. The smallest amount of a chemical combination is the atom. From the relative weights in which elements react to form compounds, it is possible to determine the relative weights of the atoms themselves. The atomic weight values (Table 34.1) express the relative weights of the elements referred to the arbitrarily assigned value of 16.00 which represents the weight of the oxygen atom. The unit of atomic weight is $\frac{1}{16}$ of the weight of an oxygen atom. Thus, because the ratio of the atomic weight of hydrogen to that of oxygen is 1.008 to 16, the atomic weight of hydrogen is 1.008, or for ordinary calculations, 1.0.

The weight of the carbon atom in atomic weight units is 12, of sulfur 32, and so on, as shown in Table 34.1. Hence a carbon atom weighs about 12 times as much as an atom of hydrogen, and $\frac{12}{16}$ as much as an atom of oxygen. Because these values all bear definite weight relations to each other, they may be expressed in any weight units desired. For convenience, the gram and pound are used most often. Thus, the atomic weight of an element expressed in grams is called a gram atom, or in pounds, a pound atom.

Molecular Weights. The atoms of the elements unite with each other to form compounds. The smallest amount of a compound that can enter into chemical reaction is the molecule, and its weight, the molecular weight, is the sum of all the atomic weights involved. For example, one atom of carbon (C) unites with one atom of oxygen (O) to form carbon monoxide (CO), and the molecular weight of carbon monoxide in atomic weight units is therefore 12 + 16 or 28. This weight may also be expressed in grams or pounds.

In the first case, it is called a gram molecule, a gram mole, or a mole; and in the second, a pound molecule or a pound mole. A pound mole contains a certain definite number of molecules. This number is the same for every substance. Molar quantities are most convenient in making the calculations involved in the numerical study of chemical reactions.

Volume and Pressure

When chemical reactions involving gases are considered, it is often necessary to know the volume relations. Thus, in the operation of a cupola, the volume of the air introduced and the volume of carbon dioxide formed are important factors. Such volumes are usually measured in cubic feet (cu ft). In order to find the weight of a given volume of gas, the pressure and temperature must also be known. Pressure

TABLE 34.1. INTERNATIONAL ATOMIC WEIGHTS
1952 Revision

Name	Symbol	Atomic Weight
Aluminum	Al	26.98
Calcium	Ca	40.08
Carbon	C	12.010
Chlorine	Cl	35.457
Hydrogen	H	1.0080
Iron	Fe	55.85
Magnesium	Mg	24.32
Manganese	Mn	54.93
Nitrogen	N	14.008
Oxygen	O	16.0000
Phosphorus	P	30.975
Silicon	Si	28.09
Sodium	Na	22.997
Sulfur	S	32.066
Titanium	Ti	47.90

is measured in ounces per square inch (oz per sq in.), pounds per square inch (psi), in inches of mercury (Hg), and sometimes in atmospheres. An atmosphere is 14.70 psi, 235.2 oz per sq in., or 29.92 in. of mercury.

Temperature

Fahrenheit and Centrigrade Scales. The temperature scales in common use are based on the freezing point and the boiling point of water. The scales are so defined that water freezes at 32°F or 0°C. At atmospheric pressure (14.7 psi), water boils at 212°F or 100°C. Thus, 100 centrigrade degrees equal 180 Fahrenheit degrees, and one centrigrade degree equals 1.8 Fahrenheit degrees. Therefore, to change from one temperature scale to the other, use is made of the equation

$$°F = 1.8\ (°C) + 32$$

Absolute Scales. The temperature of a substance cannot be lowered indefinitely. The lower limit of temperature is known as the absolute zero. This temperature, on the centigrade scale, is −273.16°. The corresponding Fahrenheit temperature is found from the above equation:

$$°F = 1.8 \times (-273.16) + 32 = -459.69°F$$

The absolute zero is taken as the starting point for the Kelvin and Rankin scales. The size of the Kelvin degree is the same as that of the centigrade degree so that a centigrade temperature is changed to a Kelvin temperature by adding it, algebraically, to 273.16. Similarly, a temperature in Fahrenheit degrees can be changed to degrees Rankin by adding 459.69 to it algebraically. For most purposes it is sufficiently accurate to round off this figure to 460. Thus 60°F becomes 520°R (460 + 60) and −16°F becomes 444°R (460 − 16). A small "t" is usually used to denote temperatures on the centigrade and Fahrenheit scales, a large "T" for Kelvin and Rankin temperatures.

CHEMICAL REACTIONS

Chemical reactions are expressed in the form of equations. The fundamental combustion reaction taking place in the cupola, the burning of carbon to form carbon dioxide, is expressed by the equation

$$C + O_2 = CO_2$$

From this equation, it is possible to calculate the weight and volume relations. The equation is chemical shorthand for the statement that one molecule (1 atom) of carbon unites with one molecule (2 atoms) of oxygen to form one molecule of carbon dioxide. Expressed in grams or pounds, it states that 12 grams or pounds of carbon react with 32 grams or pounds of oxygen to form 44 grams or pounds of carbon dioxide.

The combustion of carbon monoxide provides an example of a reaction involving only gases. The equation

$$CO + \tfrac{1}{2}\ O_2 = CO_2$$

states that one mole of carbon monoxide reacts with one-half mole of oxygen to form one mole of carbon dioxide. If we express the weight relationships in pounds, we have 28 lb (12 + 16) of carbon monoxide reacting with 16 lb (½ x 32) of oxygen to give 44 lb (12 + 32) of carbon dioxide. Any chemical reaction can be set up in the form of an equation and the relationship among the reactants and products can be evaluated quantitatively in a similar manner.

PRESSURE-VOLUME-TEMPERATURE RELATIONSHIPS

The simplest relationship between the volume and pressure of a gas is expressed by Boyle's Law, which states that at constant temperature, the volume varies inversely as the pressure. This means that a gas having a given volume at one unit of pressure will have only half that volume at two units of pressure. The general statement of the relation between the volume of a gas and its temperature is known as Charles' Law, which may be stated as follows: when the pressure remains constant, the volume of a gas varies directly as its absolute temperature.

The two simple gas laws may be expressed as follows:

Boyle $\quad V \text{ varies as } \frac{1}{P}$

Charles $\quad V \text{ varies as } T$

Combining: $\quad V \text{ varies as } \frac{T}{P}$

Introducing a constant proportionality, *R*,

$$V = R \times \frac{T}{P}$$

$$\text{or } PV = RT$$

in which

P = pressure
V = volume
R = gas constant
T = absolute temperature

A third useful concept is the Law of Avogadro which states that equal volumes of gases, under the same conditions of temperature and pressure, contain the same number of molecules. We have previously taken note of the fact that a mole of any substance contains the same number of molecules as a mole of any other substance. Now we see that a mole of any gas occupies the same volume as a mole of any other gas at the same pressure and temperature. The volume occupied by a pound molecule (molecular weight expressed in pounds) of any gas has been found ideally to be 379.5 cu ft at a temperature of 60 F and a pressure of 29.92 in. of mercury. Avogadro's Law is introduced into the simple gas equation by multiplying the gas constant by the number of gram molecules or pound molecules (n), thus:

$$PV = nRT$$

This equation is precise only for a hypothetical gas in which the volume of the molecules themselves is negligible and there are no forces of attraction or repulsion between the molecules. For this reason, it is known as the law of the perfect gas. Although it fails at very low temperatures and high pressures, the equation is adequate for calculations involving cupola operation.

When using the gas equation, one must be careful to be consistent in the choice of units. Thus the value of R for any gas may be taken as 10.73, but this value is correct only when P is expressed in psi, V in cu ft, T in degrees Rankin, and n in pound moles. It should also be noted that P must be the absolute pressure (not gage pressure) and T the absolute temperature (not Fahrenheit or centrigrade).

Suppose we wish to know the volume of gas produced when one pound of carbon is burned in air. We have already seen that one pound mole of carbon reacts with one pound mole of oxygen to produce one pound mole of carbon dioxide and that, at 60 F and atmospheric pressure, one pound mole of any gas occupies 379.5 cu ft. Thus when 12 lb (one pound mole) of carbon are burned, approximately 380 cu ft of oxygen are used and 380 cu ft of carbon dioxide are formed.

In cupola operation, this oxygen is supplied by the blast air. Atmospheric air contains approximately 21 per cent oxygen by volume (a more accurate figure would be 20.9), and therefore, the necessary volume of blast air is $380 \div 0.21 = 1{,}810$ cu ft. Because air contains 79 per cent nitrogen, this volume of air contains $1{,}810 \times 0.79 = 1{,}430$ cu ft of nitrogen. The nitrogen will pass through the cupola unchanged, because it is an inert gas. Therefore, the total volume of gas passing out of the cupola, if the combustion were complete, would consist of 380 cu ft of carbon dioxide and 1,430 cu ft of nitrogen, or a total of 1,810 cu ft, which exactly equals the volume of air introduced in the blast.

In order to express these volumes in terms of one pound of carbon, it is necessary only to divide by 12, the molecular weight of carbon (the same as the atomic weight since the carbon molecule is considered in calculations to contain but one atom). Thus if 12 lb of carbon produce 380 cu ft of carbon dioxide, one pound will produce $380 \div 12$ or 31.6 cu ft, and the total gas produced will be $1{,}810 \div 12$ or 150.8 cu ft, which is the same as the volume of air used.

In the preceding discussion it has been assumed that the gases are at 60 F and one atmosphere pressure. Suppose it is required to know the volume of air at 80 F and 29.60 in. pressure needed to burn one pound of carbon to carbon dioxide. It is necessary here to make use of the gas equation as follows:

$$P_1V_1 = nRT_1$$

$$\text{or } \frac{P_1V_1}{T_1} = nR$$

$$\text{and } \frac{P_2V_2}{T_2} = nR$$

Since n and R are constant,

$$\frac{P_1V_1}{T_1} = \frac{P_2V_2}{T_2}$$

Solving for V_2,

$$V_2 = \frac{P_1V_1T_2}{T_1P_2}$$

We know that 150.8 cu ft of air are required at 60 F and 29.92 in. pressure. Therefore,

$P_1 = 29.92$ in. $\quad P_2 = 29.60$ in.
$V_1 = 150.8$ cu ft $\quad V_2 = ?$
$T_1 = 520°R\,(60 + 460)$ $\quad T_2 = 540°R\,(80 + 460)$

Substituting and solving,

$$V_2 = \frac{29.92 \times 150.8 \times 540}{520 \times 29.60} = 158.2 \text{ cu ft}$$

The same result can be obtained more directly by substituting the known value of the gas constant, R, into the gas equation,

$$PV = nRT$$

$$\text{or } V = \frac{nRT}{P}$$

$R = 10.73$, if P is expressed in psi, n in pound moles, V in cu ft, and T in degrees R. The pressure (29.60 in.) is converted, first to atmospheres by dividing by 29.92, then to psi by multiplying by 14.70:

$$P = \frac{29.60 \times 14.70}{29.92} = 14.54 \text{ psi}$$

As in the previous calculation, $T = 540°R$. The number of pound moles, n, in the oxygen reacting with one pound of carbon is $1/12$, since the molecular weight of carbon is 12, and since each mole of carbon requires one mole of oxygen. Substituting and solving,

$$V = \frac{1/12 \times 10.73 \times 540}{14.54} = 33.21 \text{ cu ft}$$

This is the volume of oxygen used in the combustion. To find the total volume of air, we divide by 0.21 and find that 158.2 cu ft of air are needed.

HEAT UNITS

In problems dealing with the generation and transfer of heat, certain arbitrary quantities of energy called heat units are used. These units are of three types:

1) A quantity of heat.
2) A quantity of heat per unit weight per unit temperature difference (heat capacity).
3) A quantity of heat per unit weight (heat content).

Heat Quantity

The basic quantity of heat is expressed as the amount of heat required to raise a unit weight of a substance through one degree temperature difference, and generally is expressed in consistent units. In the metric system, the basic heat unit is the calorie, which is the amount of heat required to increase the temperature of one gram of water from 15° to 16°C. In industrial operations, large heat units are more convenient, and, therefore the kilogram calorie (kcal), equal to 1,000 calories, generally is used.

In the English system, the basic heat unit is the British thermal unit, Btu, which is the amount of heat required to increase the temperature of one pound of water from 60° to 61°F. The relation between the British thermal unit and the calorie is as follows:

1 Btu = 252 calories
1 calorie = 0.00397 Btu
1 kcal = 3.97 Btu

Heat Capacity

The heat capacity of a substance is defined as the quantity of heat necessary to increase the temperature of unit weight one degree. Heat-capacity units are numerically equivalent in both systems of units. That is, the heat capacity in calories per degree C per gram are the same numerically as heat capacities in Btu/degree F/lb. This very convenient relationship arises from the fact that the calorie and Btu are defined in such a manner that the heat capacity of water is numerically equal to 1.0 in both systems.

Heat capacity, or specific heat (C), varies with temperature and pressure. The heat capacity of a gas is greater at constant pressure than at constant volume because work is done when a gas expands against a constant pressure. For the purpose of solving problems in cupola operation only the constant-pressure value $(C\ )$ is used, because no effort is made to maintain constant volume, and because the pressure is always close to atmospheric.

It is necessary, however, to consider the fact that the specific heat of a substance varies with temperature. Equations have been developed to express heat capacity as a function of temperature. For the usual types of calculations, however, it is convenient to use the mean specific heat $(\overline{C_p})$, which is the average value over a specified range of temperature. The mean specific heats of a number of substances are given in Table 48 for the range 60°F to t°F at various values of t from 100 to 3200°.

The data of Table 34.2 were obtained from these sources. The mean specific heats of the gases were calculated from the Bureau of Standards Compilation.[1] The values for slag were calculated from a combination of the heat capacities of two moles of $CaO \cdot SiO_2$, one mole of $CaO \cdot Al_2O_3 \cdot 2SiO_2$, and one mole of $CaO \cdot MgO \cdot 2SiO_2$.[2] The heat of fusion of slag was estimated to be 160 Btu per pound.

The heat capacity of liquid slag was taken as 0.286 Btu per pound per degree F.[3] The mean specific heat of pig iron was calculated by combining the values of Darken and Smith for pure iron[4] with those of Kelley[2] for cementite (Fe_3C). The values may be interpolated to obtain results at other carbon contents. It is probably best to use for per cent C the sum of

1. Rossini, F. D., et al., "Selected Values of Properties of Hydrocarbons", Circular of the National Bureau of Standards C461 (1947).
2. Kelley, K. K., "High Temperature Heat Content, Heat Capacity and Entropy Data for Inorganic Compounds," U. S. Bureau of Mines *Bulletin* 476 (1949).
3. Schwartz, Carl, *Archiv. Eisenhüttenwes.*, *7*, 281 (1933).
4. Darken, L. S. and R. P. Smith, *Ind. Eng. Chem.*, *43*, 1815 (1951).

TABLE 34.2. MEAN SPECIFIC HEATS

$\overline{C_p} = H/t - 60$ Btu per lb per deg F

t(°F)	O_2	H_2	H_2O	N_2	CO	CO_2
100	0.2188	3.420	0.4448	0.2482	0.2485	0.2022
200	0.2203	3.434	0.4472	0.2485	0.2488	0.2086
300	0.2221	3.442	0.4499	0.2488	0.2493	0.2145
400	0.2240	3.448	0.4529	0.2493	0.2501	0.2201
500	0.2259	3.452	0.4562	0.2500	0.2511	0.2253
600	0.2279	3.455	0.4597	0.2509	0.2522	0.2301
700	0.2299	3.458	0.4634	0.2520	0.2535	0.2346
800	0.2318	3.462	0.4674	0.2531	0.2549	0.2388
900	0.2337	3.466	0.4715	0.2544	0.2564	0.2428
1000	0.2355	3.470	0.4757	0.2558	0.2580	0.2465
1100	0.2373	3.475	0.4800	0.2572	0.2596	0.2500
1200	0.2390	3.480	0.4844	0.2586	0.2611	0.2533
1300	0.2406	3.487	0.4888	0.2600	0.2627	0.2564
1400	0.2420	3.494	0.4932	0.2614	0.2642	0.2593
1500	0.2434	3.501	0.4976	0.2628	0.2657	0.2620
1600	0.2448	3.510	0.5021	0.2642	0.2672	0.2646
1700	0.2461	3.519	0.5066	0.2656	0.2686	0.2671
1800	0.2473	3.528	0.5111	0.2669	0.2700	0.2694
1900	0.2484	3.538	0.5156	0.2682	0.2713	0.2716
2000	0.2495	3.549	0.5201	0.2695	0.2726	0.2737
2100	0.2506	3.460	0.5245	0.2707	0.2739	0.2757
2200	0.2517	3.572	0.5289	0.2719	0.2751	0.2776
2300	0.2527	3.584	0.5334	0.2732	0.2763	0.2795
2400	0.2536	3.596	0.5375	0.2742	0.2774	0.2813
2500	0.2545	3.608	0.5415	0.2753	0.2784	0.2830
2600	0.2554	3.620	0.5456	0.2764	0.2794	0.2845
2700	0.2562	3.632	0.5496	0.2774	0.2804	0.2860
2800	0.2570	3.644	0.5536	0.2784	0.2814	0.2875
2900	0.2578	3.656	0.5575	0.2793	0.2823	0.2889
3000	0.2585	3.668	0.5614	0.2802	0.2831	0.2902
3100	0.2593	3.680	0.5652	0.2811	0.2840	0.2915
3200	0.2600	3.692	0.5688	0.2819	0.2848	0.2927

t(°F)	Slag (solid)	Slag (liquid)	Pig Iron (solid)		Pig Iron (liquid)	
			2% Carbon	4% Carbon	2% Carbon	4% Carbon
100	0.1809		0.1200	0.1308		
200	0.1893		0.1223	0.1326		
300	0.1967		0.1245	0.1353		
400	0.2032		0.1275	0.1403		
500	0.2089		0.1292	0.1404		
600	0.2139		0.1309	0.1409		
700	0.2183		0.1327	0.1417		
800	0.2223		0.1346	0.1428		
900	0.2258		0.1367	0.1441		
1000	0.2291		0.1392	0.1457		
1100	0.2321		0.1422	0.1475		
1200	0.2349		0.1458	0.1497		
1300	0.2374		0.1500†	0.1523†		
1400	0.2397		0.1671††	0.1622††		
1500	0.2418		0.1658	0.1616		
1600	0.2437		0.1647	0.1611		
1700	0.2455		0.1638	0.1608		
1800	0.2473		0.1631	0.1606		
1900	0.2490		0.1626	0.1604	0.2208	0.2221
2000	0.2506		0.1622	0.1604	0.2187	0.2197
2100	0.2522		0.1620	0.1604	0.2168	0.2176
2200	0.2538		0.1619	0.1605	0.2151	0.2157
2300	0.2555		0.1618	0.1607	0.2136	0.2140
2400	0.2571	0.3256	0.1618	0.1608	0.2122	0.2124
2500		0.3239	0.1619	0.1611	0.2110	0.2109
2600		0.3224	0.1620	0.1613	0.2099	0.2095
2700		0.3210	0.1622	0.1616	0.2089	0.2083
2800		0.3198	0.1624	0.1619	0.2079	0.2072
2900		0.3187	0.1627	0.1623	0.2070	0.2062
3000		0.3176			0.2062	0.2052
3100		0.3166			0.2054	0.2043
3200		0.3156				

† alpha
†† gamma

the silicon and carbon contents in making the interpolation.

Heat Content

When a substance is heated from one temperature to another, the quantity of heat required to change the temperature is known as the heat content of the substance, sometimes called the "sensible" heat. As used here, the heat content refers to the number of Btu per pound (or cal per gm) or Btu per pound mole (or cal per gram mole) to heat the substance from 60°F to its specified temperature. The symbol used here for heat content is *H*, and may be defined by the relation

$$H = \overline{C_p}\ (t - 60)$$

Heat contents expressed in calories per gram (or calories per gram mole) are converted to heat contents in Btu per pound (or Btu per pound mole) by multiplying by 1.8, remembering that the datum line (60°F = 15.6°C) must be the same for both.

Standard heats of formation and combustion, which later will be considered in detail, are expressed in the same basic heat units per unit weight, usually in calories per gram molecule. These quantities, when multiplied by 1.8, give the equivalent values expressed in Btu per pound molecule.

CALCULATION OF HEAT REQUIREMENT

Heat of Fusion

At the freezing point, heat is evolved and the rate of cooling is thereby decreased. This is indicated by a change of slope in the cooling curve. At the freezing point of pure chemical compounds, the cooling rate is reduced to zero, and the curve becomes a horizontal line and remains so until all of the substance has solidified.

Conversely, when a substance is heated, the temperature rises until the melting point is reached. At this point heat is absorbed in extra quantity equivalent to the work done in the change of state from solid to liquid, and the temperature remains constant until the entire mass is melted. The heat absorbed is called the *heat of fusion*, and can be expressed in Btu per lb.

Heat of Vaporization

When a liquid substance is heated, the temperature rises until the boiling point is reached (the temperature at which the vapor pressure of the substance is equal to the atmospheric pressure). Heat is then absorbed in an amount equivalent to the work done in the change of state from liquid to gas, and the temperature remains constant until the entire mass has been vaporized. The heat absorbed in this process is called *heat of vaporization* and can be expressed in Btu per lb. This constant finds application in the calculations of cupola operation only in the consideration of the evaporation of moisture contained in the coke.

Examples

The quantities of heat defined in the preceding paragraphs are used in the calculation of the total quantity of heat required to produce certain effects. For example, the heat required to raise the temperature of 10 lb of ice at 32 F to steam at 212 F, at atmospheric pressure, is obtained by adding together the following items:

Heat of fusion (change of ice to water) [5]	10 x 143.6 =	1,436 Btu
To heat water from 32 to 212 F	10 x 1 x 180 =	1,800 Btu
Heat of vaporization (water to steam) [5]	10 x 972.9 =	9,729 Btu
	Total	12,965 Btu

5. The values of the heat of fusion of ice and heat of vaporization of water are taken from Osborne, Stimson, and Ginnings, *Journal of Research*, National Bureau of Standards, *23*, 261 (1939).

Table 34.2 has been so designed that the heats of fusion of iron and slag have been included in the mean heat capacities of the liquids. Thus, to find the heat necessary to melt one ton of iron (2 per cent carbon) and bring it from a temperature of 60 F to a pouring temperature of 2800 F, it is necessary only to multiply the weight (2000 lb) by the mean heat capacity (0.2079) and by the temperature change (2740°):

$$2000 \times 0.2079 \times 2740 = 1{,}139{,}300 \text{ Btu or } 569.6 \text{ Btu per lb}$$

HEAT OF REACTION

In all chemical reactions heat is either evolved or absorbed. In the first case, the reaction is called exothermic, and the heat value is expressed as positive (+) because heat is produced in the system as the reaction proceeds from left to right. For example:

$$C + O_2 = CO_2 + \text{heat}$$

In the second case, it is called endothermic, and the heat value is negative (−) because heat must be supplied to the system to make the reaction proceed from left to right. For example:

$$CO_2 + C = 2CO - \text{heat}$$

In thermochemical calculations, it is customary to use the plus sign (+) when heat is produced and the minus sign (−) when heat is absorbed. It is of passing interest to note that in thermodynamics, the signs are reversed. The thermochemical convention is adopted here.

The heat of reaction accompanying a chemical change is dependent upon the nature of the reacting substances and products, and also upon their physical states. Because heat of reaction is affected by temperature and pressure, it is customary to refer to a standard heat of reaction, which is based on the assumption that the reaction has proceeded under a pressure of one atmosphere (29.92 in. of mercury) and starts and ends at 60 F. (A base temperature of 25 C is usually used in the metric system.)

The state of the substances involved in a reaction is designated by a letter in parentheses following the chemical formula. Thus (*g*) indicates the gaseous, (*l*) the liquid, and (*s*) the solid state. Of less importance in this discussion are certain other symbols that are used to designate some characteristic condition accompanying the state in question, particularly with respect to solids, which may exist in more than one modification. For example, *C* (coke) means solid carbon in the form of coke and *S* (*m*) stands for solid sulfur in the monoclinic form.

Combustion is a special type of chemical reaction in which certain substances, called fuels, combine with oxygen (usually obtained from atmospheric air) producing heat and light. The actual phenomena of combustion are familiar in the burning of coals for heating, the explosion of gasoline vapor for propulsion, and the burning of a candle for light. The heat of combustion is the measure of the quantity of energy produced in oxidation reactions of the types noted.

HEAT OF FORMATION

The heat of formation of a chemical compound is a special case of the standard heat of reaction wherein the elements are the reactants and the compound under consideration is the only product. Heats of formation always are expressed with reference to a standard state, and represent the quantity of heat evolved or absorbed when one mole of the compound is formed from the elements in a reaction beginning and ending at 60 F (or often at 25 C) and at one atmosphere pressure. The heat of formation is positive when heat is liberated and negative when heat is absorbed.

Table 34.3 shows standard heats of formation of the important compounds involved in cupola operation. The data were taken from the Bureau of Standards Compilation.[6] The standard states of the elements from which these compounds are formed are the stable states at 60 F (or, for the second column, 25 C). The standard state of aluminum is the solid metal, for oxygen it is gaseous O_2, etc.

Graphite is the commonly accepted standard state for carbon; the values of Table 34.3 are based on this convention. The heat of combustion of carbon in the form of coke is a more useful result for purposes here; these values will be found in Table 34.4, along with other useful heats of reaction.

THERMOCHEMICAL CALCULATIONS

The Law of Hess

By the law of the conservation of energy, the quantity of energy required to decompose a chemical compound, at a given temperature and pressure, is exactly equal to the energy evolved when the compound is formed from its elements. This consideration leads to the law of constant heat summation, or the Law of Hess, which states that the total heat of reaction in a chemical process is the same whether the reaction takes place in one or in several steps. The total change in the heat content of a system depends upon the temperature, pressure, and the state at the beginning and end of the process, and is independent of the path followed in the process.

6. Rossini, F. D. et al., *Selected Values of Chemical Thermodynamic Properties,* Circular of the Nat'l Bur. of Stds, 500 (1952).

By means of this principle, it is possible to calculate the heat of formation of a compound from a series of reactions not involving the direct formation of the compound from the elements. For example, pure carbon monoxide cannot be prepared by the direct union of carbon and oxygen, but carbon dioxide can be prepared, and the heat of the reaction can be measured. Carbon monoxide, made in some other way, such as by the action of sulphuric acid on formic acid or sodium formate, can be oxidized to carbon dioxide, and the heat of this reaction can be determined. Thus at 60°F

1) $C_{(Coke)} + O_2 = CO_2 +$ 173,570 Btu, or 14,452 Btu per lb of C

2) $CO + \frac{1}{2} O_2 = CO_2 +$ 121,745 Btu, or 10,137 Btu per lb of C

TABLE 34.3. HEATS OF FORMATION

Compound	Molecular Weight	kcal per gram mole[a]	Btu per lb mole[b]	Btu per lb[b]
Al_2O_3	101.96	399.09	718,360	7045.5
$Al_2O_3 \cdot SiO_2$	162.05	644.6	1,160,300	7160
CaO	56.08	151.9	273,400	4876
$CaCO_3$	100.09	288.45	519,210	5187.4
$CaCO_3MgO_3$	184.42	556	1,001,000	5430
CaC_2	64.10	15	27,000	420
$CaO \cdot SiO_2$	116.17	378.0	680,400	5857
$2CaO \cdot SiO_2$	172.25	538.5	969,300	5627
$3CaO \cdot SiO_2$	228.33	688.4	1,239,100	5427
$CaO \cdot Al_2O_3$	158.04	551c	992,000c	6280c
$2CaO \cdot Al_2O_3$	214.12	704	1,267,000	5920
$3CaO \cdot Al_2O_3$	270.20	861	1,550,000	5740
$4CaO \cdot Al_2O_3$	326.28	1026	1,847,000	5660
$12CaO \cdot 7Al_2O_3$	1386.68	4617	8,311,000	5993
$3CaO \cdot Al_2O_3 \cdot 2SiO_2$	390.38	1303	2,345,000	6008
$CaO \cdot Al_2O_3 \cdot 6SiO_2$	518.58	1828	3,290,000	6345
$4CaO \cdot Al_2O_3 \cdot Fe_2O_3$	485.98	1211	2,180,000	4485
CaS	72.15	115.3	207,500	2877
CO_2	44.01	94.052	169,294	3846.7
CO	28.01	26.416	47,549	1697.6
C_{coke}	12.01	-2.38d	-4,280d	-356d
H_2O (g)	18.016	57.798	104,036	5774.7
H_2O (l)	18.016	68.317	122,971	6825.6
FeO	71.85	63.7	114,700	1596
Fe_3O_4	231.55	267.0	480,600	2076
Fe_2O_3	159.70	196.5	353,700	2215
$FeO \cdot SiO_2$	131.94	276	497,000	3760
$2FeO \cdot SiO_2$	203.79	343.7	618,700	3036
Fe_3C	179.56	-5.0	-9,000	-50
FeSi	83.91	19.2	34,600	412
FeS	87.92	22.72	40,900	465.2
MgO	40.32	143.84	258,910	6421
$MgCO_3$	84.33	266	479,000	5680
$MgO \cdot SiO_2$	100.41	357.9	644,200	6416
$2MgO \cdot SiO_2$	140.73	488.2	878,800	6244
MnO	70.93	92.0	165,600	2335
Mn_3O_4	228.79	331.4	596,500	2607
Mn_2O_3	157.86	232.1	417,800	2646
MnO_2	86.93	124.5	224,100	2578
MnS	87.00	48.2	86,800	997
$MnO \cdot SiO_2$	131.02	302.5	544,500	4156
SiO_2	60.09	205.1	369,200	6144
Na_2CO_3	106.00	270.3	486,500	4590
SO_2	64.07	70.96	127,730	1993.6
TiO_2	79.90	218.0	392,400	4911

NOTE: See Table 50 for footnotes.

TABLE 34.4. HEATS OF REACTION

Reaction	kcal[a]	Btu.[b]	Btu. per lb[c]
$C_{coke} + O_2 = CO_2$	96.43[d]	173,570[d]	14,452 /lbC[d]
$C_{coke} + \frac{1}{2}O_2 = CO$	28.79[d]	51,820[d]	4,315 /lbC[d]
$CO + \frac{1}{2}O_2 = CO_2$	67.636	121,745	4,346.5/lbCO
$\frac{1}{2}CO_2 + \frac{1}{2}C_{coke} = CO$	−19.42[d]	−34,960[d]	−2,910 /lbC[d]
$H_2O_{(g)} + C_{coke} = CO + H_2$	−29.00[d]	−52,210[d]	−2,898 /lbH_2O[d]
$CaCO_3 = CaO + CO_2$	−42.5	−76,500	−764 /lb$CaCO_3$
$CaCO_3 \cdot MgCO_3 = CaO + MgO + 2CO_2$	−72	−130,000	−700 /lbCaMg$(CO_3)_2$
$MgCO_3 = MgO + CO_2$	−28	−50,000	−600 /lb$MgCO_3$

a. At 25°C.
b. At 60°F.
c. Estimated
d. Based on P. H. Dewev and D. R. Harper: *J. Res.*, Nat'l. Bur. Stds., *21*, 457 (1938)

Subtracting 2) from 1) algebraically,

$$C_{(Coke)} + \frac{1}{2} O_2 = CO + 51,820 \text{ Btu, or } 3,315 \text{ Btu per lb of C}$$

and these are the figures shown in *Heats of Reaction* Table 34.4.

Thermochemical equations, in general, may similarly be combined according to the rules of algebra, and the Law of Hess thus applied to any series of reactions.

The heat evolved or absorbed in any chemical reaction can be calculated from the heats of formation of the reacting compounds and the compounds formed in the reaction. In cupola operation, heats of combustion and decomposition are of special importance. In making such calculations, the equation of the reaction is first set up, and then the pound molecular heat of formation of each compound in Btu entering into or produced by the reaction is taken from Table 34.3.

The standard heat of formation of an element is considered to be zero except in the case of carbon in coke, as explained above. The total heat of formation of the reactants is subtracted algebraically from the total heat of formation of the products, and the result is the standard heat of reaction. This is the quantity of heat absorbed or evolved when the reaction is considered to have taken place at 60°F.

Examples

Combustion. As an example of a combustion reaction, the heat evolved when carbon monoxide unites with oxygen to form carbon dioxide is calculated as

Heats of Formation (Table 34.3)

$$CO\ (47,549\ \text{Btu}) + \frac{1}{2}\ O_2\ (0\ \text{Btu}) = CO_2\ (169,294)\ \text{Btu})$$

Heat in product	169,294 Btu
Heat in reactants	47,549 Btu
Subtract Algebraically	
Heat of combustion	121,745 Btu

The complete reaction is now written as

$$CO + \frac{1}{2}O_2 = CO_2 + 121,745 \text{ Btu}$$

which means that when 28 lb of carbon monoxide unite with 16 lb of oxygen, 44 lb of carbon dioxide are produced and 121,745 Btu are evolved. If it is desired to express this result in terms of pounds of carbon, the total molecular heat of combustion is divided by the atomic weight of carbon (12.01):

$$121,745 \div 12.01 = 10,137 \text{ Btu per lb of carbon}$$

This is the heat evolved when the reaction takes place at 60°F. Of course this reaction does not actually take place at 60°, but in order to avoid the necessity of calculating heats for formation at other temperatures, it is convenient to use the heat that would be released if the reaction were to take place at 60°F.

Decomposition. As an example of a decomposition reaction, the heat absorbed when the limestone used as a flux in cupola operation breaks down into lime and carbon dioxide is calculated as*

Heats of Formation (Table 34.3)

$$CaCO_3\ (519,210\ \text{Btu}) = CaO\ (273,400\ \text{Btu}) + CO_2\ (169,294\ \text{Btu})$$

Heat in products	442,700 Btu
Heat in reactants	519,210 Btu
Subtract Algebraically	
Heat of decomposition	−76,500 Btu

The complete reaction is now written as

$$CaCO_3 = CaO + CO_2 - 76,500 \text{ Btu}$$

which means that, when 100 lb of pure calcium carbonate are decomposed, 56 lb of calcium oxide (lime) and 44 lb of carbon dioxide are produced, and that heat is absorbed to the extent of 76,500 Btu. To cause the reaction to take place, this quantity of heat must be supplied from some external source. In the case of the cupola, the heat is supplied by the combustion of coke. As in the previous example, the −76,500 Btu is the standard molecular heat of decomposition. The quantity of heat required per pound is the molecular heat of decomposition divided by 100 (the molecular weight of calcium carbonate) or −765 Btu.

It should be stated here that the heat of formation of CO_2 is very accurately known, but the heat of formation of CaO is uncertain to the extent of several hundred Btu. The result of the calculation can, of course, be no more accurate than the numbers used in the calculation. Therefore, the standard molecular heat of decomposition may be in error by several hundred Btu. For this reason the result is rounded off to the nearest hundred Btu.

Slag Formation. In cupola operation, the lime produced in the preceding reaction will react with silica from the coke ash or the sand adhering to the scrap, to form calcium silicate, one of the components of the slag. The reaction is written as

Heats of Formation (Table 34.3)

$$CaO\ (273,000\ \text{Btu}) + SiO_2\ (369,200\ \text{Btu}) = CaSiO_3\ (680,400\ \text{Btu})$$

Heat in product	680,400 Btu
Heat in reactants	642,600 Btu
Subtract Algebraically	
Heat of reaction	37,800 Btu

*Application of this reaction, Chapter 15.

The complete equation is now written

$$CaO + SiO_2 = CaSiO_3 + 37{,}800 \text{ Btu}$$

which means that, when 56 lb lime and 60 lb of silica react, 116 lb of slag are produced with the evolution of 37,800 Btu (or 378 Btu per lb of limestone). Thus, while 765 Btu are necessary to decompose one pound of limestone, 378 Btu are produced when the lime formed reacts with silica, so that the net heat loss is 387 Btu per lb of limestone.

Moisture Decomposition. Another reaction in the cupola, the effect of which is receiving much more attention than was formerly the case, is the decomposition of the moisture in the blast air by the carbon of the coke to form carbon monoxide and hydrogen, according to the equation

Heats of Formation (Table 34.3)

$$\begin{array}{cccc} H_2O_{(g)} & C_{(Coke)} & CO & H_2 \\ 104{,}036 \text{ Btu} & + -4{,}280 \text{ Btu} = & 47{,}549 \text{ Btu} & + 0 \text{ Btu} \end{array}$$

Heat of reaction

$$47{,}549 + 4{,}280 - 104{,}036 = -52{,}210.$$

This reaction is endothermic and heat has to be applied to cause it to take place. In the cupola, this heat must be supplied by combustion of coke. Assuming that the effluent gas contains 13 per cent CO_2, the efficiency of the coke combustion is 64.6 per cent (Table 34.5).

In perfect combustion

12 lb C produce 173,570 Btu (Table 34.4)

At 64.6 per cent efficiency

12 lb C produce 173,570 x 0.646 = 112,100 Btu

$$112{,}100 \div 12 = 9{,}340 \text{ Btu per lb C}$$

To supply the necessary heat, the weight of carbon required is

$$\frac{52{,}210}{9{,}340} = 5.59 \text{ lb C}$$

TABLE 34.5. COKE COMBUSTION

CO_2 %	Heat Developed, Btu per lb Carbon			Efficiency of Combustion
	CO_2	CO	Total	%
0	000	4320	4320	29.9
1	420	4190	4610	31.9
2	860	4060	4920	34.0
3	1320	3920	5240	36.3
4	1800	3780	5580	38.6
5	2300	3630	5930	41.0
6	2820	3470	6290	43.5
7	3360	3310	6670	46.1
8	3930	3140	7070	48.9
9	4510	2970	7480	51.8
10	5120	2790	7910	54.7
11	5780	2590	8370	57.9
12	6460	2390	8850	61.2
13	7170	2170	9340	64.6
14	7900	1950	9850	68.2
15	8680	1720	10400	72.0
16	9510	1480	10990	76.0
17	10400	1210	11610	80.3
18	11320	940	12260	84.8
19	12300	640	12940	89.5
20	13320	340	13660	94.5
21	14450	000	14450	100.0

To decompose 18 lb of water, 12 lb of carbon are consumed in the reaction and 5.59 lb C are required by the reaction. Therefore, a total of 17.59 lb of carbon are needed. This is equivalent to

$17.59 \div 18 = 0.977$ lb C per lb of H_2O

$0.977 \div 0.90 = 1.09$ lb of coke (containing 90 per cent carbon) per lb of H_2O

Before use can be made of these relationships, it is necessary to determine the moisture content of the blast air in grains per cu ft, corrected for standard conditions. This variable is called "humidity" and usually is determined by means of a sling psychrometer, by which the dry- and wet-bulb temperatures of the air are measured. The calculation of humidity from these variables is difficult and use generally is made of a psychrometric chart, such as that shown on page 811, *Chemical Engineers' Handbook*, 3rd Edition. Easier to use, however, is the nomographic chart (Fig. 34.1) by Herres and Lorig.[7]

A straight edge, placed on the dry-bulb temperature on Scale T_{db} and on the wet-bulb temperature on Scale T_{wb}, will give a reading on Scale G of grains of water per lb of dry air. The straight edge is then placed on the dry-bulb temperature on Scale T_{db} and the intersection of the wet-bulb and dry-bulb lines at the right of the chart, and a reading of cu ft of air plus water vapor per lb of dry air is taken on Scale V. Dividing the first reading by the second and making the indicated barometric correction, gives the grains of water vapor per cu ft of air actually entering the cupola.

The crossing lines to the right in Fig. 34.1 are necessary because the volume of a pound of air varies with the degree of saturation with moisture. Dry-bulb (sloping) and wet-bulb (dotted) lines intersect at the top of the dry-bulb line when the two temperatures are equal, a condition indicating that the air is completely saturated with water vapor. The intersections to the right of lower wet-bulb temperatures with given dry-bulb temperatures, show that the air is only partially saturated and will occupy less volume per lb of dry air. The lower end of the dry-bulb temperature line indicates completely dry air.

For example, if the dry-bulb temperature is 62°F and the wet-bulb temperature is 55°F, Line G indicates 53 grains of water vapor per lb of dry air, and Line V that the volume of dry air and water vapor is 13.3 cu ft per lb of dry air. Dividing 53 by 13.3 gives 4.0 grains of moisture per cu ft of blast air, under standard conditions. To correct for atmospheric pressure, use the formula

$$\frac{G \times B}{V \times 29.92} = H = \text{grains of moisture per cu ft blast air at observed conditions}$$

Thus if B = 29.50

$$\frac{53 \times 29.50}{13.3 \times 29.92} = 3.9 \text{ grains water per cu ft}$$

7. Herres, S. A., and C. H. Lorig, "Cupola Blast Control," AMERICAN FOUNDRYMAN, *4*, no. 9, p. 14 (1942).

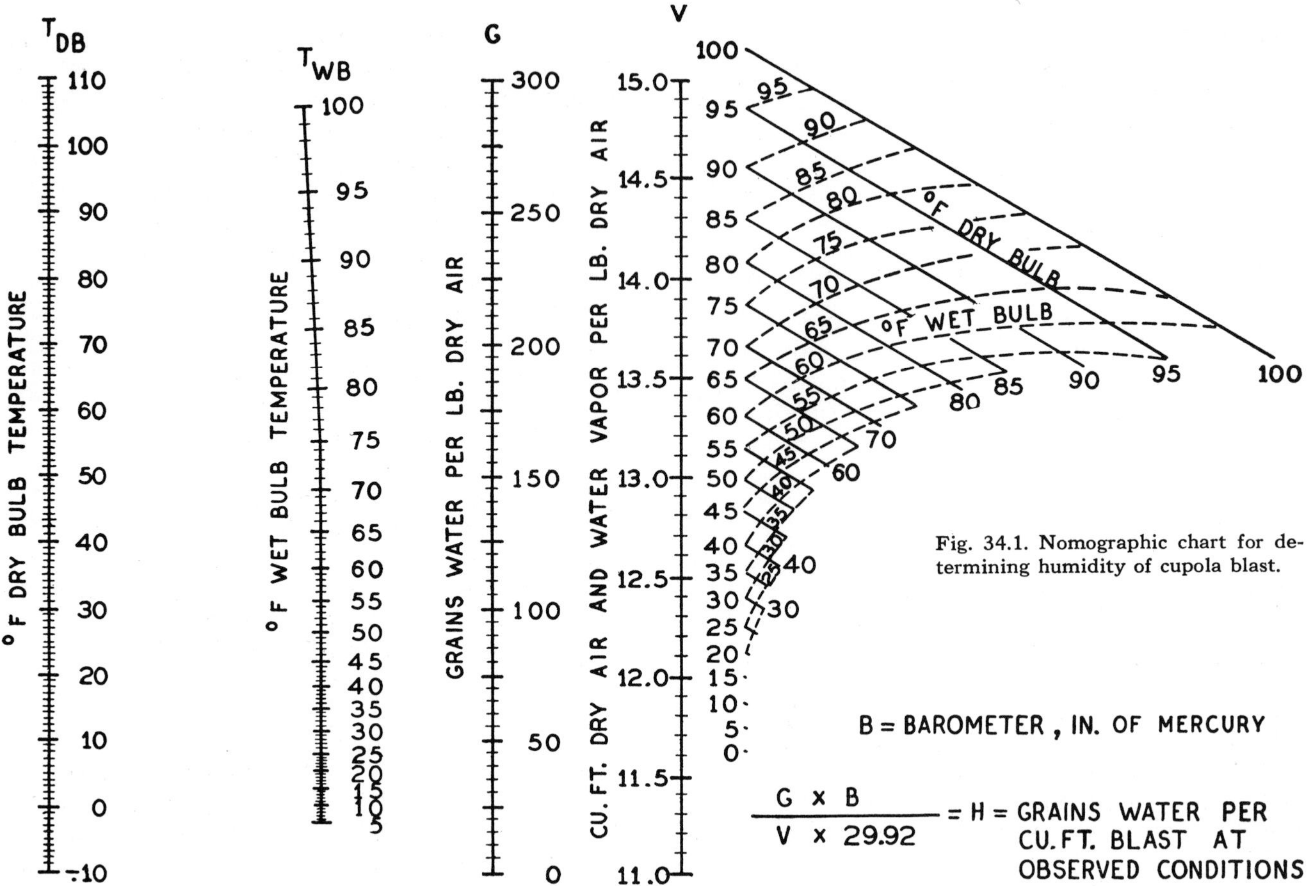

Fig. 34.1. Nomographic chart for determining humidity of cupola blast.

Heat Balance

Heats of reaction are affected by temperature and pressure. Because cupola operations are carried out at practically constant pressure, there is no reason for considering the effect of pressure in this discussion.

Standard heats of reaction are more or less ideal, in that they are calculated on the assumption that the chemical changes involved have taken place at 60°F (or at 25°C). It is obvious that no such condition actually is present in industrial operations, such as the melting of iron in the cupola by means of heat generated by the combustion of coke. The reactants may enter the system at different temperatures and the products may leave at still different ones. The effect of heat on such reactions may be calculated from the standard heats of reactions and the specific heats of the reactants and products.

The heat of reaction at constant pressure, corresponding to any conditions of temperature, is equal to the algebraic sum of the heat evolved in bringing all entering materials to their standard states at 60°F, plus the standard heat of reaction, minus the heat absorbed in bringing all resultant products to their respective final temperatures and states. This relationship may be expressed in the form of a heat balance:

$$\begin{aligned} \text{Heat Input} &= \text{Heat Output} \\ \text{Heat Input} &= H_r + Q_{60} \\ \text{Heat Output} &= H_p + Q \end{aligned}$$

where

H_r is the heat content of all reactants above their standard states at 60°F,

H_p is the heat content of all products above their standard states at 60°F,

Q_{60} is the standard heat of reaction at 60° F, and

Q is the heat effect of the process under existing conditions:

Q here is the heat made available by the process for other purposes. In the case of a cupola heat balance, it is simply the heat lost to the surroundings.

Example of a Heat Balance

The significance of the preceding statements can best be seen in an actual example. The equation for the complete combustion (Q_{60}) of carbon is

$$C_{(Coke)} + O_2 = CO_2 + 173{,}570 \text{ Btu at } 60°F$$

Suppose the oxygen is supplied in the form of air at 350°F and carbon at 60°F, and that the carbon dioxide produced leaves at 750°F

C supplied: 1 lb mole (12 lb)
O_2 supplied: 1 lb mole (32 lb)
Air supplied: $1.0 \div 0.21 = 4.76$ lb moles (air contains 21% O_2)
N_2 present: $4.76 - 1 = 3.76$ lb moles (105.3 lb)
CO_2 produced: 1 lb mole (44 lb)

Mean Specific Heats (Table 34.2):

$\overline{C_p}$ (60° – 350°F) O_2: 0.2230 Btu/lb/°F
N_2: 0.2490 Btu/lb/°F
$\overline{C_p}$ (60° – 750°F) CO_2: 0.2367 Btu/lb/°F
N_2: 0.2525 Btu/lb/°F

Heat contents of reactants:

$$H_{O_2} = 290 \times 32 \times 0.2230 = 2070 \text{ Btu}$$

$$H_{N_2} = 290 \times 105.3 \times 0.2490 = 7610 \text{ Btu}$$

$$H_r = 9680 \text{ Btu}$$

Heat contents of products:

$$H_{CO_2} = 690 \times 44 \times 0.2367 = 7{,}190 \text{ Btu}$$

$$H_{N_2} = 690 \times 105.3 \times 0.2525 = 18{,}360 \text{ Btu}$$

$$H_p = 25{,}550 \text{ Btu}$$

$$Q_{60} = 173{,}570$$
$$H_r = 9{,}680$$
$$\text{Total} = 183{,}250$$
$$H_p = 25{,}550$$
$$Q = 157{,}700$$
$$Q \div 12 = 13{,}140 \text{ Btu per lb carbon}$$

Heat Balance

Input		Output	
H_{Coke} =	0 Btu	H_{CO_2} =	7,190 Btu
H_{O_2} =	2,070 Btu	H_{N_2} =	18,360 Btu
H_{N_2} =	7,610 Btu	Q =	157,700 Btu
Q_{60} =	173,570 Btu		
	183,250 Btu		183,250 Btu

Thus, it is shown that, under these conditions, a pound of carbon provides 13,140 Btu.

HEAT BALANCE OF A CUPOLA OPERATION

The melting of iron in a cupola depends upon the development and use of heat, just as the operation of a successful business depends upon the procurement and use of money. By studying the sources of income and expenditure of money, a business can be made more efficient. Likewise, a study of the sources of heat in a cupola, and the disposition of this heat, makes it possible to improve the efficiency of the melting operation and to understand it better.

A heat balance of a cupola is simply a statement of where the heat comes from and where it goes. Just as in a financial statement, every unit of "income" must be accounted for as heat "expenditure." Depending upon the purposes for which the heat balance is made, it can be either quite simple or highly complicated. The type of heat balance discussed in this section is comparatively simple.

The calculation of a heat balance for a cupola operation requires that the necessary information and data be reasonably exact and measured with as much care as practical. Data should be acquired at a time in the heat when operation of the cupola is reasonably stable. For example, a useful heat balance usually cannot be made during the first 2 hr of a heat, during the last hour, within 1 hr after the charging of a coke "booster," or within 30 min after a change in the blast rate.

The preparation and study of a heat balance will frequently show possibilities for more economical operation. Any improvement in thermal efficiency, however, must be considered in relation to practical foundry operations and the quality of the iron. For example, thermal efficiency may be increased by reducing the size of the coke charge or by increasing the blast rate, but at the same time the melting rate and tapping temperature may be affected so as to make the increased thermal efficiency impractical.

It is necessary in cupola operation to reach a compromise between the desired high thermal efficiency and the desired operating and metallurgical characteristics that accompany lower thermal efficiency. Because of the necessity for satisfying certain metallurgical considerations, thermal efficiency cannot be taken as an infallible criterion of cupola operation.

The calculation of a heat balance for a cupola operation requires knowledge of the sources and disposition of heat. Most of the heat is furnished by combustion of the coke. Even though the coke furnishes much heat, only a portion of the total potential heat in the coke can be made available. This situation is the major compromise required by the desire for a high thermal efficiency and the need for desirable metallurgical characteristics.

If conditions in the melting zone were made so oxidizing that the coke was burned entirely to carbon dioxide so as to produce all of the potential heat in the coke, the iron passing through this zone would also be burned or oxidized and rendered unfit for most castings. Some heat is provided by oxidation of iron, silicon, and manganese in the metal charge. In the case of a hot-blast cupola, heat is also furnished by the air blast. When added together, these values represent the heat input to the operation.

Part of the heat developed in a cupola is absorbed in melting the iron and superheating it to the tapping temperature. Heating, formation, and melting of the slag requires heat, as does the elimination of moisture from the coke charge, and the calcining of the limestone. Much of the heat developed in a cupola passes out of the stack in the form of hot stack gases. The temperature of the stack gases is an indication of their "sensible" heat. High temperatures of the stack gases contribute greatly to low thermal efficiency and poor economy.

Stack gases, however, contain another very large proportion of the total heat available in the cupola. This is the "latent" heat resulting from the fact that the stack gases must contain for metallurgical reasons an appreciable quantity of carbon monoxide gas. The large amount of this latent heat in a cupola is shown impressively by the amount of heat developed when the stack gases ignite at the charging door. Whether the gases ignite or not, this same large amount of heat is being lost and is not available for melting. Some heat is also required to decompose the moisture in the air blast, and a large amount of heat is lost by radiation from the hot cupola to the surrounding air.

These items of heat input and heat output can be summarized as follows:

Heat Input

1. Potential heat in the coke (calorific value of the coke)

2. Oxidation of iron, silicon, and manganese
3. Sensible heat in the air blast

Heat Output

1. Heating, melting, and superheating of the iron
2. Calcining of limestone
3. Formation, melting, and superheating of slag
4. Decomposition of moisture in the blast
5. Sensible heat in the stack gas
6. Latent heat in the stack gas
7. Radiation from the cupola

Two ratios are used to express the thermal efficiency of a cupola. The first is called "melting efficiency" and is based on the amount of total potential heat input that is recovered in the form of hot iron. Of course, it is most desirable and most economical to get as much heat as possible to accomplish this. Therefore, it is desirable to keep melting efficiency as high as possible without jeopardizing the metallurgical quality of the iron.

Melting efficiency, per cent =

$$\frac{\text{Heat present in the iron}}{(\text{Potential heat in the coke}) + (\text{heat from oxidation of iron, silicon, and manganese}) + (\text{sensible heat in the air blast})} \times 100$$

The second ratio that expresses thermal efficiency is called "combustion efficiency" and refers only to the efficiency with which the coke is burned. It has already been pointed out that only part of the potential heat in the coke can be utilized. The latent heat in the stack gas is never developed as useful heat and always represents a thermal loss in the cupola.

Combustion efficiency =

$$\frac{(\text{Potential heat in the coke}) - (\text{Latent heat in the stack gas})}{\text{Potential heat in the coke}} \times 100$$

The melting efficiency of a cupola is high as compared with other fuel-fired melting furnaces. This is caused by the fact that the metal to be heated is mixed with the fuel and is in close contact with the source of heat. This situation produces excellent heat transfer characteristics. The melting efficiency of a cupola is usually between 30 and 50 per cent, as compared with about 20 to 30 per cent in regenerative open hearth furnaces where the metal is melted out of direct contact with the fuel.

On the other hand, the combustion efficiency of a cupola is about 60 to 70 per cent, lower than for many other types of fuel-fired furnaces because full use cannot be made of the heat content of the coke without interfering with metallurgical requirements.

Calculation of a Heat Balance

Table 34.6 indicates basic information necessary to calculate *a heat balance;* the remaining pages of this Chapter 34 concern an example. The data are based on the operation of a 66 in. cupola melting iron for chilled car wheels. The use of a heated blast is assumed to illustrate the method.

TABLE 34.6. OPERATING DATA FOR CUPOLA

1. Weight of metal charge, lb	2,642
2. Weight of coke charge, lb	275
3. Weight of limestone charge, lb	34
4. Melting rate, tons of iron charged per hour	21.91
5. Coke-burning rate, lb per hr	4,556
6. Limestone charged, lb per hr	562
7. $CaCO_3$ content of limestone, %	97.15
8. Blast rate, cfm	7,800
9. Blast volume, cu ft per hr	468,000
10. Temperature of air blast, °F	350
11. Dry-bulb temperature, °F	62
12. Wet-bulb temperature, °F	55
13. Barometric pressure, inches of mercury	29.50
14. Average tapping temperature at spout, °F	2,710
15. Fixed carbon content of coke (by analysis), %	91.0
16. Carbon content of iron charged, %	2.50
17. Carbon content of iron tapped, %	3.10
18. Silicon content of charge, %	0.66
19. Silicon content of iron tapped, %	0.58
20. Manganese content of charge, %	0.75
21. Manganese content of iron tapped, %	0.52
22. CO_2 content of stack gas (by analysis), %	13.0
23. Temperature of stack gases (before ignition), °F	850
24. CaO content of slag, %	20.52
25. FeO content of slag, %	2.0

As in any calculation, it is necessary to deal with consistent units of measurement. For this example, the hour is used as the unit of time, and it is assumed that the data were obtained over a period of time when the operation of the cupola was stable and uniform.

Heat Input

1) Potential Heat in the Coke

Weight of coke, lb per hr (Table 34.6)	4,556 lb
Carbon (fixed) in coke	91.0 %
Weight of fixed carbon 4,556 x 0.910 =	4,146 lb
Heat in burning 1 lb C to CO_2	14,452 Btu
Potential Heat 4,146 x 14,452 =	59,920,000 Btu
Iron charge, per hr (Table 34.6) 21.91 x 2,000 =	43,820 lb
Carbon content of iron charged	2.50 %
Carbon content of iron tapped	3.10 %
Loss of carbon to iron	0.60 %
or 43,820 x 0.0060 =	263 lb

It is necessary at this point to know the amount of carbon lost in the decomposition of moisture. This will be calculated later, but it may be estimated by using the relationship that the percentage of carbon lost is roughly the same numerically as the number of grains of water/cu ft (p. 289).

Approximate loss of carbon in decomposing moisture 4,146 x 0.039 =	162 lb
Total carbon lost	425 lb
Potential heat of this carbon 425 x 14,452 =	6,140,000 Btu
Net potential heat	53,780,000 Btu

2) Oxidation of Iron, Silicon and Manganese

a) Oxidation of iron

Weight of slag formed per hr *(next page)*	1,491 lb
FeO content of slag	2.0 %
or 1,491 x 0.020 =	30 lb
Heat of formation of FeO, per lb (Table 34.3)	1,596 Btu

Heat produced by oxidation of iron
1,596 x 30 = 48,000 Btu

b) Oxidation of silicon
Silicon in charge 0.66 %
Silicon in melt 0.58 %
Silicon oxidized 0.08 %
Iron charged per hour 43,820 lb
Silicon oxidized 43,820 x 0.0008 = 35 lb
Heat of formation of SiO_2, per mole
369,200 Btu
Heat of formation of SiO_2, per lb Si
369,200 ÷ 28.09 = 13,140 Btu
Heat produced by oxidation of silicon
35 x 13,140 = 460,000 Btu

c) Oxidation of manganese
Manganese in charge 0.75 %
Manganese in melt 0.52 %
Manganese oxidized 0.23 %
Iron charged per hour 43,820 lb
Manganese oxidized 43,820 x 0.0023 = 101 lb
Heat of formation of MnO, per mole
165,600 Btu
Heat of formation of MnO, per lb Mn
165,600 ÷ 54.93 = 3,015 Btu
Heat produced by oxidation of manganese
101 x 3,015 = 304,000 Btu

3) Sensible Heat in the Air Blast
Stack gas analysis

CO_2	(Table 34.6)	13.0 %
CO	(Table 34.5)	13.2 %
N_2	(Table 34.5)	73.8 %

Since equal volumes of gas contain the same number of molecules,

1 mole of stack gas contains
CO_2 0.130 moles
CO 0.132 moles
N_2 0.738 moles

1 mole of stack gas is produced from
0.130 + 0.132 = 0.262 moles carbon
or 0.262 x 12 = 3.14 lb carbon
Coke charged, per hr 4,556 lb
Carbon charged, per hr 4,146 lb
Carbon lost to iron and in decomposition of moisture *(prior page)* 425 lb
Carbon burned, per hr 3,721 lb
Moles of stack gas produced per hr 3,721 ÷ 3.14 = 1,185 moles
Stack gas contains
CO_2
1,185 x 0.130 = 154 moles
or 154 x 44 = 6,780 lb
CO
1,185 x 0.132 = 156 moles
or 156 x 28 = 4,370 lb
N_2
1,185 x 0.738 = 875 moles
or 875 x 28 = 24,500 lb

Oxygen required
for CO_2 154 moles
for CO 156 ÷ 2 = 78 moles
Total 232 moles

Air required 232 ÷ 0.21 = 1,105 moles
which contains
O_2
232 moles or 232 x 32 = 7,420 lb
N_2 (as above)
875 moles or 24,500 lb
Total weight of dry air used 31,920 lb
Weight of moisture in blast *(next page)*
237 lb
Mean specific heats from 60 to 350°F (Table 34.2)
O_2 0.2230 Btu/lb/deg F
N_2 0.2490 Btu/lb/deg F
H_2O 0.4514 Btu/lb/deg F
Heat content (sensible heat) of the blast air at 350°F
O_2 7,420 x 0.2230 x 290 = 480,000 Btu
N_2 24,500 x 0.2490 x 290 = 1,769,000 Btu
H_2O 237 x 0.4514 x 290 = 31,000 Btu
Total 2,280,000 Btu

4) Total Heat Input per Hour
Net potential heat in the coke 53,780,000 Btu
Oxidation of elements
Fe 48,000 Btu
Si 460,000 Btu
Mn 304,000 Btu
Total 812,000 Btu
Sensible heat in the air blast 2,280,000 Btu
Total heat input per hour 56,870,000 Btu

Heat Output

1) Heating, Melting, and Superheating of the Iron
Iron changed per hour 43,820 lb
Weight of FeO in slag (p. 287) 30 lb
Weight of Fe oxidized to FeO

$$\frac{30 \times 55.8}{71.8} = 23 \text{ lb}$$

Iron tapped 43,800 lb
Temperature of iron charged (Table 34.6) 62°F
Temperature of iron tapped 2,710°F
Carbon content of tapped iron 3.10 %
Mean specific heat from 62 to 2,710°F (Table 34.2) 0.2085 Btu/lb/deg F
Heat content of iron at tapping temperature
2,648 x 0.2085 x 43,800 = 24,180,000 Btu

2) Calcining of Limestone
Weight of stone charged per hour 562 lb
$CaCO_3$ content of limestone 97.15 %
Weight of $CaCO_3$ charged 546 lb
Heat of decomposition of $CaCO_3$ (Table 34.4) per lb $CaCO_3$ 764 Btu
Heat of calcining limestone, per hour
546 x 764 = 417,000 Btu

3) Formation, Melting, and Superheating of Slag
a) Weight of slag produced per hour
Weight of $CaCO_3$ in limestone 546 lb
Moles of $CaCO_3$ charged (equals moles of CaO formed) 546 ÷ 100 = 5.46 moles
Weight of CaCO in slag
5.46 x 56.1 = 306 lb

CaO content of slag 20.52 %

Weight of slag formed per hour

306 ÷ 0.2052 = 1,491 lb

b) Heat of slagging reactions

The slagging reactions may be represented by

Heats of formation (Table 34.3)

CaO	SiO_2	$CaO \cdot SiO_2$
273,400 Btu +	369,200 Btu =	680,400 Btu

Heat of reaction

680,400 − 642,600 = 37,800 Btu

Weight of $CaCO_3$ needed to form one mole of $CaO \cdot SiO_2$ 100 lb

Heat of slagging reactions per lb of $CaCO_3$ 378 Btu

Heat of slagging reactions

378 x 546 = 206,000 Btu

c) Heat content of slag at 2,710°F

Mean specific heat of slag from 62 to 2710° F 0.3209 Btu/lb/deg F

Weight of slag formed per hour

1,491 lb

Heat content of molten slag

1,491 x 0.3209 x 2,648 = 1,267,000 Btu

Heat available from slagging reactions

206,000 Btu

Net heat required for slag

1,061,000 Btu

4) Decomposition of Moisture in the Blast

Weight of dry air used	31,920 lb
Dry-bulb temperature	62° F
Wet-bulb temperature	55° F
Barometric pressure	29.50 in. Hg

From calculations on p. 289, moisture per lb of dry air

$$\frac{53 \times 29.50}{29.92} = 52 \text{ grains}$$

Grains per pound 7,000

Total moisture in blast per hour

$$\frac{31,920 \times 52}{7,000} = 237 \text{ lb}$$

Since one mole of carbon (12 lb) is required to decompose one mole of water (18 lb), the carbon required is

$$\frac{237 \times 12}{18} = 158 \text{ lb}$$

Heat required per lb H_2O (Table 34.4)

2,898 Btu

Heat required for decomposition of water in the blast 237 x 2,898 = 687,000 Btu

5) Sensible Heat in the Stack Gas

Stack gas contains

CO_2	6,780 lb
CO	4,370 lb
N_2	24,500 lb
H_2	$\frac{237 \times 2}{18} =$ 26.3 lb
Temperature of stack gas	850° F

Mean specific heat of gases from 60 to 850°F

CO_2	0.2408 Btu/lb/deg F
CO_2	0.2556 Btu/lb/deg F
N_2	0.2538 Btu/lb/deg F
H_2	3.463 Btu/lb/deg F

Heat content of stack gases

CO_2	6,780 x 0.2408 x 790 = 1,290,000 Btu
CO	4,370 x 0.2556 x 790 = 882,000 Btu
N_2	24,500 x 0.2538 x 790 = 4,912,000 Btu
H_2	26.3 x 3.463 x 790 = 72,000 Btu
Total	7,156,000 Btu

6) Latent Heat in the Stack Gas

The CO may be burned to CO_2 as in the Griffin hot blast system (Chapter 7 PAGE 64) and part of the heat recovered.

Weight of CO in stack gas 4,370 lb

Heat of combustion per lb CO (Table 50) 4,346 Btu

Heat of combustion of CO

4,346 x 4,370 = 18,992,000 Btu

7) Radiation From the Cupola

Total heat output acounted for so far

Heating, melting, and superheating of the iron	24,180,000 Btu
Calcining of limestone	417,000 Btu
Formation, melting, and superheating of the slag	1,061,000 Btu
Decomposition of moisture in the blast	687,000 Btu
Sensible heat in stack gas	7,156,000 Btu
Latent heat in stack gas	18,992,000 Btu
Total	52,493,000 Btu
Total heat input per hour	56,870,000 Btu
Radiation loss from the cupola, by difference	4,377,000 Btu

SUMMARY

Heat Input

Net potential heat of coke

53,780,000 Btu

Oxidation of elements

Fe	48,000 Btu
Si	460,000 Btu
Mn	304,000 Btu
Total	812,000 Btu

Sensible heat in air blast

O_2	480,000 Btu
N_2	1,769,000 Btu
H_2O	31,000 Btu
Total	2,280,000 Btu

Total heat input 56,870,000 Btu

Heat Output

Heating, melting, and superheating of iron 24,180,000 Btu

Calcining of limestone

417,000 Btu

Formation, melting, and superheating of slag 1,061,000 Btu

Decomposition of moisture in the blast 687,000 Btu

Sensible heat in the stack gas

CO_2	1,290,000 Btu
CO	882,000 Btu
N_2	4,912,000 Btu
H_2	72,000 Btu
Total	7,156,000 Btu

Latent heat in the stack gas
18,992,000 Btu

Radiation from the cupola
4,377,000 Btu

Total heat output 56,870,000 Btu

Reference to the summary will indicate the relative error involved in neglecting any of the heat effects involved. The heat of oxidation of iron, the sensible heat of water in the blast, and of hydrogen in the stack gas can safely be neglected. The sources and disposition of heat are shown graphically in Fig. 34.2.

Efficiency

Melting efficiency =

$$\frac{\text{Heat present in the iron x 100}}{\text{(Potential heat in the coke) + (heat from oxidation of the elements) + (sensible heat in the air blast)}} =$$

$$= \frac{24{,}180{,}000}{59{,}920{,}000 + 812{,}000 + 2{,}280{,}000} \times 100 = 38.37$$

Combustion efficiency =

$$\frac{\text{(Potential heat in the coke)} - \text{(Latent heat in the stack gas)}}{\text{Potential heat in the coke}} \times 100 =$$

$$= \frac{59{,}920{,}000 - 18{,}992{,}000}{59{,}920{,}000} \times 100 = 68.30\%$$

Alternative Method

The following alternative method of making a heat balance is more accurate and, in the long run, easier to perform than the more traditional method just described. It is based on a general application of the Law of Hess. The heat contents of materials entering and leaving the cupola are calculated in the same way as in the previous method, but all chemical changes are lumped together and calculated in one step. This requires the compiling of a complete material balance.

While the quantities of materials entering and leaving need not be known with greater accuracy than in the former method, the material balance must be completely consistent so that exactly the same amount of each element is shown entering and leaving the cupola. For this purpose it is most convenient to express all quantities in terms of pound moles. The method will be illustrated on the basis of the data in Table 34.6.

MATERIAL BALANCE

Input

1) Metal — Pound Moles
   a) Fe 43,820 ÷ 55.85 = 784.60
   b) Si 43,820 x 0.0066 ÷ 28.09 = 10.30
   c) Mn 43,820 x 0.0075 ÷ 54.93 = 5.98
   d) C 43,820 x 0.0250 ÷ 12.01 = 91.22
2) Limstone
   a) $CaCO_3$ 562 x 0.9715 ÷ 100.09 = 5.46
   b) SiO_2 562 x 0.0285 ÷ 60.09 = 0.27
3) Coke
   a) C 4,556 x 0.910 ÷ 12.01 = 345.21
   b) SiO_2 4,556 x 0.090 ÷ 60.09 = 6.82
4) Refractory loss
   a) SiO_2 Silicon in slag and melt minus silicon in iron, coke and limestone
   9.04 + 17.06 − 10.30 − 0.27 − 6.82 = 8.70
5) Air
   a) O_2 Oxygen required to burn the coke calculated as on p. 293, plus that needed to oxidize iron, silicon and managese
   232 + 0.21 + 1.26 + 0.91 = 234.38
   b) N_2 234.38 x 0.79 ÷ 0.21 = 881.75
   c) H_2O Calculated as on p. 294
   237 ÷ 18.02 = 13.16

Output

1) Metal
   a) Fe 784.60 − 0.42 (see slag below) = 784.18
   b) Si
   43,800 (see p. 293) x 0.0058 ÷ 28.09 = 9.04
   c) Mn 43,800 x 0.0052 ÷ 54.93 = 4.15
   d) C 43,800 x 0.0310 ÷ 12.01 = 113.05
2) Slag
   a) CaO Equals moles $CaCO_3$ charged 5.46
   or 5.46 x 56.08 = 306 lb
   Total weight of slag (p. 293) 1,491 lb
   b) FeO 1,491 x 0.020 ÷ 71.85 = 0.42
   or 0.42 x 71.85 = 30 lb
   c) MnO Equals loss of Mn from metal
   5.98 − 4.15 = 1.83
   or 1.83 x 70.93 = 130 lb
   d) SiO_2 1,491 − 306 − 30 − 130 = 1,025 lb
   or 1,025 ÷ 60.09 = 17.06
3) Stack gas
   a) CO_2 from combustion of coke (p. 293) plus amount obtained from calcining $CaCO_3$ 154 + 5.46 = 159.46
   b) CO from combustion of coke and decomposition of moisture
   156 + 13.16 = 169.16
   c) H_2 from decomposition of water 13.16
   d) N_2 as above 881.75

To find the heat involved in all the chemical reactions taking place in the cupola, this material balance is now treated like a chemical reaction. The number of moles of each reactant and product is multiplied by the molar heat of formation. The net increase in heat of formation gives the heat effect of the reactions. Elements in the metal and the slag are realistically combined in Table 34.7.

HEAT BALANCE

The sensible heat of the stack gas should be recalculated. The other heat content figures may be taken from the former calculation.

TABLE 34.7. MATERIAL BALANCE

Input	moles	Heat of formation, Btu/hr	Output	moles	Heat of formation, Btu/hr
Metal			Metal		
Fe_3C	91.22	−821,000	Fe_3C	113.05	−1,017,400
FeSi	10.30	356,400	FeSi	9.04	312,800
Mn	5.98	0	Mn	4.15	0
Fe	500.64	0	Fe	435.99	0
Limestone			Slag		
$CaCO_3$	5.46	2,834,900	$CaO \cdot SiO_2$	5.46	3,715,000
SiO_2	0.27	99,600	$MnO \cdot SiO_2$	1.83	996,400
Coke			$FeO \cdot SiO_2$	0.42	208,700
C	345.21	−1,477,500	SiO_2	9.35	3,452,000
SiO_2	6.82	2,517,900	Stack Gas		
Refractory			CO_2	159.46	26,995,600
SiO_2	8.70	3,212,000	CO	169.16	8,043,400
Air			H_2	13.16	0
O_2	234.28	0	N_2	881.75	0
N_2	881.75	0			
H_2O	13.16	1,369.100			
Totals		8,091,400			42,706,500

Net heat of chemical change per hour
42,706,500 − 8.091,400 = 34,615,100 Btu

Heat Content of Stack Gas

Weight of gas

CO_2	159.46 x 44.01 =	7,017 lb
CO	169.16 x 28.01 =	4,738 lb
H_2	13.16 x 2.02 =	26.6 lb
N_2	881.75 x 28.02 =	24,707 lb

Heat content

CO_2	7,017 x 0.2408 x 790 =	1,334,800 Btu
CO	4,738 x 0.2556 x 790 =	956,700 Btu
H_2	26.6 x 3.463 x 790 =	72,800 Btu
N_2	24,707 x 0.2538 x 790 =	4,953,800 Btu
Total		7,318,100 Btu

Heat Input

Blast preheat	2,280,000 Btu	
Chemical charges	34,615,000 Btu	
Total		36,895,000 Btu

Heat Output

Heat content of iron	24,180,000 Btu	
Heat content of slag	1,267,000 Btu	
Heat content of stack gas	7,318,000 Btu	
Radiation loss (by difference)	4,130,000 Btu	
Total		36,895,000 Btu

EFFICIENCY

In calculating the melting efficiency the heat of oxidation of the elements may be neglected or may be calculated as on p. 292. Melting efficiency =

$$\frac{24,180,000}{59,920,000 + 2,280,000} = 38.87\%$$

For the combustion efficiency the total latent heat in the stack gas should be calculated as follows:

From Table 50:

$$CO + \tfrac{1}{2} O_2 = CO_2 + 121,745 \text{ Btu}$$

From Table 49:

$$H_2 + \tfrac{1}{2} O_2 = H_2O + 104,036 \text{ Btu}$$

Latent heat of CO:

$$169.16 \times 121,745 = 20,594,000 \text{ Btu}$$

Latent heat of H_2:

$$13.16 \times 104,036 = 1,369,000 \text{ Btu}$$

Total 21,963,000 Btu

Combustion efficiency

$$\frac{59,920,000 - 21,963,000}{59,920,000} = 63.35\%$$

Fig. 34.2. Diagram of a heat balance in a cupola.

HEAT INPUT

POTENTIAL HEAT OF COKE
% BTU/HR
94.54 53,800,000

OXIDATION OF ELEMENTS
1.41 800,000

SENSIBLE HEAT OF BLAST
4.05 2,300,000

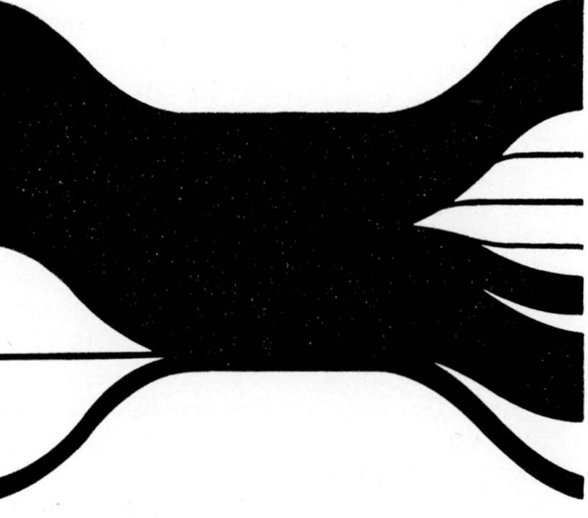

HEAT OUTPUT

HEAT CONTENT OF IRON
% BTU/HR
42.50 24,200,000
CALCINING
0.70 400,000
HEAT CONTENT OF SLAG
1.93 1,100,000
DECOMPOSITION OF H2O
1.23 700,000
SENSIBLE HEAT IN STACK GAS
12.48 7,100,000
LATENT HEAT IN STACK GAS
33.41 19,000,000
RADIATION FROM CUPOLA
7.75 4,400,000

SCALE: = 8,530,000 BTU/HR

CHAPTER 35

Metallurgy of the Cast Irons

I. CAST IRONS AS A GROUP

The alloys of iron and carbon can be classified into two groups—the steels and the cast irons. The cast iron group includes white iron, gray iron, malleable iron and ductile iron. Although primarily alloys of iron and carbon, all of these alloys contain significant amounts of silicon, manganese, phosphorus, sulfur and, on occasion, the alloying elements nickel, chromium, molybdenum, vanadium, copper, and some others.

Satisfactory definition of the terms steel and cast iron is difficult, and must be made by reference to the iron-iron carbide diagram, Fig. 35.1.

Steel can be defined as an alloy of iron and carbon containing such amounts of carbon that the alloy can be made 100 per cent austenite by heating into the single phase austenite region, as shown on the diagram (austenite is designated on the diagram by gamma, γ). Since the greatest extent of this region is at 2 per cent carbon, steel is an alloy of iron and carbon containing less than 2 per cent of carbon in terms of this diagram.

The cast irons are alloys of iron and carbon containing amounts of carbon in excess of the amount which can be retained in solid solution in austenite, and in terms of this diagram are alloys containing more than 2 per cent of carbon.

The diagram indicates that alloys of more than 2 per cent carbon will contain substantial amounts of the hard brittle compound cementite (Fe_3C) or its decomposition product, graphite, in addition to the austenite. Both cementite and graphite lower the plasticity of austenite in the cast irons to the point where forging is not practiced. A fundamental distinction between steel and the cast irons is that steel can be forged, and is available in both the forged and cast condition, whereas the various cast irons are employed in general only in the cast condition.

The presence of alloying elements changes the extent of the austenite region. Commercial cast irons ordinarily contain significant amounts of silicon. The lower diagram of Fig. 35.2, which is for the alloys of iron and carbon containing 2 per cent of silicon, shows that the extent of the austenite or gamma region is reduced to a maximum of 1.50 per cent carbon by the presence of silicon.

A similar change is effected by chromium, molybdenum, vanadium, and other elements which may be present. This change in the extent of the austenite region makes it difficult to frame a valid definition distinguishing between steel and cast iron on the basis of a stated carbon content, but in general the cast irons can be regarded as alloys of iron and carbon containing more than 2 per cent carbon, and steel as an alloy containing less than this amount.

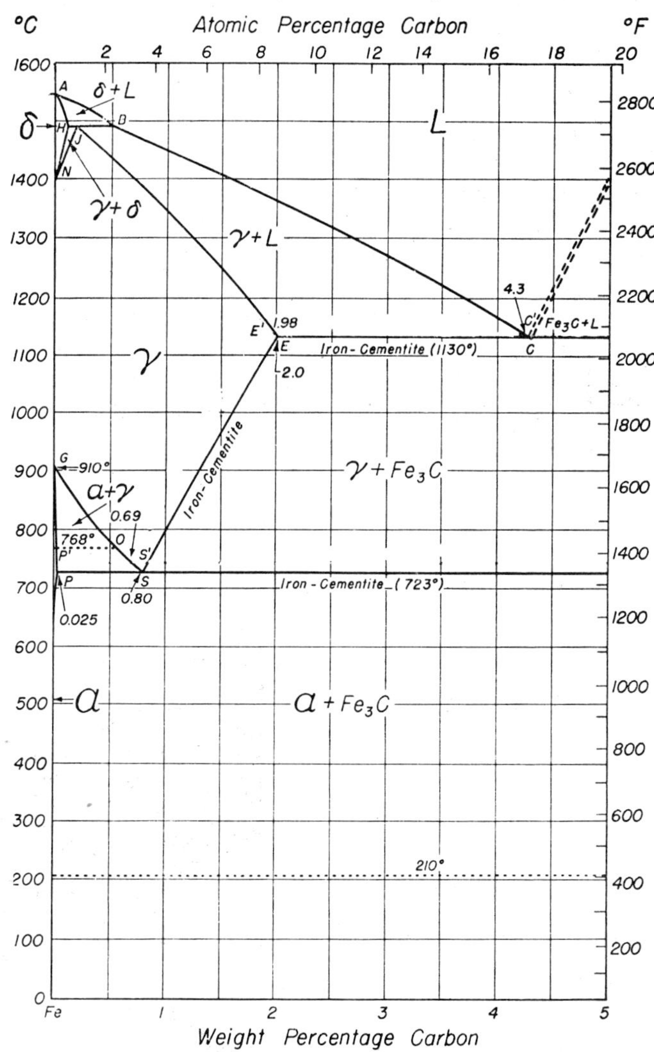

Fig. 35.1. Iron-iron carbide diagram. The symbol γ*(gamma)* designates austenite, the symbol α*(alpha)* ferrite or alpha ferrite. (Diagram from *American Society of Metals Handbook*, 1948, with modification.)

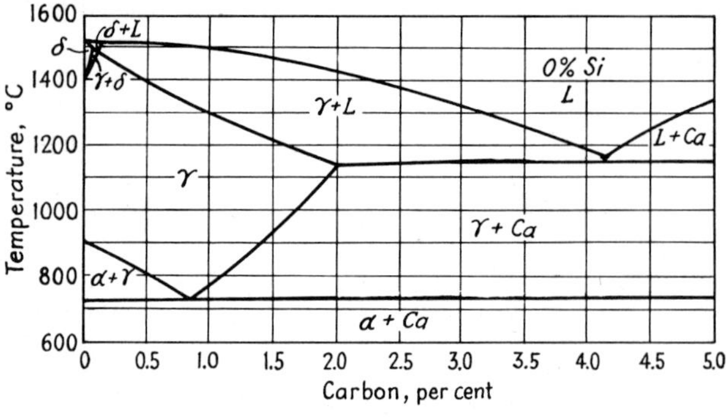

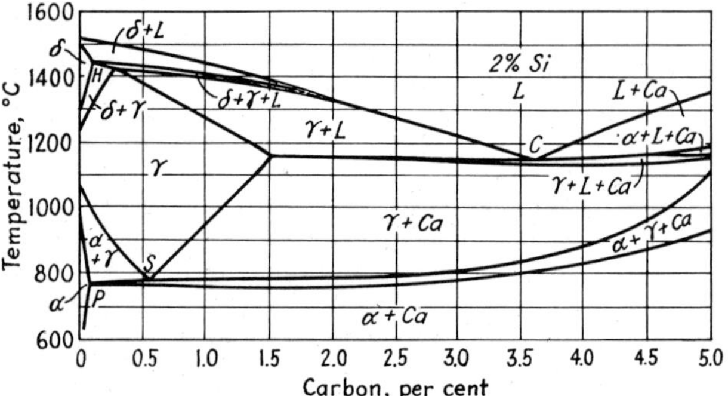

Fig. 35.2. The iron-iron carbide diagram, *(above)* and diagram for the series of iron carbon alloys containing 2.00 per cent silicon presented *(below)* to show the effect of silicon. Austenite is designated by the symbol γ*(gamma)* and iron carbide *(Fe_3C)* by the symbol *Ca*.

This chapter deals with the microstructure and properties of the several kinds of cast irons. The cast irons are among the most complex and sensitive of alloys. The discussion here is of necessity incomplete; essential aspects of the metallurgy of these important materials of interest to those engaged in cupola melting will be reviewed.

Although every effort is made to simplify the discussion, it is necessary to employ the appropriate phase diagrams in defining the structures present in the irons and their relation to engineering properties.

II. WHITE AND CHILLED IRON

Gray cast iron is described as gray because a portion of the carbon is present as elemental or free carbon in the form of graphite, which darkens the fracture.

White cast iron is definable as cast iron which contains no free carbon and a substantial portion of the carbon is combined with iron to form a compound designated as iron carbide or cementite. This compound is represented by the chemical formula Fe_3C.

Cementite is a hard, brittle substance (over 750 Brinell), and its presence as a part of the structure of white iron accounts for the hardness, brittleness and abrasion resistance of this alloy. The light etching, massive crystals of Fig. 35.3 are cementite. Due to the absence of graphite and the presence of massive cementite, the fracture of white iron is white and lustrous in appearance as opposed to the fracture of gray iron. Rapid cooling favors the formation of the white fracture. For this reason iron castings or portions of iron castings having a white fracture are referred to as chilled iron.

Although white iron has less extensive direct application than the other forms of iron, it is discussed first because an understanding of its structure is essential to the metallurgy of both gray and malleable iron.

The structures of the cast irons are highly complex, and of necessity will be discussed in terms of the appropriate versions of the diagrams for the iron-carbon or iron-carbon-silicon systems presented in Figs. 35.1, 35.2 and 35.4. This discussion assumes a knowledge of these diagrams and their interpretation.

If the reader has not had an opportunity to become familiar with phase diagrams, he should understand that the diagram is divided in fields separated by lines connecting temperature composition points, and that if a point in a field is selected as representing a certain composition of alloy at a certain temperature, then the structure of the alloy is made up of the phases or constituents marked on this field.

Changing the temperature of the alloy within the field may change the relative amounts and compositions of the phases, but the alloy will still consist of the same phases. These diagrams are valid at low rates of heating and cooling permitting an approach to equilibrium. Such rates of heating and cooling may be approached when cast irons solidify and cool in sand molds in regular foundry practice.

The origin and description of the structures present in white iron are described in terms of the diagrams of Figs. 35.1 and 35.4. Before undertaking this description, it will be necessary to define a number of terms used in designating the microconstituents of irons and steels.

Allotropic Forms of Iron

The element iron exists in two allotropic or crystalline forms. In certain ranges of temperature the existing form or arrangement is described by the crystallographer as the alpha (α) or body centered cubic. In an intermediate range of temperature the iron atoms assume a different arrangement in space described as gamma (γ) or face centered cubic. The vertical line of Fig. 35.1 at zero carbon describes the element iron, and defines the ranges of existence of the two forms of iron.

The alpha form exists at temperatures up to 910 C (1670 F) point *G*, and also in the range from 1400 to 1539 C (2552 – 2802 F) at which temperature of the iron becomes molten. The gamma form of iron exists in the intermediate range of temperature from 910 to 1400 C (1670 – 2552 F). The extent of the existence of the gamma form is increased by the presence of carbon, and the gamma form is capable of existing down to 723 C (1333 F) in the presence of 0.80 per cent or more of carbon. It follows that when pure iron is heated to 910 C (1670 F) a rearrangement of the atoms in the iron takes place, and the alpha form changes to the gamma. These changes in the form of iron are reversible, and the gamma changes to alpha on cooling through the 910 C (1670 F) point.

The two forms of iron differ in their properties. Gamma iron is more plastic, has a higher density and is nonmagnetic. Alpha iron is magnetic below a

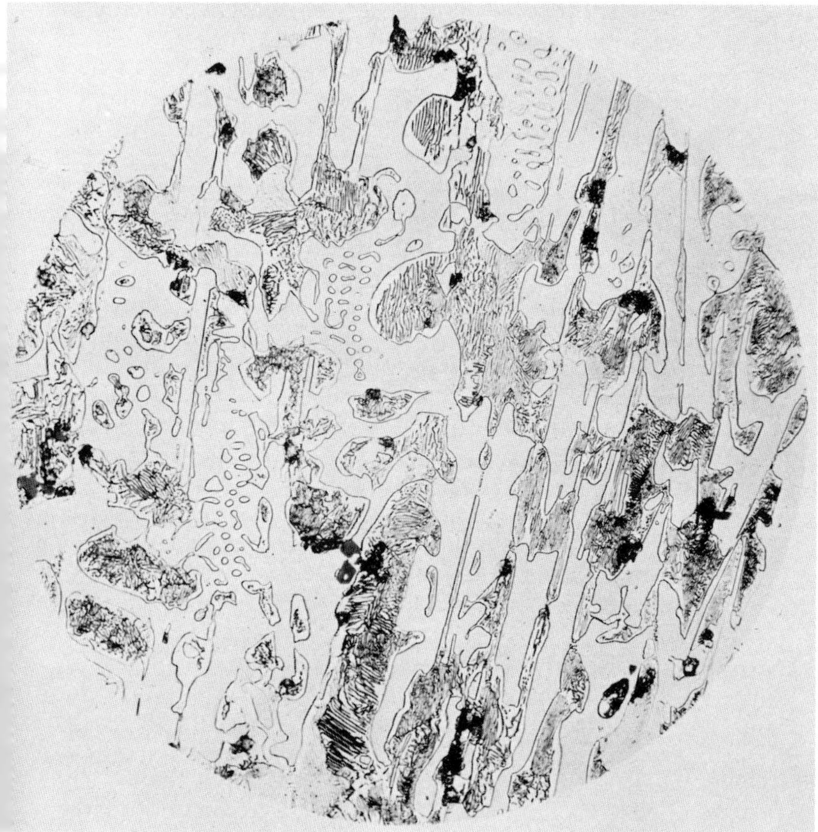

Fig. 35.3. Hypoeutectic white iron. Nital etch, 250 × (from S. C. Massari).

Fig. 35.5. Microstructure of an eutectic iron, 500 × (from H. A. Schwartz, National Castings Company).

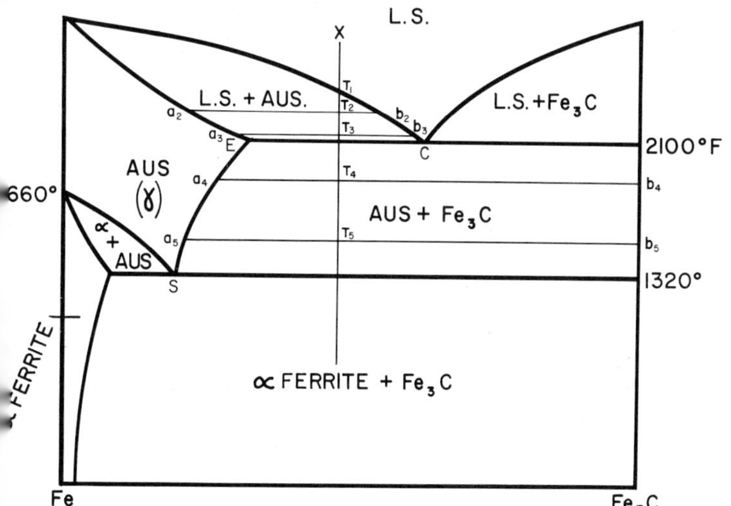

Fig. 35.4. Simplified version of iron-iron carbide diagram of *Fig. 35.1.* Note that diagram is not drawn to scale. LS stands for liquid solution or melt.

TABLE 35.1. INFLUENCE OF SILICON ON PROPERTIES* OF ANNEALED FERRITE (Yensen)

Si, %	Tensile Strength, psi	Yield Strength, psi	Elongation, %
0	34000	17000	60
1	47000	30000	50
2	60000	42000	50
3	73000	55000	20
4	86000	68000	20

* The Brinell hardness may be computed with reasonable accuracy by dividing the tensile strength by 500.

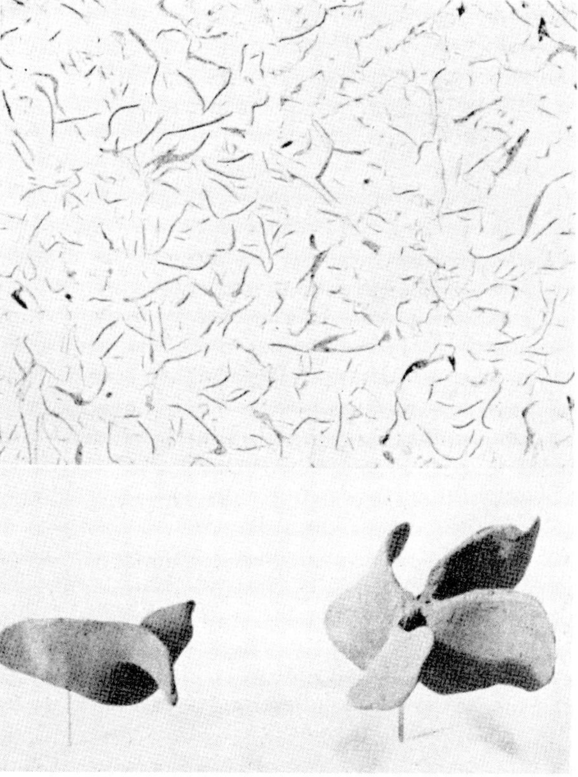

Fig. 35.6. Microstructure and space models of flake graphite. Unetched, 150 × (from J. T. MacKenzie).

certain range of temperature. The important difference in this discussion is in the extent of solubility of carbon in the two forms. This solubility is defined on the diagram (Fig. 35.1) by the extent of the two regions marked α, and γ. The maximum solubility in alpha iron in the lower range of temperature occurs at 720 C (1328 F), and is 0.025 per cent carbon at 723 C (1333 F) point *P*, and the maximum solubility in the gamma form is 2.00 per cent C at 1130 C (2066 F) point *E*.

Since the carbon rich phase cementite or graphite is not indicated as existing in the gamma or alpha fields, it follows that the carbon is in solution in the two forms of iron in these ranges of temperature and composition. If the carbon content of the alloys is increased by moving to the right of the alpha and gamma fields, the additional carbon in excess of the amount soluble in the iron crystals appears as the carbon rich phase, iron carbide (see fields marked gamma plus carbide, and alpha plus carbide).

Structural Constituents in Iron

The structural constituents commonly appearing during the solidification and transformation of white iron, in addition to cementite, are austenite, ferrite, and pearlite.

Austenite may be defined as a solid solution of carbon in the gamma or face centered cubic form of iron. The carbon atoms are relatively small, and are able to take positions between the iron atoms in the gamma iron crystals, and the resulting dispersion is a true solution. As previously mentioned, the maximum amount of carbon which can be held in solution in this manner is 2 per cent. Austenite is relatively soft, moderately strong and is ductile and forgeable. It is nonmagnetic. This solution may contain other elements in addition to carbon and silicon, and the various alloying elements occur in solution in the austenite when they are present in the iron or steel.

The presence of these elements changes the extent of solubility of carbon in the iron, and their presence changes the extent of the austenite region from the 2 per cent maximum found in alloys containing only iron and carbon. The mechanical properties of austenite are influenced by the amount of the solute elements. The range of temperature within which austenite is stable is also altered by the presence of the solute elements. Increasing carbon in solution lowers the minimum temperature of stability under equilibrium conditions from 910 C (1670 F), its value in solutions approaching pure iron, to 723 C (1333 F) at 0.80 per cent carbon (Fig. 35.1).

Ferrite (sometimes designated as α Ferrite) is a solid solution of carbon in the alpha or body centered cubic form of iron. The amount of carbon which can be dissolved in ferrite is limited, and is a maximum of about 0.025 per cent in the low range of temperature (maximum extent of alpha region, point *P*, Fig. 35.1). This is in contrast to the high solubility of carbon in the face centered cubic austenite solution. The transformation of the face centered cubic form of iron to the body centered or alpha form on cooling results in a precipitation of carbon, usually in the combined form as cementite.

Ferrite may contain other elements in solution in addition to carbon. Silicon and the alloying elements when present in steel and cast iron are dissolved in the ferrite. Ferrite is relatively soft and ductile. Its properties are determined by the amount of carbon and solute elements present. Table 35.1 gives the mechanical properties of ferrite as influenced by increasing silicon content. Ferrite appears under the microscope as light etching crystals (Fig. 35.18). At ordinary temperatures ferrite is magnetic.

In addition to occurring as relatively large or massive crystals, ferrite and cementite occur in alloys of iron and carbon as a two phased constituent designated as pearlite. Pearlite is made up of thin, alternate lamellae of ferrite and cementite. These platelike crystals of cementite and ferrite are shown in cross section in the pearlite of Fig. 35.8. In terms of the equilibrium diagram of Fig. 35.1, pearlite is formed when austenite of 0.80 per cent C content transforms in the eutectoid manner at the temperature-composition point *S*, which is designated as the eutectoid point.

When silicon and alloying elements are present in the alloy the eutectoid point is displaced to a lower carbon percentage. At 2 per cent silicon the eutectoid point is shifted from 0.80 per cent to 0.60 per cent C, and pearlite in an alloy with 2 per cent of silicon contains the proportion of ferrite and cementite giving the structure a carbon content of 0.60 per cent.

The mechanical properties of pearlite are dependent on a number of factors including the thickness of the lamellae. Increasing cooling rates promotes fineness of structure and the finer pearlites are harder and stronger. Strength and hardness may exceed 120,000 psi and 225 Brinell. Fine pearlites are not resolved at low magnifications under the microscope. Fine pearlites appear as dark etching, unresolved structures in photomicrographs (Fig. 35.9).

Solidification and Transformation of White Iron

The solidification and transformation of a typical white iron will be discussed in terms of the diagram of Fig. 35.4, a simplified version of Fig. 35.1 not drawn to scale. The alloy selected is a hypoeutectic iron of 3.00 per cent C, the alloy being represented by the vertical line marked x at this percentage of carbon. At the temperature x the alloy is completely molten as a solution of carbon and silicon in iron.

As the alloy is cooled from x to point T_1 the alloy remains molten. At point T_1 the alloy is entering the field marked austenite plus melt, and it follows that solidification is starting with the formation of crystals of the solid solution, austenite. These crystals are complex in shape, having a central axis from which branches originate to give the peculiar branched, treelike structure described by the metallographer as dendritic. Although the external shape of the crystals is complex, the growing crystals of austenite are true crystals in every sense.

As the temperature falls from point T_1 to point T_2 solidification progresses with the formation of more austenite dendrites, and a corresponding decrease in the amount of remaining liquid. At a point within a two phased field, it is possible to determine the relative amounts of the phases present at the temperature point in question in accordance with well defined rules for the interpretation of these diagrams.

This determination is accomplished at T_2 by drawing the horizontal line a_2 b_2 through the temperature point T_2. At temperature T_2 the entire amount of metal in the system is represented by the horizontal line. At this temperature, the amount of solid austenite is proportional to the line segment T_2 b_2 and the amount of remaining liquid is proportional to the line segment a_2 T_2. Since the segment T_2 b_2 is approximately one-fifth of the line a_2 b_2, it follows that the system is approximately one-fifth solid and four-fifths liquid at T_2. If the rule is applied at T_3, where the total amount of metal in the system is represented by the line a_3 b_3, it is demonstrated that solidification is continuing with an increase in solid austenite and a decrease in the remaining liquid.

As the temperature falls in the two phased field, the composition or chemical analysis of both solid and liquid change continuously. The precipitation of austenite, which contains less carbon than the original liquid of 3 per cent carbon, enriches the remaining liquid in carbon. At T_2 the composition of the remaining liquid is determined by projecting point b_2, and at T_3 by projecting point b_3 to the composition axis. It follows that the composition of the remaining liquid is changing in accordance with the line T_1 C and is approaching the composition of the eutectic point *C*.

The composition of the austenite can be determined at the respective temperatures by projecting points a_2 and a_3 and approaches the value of point *E* as the temperature in the system approaches the eutectic horizontal EC.

As the temperature approaches the horizontal EC, it is apparent that the system still contains approximately 50 per cent liquid. The composition of this remaining liquid is approaching the eutectic composition C of 4.3 per cent carbon. Since no liquid exists in the field below the horizontal, the temperature must become constant during the period of solidification of this remaining liquid. The term eutectic, meaning lowest melting, is applied to such minimum points as *C* and to the remaining liquids of corresponding composition. Eutectic liquids solidify at constant temperature or within a very narrow range of temperature in ferrous alloys.

The manner of solidification of eutectic compositions is characteristic, and is accomplished by the simultaneous or alternate formation of two kinds of crystals to produce a dispersion which is characteristic of the particular alloy. In this case the two phases are austenite and iron carbide.

Although the microstructure of Fig. 35.5 was made at room temperature, the structure shown gives an approximation of the eutectic structure, the dark areas representing the austenite and the light areas the hard cementite. The eutectic structure is designated as ledeburite. After completion of eutectic solidification, the alloy is entirely solid, and consists of the primary dendrite of austenite plus the ledeburite or eutectic dispersion of austenite and cementite. Figure 35.3 shows the total structure. The large dark areas represent sections through primary dendrites. The intervening finely dispersed structure is the ledeburite.

The temperature is now free to fall and cooling continues through the austenite plus carbide region with precipitation of more carbon in the form of cementite from the austenite. At temperature T_4, the horizontal line determination gives the amount of cementite as proportional to the segment a_4T_4 and the amount of austenite as T_4b_4. The composition of the austenite at T_4 is given by the projection of point a_4 to the composition axis. At T_5 the amount of cementite has increased to a_5T_5 with a corresponding decrease in the amount of remaining austenite. As a result of the continuing precipitation of the carbon rich cementite, the remaining austenite has been reduced in carbon content to the value determined by projecting point a_5.

Application of the horizontal line determination shows that cooling through this region results in a continuing precipitation of iron carbide from the austenite, and that the remaining austenite is reduced in carbon, changes its composition in accordance with line ES, and approaches the composition of the eutectoid point *S*. At *S* a reaction occurs at constant temperature in the eutectic manner. Since the reaction involves the transformation of a solid solution instead of a liquid solution, the point *S* is designated the eutectoid point and the horizontal line passing through this point as the eutectoid line.

At this eutectoid temperature and under equilibrium conditions the remaining austenite transforms, and produces the lamellar dispersion of alternate crystals of ferrite and iron carbide previously designated as pearlite. The microstructure now consists of relatively large or massive crystals of cementite, and pearlite. In cooling from the eutectoid temperature to ambient temperature the only change is a slight increase in the amount of cementite by precipitation from the ferrite solution.

The final microstructure is illustrated in Fig. 35.3 where the darker areas are pearlite which is not resolved into its platelike structure at the magnification employed. The larger dark areas are sections through the primary dendrites formed during the solidification of the iron. The small dark areas intimately dispersed with the white cementite represent the secondary austenite formed during the solidification of the eutectic structure. Both the primary and the eutectic crystals of austenite have transformed to pearlite.

Two types of cementite crystals are present. These are the large or so called "massive" crystals which formed as one constituent of the eutectic solid, and the small or lamellar crystals which formed as part of the pearlite at the eutectoid temperature.

In the case of the solidification of an alloy of eutectic composition, 4.3 per cent carbon, no precipitation of primary dendrites of austenite occurs and the entire mass of liquid solidifies as the eutectic structure, ledeburite. As cooling continues transformation takes place in the same manner as in the case of the lower carbon iron, with the final structure again consisting of massive cementite and pearlite.

Figure 35.5 shows that microstructure of an iron of this composition.

Irons of hypereutectic composition solidify with the formation of primary iron carbide as solidification proceeds through the Melt + Carbide field at the upper right of the diagram. This precipitation is followed by the transformation of the remaining liquid to ledeburite at the eutectic temperature. Increasing the carbon content of the white iron increases the hardness of the iron as a result of increased massive cementite in the structure, and it is the presence of the massive cementite which accounts for the high compressive strength and abrasion resistance of the white or chilled irons.

III. GRAY CAST IRON

Figure 35.6 shows the microstructure of a gray cast iron. It consists of a dispersion of the dark gray inclusions of graphite set in a continuous medium or matrix. The lower part of Fig. 35.6 shows models of graphite flakes, and represents the simplest form or shape of graphite flake which occurs in cast iron. In gray iron the graphite inclusions have replaced the massive cementite of the white irons, and it is the presence of the soft, friable graphite which confers on gray iron its unique properties of machinability, wear resistance, absence of ductility, low shrinkage characteristics in the foundry, and the gray fracture.

Graphitization in Gray Iron

Iron carbide or cementite is not a stable compound. It tends to decompose in accordance with this reaction –

$$Fe_3C \rightarrow 3\,Fe + C$$

The carbon liberated by the decomposition is in the form of graphite.

The rate of decomposition of the carbide is influenced by a number of factors among which are the carbon and silicon contents. High carbon and high silicon in the alloy promote rapid decomposition of the carbide, or may prevent the formation of the carbide during solidification. Steel is ordinarily free of graphite because of its relatively low carbon and silicon contents, and the high rates of cooling to which it is subject.

The carbon is maintained in its combined state in white iron, either by controlling the carbon and silicon contents in a low range, by fast cooling, or by both of these measures. The primary function of silicon in gray iron is the promotion of graphite formation, and gray iron is distinguished from white iron by the formation of graphite instead of cementite during solidification and proeutectoid transformation.

Stable and Metastable Solidification

As a result of this instability of the carbide phase, the iron-iron carbide diagram of Fig. 35.1 is not regarded as a stable or equilibrium diagram, and is referred to as the metastable diagram. The equilibrium diagram is one where the second phase in the solid alloys of the system is graphite, and it follows that no ferrous alloy containing iron carbide is in the equilibrium state.

The low rate of decomposition of cementite in steel and white iron permits the use of the metastable diagram for the discussion of the origin of structures in these materials when cooling rates are appreciable. As room temperature is approached the rate of decomposition of cementite becomes infinitesimal, and steel and cast iron can be held indefinitely at ordinary temperatures without detectable change.

Gray cast iron ordinarily contains cementite as a part of the matrix structure, usually as a constituent of pearlite, and because of the presence of carbon as graphite and as cementite, both the stable and metastable diagrams must be employed in the discussion of the solidification and transformation of gray iron.

Gray iron is seen to consist of a dispersion of graphite flakes in a matrix or continuous structure. The properties of the iron are determined by the two factors:

1. The character of the matrix structure.
2. The amount of graphite present, and the nature of the graphite dispersion.

Matrix Structures

The matrix structure of cast iron can be varied, and may consist of any one of the several structures found in steel in its various conditions as to heat treatment and composition. As a result of this similarity, gray iron is often described as a dispersion of graphite flakes in steel. All pearlite, pearlite and ferrite, all ferrite, austenite, martensite, and tempered martensite are among the possible matrix structures for gray iron.

Martensite is the structure produced by cooling austenite from a temperature above the eutectoid range to room temperature at a rate exceeding a certain critical rate. It is a light etching structure, and consists of Widmanstätten plates of body centered tetragonal iron supersaturated with carbon. These plates are dispersed in a variable amount of retained austenite, and appear as needle-like or acicular crystals under the microscope. Figure 35.7 shows the microstructure of a martensitic iron.

Martensite is the hardest and strongest structure which can be produced in a given iron or steel with the exception of cementite. It is ordinarily obtained by quenching iron or steel in oil or water from a temperature above the eutectoid range.

If martensite is heated or tempered in the range of temperature from 250 F to 1300 F (121-704 C) the microstructure designated as tempered martensite is produced. It is a dark etching structure consisting of very small particles of cementite dispersed in ferrite resulting from the breakdown of the supersaturated solution and the retained austenite.

The formation of tempered martensite is accompanied by stress relief and progressive softening dependent on the tempering temperature employed. High temperatures produce the softer structures. Tempered martensites were formerly designated as secondary troostite or sorbite. Martensitic and tempered martensitic structures are occasionally produced in iron by quenching and tempering when unusually high tensile strength is required.

For most applications the desirable and readily pro-

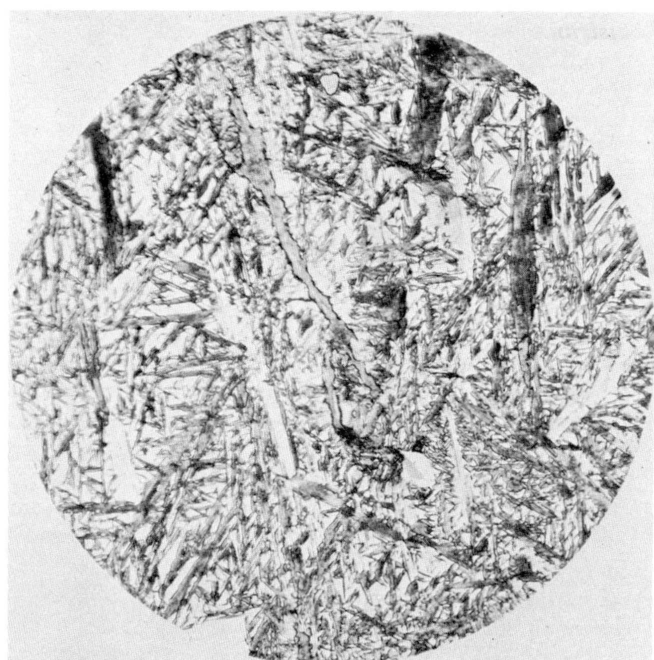

Fig. 35.7. Microstructure of a martensitic iron showing martensite and retained austenite as a matrix for the graphite flakes. Nital etch, 560 × (from S. C. Massari).

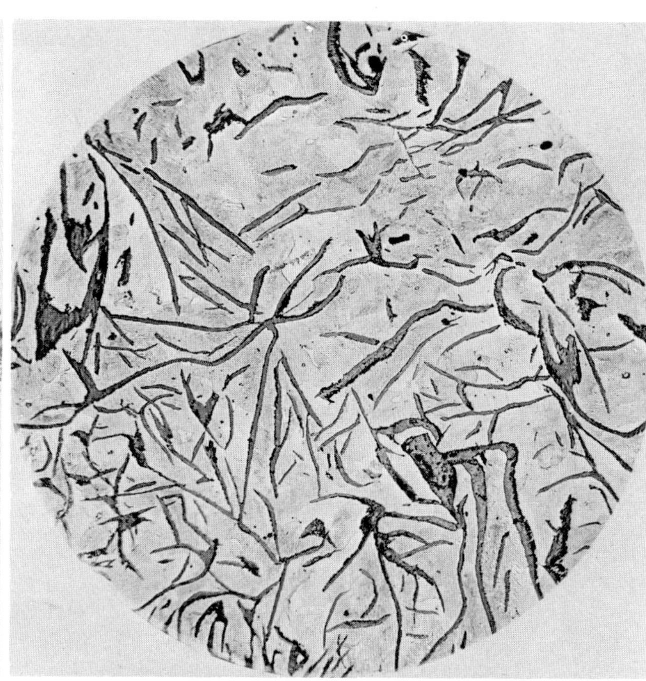

Fig. 35.9. Type *A* graphite flakes. Unresolved fine pearlite as matrix structure. 100 ×.

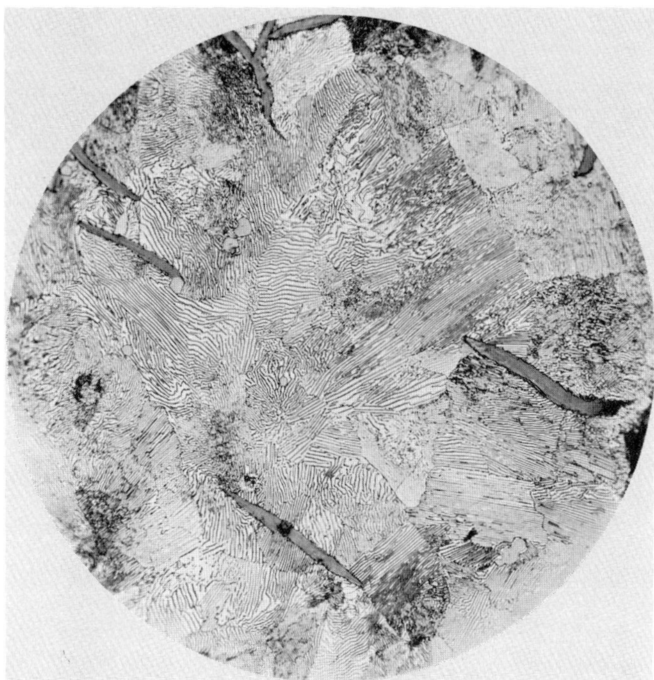

Fig. 35.8. Graphite flakes in a matrix of 100 per cent pearlite. Picrical and *HCl* etch, 320 × (from S. C. Massari).

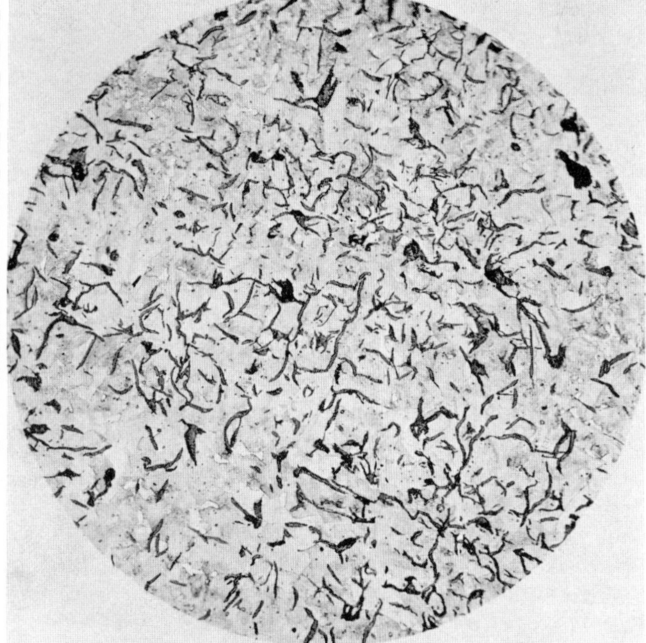

Fig. 35.10. Type *E* graphite flakes. 100 ×.

duced matrix structure is 100 per cent pearlite (Fig. 35.8). This structure gives the best combination of strength, wear resistance, machinability and bearing properties for many machine parts. The appearance of ferrite in increasing amounts with the pearlite results in a lowering of strength and wear resistance, but increases the ease of machining under some circumstances.

Gray irons with 100 per cent ferrite as a matrix structure are not common, but are produced in special cases. Such irons may have satisfactory tensile properties combined with a maximum of machinability. Fig. 35.18 shows the microstructure of an iron containing some ferrite (the large light areas) in the matrix.

Certain alloyed irons containing amounts of nickel ranging from 5 to 30 per cent have matrix structures consisting of martensite and austenite (Fig. 35.7). With the larger amounts of nickel, which has a stabilizing effect on the austenite, the matrix will remain 100 per cent austenite to ambient temperatures. Austentitic irons are produced for highly specialized wear resistance and corrosion resistance application.

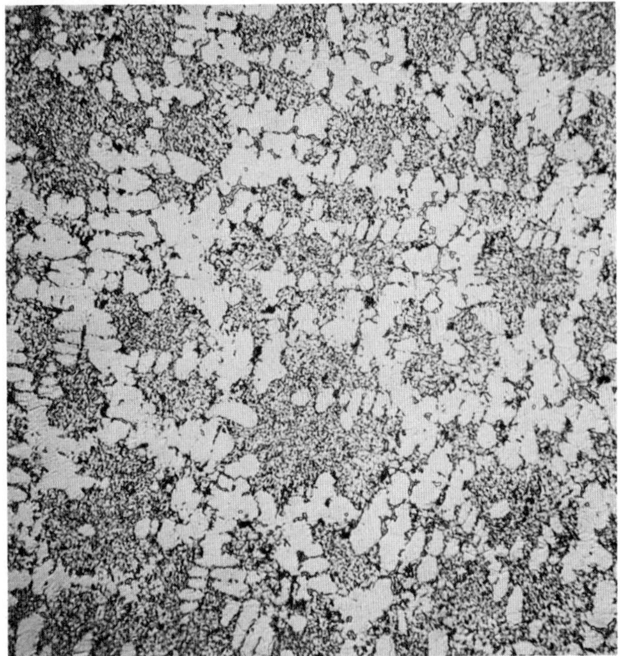

Fig. 35.11. Fine eutectiform graphite type *D*. 200 ×.

In view of the great variation possible in the matrix structure, it is important to consider the factors determining this structure. Carbon content, silicon content, cooling rate, and alloy content are among these factors.

Increasing carbon and silicon contents in cast iron promote the appearance of massive ferrite in the microstructure and as a result have a softening and weakening effect on the iron. Low rates of cooling produced by a large casting section tend to result in increasing amounts of ferrite, and coarser and softer pearlites.

A fundamental principle of gray iron metallurgy is the balancing of silicon content against section size in order to retain a proper matrix structure and a gray fracture. Heavy section castings should have low silicon contents, and light section castings should have high silicon contents to offset the more rapid cooling rate in thin sections. To a degree permitted by other considerations such as melting practice, a similar variation in carbon content may be desirable with the lighter section castings permitting the higher carbon contents.

Graphite Distribution

The second general factor determining the mechanical properties in addition to the matrix structure is the graphite phase, which varies from iron to iron not only in the amount of graphite present but in the nature of the arrangement of the graphite flakes and in their size. Figs. 35.9, 35.10 and 35.11 show typical graphite flake arrangements. Fig. 35.9 illustrates the desirable, random distribution of the graphite. This arrangement is sometimes described as normal as opposed to the pattern or abnormal distributions shown in Figs. 35.10 and 35.11.

The graphite flake pattern is highly significant in determining the mechanical properties of cast iron. The abnormal arrangements tend to produce more or less continuous planes of weakness in the iron to the detriment of the tensile strength, transverse strength and deflection, wear resistance, and fatigue resistance. The most desirable distribution is one where the flakes are of moderate size and have the normal arrangement of Fig. 35.9.

Figure 35.12 presents a graphite distribution chart. The normal arrangement at the left is designated as type *A*, and the abnormal arrangements at the right as types *D* and *E*.

Type *B*, commonly called the rosette distribution, is indicative of a tendency towards the *D* and *E* types. Types *B*, *D* and *E* are often associated with massive ferrite in the matrix. This ferrite is intimately dispersed with the finely divided graphite and contributes to the poor mechanical properties, and wear resistance of the types *B*, *D* and *E* irons (Fig. 35.13). The presence of the fine graphite-ferrite dispersion may result in a seriously pitted machined surface.

Type *C* graphite is characteristic of hypereutectic irons and is not common in commercial gray irons. This structure is typical of high carbon pig irons where the first solid to form during solidification is the long straight graphite flakes shown under type *C* of the chart. These peculiar flakes are absent in eutectic or hypoeutectic irons.

The carbon content, melting practice, solidification and transformation rate (which is determined mainly by casting section size) and degree of inoculation are among the factors determining graphite distribution.

High tensile strength cast irons are produced by lowering the carbon content of the iron with a consequent reduction of the amount of graphite in the structure. Such irons are commonly melted with carbon contents in the range of 2.7 per cent C to 3.1 per cent and tensile strengths in excess of 40,000 psi.

Fig. 35.12. AFA-A.S.T.M. illustrations of types of graphite flakes in gray cast iron. Reduced for reproduction here, in the recommended practice charts are shown at 100 ×.

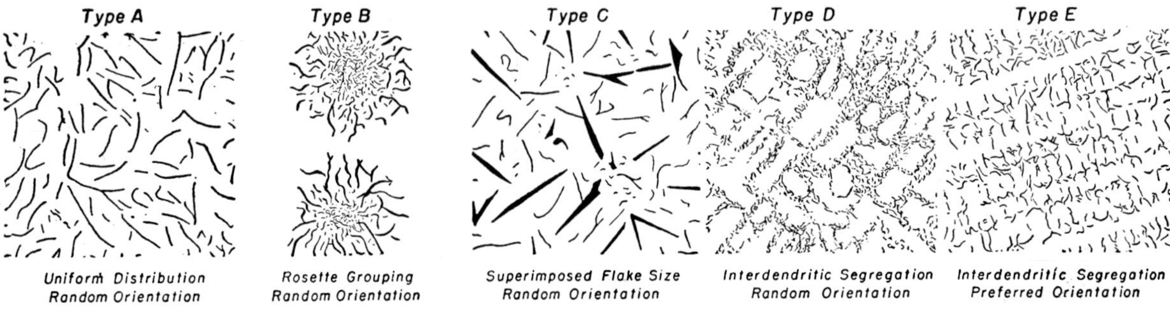

Unfortunately lowering of the carbon content to this range results in an increased tendency towards types *B*, *D* and *E* distributions. Special measures, such as late additions to the ladle, must be taken in the case of the low carbon irons to preserve the type *A* graphite distribution.

In the production of electric furnace irons, high superheating temperatures, and prolonged holding in the furnace at high temperature create an increased tendency towards the unfavorable graphite patterns.

Rate of solidification is a primary factor in determining graphite pattern type. High rates of solidification increase the tendency for unfavorable graphite distribution, and as a consequence light section castings are particularly prone to develop *D* and *E* graphite. In addition castings of moderate section tend to develop type *D* graphite at the surface where eutectic solidification is rapid.

Figure 35.14 is a section at the surface of a 1.20 inch transverse bar and shows pronouncedly type *D* distribution. The structure of this bar at a distance beneath the surface was mainly type *A*. Inoculation, which is a ladle addition process, is required in the case of light section, high strength irons of low carbon content for the production of good graphite distribution. The subject of inoculation will be treated in detail in subsequent paragraphs.

Solidification and Transformation of Gray Iron

Since the commercial gray irons contain significant amounts of silicon, a ternary diagram for the system iron-carbon-silicon must be employed in their discussion rather than the binary iron-carbon diagram. The lower diagram of Fig. 35.2 represents a section through the highly complex ternary system at two per cent silicon. This section has the appearance of a binary diagram, and in general can be interpreted in the same manner. The two per cent silicon section is ordinarily employed in discussing the solidification and transformation of gray irons because this amount of silicon is representative of commercial irons.

As previously mentioned the presence of silicon effects changes in the extent and positions of the regions of the binary diagram. Comparison of the diagrams of Fig. 35.2 shows that 2 per cent of silicon brings about these important changes from the iron-iron carbide diagram:

1. The eutectoid point is shifted from .80 per cent C to .60 per cent C.
2. The greatest extent of the single phased austenite region is lowered from 2.00 per cent C to 1.50 per cent C.
3. The horizontal eutectoid line is changed to the narrow eutectoid zone and the temperature of the eutectoid reaction is raised.
4. The eutectic point at 4.30 per cent C is shifted to 3.60 per cent C.
5. The eutectic line becomes a narrow eutectic zone.

The solidification and transformation of gray iron in accordance with the lower diagram of Fig. 35.2 have been described by Alfred Boyles. In his classical research Boyles quenched small melts of solidifying and transforming gray irons from the various temperature composition regions delineated by the diagram. From the resulting quenched microstructures Boyles was able to deduce the sequence of events during solidification and transformation of an iron solidifying as gray iron. This sequence is discussed in terms of the diagram of Fig. 35.15 which is a simplification of the ternary section diagram of Fig. 35.2. The four photomicrographs of Fig. 35.16 summarize the results of his quenching experiments.

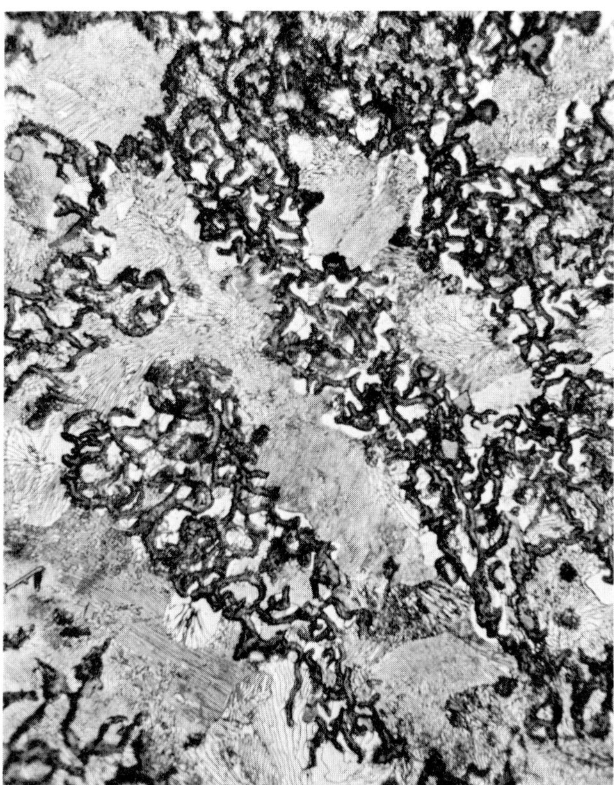

Fig. 35.13. Type *D* graphite flakes. Matrix is partly fine pearlite with light etching ferrite intimately associated with the graphite. Etch 5 per cent nital, 500 ×.

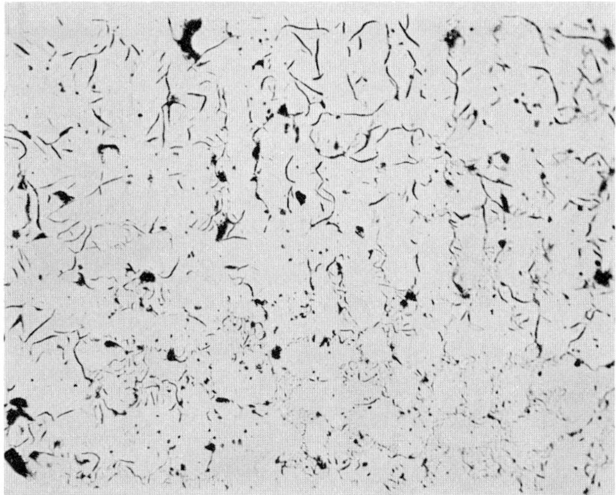

Fig. 35.14. Gray iron showing type *D* graphite. Unetched, 100 ×.

The solidification and transformation of hypoeutectic gray iron of the composition represented by the vertical line of Fig. 35.15 will be discussed in detail.

At point T_1 solidification starts with the formation of primary dendrites of austenite, and as the tempera-

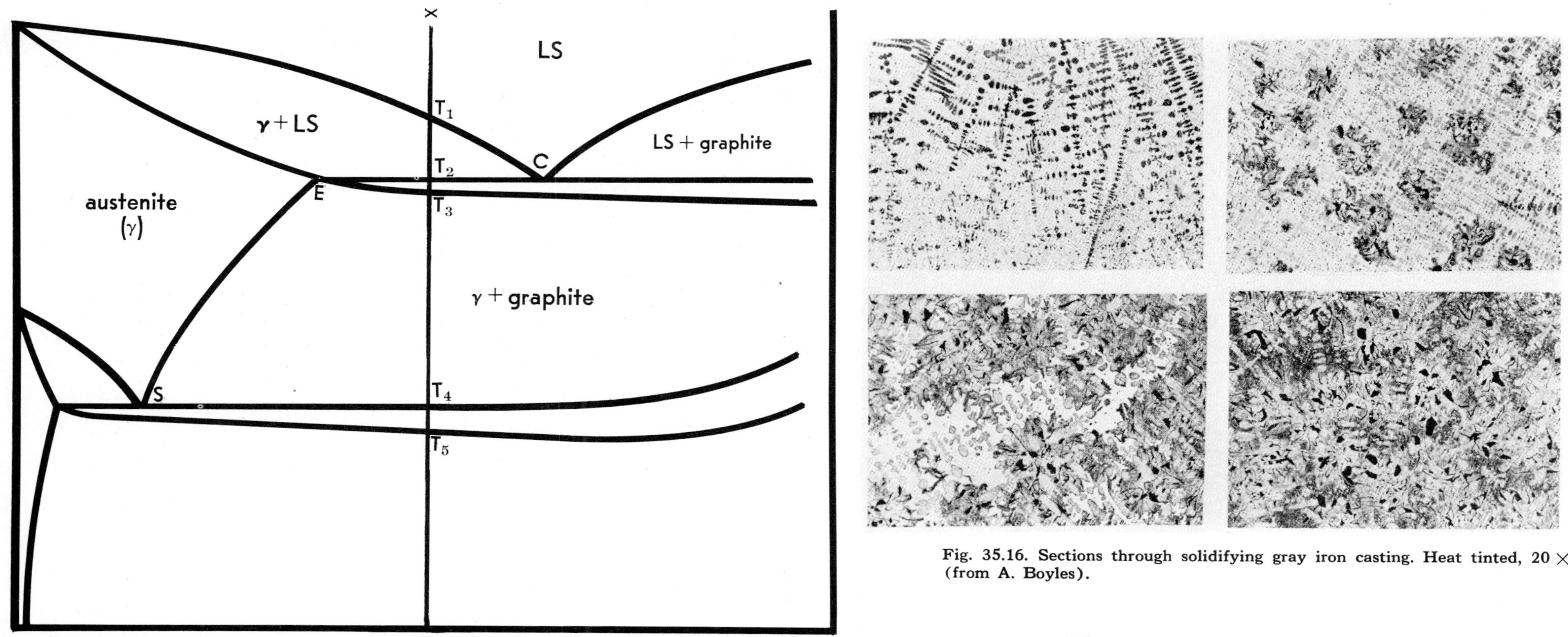

Fig. 35.15. Section through iron carbon-silicon ternary system diagram, simplified and not drawn to scale.

Fig. 35.16. Sections through solidifying gray iron casting. Heat tinted, 20 × **(from A. Boyles).**

ture falls more solid austenite forms. The upper left hand photomicrograph of Fig. 35.16 shows the structure produced by quenching from a point in this region. This micrograph pictures the primary dendrites as the darker branched crystals in a light etching background.

This light etching constituent is the structure produced by quenching the remaining liquid. Quenching the partially solidified samples from successively lower temperatures in this field would demonstrate an increasing amount of dendrite and a decreasing amount of liquid. The austenite dendrites are lower in carbon content than the liquid from which they are forming, and as a result the remaining liquid is enriched in carbon by the precipitation, and changes its composition in accordance with the line T_1C. As the temperature approaches the eutectic interval the remaining liquid approaches the eutectic point *C* in composition.

As the eutectic interval T_2T_3 is approached the system is approximately half solid as austenite dendrites, and half remaining liquid now of eutectic composition. Eutectic solidification starts at centers of crystallization or nuclei, and continues by forming spherical cells between and around the primary dendrites. A sample quenched in the eutectic range between the points T_2 and T_3 shows a number of these cells in cross-section and they develop between the dendrites. The upper right hand photomicrograph of Fig. 35.16 reveals these cells as they grow in the remaining liquid.

Figure 35.17 is an enlarged view of two of these cells. Sections through the branches of the austenite dendrites are also evident. This picture shows that the eutectic cell in gray iron is made up of the two phases – graphite and austenite. The graphite is present as the lighter gray, irregular, thin crystals in a background of austenite.

The pictures of Figs. 35.16 and 35.17 were taken from specimens prepared and photographed at room temperature after quenching. As a result the areas described as austenite at the solidification temperature appear in the photomicrographs not as austenite but as martensite, formed during the quench and subsequently lightly tempered.

Picture 35.17 is highly significant, and makes evident the reason for the peculiar flattened graphite form which is characteristic of gray iron. The flakes grow edgewise at the interface between the cell and the remaining liquid, and sidewise growth of flakes is inhibited by the enveloping austenite which is precipitated simultaneously with the graphite. Their growth is dependent on diffusion of carbon in the liquid to the growing edge.

This concept affords an explanation for the pronounced effect of cooling or solidification rate on the form and size of graphite flakes. The rate of cooling determines the time available for diffusion as well as the degree of undercooling, which in turn determines the rate of nucleation of new edges. High rates of cooling, and undercooling are associated with the finely divided intricate graphite patterns of the *B, D* and *E* types.

The lower left picture of Fig. 35.16 shows a later stage in the progress of solidification with an increase in the number and size of the eutectic cells and a corresponding decrease in the remaining liquid. Sections through the branches of the primary dendrites are visible, and it should be noted that these areas are free of graphite, and that the graphite is confined to the eutectic cells. In hypoeutectic irons all graphite is interdendritic. This becomes evident as an interdendritic pattern of graphite when the flakes are small as in the case of the *D* and *E* irons.

The lower right hand picture represents the final state of solidification with the disappearance of the liquid. The structure now consists of a dispersion of graphite in austenite. Under equilibrium conditions solidification is completed at the lower boundary of the eutectic region at point T_3. At more rapid rates of cooling than permit an approach to equilibrium, undercooling results and this undercooling has been correlated with unfavorable graphite dispersions.

An important aspect of this mechanism of graphite formation is that the graphite pattern is determined during solidification. Factors which effect the manner of eutectic solidification and cell formation are the factors which determine the graphite pattern. Among these are the rate of heat extraction, the degree of nucleation, which can be controlled by ladle additions, and surface energy effects. Prior to the research by Boyles these matters were poorly understood, and many considered that gray irons solidified in the metastable manner as a dispersion of austenite and carbide, and that graphite formed subsequent to solidification by decomposition of carbide.

Upon completion of freezing under equilibrium conditions, the austenite has the composition with respect to carbon marked by point *E* Fig. 35.15. Cooling through the interval T_3T_4 results in a continuing precipitation of carbon as graphite from the austenite. As a result the remaining austenite changes its composition in accordance with the line ES and approaches the eutectoid boundary at point *S*.

The graphite precipitated in this range does not produce a new flake structure, but is deposited on the flakes formed during eutectic solidification. This is in keeping with the statement that the pattern of graphite dispersion is determined during eutectic freezing.

At lower rates of cooling and under conditions approaching equilibrium the remaining austenite, now

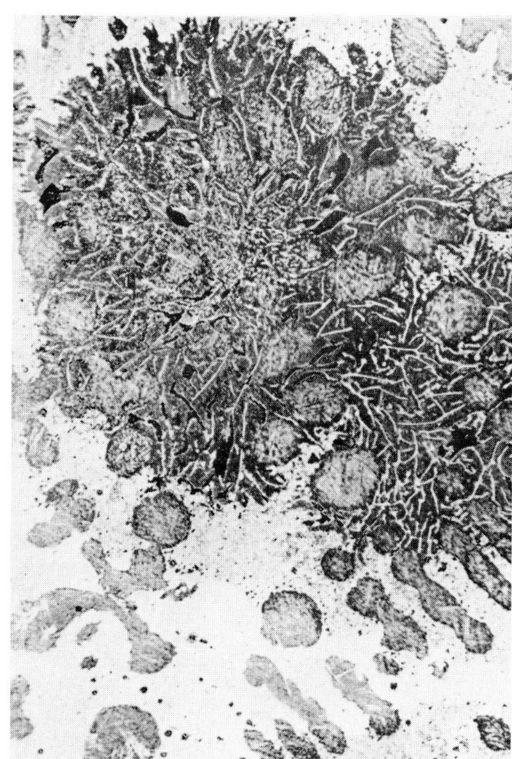

Fig. 35.17. Section through eutectic cells in partially solidified sample. Heat tinted, 100× (from A. Boyles).

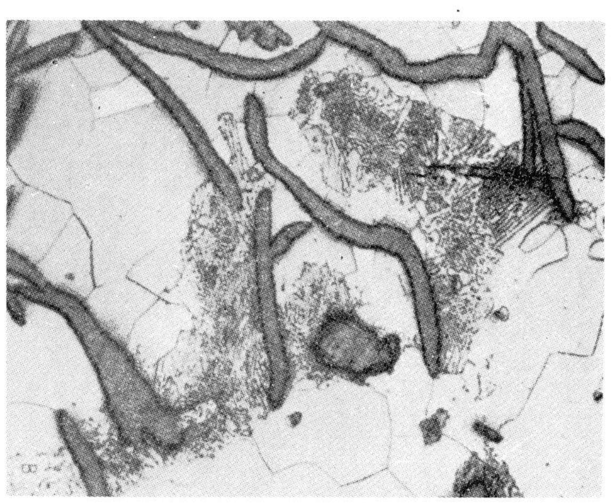

Fig. 35.18. Pearlite and light etching ferrite as a matrix in gray iron.

of eutectoid composition, undergoes the eutectoid transformation to pearlite in the range T_4T_5. The resulting structure is pictured in Fig. 35.8 which shows graphite flakes dispersed in a pearlitic matrix. For most applications this is the desired structure possessing the most satisfactory combination of mechanical properties.

At low rates of cooling as in the case of heavy section castings, or in the case of an excessively high silicon and carbon content for the section, the iron carbide or cementite of the eutectoid is rendered unstable and ferrite appears adjacent to the graphite flakes as a part of the matrix (Figs. 35.13 and 35.18). The presence of this massive ferrite in increasing

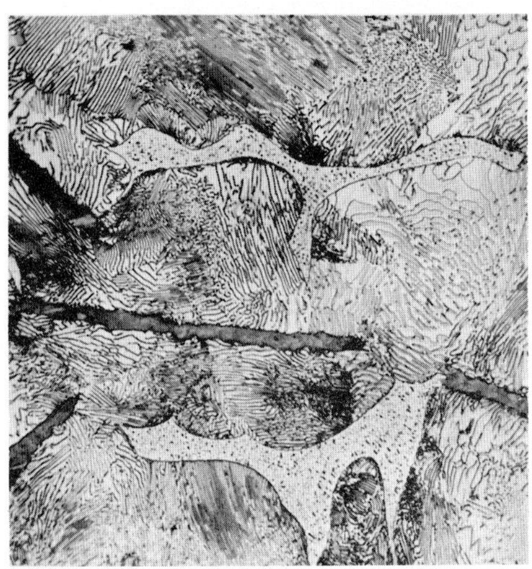

Fig. 35.19. Steadite (phosphide eutectic) in cast iron. Nital etch, 500 ×.

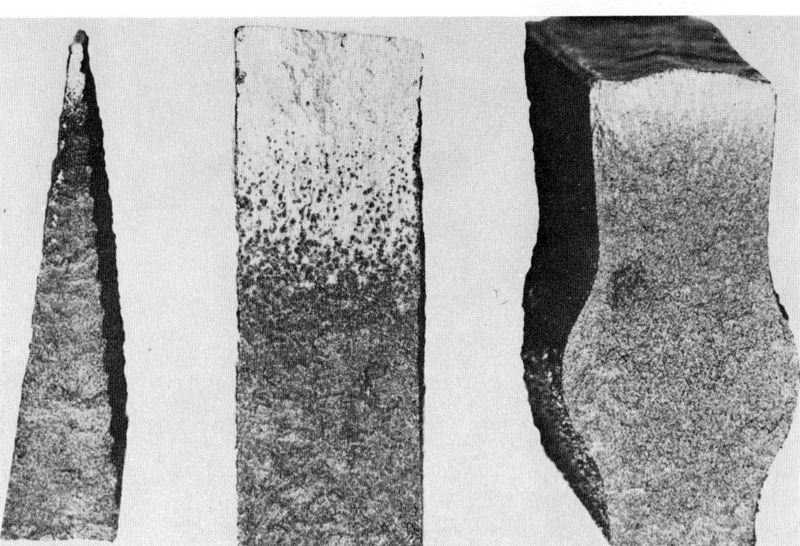

Fig. 35.20. Chill test specimens for gray cast iron.

amounts results in a lowering of hardness and a loss of strength properties, but may under some circumstances, where surface finish is not a primary consideration, result in an increase in machinability.

With rapid cooling through the eutectoid range the transformation is suppressed and undercooling occurs. Undercooling results in a finer pearlite in the matrix and a harder and stronger iron. With increased undercooling there is an increasing tendency towards an acicular, martensitic or bainitic structure such as pictured in the photomicrograph of Fig. 35.7. The presence of alloying elements such as nickel, chromium, molybdenum and vanadium in the iron ordinarily increases the tendency towards a harder matrix structure with improved mechanical properties. In the presence of sufficient nickel the eutectoid or acicular transformation may be completely suppressed with a resulting austenitic matrix at ambient temperature. The carbide forming and stabilizing elements chromium, molybdenum, and vanadium are particularly effective in preventing the formation of massive ferrite as a part of the matrix structure.

The solidification of a gray iron of eutectic composition proceeds in the same manner as for the hypoeutectic iron just described except that the primary dendrites of austenite are absent and the entire solid, at the moment solidification is completed, consists of the eutectic dispersion of austenite and graphite flakes. Cooling and transformation to ordinary temperatures then proceeds as outlined. Hypereutectic irons form graphite as the proeutectic phase, and this graphite may appear on the molten iron as kish floating on the surface.

Phosphorus and Steadite Formation

In the presence of phosphorus beyond approximately 0.10 per cent, an additional constitutent appears in the microstructure. Phosphorus concentrates in the remaining liquid during eutectic cell formation, and in the presence of sufficient phosphorus, this concentration results in the formation of a phosphorous rich structure known as steadite.

Steadite is the last solid to form in these irons, final solidification occurring in the range of 1750 to 1800 F (954-982 C). Steadite contains approximately ten per cent phosphorus, and the amount of steadite increases with increasing phosphorous content. It is a eutectic type structure consisting of iron with phosphorus in solution and iron phosphide (Fe_3P). When cooling is rapid cementite may be present as a third component.

Fig. 35.19 shows the microstructure of steadite. It is a hard, brittle substance. When etching is performed in the usual manner, steadite appears as a light etching constituent. At sufficient magnification, its complex structure is revealed.

With increasing phosphorous content, steadite tends to form a network structure outlining the eutectic cells. If present in large amounts, steadite is detrimental to machinability and mechanical properties, particularly impact strength. Large amounts of steadite may result in microshrinkage and porosity brought about by solidification contraction during the solidification of the steadite.

Irons for critical applications generally carry a maximum specification of 0.20 per cent phosphorus. Phosphorus increases the fluidity of cast iron, and irons for light section castings may carry a higher phosphorous specification. Steadite should be avoided in irons alloyed with molybdenum since this element enters into the composition of the steadite with an increase in volume of this constituent, and an increased tendency toward porosity.

It is evident that a given iron may solidify in either the metastable or the stable manner. If solidification occurs in the stable manner, the two phases of the eutectic are austenite and graphite, and transformation proceeds with a continuing precipitation of graphite down to the eutectoid range; a gray iron results. If the iron solidifies in the metastable manner, the two phases of the eutectic solid are austenite and iron carbide. In this case transformation proceeds with the deposition of more cementite; a white iron free of graphite is produced.

Chilling Tendency

The tendency for an iron to solidify in the metastable manner as white iron is referred to as the chilling tendency. At high rates of cooling as in light sections an iron tends towards metastable solidification and a white fracture. At a lower rate of cooling and in heavier section, the same iron will solidify in the stable manner with a gray fracture.

Since cooling proceeds more rapidly in thin sections and at corners and edges, a chilling tendency which is too high for a particular casting may result in chilled edges and sections with consequent difficulty in machining.

Carbon and silicon contents are primary factors in determining chilling tendency. Increasing carbon and silicon contents lower chilling tendency, and irons for light section castings require a higher total content of these elements when white fracture and machining problems are to be avoided.

Control of chilling tendency is an important aspect of gray iron metallurgy. Measurement of chilling tendency is accomplished by pouring test castings which are subject to differential cooling rates.

Figure 35.20 shows the fractures of typical chill test castings. In the case of the wedge shaped specimen the difference in cooling rate results from varying sections. The variation in rate in the two chill blocks is accomplished by pouring against a metal portion or chill in the mold.

Inspection of the fractures shows an all white portion adjacent to the chilled end, and a partially white or mottled zone intermediate between the white and all gray portions. Chilling tendency is determined by measurements of the zones in the fracture, and is reported as clear chill, which includes only the all white zone, and total chill, which includes both the white and mottled zones.

The key hole section chill test specimen at the right of Fig. 35.20 permits an inspection of the gray fracture produced in the relatively heavy section. A low chilling tendency may be associated with a coarse, open fracture when the iron is cast in heavy section. A fracture of this nature is indicative of a poor matrix structure containing massive ferrite and large graphite flakes, of low Brinell hardness, poor mechanical properties and generally is a result of carbon and silicon contents too high for the section.

Various aspects of melting practice are important in determining chilling tendency and mechanical properties. Factors are the nature of the metallic charge or heredity, the superheating temperature, time at temperature, pouring temperature and the application of ladle additions. High superheating temperature in the electric furnace is associated with high chilling tendency and abnormal structures with type *D* and *E* graphite. Much careful research remains to be done in the area of evaluation of the role of melting practice in determining microstructure, properties, and chilling tendency.

Inoculation

Certain ladle additions provide an important means of controlling chilling tendency and graphite distribution. Control accomplished by these additions is referred to an inoculation. Inoculation may be defined as a late addition of an element or elements to the molten iron, made primarily for the purpose of controlling microstructure and chilling tendency to a degree not explainable on the basis of composition change of the iron.

Graphite is a recognized inoculating agent, and its addition to the ladle immediately before pouring produces improvement in microstructure and properties not obtainable by the same increase in carbon content brought about by addition to the cold furnace charge. Late addition is an essential feature of the inoculation process and the effect of inoculation is transient and tends to disappear with the passage of time.

Among the substances employed as inoculating agents are: graphite; certain grades of ferrosilicon containing small amounts of calcium and aluminum; calcium-silicon with calcium in the range of 30 to 33 per cent; and certain complex alloys containing various combinations of aluminum, calcium, zirconium, manganese, titanium, barium, and chromium with silicon as a base element.

The exact mechanism of inoculation has not been determined. It has been demonstrated that successful inoculation is accompanied by an increase in the number of eutectic cells and a decrease in eutectic cell size. It is considered that this increase in number of cells is accomplished by nucleation of eutectic solidification and the graphite phase.

In the absence of inoculation, irons tend to undercool, and this undercooling is associated with the formation of type *D* and *E* graphite, and a high chilling tendency. Inoculated irons solidify at a markedly higher temperature, have a lower chilling tendency, and tend to have type *A* graphite distribution and an all pearlite matrix.

Certain inoculants are classified as balanced or stabilizing inoculants as opposed to the simple chill reducing inoculants. These stabilizing inoculants contain carbide stabilizing elements such as chromium, manganese, titanium and zirconium. Irons treated with these alloys are less section sensitive, and the application of these alloys results in a reduction of chill at edges and in light sections, production of type *A* graphite, elimination of massive ferrite in heavy sections, and a refinement of graphite distribution.

Composition and Properties of Gray Iron

Table 35.2 gives the composition range for the elements present in unalloyed gray cast irons normally produced in commercial practice.

As previously noted carbon occurs in iron in the combined form as iron carbide or cementite, and in the free form as graphite. Increasing the carbon content beyond the amount in combined form results in an increase in the amount of graphite present with a consequent lowering of tensile and transverse strength,

TABLE 35.2. COMPOSITION RANGE
For UNALLOYED GRAY CAST IRON

Element	Range
Carbon	2.60 - 3.75%
Silicon	1.25 - 2.75%
Manganese	0.40 - 0.90%
Phosphorus	0.05 - 1.00%
Sulfur	0.05 - 0.14%

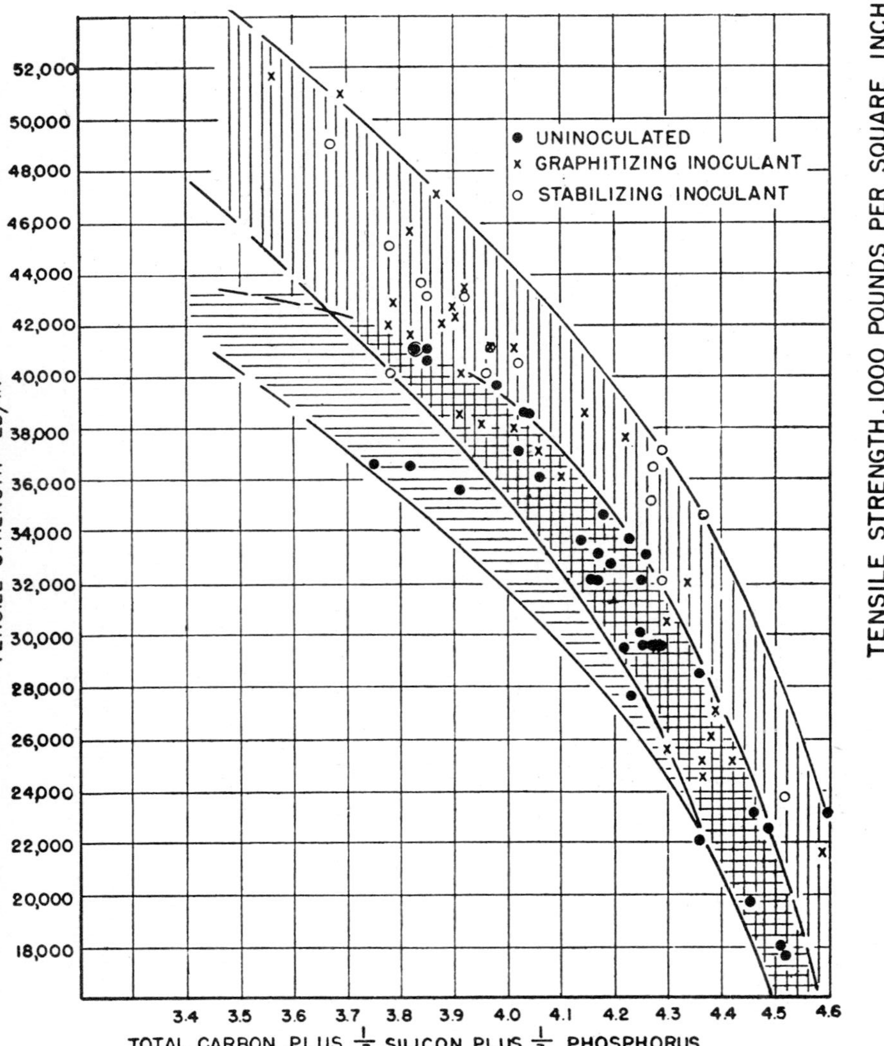

Fig. 35.21. Carbon equivalent and tensile strength relationship of inoculated and uninoculated cast irons.

TENSILE STRENGTH, 1000 POUNDS PER SQUARE INCH

100 95 90 85 80 75 70 65 60 55 50 45 40 35 30 25 20 15 10

BRITISH TONS/IN.²

45 40 35 30 25 24 23 22 21 20 19 18 17 16 15 14 13 12 11 10 9 8 7 6 5

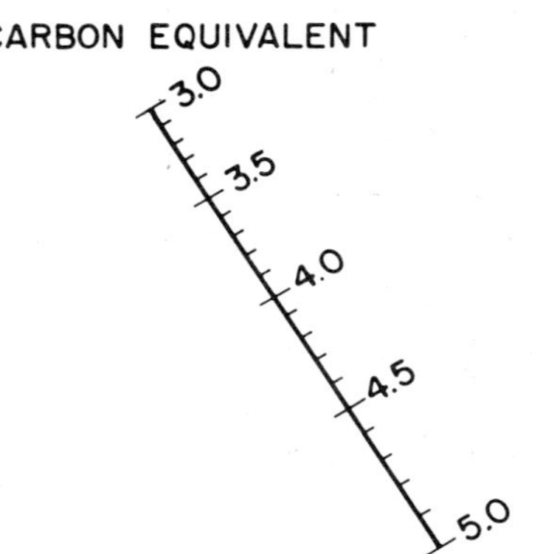

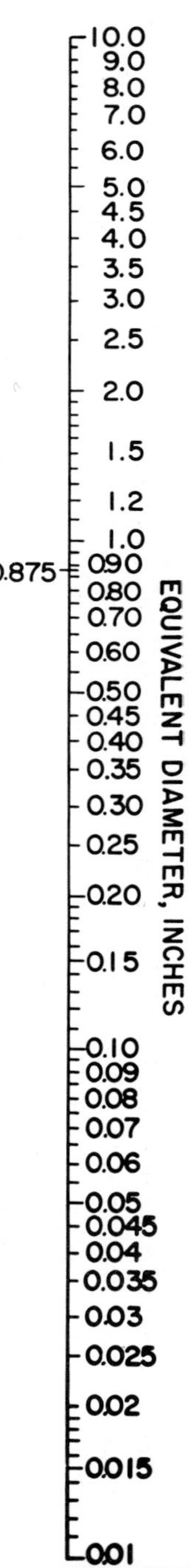

Fig. 35.22. Tensile strength nomograph for unalloyed sand cast gray iron.

TABLE 35.3. EFFECT of ALLOYS on the TENSILE STRENGTH of UNINOCULATED CAST IRON IN THE RANGE OF TC 3.30% and Si 2.0%

Alloy	Max % used	% Increase in Strength for each 1%	Remarks
Mo	1.00	40	chilling tendency mild
Cr	0.50	20	chilling tendency strong
V	0.35	45	chill. tendency very strong
Ni	3.00	10	chill. tend. weak or negative
Cu	1.50	10	chill. tend. weak or negative
Mn	—	10	chilling tendency weak

Brinell hardness and modulus of elasticity. The elastic modulus ranges from 12 to 18 million psi in engineering gray irons.

Increasing carbon content increases fluidity of the molten iron. As a result of the expansion taking place during graphite formation, increasing carbon content reduces solidification contraction and shrinkage. Increasing carbon content improves machinability. Increasing carbon content increases the damping capacity of cast irons.

The role of silicon in cast iron can be summarized in these statements. Silicon acts as a graphitizer and chill reducer, and irons for thin section castings should be high in silicon. Silicon strengthens and hardens ferrite (Table 35.1) and in this manner increases the strength of irons. Silicon alters the equilibrium diagram. Silicon lowers the solubility of carbon in molten iron, and cupola irons high in silicon tend to run lower in total carbon content.

Both silicon and carbon are chill reducers and graphitizers, and the combined effect of these elements can be represented by a value called the carbon equivalent. Phosphorus increases the effectiveness of carbon and silicon. The expression for carbon equivalent is

$$\text{Carbon Equivalent} = C + \frac{Si}{3} + \frac{P}{3}$$

or the carbon equivalent is the total carbon content plus one third of the silicon content plus one third of the phosphorous content.

Figure 35.21 shows the relationship between tensile strength of gray iron and carbon equivalent, and establishes the range of tensile strength in gray irons. The width of the band represents the variation in strength at any given composition level resulting from variations in graphite distribution and matrix structure. As indicated by the data, the use of inoculants is effective in controlling these variations and improving properties.

Cast irons are section sensitive. With progressively lighter sections an iron of a given carbon equivalent becomes progressively harder and stronger and finally develops a white fracture. The nomograph Fig. 35.22 establishes the relationship between carbon equivalent, section size and tensile strength for gray iron.

If a straight edge is placed on a given carbon equivalent and rotated, the section sizes are read from the right hand ordinate, and the corresponding tensile strengths at the left. The values for strength are approximations because of the many variables, such as degree of inoculation, etc., but the chart is a useful guide in selecting the proper composition for a specified tensile strength in a given section.

As a result of the section sensitivity of gray iron, American specifications recognize three standard test bar sections: 0.875, 1.2, and 2 in.

The relationship between the hardness and strength of cast iron is not as direct as is the case with steel. In general the hardness increases with strength and will vary from approximately 150 to 275 Brinell as the tensile strength increases from 20,000 to 60,000 psi. However, it is possible to markedly increase the tensile and transverse strength of gray iron by inoculation, and at the same time slightly decrease the Brinell hardness.

The primary function of manganese in gray iron is to combine with sulfur to form manganese sulfide, which appears in the microstructure as small gray, equiaxed inclusions. The amount of manganese regarded as necessary to neutralize sulfur is generally given as three times the sulfur content. In practice an excess of manganese of 0.2 per cent or 0.3 per cent above the amount required to combine with the sulfur is employed. Excess or free manganese acts as a pearlite stabilized and inhibits formation of massive ferrite as a part of the matrix structure.

In the presence of sufficient manganese, sulfur in amounts up to about 0.18 per cent is not harmful to cast iron. Sulfur, when uncombined with manganese, is a powerful chill inducer and carbide stabilizer, and most specifications limit the sulfur content to 0.14 per cent.

As previously discussed phosphorus in excess of about 0.10 per cent in the iron forms the hard brittle constituent steadite as part of the microstructure. The presence of excessive steadite decreases machinability, increases porosity and lowers impact strength; many specifications limit the phosphorous content to 0.20 per cent maximum. Phosphorous promotes fluidity of molten iron, but it is only one-third as effective as a corresponding amount of carbon increase.

Alloy Cast Irons

The term alloy cast iron is applicable to cast irons to which elements such as nickel, chromium, molybdenum, vanadium, copper and titanium are added to improve mechanical properties or to obtain special properties such as corrosion resistance.

The alloying elements are effective in improving properties in these ways:

1. By dissolving in ferrite with a consequent strengthening and hardening of the iron.
2. By improving the graphite distribution.
3. By preventing the formation of massive ferrite in the matrix.
4. By increasing the tendency towards finer pearlite, acicular, or austenitic matrix structures.
5. By decreasing the section sensitivity of the iron.
6. By increasing the hardenability of the iron during heat treatment.
7. By increasing or decreasing chilling tendency.

The alloying elements can be classified as carbide stabilizers which tend to increase chilling tendency, and as graphitizers which tend to reduce chilling tendency. Chromium, molybdenum, vanadium, and titanium are chill inducers, while nickel and copper reduce chilling tendency.

Figures 35.23 and 35.24 summarize the effect of the several elements on chilling tendency. Table 35.3 gives information concerning the effectiveness of the elements in increasing tensile properties.

Alloy irons are produced containing combinations of elements. Useful compositions contain combinations of nickel or copper with the carbide stabilizing elements molybdenum, chromium and vanadium in such proportions that the effect on chilling tendency is balanced.

There are special corrosion resistant and temperature resistant irons high in nickel and chromium

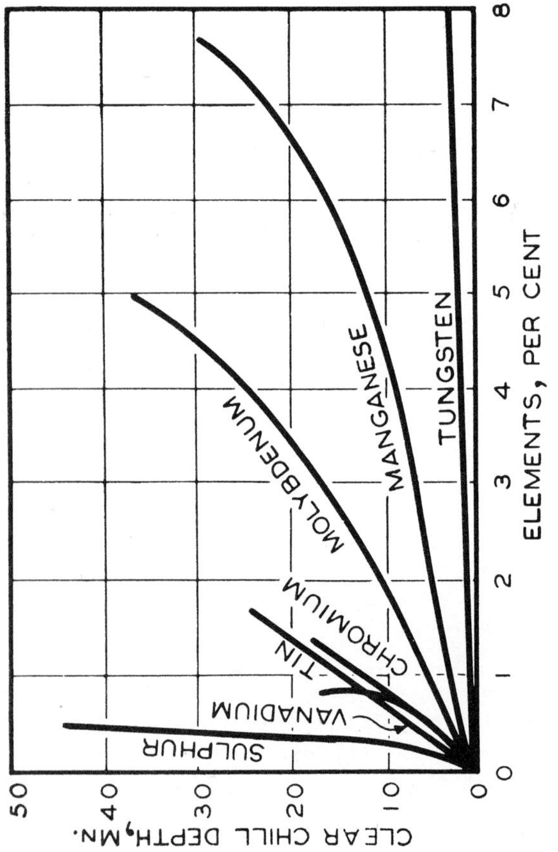

Fig. 35.23. Comparative influence of various elements on chill depth (elements which increase the depth of chill).

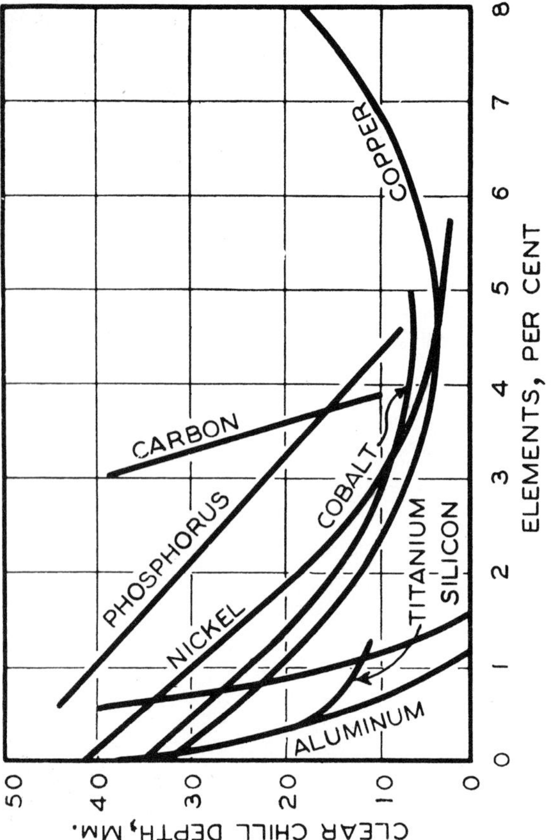

Fig. 35.24. Comparative influence of various elements on chill depth (elements which decrease depth of chill).

contents. With sufficient nickel, the matrix structure becomes austenitic at ambient temperature.

Heat Treatment of Gray Iron

Gray iron castings are generally employed in the cast condition without heat treatment.

Under special circumstances gray iron castings are subjected to heat treatment. The treatments are stress relieving, annealing, hardening and drawing, surface hardening by induction and flame heating.

In common with all cast metals, gray iron castings may contain residual stresses resulting from variance in the rate of cooling of different casting sections. These internal stresses may entail a loss of strength and a tendency for the castings to distort in machining.

Stresses may be relieved by heating to a temperature in the range 950 F to 1200 F (510 – 649 C), holding, and slow cooling. The degree of stress relief increases with temperature. Unfortunately heating to temperatures above 1050 F (566 C) is accompanied by loss of strength at an appreciable rate as a result of graphitization.

It is recommended that stress relief should be accomplished by temperatures not exceeding 1050 F (566 C) in the case of unalloyed irons when appreciable softening is to be avoided. Alloyed irons may in some cases be heated to 1200 F (649 C) without undue loss of strength.

Gray iron is sometimes subjected to annealing treatments to improve machinability. These softening treatments convert pearlite to graphite and ferrite and decrease the strength properties. In most cases subcritical holding between 1300 – 1400 F (705 – 760 C) is recommended. When enough softening is not obtained by holding in this range, temperatures above the critical 1450 – 1650 F (788 – 899 C) may be used, followed by slow cooling through the critical range.

When machining problems result from chilled portions of a casting and massive carbides in the structure, castings may be salvaged by high temperature annealing. For softening, and decomposition of carbides, it is necessary to employ temperatures between 1650 F to 1750 F (899 – 955 C) with holding times ranging up to three hours plus one hour per inch of section.

Cooling rate from these temperatures is determined by the property requirements. If maximum machinability is required, slow cooling in the furnace is recommended. Where strength and wear resistance with a pearlitic matrix are desired, air cooling may be employed. Since these very high temperature anneals involve scaling, distortion of castings, and a high cost, every effort should be exerted to avoid massive carbides and chilled castings.

The wear resistance and strength of cast iron may be improved by conventional hardening and drawing treatments. Hardening is accomplished by heating to a temperature above the critical range to produce a structure consisting of austenite in equilibrium with graphite, holding, and quenching to obtain cooling in excess of a critical rate, thereby producing a microstructure of martensite and graphite.

The austenitizing or holding temperature will vary with the composition of the iron, and will usually exceed 1500 F (816 C). Castings should be removed from the quenching bath before cooling completely to ambient temperature (recommend 300 F, 149 C) and promptly transferred to the tempering furnace. The relationship between tempering temperature and mechanical properties of a low silicon gray iron is shown in Fig. 35.25.

Gray iron may be surface hardened by flame heating or induction heating at the surface followed by quenching. For a detailed discussion of these and the other treatments the reader is referred to the AFS CAST METALS HANDBOOK.

IV. MALLEABLE CAST IRON

Malleable cast iron may be defined as a ductile ferrous alloy produced by the heat treatment of white cast iron. As ordinarily made in American practice, malleable iron has a microstructure consisting of compacted inclusions of graphite, called temper carbon modules, in a matrix of ferrite or some other decomposition product of austenite (Figs. 35.26 and 35.27).

The production in the mold of a white iron casting free of graphite flakes is an essential step in the production of malleable iron. When graphite forms during solidification, as is the case with gray iron, it tends to form as flattened extended inclusions or flakes. These flakes, as opposed to the equiaxed modules of malleable iron, interrupt the continuity of the matrix, and their presence results in the negligible ductility which is a characteristic of gray iron.

In the production of malleable iron, a white iron is subjected to an annealing treatment (usually in the range of 1800 F to 1200 F, (982 – 649 C). This treatment results in the decomposition of massive cementite to form graphite, and when graphite is formed in this manner in the solid, it forms as compacted inclusions described as temper carbon. This distribution of the graphite interrupts the matrix to a minimum degree and results in an alloy which is highly machinable, and at the same time is sufficiently tough and ductile for farm implement parts, automotive parts, pipe fittings and general hardware.

Figures 35.3 and 35.28 show the microstructure of white iron and as cast malleable iron. The origin of these structures is discussed earlier in this chapter in connection with the solidification of white iron. Malleable irons are hypoeutectic in composition, and the as-cast structure shows evidence of the formation during solidification of primary dendrites of austenite, and the eutectic structure, ledeburite, consisting of a dispersion of austenite and massive cementite. As cooled in the mold the austenite ordinarily transforms to pearlite, and the final structure of the casting as removed from the mold is made up of pearlite and light etching massive cementite (Fig. 35.28), and is necessarily free of graphite at this stage in the production of a malleable part. The necessity for a white casting which is free of graphite as the casting is removed from the mold is a fundamental of the metallurgy of malleable iron.

The factors determining whether a given iron will solidify as white iron or as gray iron containing flakes are discussed in the paragraphs dealing with stable and metastable solidification, and with chilling tendency. The primary factors are carbon content, silicon content and the cooling rate, which is determined

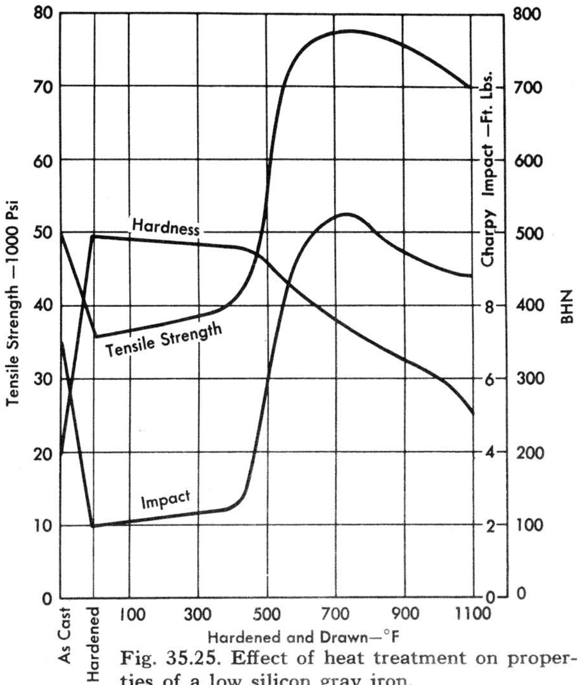

Fig. 35.25. Effect of heat treatment on properties of a low silicon gray iron.

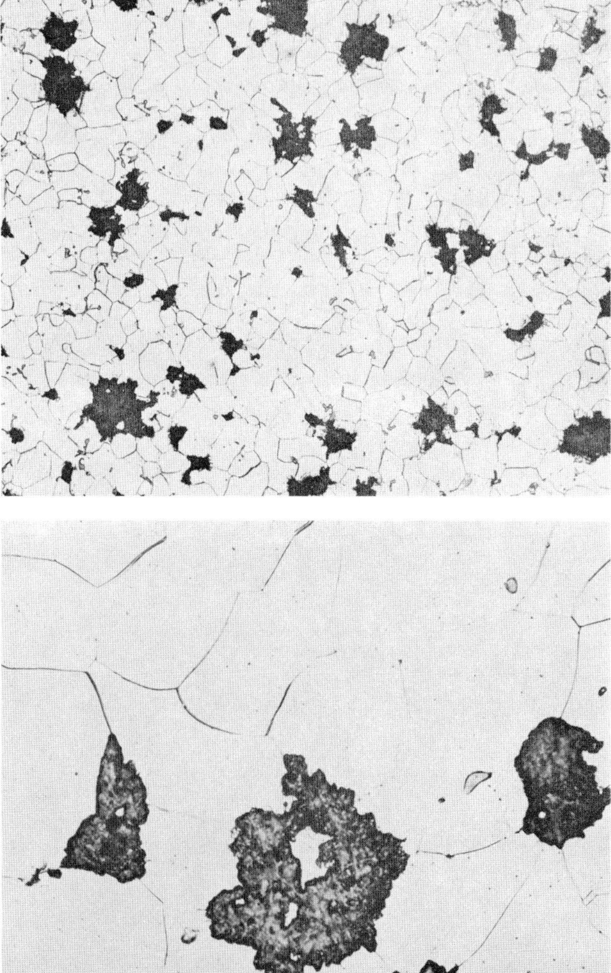
Fig. 35.26. Ferritic malleable iron showing temper carbon in a matrix of ferrite with ferrite grain boundaries clearly visible. *Above:* 100 ×, *below:* 500 × (courtesy Malleable Founders Society *Malleable Iron Castings*, 1960).

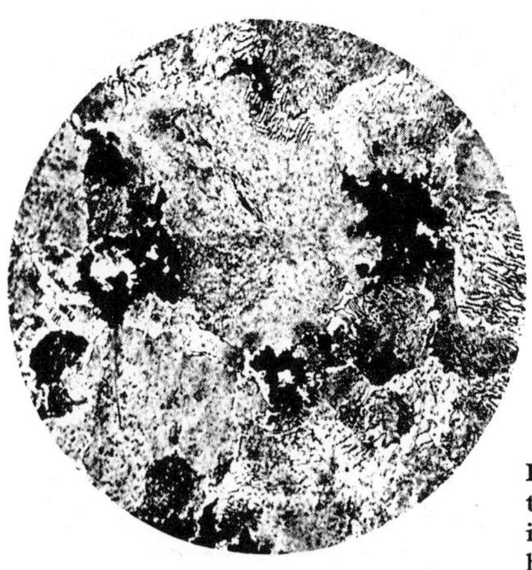

Fig. 35.27. Pearlitic malleable iron; temper carbon in a matrix of fine pearlite. 100 × (from M.F.S. *American Malleable Iron,* 1944).

Fig. 35.29. Photograph of three fractures *(right)* of castings poured as a malleable heat progresses. The transition from gray through a mottled to a white fracture is indicated (from M.F.S. *Malleable Iron Castings,* 1960).

Table 35.4

Carbon	1.75–3.00%
Silicon	.60–1.70%
Manganese	less than .65%
Phosphorus	less than .20%
Sulfur	less than .20%

mainly by the section size of the casting. In the production of a malleable casting with the essential white structure it is necessary to control these factors within close limits.

Since both carbon and silicon in increasing amounts promote the formation of stable solidification and graphite formation during freezing, malleable cast irons of normal composition must contain less of these elements than is the case with gray iron of comparable section. Table 35.4 gives the composition range which will include malleable irons made in ordinary production.

Comparison of these composition ranges with those for gray iron in Table 35.2 shows that the malleable irons run lower in carbon and silicon, although the ranges overlap.

The necessity for the white, graphite free structure as cast requires that malleable irons of ordinary compositions be cooled rapidly in the mold in light section. Most malleable parts have sections of less than ½-in. However, sections up to one in. are commonly cast, and heavier sections are produced in special practice. Small parts with $\frac{1}{16}$-in. section are successfully made.

Melting Practice

Molten iron for malleable castings is produced in the cupola, air furnace, or the electric furnace, and by employing a combination of the cupola with the air furnace, or electric furnace in the process referred to as duplexing.

The cupola is not adaptable to the direct production of the lower carbon malleable irons because of carbon pick up and difficulty with carbon and temperature control. However, the higher carbon grades are produced directly from cupola iron. Such irons are used for the manufacture of pipe fittings and similar light section parts where fluidity and soundness are more important than high strength and ductility.

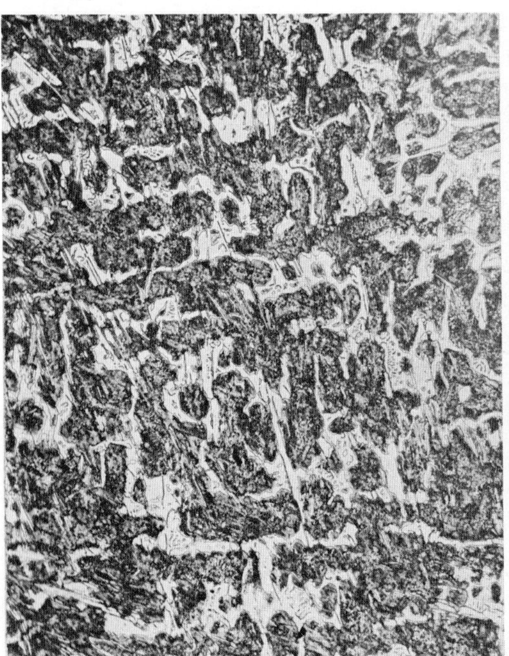

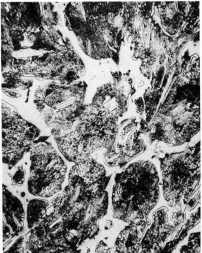

Fig. 35.28. White iron in an unheat-treated malleable casting; massive cementite (white) in background of dark etching pearlite. *Left:* 100 ×, *above:* 500 × (from M.F.S. *Malleable Iron Castings,* 1960).

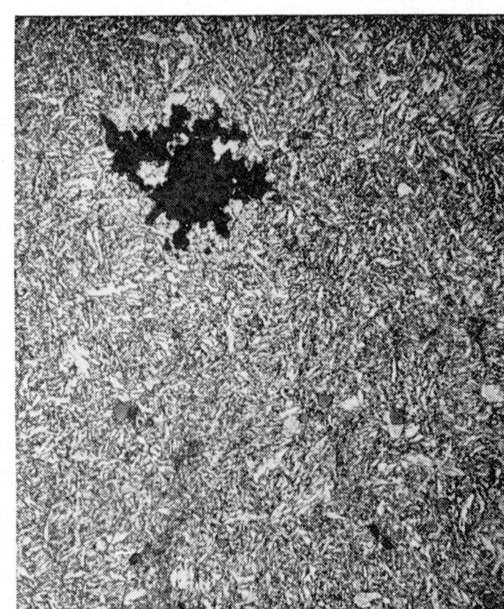

Fig. 35.30. Tempered martensitic matrix in a *pearlitic* malleable iron. Castings were quenched and tempered after completion of first stage graphitization; picture shows a single graphite inclusion. 500 × (from M.F.S. *Malleable Iron Castings,* 1960).

The air furnace has been employed since the advent of the malleable industry as a solution to the problem of producing low carbon irons. The modern air furnace is a shallow reverberatory type furnace ranging in capacity from 20 to 60 tons. Furnaces of this type are usually fired with powdered coal or oil. In the batch or direct melt process – as opposed to duplexing with the cupola – cold charges consisting of domestic returns, steel, pig and ferro-alloys are made. Melting times vary with furnace capacity but range from six hours. The air furnace has the advantage of no direct contact of the metal with coke, thus permitting the production of lower carbon irons by elimination of the carbon pick up experienced in cupola melting. In addition carbon reduction by oxidation is experienced in the later or refining stages of the heat. Carbon reductions of from 0.50 per cent carbon or more in the metal are obtained. Silicon and manganese losses occur in the earlier stages of the heat.

As a result of analysis changes during the course of melting and refining in the air furnace, there is a progressive increase in the tendency of the iron to solidify with a white fracture. To check progress in malleable melting the metallurgist may pour a series of test castings of comparable section to the production castings. Examination of the fracture shows the change in chilling tendency. Fig. 35.29 presents the fractures of such sprue tests.

In large scale production, economy and other advantages are obtained by charging the air furnace with liquid iron from the cupola in the duplexing process. Liquid metal may be charged in batches, or the air furnace may be attached to the cupola and the iron tapped continuously. Cupola practice is regulated to produce a low carbon iron, and a further reduction in carbon, superheating, and composition adjustment are effected in the air furnace.

An increasing amount of malleable iron is being produced by duplexing between the cupola and the electric furnace. The electric furnace employed is usually of the direct arc type, and provides the same general advantages as the air furnace with improved composition and temperature control.

Annealing of Malleable Iron

As taken from the mold and cleaned, malleable castings are hard and brittle, have a microstructure which contains massive cementite and is free of graphite (Figs. 35.3 and 35.28). This structure must be converted to the soft ductile structures of Figs. 35.26 and 35.27 containing temper carbon modules by heat treatment or annealing at temperatures ranging up to 1800 F (982 C).

Annealing is accomplished in both batch and continuous furnaces. In the batch process castings are packed in sealed pots or boxes and surrounded by a supporting packing material such as sand, gravel or mill scale. The containers are stacked in oil, coal, or gas fired, periodic furnaces, subjected to extended annealing cycles for periods of up to ten days. The sealing in boxes is necessary to avoid undue oxidation, scaling and decarburization.

More modern annealing practice utilizes electric or radiant tube, gas fired, continuous furnaces with controlled atmospheres. The controlled atmosphere allows stacking the castings in open baskets and shortens the annealing cycle by permitting more rapid temperature changes. Annealing in this type of equipment requires from 36 to 72 hr.

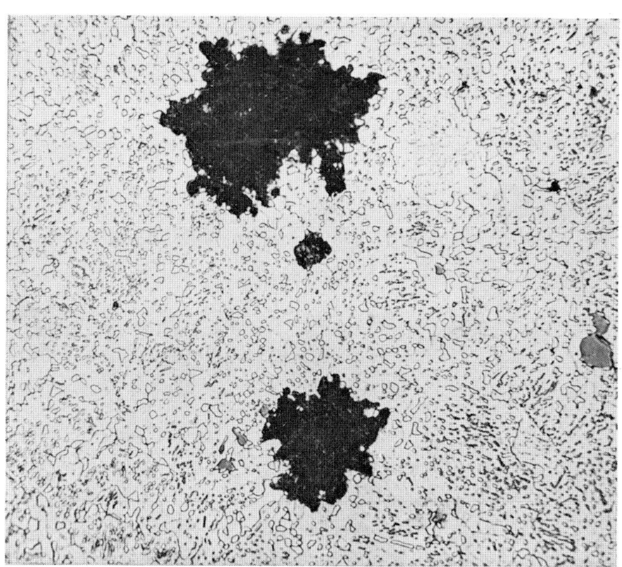

Fig. 35.31. Pearlitic malleable iron with a *spheroidized* matrix consisting of spheroidal particles of iron carbide dispersed in ferrite. 500 × (from M.F.S. *Malleable Iron Castings*, 1960).

Batch type controlled atmosphere furnaces are also employed.

Malleable iron is produced in two general types in American practice depending on the microstructure of the matrix. If the castings are annealed and heat treated to produce a matrix which is entirely ferrite, the iron is designated as ferritic malleable. Fig. 35.26 shows the microstructure of a ferritic malleable iron.

Superior strength and hardness at the sacrifice of some ductility may be produced by annealing and heat treating to a final matrix structure containing combined carbide dispersed in ferrite. This final structure may be pearlite or some other structure containing combined carbon. (Figs. 35.27, 35.30, 35.31 and 35.32). With the exception of those with a ferrite matrix structure, all malleable irons are pearlitic malleable. Pearlitic malleable irons constitute a relatively new and important engineering material exhibiting a combination of high strength, yield strength, machinability and toughness suitable for many machine parts.

A third general type of malleable, designated as white heart malleable, has been produced in European practice. In this practice light section castings are subjected to a prolonged anneal in an oxidizing atmosphere resulting in removal of free carbon by oxidation and the production of a ferrite matrix free of carbon. The absence of temper carbon results in a white fracture as opposed to the dark fracture of American or black heart malleable.

Figure 35.33 presents a typical time-temperature cycle for production of a ferritic malleable. The metallurgical changes occurring during annealing are complex and will be discussed in terms of the lower diagram of Fig. 35.2, which represents a section thru the ternary system for iron-carbon-silicon alloys.

At ambient temperature and as taken from the mold, the white malleable casting has a microstruc-

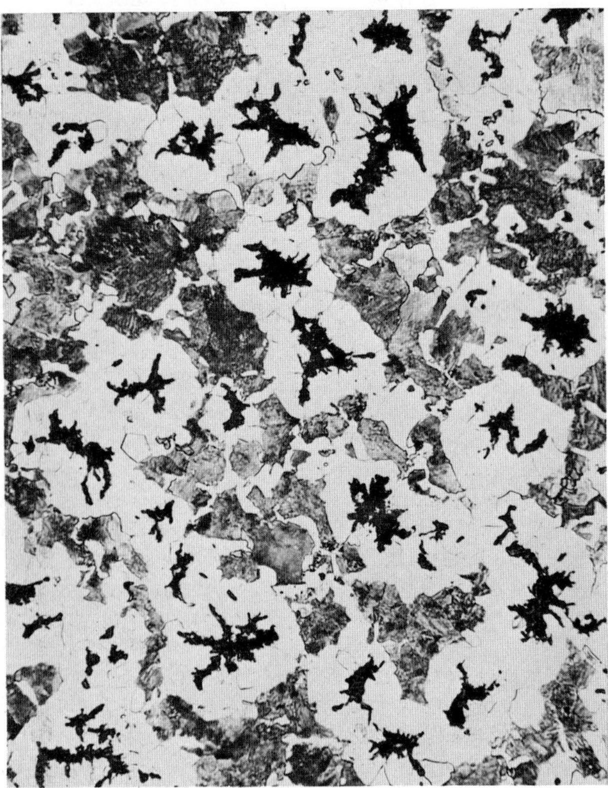

Fig. 35.32. A matrix of ferrite and pearlite in a *bull's eye* malleable. Temper carbon modules surrounded by light etching ferrite give the *bull's eye* appearance; balance of structure is dark etching pearlite. Nital etch, 100 × (from M.F.S. *Malleable Iron Castings*, 1960).

ture consisting of pearlite and massive cementite. Since pearlite is made up of alternate lamillae of cementite and ferrite, the two phases present are ferrite and cementite (Fig. 35.8). This is indicated on the lower region of the diagram of Fig. 35.2 where the two phases are designated as α (ferrite) and Ca (standing for the carbide or cementite phase).

When the malleable casting of a composition in the range of 2 to 3 per cent C is slowly heated and enters the three phased eutectoid region marked $\alpha + \gamma +$ Ca (where the symbol γ represents austenite), the pearlite transforms to austenite. At low heating rates this transformation is completed in or near the eutectoid interval and the iron enters the two phased region consisting of γ or austenite and massive cementite. The temperature attained in this region is marked by the first horizontal on the cycle diagram of Fig. 35.33 at approximately 1600 F (870 C). The iron is now held at this temperature for a prolonged period.

As previously noted in the paragraph dealing with graphitization in gray iron and with stable and metastable solidification, iron carbide or cementite is not a stable compound and tends to decompose in accordance with this reaction in the region of holding during annealing

Fe_3C (cementite) $\rightarrow$ 3Fe (austenite) + C (graphite)

The prolonged holding indicated by the upper plateau of the cycle of Fig. 35.33 is designed to effect the complete dissociation of the cementite and to bring the alloy into equilibrium with the structure consisting of the two phases, austenite and graphite.

When the graphite forms in this range of temperature in the solid iron it forms as compacted inclusions or the temper carbon modules pictured in Figs. 35.26 and 35.27. Graphitization in this upper range of temperature is referred to as first stage malleabilization or graphitization.

The rate of decomposition and the period of holding time at the elevated temperature are determined by a number of factors among the most important of which are carbon content, silicon content and holding temperature. Both carbon and silicon in increasing amounts increase the rate of dissociation and the economy of the process. This circumstance requires that the maximum silicon content, consistent with obtaining a white casting free of graphite and mottle, be employed in order to attain equilibrium at the annealing temperature in the shortest possible time. Careful attention is given to balancing the silicon content against section size of the casting with the lighter sections permitting the higher silicon content.

The present trend in the industry is towards higher annealing temperatures and shorter annealing cycles with attendant economy of furnace time. Fig. 35.34 shows a short cycle employing a temperature of approximately 1750 F (955 C). Temperatures ranging up to 1800 F (982 C) are employed. Although high temperatures shorten annealing times, they are associated with increased oxidation and scaling, increased distortion of castings, shorter furnace life, increased fuel and furnace expenditures, and a tendency towards lower mechanical properties in the final product.

Upon completion of first stage annealing the castings are slowly cooled to or near the eutectoid zone in the temperature range of 1400 to 1200 F (760-649 C) (Figs. 35.2 and 35.15). Cooling from the maximum temperature to this range involves a precipitation of more carbon from the austenite with a resulting lowering of the carbon content of the remaining austenite, which approaches the eutectoid content defined by the eutectoid point *S* of the phase diagram.

If the cooling rate is low, precipitation in this range is in the form of additional graphite on the surface of the existing nodules, and the alloy approaches the eutectoid range as graphite nodules dispersed in austenite of eutectoid composition. The malleabilizing cycles are designed to accomplish this result.

With sufficiently rapid cooling austenite of eutectoid composition transforms to pearlite in or below the narrow, three phased eutectoid range. However, if cooling is slow (3 to 30 F/hr) or if the iron is held in the eutectoid range (Figs. 35.2 and 35.15) transformation occurs in the stable equilibrium manner to ferrite and graphite with continuing deposition of carbon.

Since cooling on down to ambient temperature after completion of austenite transformation does not produce a discernable alteration in the microstructure, the final product of the cycles of Figs. 35.33 and 35.34 is ferritic malleable iron, illustrated in photomicrograph Fig. 35.26. Graphitization in or near the eutectoid range is referred to as second stage malleabilization or graphitization.

An important aspect of the metallurgy of malleable iron is the number, size and shape of the temper car-

Fig. 35.33. Typical annealing cycle used in *pot-type* annealing furnaces for standard grades of ferritic malleable iron (*above*).

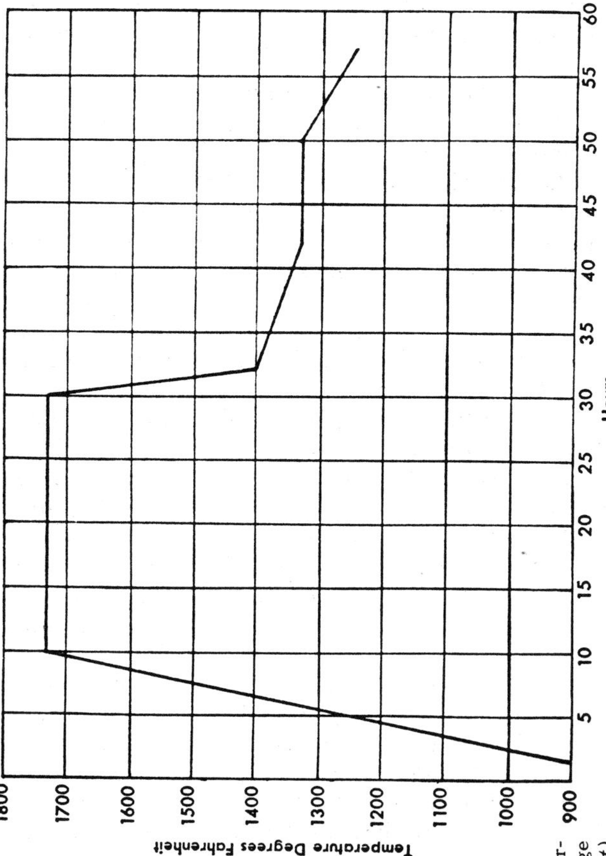

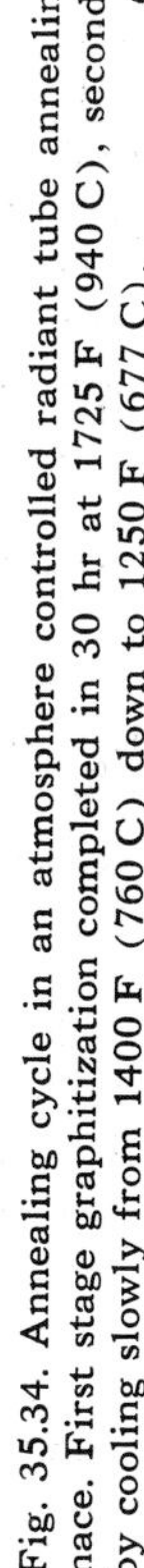

Fig. 35.34. Annealing cycle in an atmosphere controlled radiant tube annealing furnace. First stage graphitization completed in 30 hr at 1725 F (940 C), second stage by cooling slowly from 1400 F (760 C) down to 1250 F (677 C). (*right*)

bon nodules. The number of nodules is dependent on a nucleation process which appears to be influenced by a large number of variables including section size of the casting, chemical analysis of the iron with respect to several elements, heating rate during malleabilization treatment, and melting conditions.

A pretreatment involving holding the iron at subcritical temperatures in the range of 600 F to 1200 F (316-649 C) is credited with increasing the number of nodules. Nodule shape will vary from an irregular inclusion to that of a more or less perfect sphere. High nodule count accelerates graphitization during annealing.

Pearlitic malleable irons have been defined as malleable irons with a microstructure containing combined carbon in the matrix structure as opposed to ferritic malleable irons where the matrix is 100 per cent ferrite and is free of carbide. Although these irons are designated as pearlitic, the pearlitic malleable irons may have pearlite, pearlite and ferrite, tempered martensite or a spheroidal type of structure as the matrix. Such irons have superior strength as a result of the hardening effect of the carbide particles dispersed in the ferrite. Microstructures of pearlitic irons are shown in Figs. 35.27, 35.30, 35.31 and 35.32.

There are many variations in the procedures for the production of pearlitic malleable. Among these are – 1. production by increasing the rate of cooling through and below the eutectoid range in order to avoid second stage graphitization, 2. production by addition of alloying elements to assist in retarding second stage graphitization, 3. production by cooling rapidly to avoid second stage graphitization followed by reheating to a temperature above the eutectoid zone, liquid quenching and then tempering and 4. production by heat treatment of a completely graphitized, ferritic malleable. All of these methods involve first stage malleabilization by holding in the elevated temperature range as in the production of ordinary standard (ferritic) malleable.

In procedure (1) continuous and rapid cooling at various rates through the eutectoid zone are substituted for the isothermal treatment and very slow cooling through this zone of the ferritic malleable cycles of Figs. 35.33 and 35.34. As a result second stage graphitization does not occur and the resulting matrix structure is one containing combined carbon or is martensitic, depending on the rate of cooling employed.

The appropriate rate of cooling may be obtained by accelerating the cooling in the furnace, by air quenching, and by liquid quenching. At rates of cooling less than the critical rate, the microstructure will be pearlite of varying degrees of fineness, or mixed structures containing pearlite and bainite, etc. At rates of cooling above the critical rate, obtained by liquid quenching, the resulting structure will be martensite. The more rapid rates of cooling are generally followed by tempering in the range of 450 to 1300 F (232-705 C) to relieve stresses, and to produce tempered martensite of the desired hardness.

If the final heating is close to 1300 F (705 C) and the heating is prolonged, a spheroidized structure consisting of spheroidal particles of carbide in a matrix of ferrite is produced. The tempered martensitic structures, when produced by tempering in the lower part of the tempering range, result in irons of maximum strength, hardness, wear resistance, but low ductility. The spheroidized irons have superior ductility and better machinability than the lamellar (pearlitic) irons.

In procedure (2) additions of a carbide stabilizing element are made to aid in suppressing second stage graphitization. Molybdenum or manganese in amounts in excess of those ordinarily employed in the iron are used for this purpose. The presence of these elements serves to prevent graphitization during the spheroidizing treatment sometimes employed as a part of procedure (1).

Method (3) is employed to convert a pearlitic matrix to a tempered martensitic structure by heating to above the critical range, austenitizing, quenching to form martensite, and tempering to the desired hardness and strength level. This is a useful procedure for treating iron with a matrix structure that does not permit meeting a hardness or yield strength specification.

Procedure (4) is useful where a limited production of pearlitic iron is desired in a plant normally producing ferritic malleable. In this procedure the fully graphitized, ferritic castings are taken after the usual production sequence, reheated to a temperature in the austenite range, held to dissolve sufficient temper carbon to provide the matrix structure, and cooled at the appropriate rate to produce the desired structure and hardness.

Influence of Malleable Iron Composition

The influence of carbon and silicon in promoting graphitization during solidification and the necessity of keeping these elements low in order to obtain a graphite free white iron as initially cast in malleable practice, have been discussed.

The role of silicon in promoting graphitization in the primary graphitization stage must also be considered. An unnecessarily low content of silicon requires a prolonged graphitizing anneal with resulting increase in cost. These considerations require a careful balancing of the silicon content of the iron against section size, with the heavier castings requiring the lower silicon and carbon contents.

An important function of manganese in all ferrous alloys is to combine with sulfur to form manganese sulfide (MnS) and to prevent the formation of an undue amount of iron sulfide (FeS), which has an embrittling effect. Theoretically, one part of manganese is required to combine with 1.7 parts of sulfur. However, it is common practice to employ an excess of manganese, and manganese contents ranging up to three times the required are employed.

Manganese is a carbide stabilizer, particularly in the eutectoid range, and is employed in larger than usual amounts in the production of pearlitic malleable to aid in the formation of combined carbon in the matrix. In the production of ferritic malleable, the manganese content must be controlled in a low range in order to avoid excessive time in the second stage of graphitization.

Excess sulfur retards both stages of graphitization. Higher sulfur contents permit casting heavier sections free of graphite, and special heavy section malleables (ranging up to 4 inches) are cast with higher than usual sulfur contents. High sulfur to manganese ratios result in increased compactness of nodules and an approach to a spherical temper carbon nodule shape.

It is desirable to keep the phosphorus content well within the limit of Table 35.4 because of embrittling effects, including temper embrittlement.

Temper embrittlement, which results in a lowered impact strength and a high nil ductility transition temperature, is associated with certain cooling and heating cycles in the range of temperature below the eutectoid zone. It is generally considered that rapid cooling from a temperature above 1150 F (621 C) following second stage graphitization will prevent or minimize the danger of temper embrittlement unless the casting is subsequently subjected to temperatures approaching 850 F (454 C) in service or as in a galvanizing treatment.

Chromium is a powerful carbide stabilizer and its presence as a tramp element in the iron originating from scrap is undesirable beyond a content of .04 to .05 per cent, because of its effect in increasing graphitizing time in the annealing treatment. The control of chromium in scrap is an important problem in the industry.

Molybdenum and copper are employed in malleable iron as alloying elements. Molybdenum increases the tensile strength of the iron, and as a carbide stabilizing element assists in retarding second stage graphitization in the production of pearlitic malleable.

Copper additions improve the mechanical properties by solution hardening the ferrite, and by rendering the iron susceptible to precipitation hardening. Copper is a graphitizing element and molybdenum-copper irons are produced in which the retarding influence of molybdenum in first stage graphitization is balanced by the copper. The molybdenum-copper irons have superior corrosion resistance.

Boron acts as a graphitizing element in malleable iron in amounts up to 0.1 per cent, and small additions (0.001 to 0.002 per cent) are employed to reduce the time required for first stage graphitization.

Bismuth is a strong carbide stabilizer and is added to iron in small percentages for the purpose of casting heavy sections free of gray or mottle in the fracture. Malleable castings may be successfully cast white in sections up to five inches with bismuth present in amounts of a few hundredths of one per cent.

Combinations of bismuth and boron additions are made with the bismuth assuring a white fracture as cast, and the boron serving as a graphitizer to offset the carbide stabilizing effect of the bismuth during the primary graphitizing stage.

Mechanical Properties of Malleable Iron

Representative tensile test properties for standard (ferritic) malleable iron are presented in Table 35.5.

The modulus of elasticity of malleable iron in tension is approximately 25,000,000 psi. Brinell hardnesses of ferritic malleable are in the range of 110 to 156. An outstanding characteristic of ferritic malleable

TABLE 35.5. TENSILE TEST VALUES

	Tensile Strength (psi)	Yield Point (psi)	Elongation % in 2 in.
Grade 32510			
Minimum	50,000	32,500	10
Most probable value	52,000	34,000	12.5
Grade 35018			
Minimum	53,000	35,000	18.0
Most probable value	55,000	36,500	20.0

TABLE 35.6. TENSILE PROPERTIES of PEARLITIC MALLEABLE IRON (Requirements of A.S.T.M. Specification *A220-55T*)

Grade	Min. Tensile Strength (psi)	Min. Yield Point or Yield Strength (psi)	Min. Elongation (% in 2 in.)	Typical BHN Range
45010	65,000	45,000	10	163-207
48004	70,000	48,000	4	163-228
53004	80,000	53,000	4	197-241
80002	100,000	80,000	2	241-269

is its machinability. Ferritic malleable is regarded as the most readily machinable and free cutting of the ferrous alloys.

Tensile properties of representative grades and Brinell ranges of pearlitic malleable are shown in Table 35.6.

The higher tensile and yield strengths and lower ductilities of the pearlitic grades are a result of the combined carbon in the complex matrix structures of this general type of malleable. Tensile strengths approaching 100,000 psi are obtained with tempered martensite as the matrix structure. As a result of the presence of combined carbon, the pearlitic irons respond readily to surface and localized hardening treatments.

V. NODULAR CAST IRON

Nodular cast iron is a cast iron with an as-cast structure containing graphite inclusions of a spheroidal shape (Fig. 35.35). These irons are produced commercially by treating molten iron of appropriate composition with magnesium or cerium metal or complex alloys containing these elements.

The presence of graphite in the spheroidal condition results in a minimum interruption of the matrix and ductilities ranging from 2.0 per cent to more than 20.0 per cent, as opposed to the near zero ductility of gray iron, where the matrix continuity is reduced by the flattened graphite flakes.

As taken from the mold the microstructure of nodular iron resembles that of pearlitic malleable in the annealed condition, with the graphite inclusion approaching a more nearly spheroidal shape than is ordinarily the case with malleable microstructures.

The matrix structure of nodular cast iron is generally pearlite, or pearlite and ferrite, as-cast. The as-cast matrix may be converted to all ferrite by annealing, or to martensite and tempered martensite by heat treatment as indicated in Fig. 35.35.

Nodular irons are referred to in the literature as ductile iron, spherulitic iron, or spheroidal iron. Ductile iron and nodular iron are the most widely used terms.

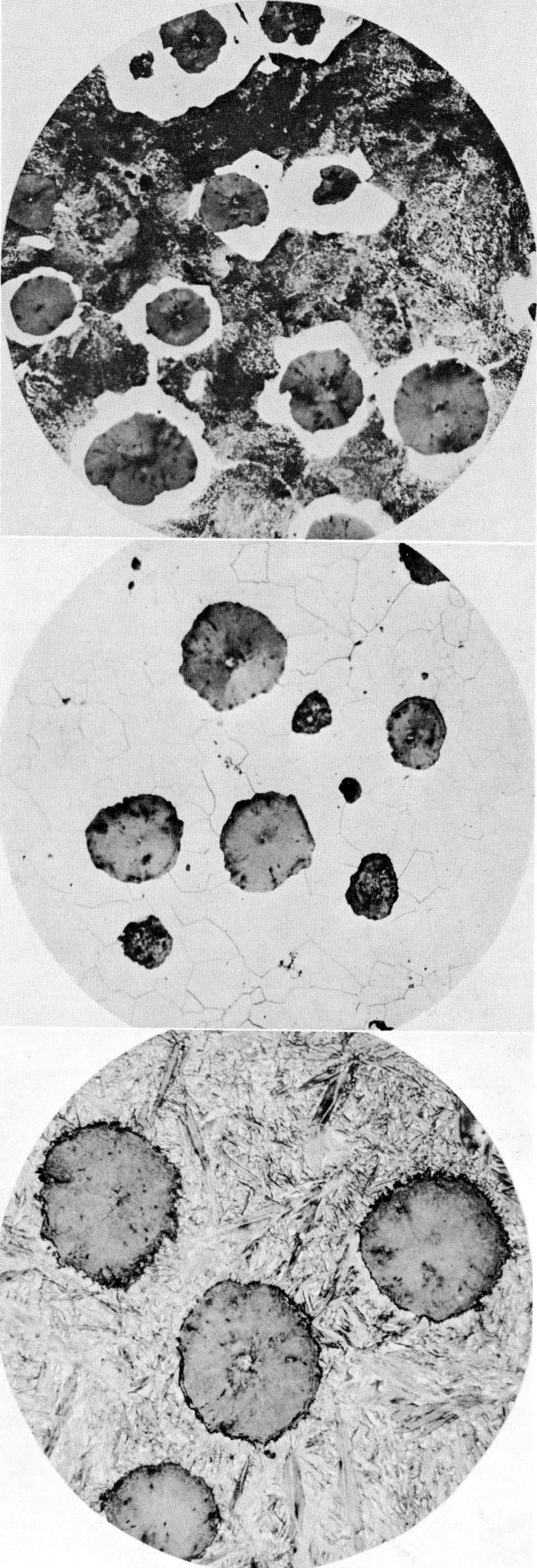

Fig. 35.35. Microstructure of nodular iron. *Top*—As Cast, 250 ×; *middle*—Annealed, 250 ×; *below*—Quenched, 340 × (courtesy International Nickel Co. *The Fundamentals of Iron and Steel Castings* by Albert P. Gagnebin, 1957).

TABLE 35.7. MAGNESIUM MASTER ALLOYS For NODULAR IRON

Alloys	Per Cent		
1. Nickel-base			
A. Nickel-magnesium	85 *Ni*	15 *Mg*	
B. Nickel-silicon-magnesium	50 *Ni*	15 *Mg*	30 *Si*
2. Silicon-base			
A. Silicon-magnesium	45 *Si*	9 *Mg*	
B. Silicon-magnesium-cerium	45 *Si*	9 *Mg*	0.5 *Ce*
3. Magnesium rich			
A. Silicon-base	62 *Si*	18 *Mg*	0.5 *Ce*
B. Nickel-base	70 *Ni*	30 *Mg*	

TABLE 35.8. COMPOSITION RANGE for NODULAR IRON

Total Carbon	3.00 - 4.20%
Silicon	1.80 - 2.80%
Manganese	0.15 - 0.90%
Phosphorus	0.10% max.
Sulfur	0.03% max.
Magnesium	0.04 - 0.10%

The discovery of the nodularizing process was announced in the mid-1940s by investigators working independently in the United States and Great Britain. American production is governed by U.S. Patents No. 2,485, 760 and 2,749,238.

Manufacture of Nodular Iron

The steps in the manufacture of nodular iron are – 1. production of a molten iron of low sulfur content, preferably under 0.03 per cent, 2. treatment of the molten iron with certain active metals, generally magnesium or cerium in commercial practice and 3. inoculation with ferrosilicon before pouring.

The base iron may be melted in the cupola (both acid and basic), the electric furnace, the air furnace and by duplexing. Since a low sulfur content is a requirement, the basic cupola, which can be operated to produce a sulfur content of less than 0.02 per cent, is finding extensive use as a melting unit.

Melting conditions may make desulfurizing outside the furnace necessary. Sulfur may be removed in a ladle or forehearth by pouring over a soda ash slag, or through injection of powdered calcium carbide by blowing with nitrogen. High sulfur content in the as-melted base iron markedly increases the cost of the magnesium addition because of the tendency of this element to combine with sulfur.

In American practice the production of the spherulitic graphite is accomplished by the addition of magnesium, or combinations of magnesium with a small amount of cerium. Additions are usually in the form of an alloy, but a limited amount of nodular iron continues to be produced by the introduction of pure magnesium. Table 35.7 gives the composition of a number of commonly employed alloys.

The introduction of magnesium involves technical difficulties due to the high chemical activity of the magnesium, its low boiling point (2024 F, 1107 C), its low specific gravity, and the low density of the high magnesium alloys. These methods of introduction are employed:

1. Introduction of pure magnesium with an inert gas, or introduction of pure magnesium in a pressure chamber or autoclave maintained at a pressure equal to the vapor pressure of magnesium at the metal temperature.
2. Addition of a bulk alloy in the ladle bottom, and rapid pouring onto the alloy.
3. Plunging of an alloy in a refractory bell.
4. The sandwich method in which the alloy is placed in a recess in the bottom of the ladle, covered with sand or steel, and the molten iron rapidly poured onto the sandwich.
5. Mechanical feeding of the alloy to the stream of molten metal as it issues from the cupola or forehearth.

The use of the alloys of Table 35.7 introduced by methods 2, 3 and 4 accounts for 95 per cent of American production.

Recovery of magnesium varies from 25 per cent to 90 per cent depending on the alloy and method employed, the temperature of the iron, the sulfur content of the iron, and other circumstances. Amounts of magnesium added vary in most cases from 1.0 to 2.5 lb/1000 lb of iron.

The introduction of the magnesium is followed by inoculation with ferrosilicon. Commonly used amounts of ferrosilicon increase the silicon content of the iron by 0.30 to 0.70 per cent.

Although not essential to the production of spheroidal graphite, the use of an inoculant results in an iron of lower chilling tendency and improved mechanical properties. Inoculation should be followed immediately by pouring.

Influence of Nodular Iron Composition

Table 35.8 gives the composition range for nodular iron.

The compactness of the graphite inclusions which approach the spheroidal in shape, permits high ductility combined with good tensile strength at high carbon levels in nodular iron. Although nodular iron contains about 10 per cent graphite by volume, its tensile properties approach within 15 per cent those of steel at similar hardness levels.

Nodular iron exhibits a chilling tendency, and increasing carbon content results in a decrease in chill accompanied by an increase in the amount of ferrite in the matrix. Increasing carbon content results in a reduction of shrinkage and riser requirements.

Increasing silicon content lowers the chilling tendency and tends to increase the amount of ferrite in the matrix. Increasing silicon content raises the hardness of ferrite by solution hardening. High silicon content tends to elevate the transition temperature in irons with an entirely ferritic matrix. Irons for impact application are produced to a maximum silicon specification.

High manganese content tends to reduce the amount of ferrite in the matrix structure. Manganese should be controlled at lower levels when high as-cast ductility is desired.

Phosphorus is detrimental to ductility. Phosphorus is held to a maximum specification of 0.10 per cent for most applications.

Residual magnesium content of the iron is critical. The majority of irons produced in American practice have a content of this element in the range of 0.04 per cent to 0.07 per cent. Low magnesium contents promote a tendency towards flake or vermicular graphite with resulting loss of ductility (Fig. 35.36).

Excessive residual magnesium acts as a powerful carbide stabilizer and tends to increase chilling tendency and shrinkage during solidification. Large amounts of magnesium increase the amount of dross formed in the metal particularly in the presence of higher than normal sulfur content.

Nickel as an alloying element in nodular iron promotes a pearlitic matrix with increased tensile strength and response to heat treatment. Nickel is introduced as a base metal in the nodularizing alloy.

When nickel is not required as an alloying element, lower treatment costs are obtained by the use of silicon base alloys (Table 35.7).

Copper base alloys have been employed as nodularizing agents, and the presence of copper is credited with improved tensile properties. Copper renders the nodular iron susceptible to precipitation hardening treatments. Chromium content is generally controlled at low levels because of chill inducing effects.

Tramp elements, originating from scrap – such as titanium, tin, lead, and arsenic – have an inhibiting effect on nodule formation, and must be held to low levels. Cerium additions are made to overcome the effects of these tramp elements.

Solidification of Nodular Iron

Research in which samples of nodular iron are quenched during freezing indicates that graphite nodules form early during eutectic solidification and grow rapidly in the partially solidified iron.

In hypoeutectic irons the graphite nodules appear between the primary dendrites as the first stage of eutectic solidification. The developing graphite nodules are very soon, if not immediately, encased in a growing layer of austenite. This graphite-austenite growth continues until solidification is completed, with the nodule growing by diffusion through the encasing austenite.

In the absence of primary dendrites, the graphite nodules are free to float in the surrounding liquid, and a tendency to float and segregate in the cope part of eutectic iron castings has been observed.

The formation of graphite during solidification, with the accompanying expansion, is of assistance in reducing solidification contraction and risering requirements. As is the case with gray iron, the higher carbon nodular irons require less risering.

The exact mechanism of the magnesium and cerium nodularizing action has not been determined. Nucleation and surface energy effects have been proposed as factors in the formation of nodules. The effect is not confined to magnesium and cerium, but may be produced by other active metals such as calcium.

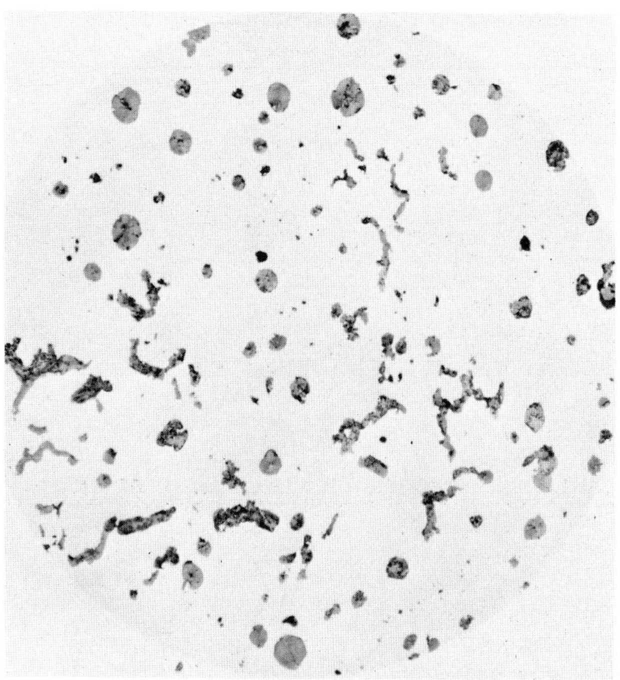

Fig. 35.36. Unacceptable graphite structure in nodular casting showing *vermicular* or *quasi-flake* graphite mixed with spheroids.

Microstructure and Heat Treatment

Although special irons such as austenitic varieties are made, the microstructure of nodular iron as ordinarily produced consists of graphite spheroids in a matrix of pearlite with a variable amount of ferrite. As a result of variations in amount of ferrite, and varying degrees of fineness of the pearlite, the as-cast ductility will range from 2 per cent to 20 per cent with corresponding variations in strength and hardness. A typical as-cast structure is in the top photomicrograph of Fig. 35.35 showing pearlite with light etching ferrite surrounding the nodules. Nodular irons are subject to chill, and as-cast microstructures may contain massive carbides.

Many nodular iron castings go into service as-cast. The balance of production is subject to heat treatment. A ferritizing anneal is employed to increase ductility, toughness and machinability. Hardness and strength are increased by rapid cooling after austenitizing. Typical heat treatments are tabulated.

A typical ferritizing anneal in the absence of massive cementite is

Heat to 1450 F (788 C)
Hold for one hr/in. of section
Cool at 20 F/hr to 1350 F (732 C)
Cool at 100 F (38 C)/hr to 800 F (427 C)

This treatment may be employed for the decomposition of massive or primary carbides

Heat to 1650 F (899 C)
Hold for 2 hr/in. of section
Cool to 1450 F (788 C) in one hr
Cool to 1350 F (732 C) at 20 F/hr
Cool at 100 F (38 C)/hr to 800 F (427 C)

TABLE 35.9. RANGE of MECHANICAL PROPERTIES Of NODULAR IRON

Tensile Strength, psi	60,000-140,000
Yield Strength, psi	40,000-120,000
Elongation, % in 2 in.	25-1
Modulus of Elasticity	22,000,000-25,000,000
Brinell Hardness	130-340

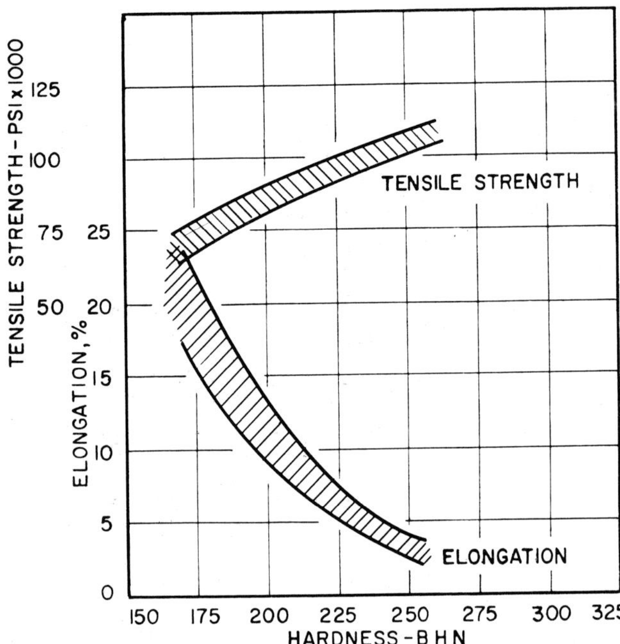

Fig. 35.37. Relationship of elongation, tensile strength, and hardness of ductile iron in the as-cast condition. (International Nickel Co.)

For higher strengths and hardness, casting may be austenitized at 1600 F (871 C) and subject to one of these treatments

1. Cool in air
2. Cool to 1450 F (788 C) in furnace and quench in air
3. Quench in air followed by temper or quench in oil followed by temper.

Properties and Application

Table 35.9 gives the range of mechanical properties of nodular iron. Low strengths with high ductilities are produced with a ferritizing anneal and ferritic matrix. The high strengths levels are attained by quenching and drawing to produce tempered martensite as a matrix structure. Figure 35.37 presents the relationship between hardness, tensile strength and ductility.

Nodular iron castings are widely applied. Typical applications include – crankshafts, engine heads, gears, clutch plates, casings, pipes, machine tool parts and automotive parts.

Nodular castings are specified where high strength combined with ductility, wear resistance, good machinability and castability are required. Castings are produced in sizes ranging from less than one lb to 40 tons or more.

Appendix

TEMPERATURE CONVERSION

NOTE:—The numbers in bold face type refer to the temperature either in degrees Centigrade or Fahrenheit which is to be converted into the other scale. If converting from Fahrenheit to Centigrade the equivalent temperature will be found in the left column. When converting from degrees Centigrade to Fahrenheit, the answer will be found in the column on the right. Interpolation factors are at the bottom right hand corner of the table.

C.		F.	C.		F.	C.		F.	C.		F.
-17.8	**0**	32	10.0	**50**	122.0	38	**100**	212	316	**600**	1112
-17.2	**1**	33.8	10.6	**51**	123.8	43	**110**	230	321	**610**	1130
-16.7	**2**	35.6	11.1	**52**	125.6	49	**120**	248	327	**620**	1148
-16.1	**3**	37.4	11.7	**53**	127.4	54	**130**	266	332	**630**	1166
-15.6	**4**	39.2	12.2	**54**	129.2	60	**140**	284	338	**640**	1184
-15.0	**5**	41.0	12.8	**55**	131.0	66	**150**	302	343	**650**	1202
-14.4	**6**	42.8	13.3	**56**	132.8	71	**160**	320	349	**660**	1220
-13.9	**7**	44.6	13.9	**57**	134.6	77	**170**	338	354	**670**	1238
-13.3	**8**	46.4	14.4	**58**	136.4	82	**180**	356	360	**680**	1256
-12.8	**9**	48.2	15.0	**59**	138.2	88	**190**	374	366	**690**	1274
-12.2	**10**	50.0	15.6	**60**	140.0	93	**200**	392	371	**700**	1292
-11.7	**11**	51.8	16.1	**61**	141.8	99	**210**	410	377	**710**	1310
-11.1	**12**	53.6	16.7	**62**	143.6	104	**220**	428	382	**720**	1328
-10.6	**13**	55.4	17.2	**63**	145.4	110	**230**	446	388	**730**	1346
-10.0	**14**	57.2	17.8	**64**	147.2	116	**240**	464	393	**740**	1364
- 9.44	**15**	59.0	18.3	**65**	149.0	121	**250**	482	399	**750**	1382
- 8.89	**16**	60.8	18.9	**66**	150.8	127	**260**	500	404	**760**	1400
- 8.33	**17**	62.6	19.4	**67**	152.6	132	**270**	518	410	**770**	1418
- 7.78	**18**	64.4	20.0	**68**	154.4	138	**280**	536	416	**780**	1436
- 7.22	**19**	66.2	20.6	**69**	156.2	143	**290**	554	421	**790**	1454
- 6.67	**20**	68.0	21.1	**70**	158.0	149	**300**	572	427	**800**	1472
- 6.11	**21**	69.8	21.7	**71**	159.8	154	**310**	590	432	**810**	1490
- 5.56	**22**	71.6	22.2	**72**	161.6	160	**320**	608	438	**820**	1508
- 5.00	**23**	73.4	22.8	**73**	163.4	166	**330**	626	443	**830**	1526
- 4.44	**24**	75.2	23.3	**74**	165.2	171	**340**	644	449	**840**	1544
- 3.89	**25**	77.0	23.9	**75**	167.0	177	**350**	662	454	**850**	1562
- 3.33	**26**	78.8	24.4	**76**	168.8	182	**360**	680	460	**860**	1580
- 2.78	**27**	80.6	25.0	**77**	170.6	188	**370**	698	466	**870**	1598
- 2.22	**28**	82.4	25.6	**78**	172.4	193	**380**	716	471	**880**	1616
- 1.67	**29**	84.2	26.1	**79**	174.2	199	**390**	734	477	**890**	1634
- 1.11	**30**	86.0	26.7	**80**	176.0	204	**400**	752	482	**900**	1652
- 0.56	**31**	87.8	27.2	**81**	177.8	210	**410**	770	488	**910**	1670
0	**32**	89.6	27.8	**82**	179.6	216	**420**	788	493	**920**	1688
0.56	**33**	91.4	28.3	**83**	181.4	221	**430**	806	499	**930**	1706
1.11	**34**	93.2	28.9	**84**	183.2	227	**440**	824	504	**940**	1724
1.67	**35**	95.0	29.4	**85**	185.0	232	**450**	842	510	**950**	1742
2.22	**36**	96.8	30.0	**86**	186.8	238	**460**	860	516	**960**	1760
2.78	**37**	98.6	30.6	**87**	188.6	243	**470**	878	521	**970**	1778
3.33	**38**	100.4	31.1	**88**	190.4	249	**480**	896	527	**980**	1796
3.89	**39**	102.2	31.7	**89**	192.2	254	**490**	914	532	**990**	1814
4.44	**40**	104.0	32.2	**90**	194.0	260	**500**	932	538	**1000**	1832
5.00	**41**	105.8	32.8	**91**	195.8	266	**510**	950	543	**1010**	1850
5.56	**42**	107.6	33.3	**92**	197.6	271	**520**	968	549	**1020**	1868
6.11	**43**	109.4	33.9	**93**	199.4	277	**530**	986	554	**1030**	1886
6.67	**44**	111.2	34.4	**94**	201.2	282	**540**	1004	560	**1040**	1904
7.22	**45**	113.0	35.0	**95**	203.0	288	**550**	1022	566	**1050**	1922
7.78	**46**	114.8	35.6	**96**	204.8	293	**560**	1040	571	**1060**	1940
8.33	**47**	116.6	36.1	**97**	206.6	299	**570**	1058	577	**1070**	1958
8.89	**48**	118.4	36.7	**98**	208.4	304	**580**	1076	582	**1080**	1976
9.44	**49**	120.2	37.2	**99**	210.2	310	**590**	1094	588	**1090**	1994

C.		F.	C.		F.	C.		F.	C.		F.
593	**1100**	2012	871	**1600**	2912	1149	**2100**	3812	1427	**2600**	4712
599	**1110**	2030	877	**1610**	2930	1154	**2110**	3830	1432	**2610**	4730
604	**1120**	2048	882	**1620**	2948	1160	**2120**	3848	1438	**2620**	4748
610	**1130**	2066	888	**1630**	2966	1166	**2130**	3866	1443	**2630**	4766
616	**1140**	2084	893	**1640**	2984	1171	**2140**	3884	1449	**2640**	4784
621	**1150**	2102	899	**1650**	3002	1177	**2150**	3902	1454	**2650**	4802
627	**1160**	2120	904	**1660**	3020	1182	**2160**	3920	1460	**2660**	4820
632	**1170**	2138	910	**1670**	3038	1188	**2170**	3938	1466	**2670**	4838
638	**1180**	2156	916	**1680**	3056	1193	**2180**	3956	1471	**2680**	4856
643	**1190**	2174	921	**1690**	3074	1199	**2190**	3974	1477	**2690**	4874
649	**1200**	2192	927	**1700**	3092	1204	**2200**	3992	1482	**2700**	4892
654	**1210**	2210	932	**1710**	3110	1210	**2210**	4010	1488	**2710**	4910
660	**1220**	2228	938	**1720**	3128	1216	**2220**	4028	1493	**2720**	4928
666	**1230**	2246	943	**1730**	3146	1221	**2230**	4046	1499	**2730**	4946
671	**1240**	2264	949	**1740**	3164	1227	**2240**	4064	1504	**2740**	4964
677	**1250**	2282	954	**1750**	3182	1232	**2250**	4082	1510	**2750**	4982
682	**1260**	2300	960	**1760**	3200	1238	**2260**	4100	1516	**2760**	5000
688	**1270**	2318	966	**1770**	3218	1243	**2270**	4118	1521	**2770**	5018
693	**1280**	2336	971	**1780**	3236	1249	**2280**	4136	1527	**2780**	5036
699	**1290**	2354	977	**1790**	3254	1254	**2290**	4154	1532	**2790**	5054
704	**1300**	2372	982	**1800**	3272	1260	**2300**	4172	1538	**2800**	5072
710	**1310**	2390	988	**1810**	3290	1266	**2310**	4190	1543	**2810**	5090
716	**1320**	2408	993	**1820**	3308	1271	**2320**	4208	1549	**2820**	5108
721	**1330**	2426	999	**1830**	3326	1277	**2330**	4226	1554	**2830**	5126
727	**1340**	2444	1004	**1840**	3344	1282	**2340**	4244	1560	**2840**	5144
732	**1350**	2462	1010	**1850**	3362	1288	**2350**	4262	1566	**2850**	5162
738	**1360**	2480	1016	**1860**	3380	1293	**2360**	4280	1571	**2860**	5180
743	**1370**	2498	1021	**1870**	3398	1299	**2370**	4298	1577	**2870**	5198
749	**1380**	2516	1027	**1880**	3416	1304	**2380**	4316	1582	**2880**	5216
754	**1390**	2534	1032	**1890**	3434	1310	**2390**	4334	1588	**2890**	5234
760	**1400**	2552	1038	**1900**	3452	1316	**2400**	4352	1593	**2900**	5252
766	**1410**	2570	1043	**1910**	3470	1321	**2410**	4370	1599	**2910**	5270
771	**1420**	2588	1049	**1920**	3488	1327	**2420**	4388	1604	**2920**	5288
777	**1430**	2606	1054	**1930**	3506	1332	**2430**	4406	1610	**2930**	5306
782	**1440**	2624	1060	**1940**	3524	1338	**2440**	4424	1616	**2940**	5324
788	**1450**	2642	1066	**1950**	3542	1343	**2450**	4442	1621	**2950**	5342
793	**1460**	2660	1071	**1960**	3560	1349	**2460**	4460	1627	**2960**	5360
799	**1470**	2678	1077	**1970**	3578	1354	**2470**	4478	1632	**2970**	5378
804	**1480**	2696	1082	**1980**	3596	1360	**2480**	4496	1638	**2980**	5396
810	**1490**	2714	1088	**1990**	3614	1366	**2490**	4514	1643	**2990**	5414
816	**1500**	2732	1093	**2000**	3632	1371	**2500**	4532	1649	**3000**	5432
821	**1510**	2750	1099	**2010**	3650	1377	**2510**	4550			
827	**1520**	2768	1104	**2020**	3668	1382	**2520**	4568			
832	**1530**	2786	1110	**2030**	3686	1388	**2530**	4586			
838	**1540**	2804	1116	**2040**	3704	1393	**2540**	4604			
843	**1550**	2822	1121	**2050**	3722	1399	**2550**	4622			
849	**1560**	2840	1127	**2060**	3740	1404	**2560**	4640			
854	**1570**	2858	1132	**2070**	3758	1410	**2570**	4658			
860	**1580**	2876	1138	**2080**	3776	1416	**2580**	4676			
866	**1590**	2894	1143	**2090**	3794	1421	**2590**	4694			

INTERPOLATION FACTORS

C.		F.
0.56	**1**	1.8
1.11	**2**	3.6
1.67	**3**	5.4
2.22	**4**	7.2
2.78	**5**	9.0
3.33	**6**	10.8
3.89	**7**	12.6
4.44	**8**	14.4
5.00	**9**	16.2
5.56	**10**	18.0

JW >∞

Formulas: C = (F − 32) 5/9 F = 9/5 C + 32

PROPERTIES OF DRY AIR

Temp., Deg F	Weight /Cu Ft, lb	Cu Ft in 1 lb of Air	Percent Volume at 70 F	Btu Absorbed by 1 Cu Ft/ Deg F	Cu Ft Warmed 1 Deg/ Btu
−20	0.0902	11.1	0.830	0.0217	46.1
−15	0.0892	11.2	0.840	0.0215	46.5
−10	0.0882	11.3	0.849	0.0213	46.9
−5	0.0873	11.4	0.858	0.0210	47.6
0	0.0863	11.5	0.868	0.0208	48.0
5	0.0854	11.7	0.877	0.0206	48.5
10	0.0845	11.8	0.886	0.0203	49.0
15	0.0836	11.9	0.896	0.0201	49.5
20	0.0827	12.0	0.905	0.0199	50.0
25	0.0819	12.2	0.915	0.0197	50.5
30	0.0810	12.3	0.924	0.0195	51.1
35	0.0802	12.4	0.934	0.0193	51.6
40	0.0794	12.6	0.943	0.0191	52.1
45	0.0786	12.8	0.953	0.0190	52.6
50	0.0778	12.9	0.962	0.0188	53.1
55	0.0771	13.0	0.971	0.0187	53.6
60	0.0764	13.1	0.981	0.0184	54.1
65	0.0756	13.2	0.990	0.0182	54.6
70	0.0749	13.3	1.000	0.0181	55.1
75	0.0742	13.4	1.009	0.0179	55.7
80	0.0735	13.6	1.019	0.0177	56.2
85	0.0728	13.7	1.028	0.0176	56.7
90	0.0722	13.8	1.038	0.0174	57.2
95	0.0715	13.9	1.047	0.0173	57.7
100	0.0709	14.0	1.057	0.0171	58.2
110	0.0696	14.3	1.075	0.0168	59.2
120	0.0684	14.5	1.094	0.0165	60.2
130	0.0673	14.8	1.113	0.0163	61.3
140	0.0662	15.0	1.132	0.0160	62.3
150	0.0651	15.3	1.151	0.0157	63.3
160	0.0640	15.6	1.170	0.0155	64.3
170	0.0630	15.8	1.189	0.0153	65.3
180	0.0620	16.1	1.208	0.0150	66.4
190	0.0611	16.3	1.227	0.0148	67.4
200	0.0601	16.6	1.245	0.0146	68.4
220	0.0584	17.1	1.283	0.0141	70.4
240	0.0567	17.6	1.321	0.0138	72.4
260	0.0551	18.1	1.359	0.0134	74.4
280	0.0536	18.6	1.396	0.0130	76.4
300	0.0522	19.1	1.434	0.0127	78.5
350	0.0490	20.4	1.528	0.0119	83.5
400	0.0461	21.7	1.623	0.0113	88.5
450	0.0436	22.9	1.717	0.0107	93.4
500	0.0413	24.1	1.811	0.0101	98.2
550	0.0393	25.4	1.906	0.0096	103.4
600	0.0374	26.7	2.001	0.0092	108.3
700	0.0342	29.2	2.190	0.0084	118.0
800	0.0315	31.7	2.378	0.0078	127.8
900	0.0292	34.2	2.567	0.0072	137.3
1000	0.0272	36.8	2.756	0.0068	147.0
1200	0.0239	41.7	3.133	0.0060	165.8

TAPER SIDE LADLE CAPACITIES IN IRON

Top Dia. in.	Bowl Size Bottom Dia., in.	Depth, in.	Top Allowance in.	Capacities in pounds — Lining Thickness, in. 1	1½	2	2¾	3½	4	4¾	5¼	6	7¼	8	9¼
20½	18	20½	2	960	*825*	715	560	425							
23	20	23	2	1400	*1230*	1080	875	695							
26	22¾	26	2	2225	2000	*1780*	1485	1230	1075						
27½	24	27½	2½		2245	*2010*	1700	1415	1240						
29	25½	29	2½		2710	*2450*	2085	1760	1560						
32	28	32	2½		3770	3440	*3000*	2565	2310	1960					
34½	30¼	34½	3		4760	4380	*3850*	3360	3050	2620					
36½	32	36½	3			5325	4710	*4150*	3790	3300	3000				
40½	35½	40½	3			7585	7010	*6085*	5620	4960	4565				
43½	38	43½	3				8700	7835	*7300*	6515	6030	5360			
46	40½	46	4				10320	9375	*8760*	7885	7340	6565			
48½	42½	48½	4				12360	11260	*10570*	9580	8950	8075			
51	44½	51	4					13400	12600	*11500*	10800	9790	8250		
55	48	55	5					17100	16100	*14800*	13990	12785	10950		
58	51	58	5					20650	19600	*18135*	17140	15800	13670		
62	54	62	5						24560	22765	*21685*	20850	17600	16200	
66	58	66	5						30780	28775	*27450*	25500	22630	21000	
72	63½	72	6							38450	36900	*34610*	31200	28935	25780
79	70	72	6							47850	46100	*44440*	39350	37000	33235
86	77	72	7							57857	55700	*52750*	48200	45500	41200

Note: (1) Based on density of molten iron at 411 lb/cu ft or 0.238 lb/cu in. (2) Italicized capacity weights are the more usual in use.

GRAINS OF MOISTURE PER POUND OF DRY AIR

Dry Bulb Temp.	Wet Bulb Temperature 62	63	64	65	66	67	68	69	70	71	72	73
90	38.0	42.7	47.6	52.0	57.0	62.3	67.2	72.5	78.0	83.9	89.8	95.1
91	36.4	41.0	46.0	50.7	55.5	60.8	65.7	71.0	76.5	82.0	88.0	93.7
92	35.0	39.4	44.2	49.0	54.0	59.1	64.0	69.5	75.0	80.6	86.5	92.0
93	33.2	38.0	42.7	47.2	52.4	57.7	62.8	68.0	73.4	78.9	84.9	90.6
94	31.8	36.2	41.0	46.0	50.8	56.0	60.9	66.0	71.8	77.3	83.3	89.0
95	30.0	34.7	39.4	44.2	49.1	54.3	59.3	64.5	70.2	75.7	81.7	87.3
96	28.7	33.0	38.0	42.5	47.6	52.8	57.8	63.0	68.7	74.0	80.0	85.7
97	27.0	31.4	36.2	41.0	46.0	51.1	56.0	61.5	67.0	72.5	78.4	84.0
98	25.3	30.0	34.7	39.6	44.2	49.7	54.5	60.0	65.3	71.0	77.0	82.4
99	24.0	28.3	33.0	38.0	42.8	48.0	53.0	58.2	63.8	69.4	75.3	80.9
100	22.2	26.8	31.6	36.1	41.1	46.3	51.7	56.8	62.1	67.8	73.7	79.3
101	20.6	25.0	30.0	34.7	39.7	44.8	50.0	55.0	60.7	66.0	72.0	77.6
102	19.0	23.6	28.2	33.0	38.0	43.1	48.1	53.7	59.0	64.5	70.5	76.0
103	17.4	22.0	26.8	31.5	36.1	41.7	46.6	52.0	57.5	63.0	69.0	74.5
104	16.0	20.4	25.2	29.9	35.0	40.0	45.0	50.2	55.9	61.3	67.3	73.0
105	14.2	19.0	23.7	28.2	33.1	38.3	43.4	48.7	54.2	59.9	65.7	71.3
106	12.8	17.1	22.0	26.7	31.8	36.9	42.0	47.0	52.7	58.2	64.0	69.7
107	11.1	15.8	20.5	25.0	30.0	35.2	40.2	45.5	51.0	56.7	62.4	68.0
108	9.7	14.0	19.0	23.6	28.4	33.7	38.7	44.0	49.4	55.0	61.0	66.5
109	8.0	12.5	17.2	22.0	27.0	32.1	37.0	42.2	47.8	53.5	59.5	65.0
110	6.2	11.0	15.8	20.5	25.3	30.5	35.7	40.8	46.2	52.0	57.8	63.4

GRAINS OF MOISTURE PER CUBIC FOOT OF DRY AIR

Dry Bulb Temp.	Wet Bulb Temperature 62	63	64	65	66	67	68	69	70	71	72	73
90	2.72	3.05	3.40	3.71	4.06	4.44	4.78	5.15	5.54	5.94	6.35	6.71
91	2.60	2.92	3.28	3.62	3.95	4.32	4.66	5.03	5.41	5.80	6.21	6.61
92	2.50	2.81	3.14	3.49	3.84	4.20	4.53	4.92	5.30	5.70	6.11	6.48
93	2.37	2.70	3.04	3.36	3.72	4.08	4.45	4.80	5.18	5.56	5.98	6.36
94	2.26	2.58	2.92	3.26	3.60	3.96	4.31	4.66	5.07	5.45	5.85	6.25
95	2.13	2.46	2.80	3.15	3.48	3.84	4.19	4.55	4.95	5.36	5.73	6.12
96	2.04	2.34	2.69	3.00	3.36	3.73	4.08	4.44	4.83	5.20	5.61	6.00
97	1.91	2.22	2.56	2.90	3.25	3.60	3.94	4.32	4.70	5.09	5.50	5.87
98	1.79	2.12	2.45	2.79	3.11	3.50	3.83	4.21	4.58	4.98	5.39	5.75
99	1.69	2.00	2.32	2.68	3.01	3.38	3.72	4.08	4.46	4.85	5.26	5.64
100	1.57	1.89	2.22	2.54	2.88	3.25	3.63	3.98	4.34	4.73	5.14	5.52
101	1.45	1.76	2.11	2.44	2.78	3.14	3.50	3.84	4.24	4.60	5.01	5.40
102	1.35	1.66	1.98	2.32	2.66	3.02	3.36	3.75	4.11	4.49	4.90	5.28
103	1.22	1.54	1.88	2.21	2.52	2.91	3.26	3.62	4.00	4.39	4.80	5.16
104	1.12	1.43	1.76	2.09	2.44	2.78	3.14	3.50	3.88	4.25	4.66	5.05
105	.99	1.33	1.65	1.97	2.30	2.67	3.02	3.39	3.76	4.15	4.55	4.93
106	.89	1.19	1.54	1.86	2.22	2.56	2.92	3.26	3.65	4.02	4.42	4.81
107	.78	1.10	1.43	1.74	2.10	2.44	2.79	3.15	3.53	3.92	4.31	4.69
108	.68	.98	1.32	1.64	1.97	2.34	2.68	3.04	3.42	3.80	4.20	4.58
109	.56	.87	1.20	1.53	1.87	2.22	2.56	2.92	3.30	3.68	4.10	4.47
110	.43	.76	1.10	1.42	1.75	2.11	2.46	2.82	3.18	3.58	3.98	4.36

PRESSURE EQUIVALENTS

Ounces per Sq. In.	Pounds per Sq. In.	Inches of Water	Inches of Mercury
0.25	0.016	0.433	0.0319
0.50	0.031	0.866	0.0638
1	0.062	1.732	0.1275
2	0.125	3.464	0.2551
3	0.187	5.196	0.3826
4	0.250	6.928	0.5102
5	0.312	8.660	0.6377
6	0.375	10.392	0.7653
7	0.437	12.124	0.8928
8	0.500	13.856	1.020
9	0.562	15.588	1.148
10	0.625	17.320	1.275
11	0.687	19.052	1.403
12	0.750	20.784	1.531
13	0.812	22.516	1.658
14	0.875	24.248	1.786
15	9.937	25.980	1.913
16	1.000	27.712	2.041
17	1.062	29.444	2.169
18	1.125	31.176	2.296
19	1.187	32.908	2.424
20	1.250	34.640	2.551
21	1.312	36.372	2.679
22	1.375	38.104	2.806
23	1.437	39.836	2.934
24	1.500	41.568	3.061
25	1.562	43.300	3.189
26	1.625	45.032	3.317
27	1.687	46.764	3.444
28	1.750	48.496	3.572
29	1.812	50.228	3.699
30	1.875	51.960	3.827
31	1.937	53.692	3.954
32	2.000	55.424	4.082
33	2.062	57.156	4.210
34	2.125	58.888	4.337
35	2.187	60.620	4.465

METRIC EQUIVALENTS

Length

1 centimeter (cm)	= 0.3937 in.	1 inch (in)	= 2.540 cm
1 meter (m)	= 3.2808 ft	1 foot (ft)	= 0.3048 m
1 meter (m)	= 1.0936 yd	1 yard (yd)	= 0.9144 m
1 kilometer (km)	= 0.6213 mile	1 mile	= 1.6093 km

Area

Sq cm	= 0.1549 sq in.	Sq in.	= 6.4516 sq cm
Sq m	=10.7638 sq ft	Sq ft	= 0.0929 sq m
Sq m	= 1.1959 sq yd	Sq yd	= 0.8361 sq m
Hectare	= 2.4710 acres	Acre	= 0.4046 hectare
Sq km	= 0.3861 sq miles	Sq mile	= 2.5900 sq km

Volume

Cu cm	= 0.0610 cu in.	Cu in.	=16.3871 cu cm
Cu m	=35.3144 cu ft	Cu ft	= 0.0283 cu m
Cu m	= 1.3079 cu yd	Cu yd	= 0.7645 cu m

Capacity

Liter	= 0.0353 cu ft	Cu ft	=28.32 liters
Liter	= 0.2641 gallon (US)	Gallon	= 3.7853 liters
Liter	=61.0250 Cu in.	Cu in	= 0.0163 liter

Weight

Gram (gm)	=15.5323 grains	Grain	= 0.0647 gm
Gram	= 0.0352 oz	Ounce (oz)	=28.3495 gm
Kilogram (kg)	= 2.2046 lb	Pound (lb)	= 0.4535 kg
Kilogram	= 0.0011 ton (short)	Ton (short)	=907.1848 kg
Long ton	= 1.1023 ton (short)	Ton (short)	=2000 lb

Pressure

1 kg per sq cm	=14.22 lb per sq in.
1 lb per sq in.	= 0.07031 kg per sq cm
1 kg per sq m	= 0.2048 lb per sq ft
1 lb per sq ft	= 4.882 kg per sq m
1 kg per sq cm	= 0.9678 normal atmosphere
1 normal atmosphere	= 1.0332 kg per sq cm
1 normal atmosphere	=14.70 lb per sq in.

DECIMAL EQUIVALENTS OF ONE INCH

1/64	.015625	33/64	.515625	17/64	.265625	49/64	.765625
1/32	.03125	17/32	.53125	9/32	.28125	25/32	.78125
3/64	.046875	35/64	.546875	19/64	.296875	51/64	.796875
1/16	.0625	9/16	.5625	5/16	.3125	13/16	.8125
5/64	.078125	37/64	.578125	21/64	.328125	53/64	.828125
3/32	.09375	19/32	.59375	11/32	.34375	27/32	.84375
7/64	.109375	39/64	.609375	23/64	.359375	55/64	.859375
1/8	.125	5/8	.625	3/8	.375	7/8	.875
9/64	.140625	41/64	.640625	25/64	.390625	57/64	.890625
5/32	.15625	21/32	.65625	13/32	.40625	29/32	.90625
11/64	.171875	43/64	.671875	27/64	.421875	59/64	.921875
3/16	.1875	11/16	.6875	7/16	.4375	15/16	.9375
13/64	.203125	45/64	.703125	29/64	.453125	61/64	.953125
7/32	.21875	23/32	.71875	15/32	.46875	31/32	.96875
15/64	.234375	47/64	.734375	31/64	.484375	63/64	.984375
1/4	.25	3/4	.75	1/2	.5	1	1.

APPROXIMATE HOLDING CAPACITY OF CUPOLA WELL*

Diameter Inside Lining, in.	Approximate Holding Capacity, lb
23	570
27	820
32	1160
37	1540
42	1990
45	2280
48	2610
54	3390
60	4050
66	4910
72	5840
78	6840
84	7960

* Above figures are based on 1) 12 in. average depth of metal, and 2) molten metal occupies 46 per cent of available volume of the well.

COLOR SCALE FOR TEMPERATURES

Color	Degrees F
Lowest visible red	885
Lowest visible red to dark red	885-1200
Dark red to cherry red	1200-1380
Cherry red to bright cherry red	1380-1500
Bright cherry red to orange	1500-1650
Orange to yellow	1650-2000
Yellow to light yellow	2000-2400
Light yellow to white	2400-2800
White to dazzling white	Above 2800

USEFUL RATIOS

Multiply	By	To Obtain
Diam. circle	3.1316	Circumference
Diam. circle	0.886	Side of equal square
U. S. gallon	0.8327	Imperial gallon
U. S. gallon	0.1337	Cubic foot
Inches of mercury	0.4912	Pounds per sq in.
Feet of water	0.4335	Pounds per sq in.
Cubic feet	62.428	Pounds of water
U. S. gallons	8.336	Pounds of water
Knots	1.152	Miles per hour

TABLE OF BRINELL HARDNESS NUMBERS (10 Millimeter Ball)

Dia. of Inden- tation	load 500 kg	1000 kg	1500 kg	2000 kg	2500 kg	3000 kg
2.00	158	315	473	632	788	945
2.05	150	300	450	600	750	890
2.10	143	286	428	572	714	856
2.15	136	272	409	544	681	817
2.20	130	260	390	520	650	780
2.25	124	248	373	496	621	745
2.30	119	238	356	476	593	712
2.35	114	228	341	456	568	682
2.40	109	218	327	436	545	653
2.45	104	208	314	416	522	627
2.50	100	200	301	400	500	601
2.55	96.3	193	289	385	482	578
2.60	92.6	185	278	370	462	555
2.65	89.0	178	267	356	445	534
2.70	85.7	171	257	343	429	514
2.75	82.6	165	248	330	413	495
2.80	79.6	159	239	318	398	477
2.85	76.8	154	231	307	384	461
2.90	74.1	148	222	296	371	444
2.95	71.5	143	215	286	358	429
3.00	69.1	138	208	276	346	415
3.05	66.8	134	203	267	334	401
3.10	64.6	129	194	258	324	388
3.15	62.5	125	188	250	313	375
3.20	60.5	121	182	242	303	363
3.25	58.6	117	176	234	293	352
3.30	56.8	114	171	227	284	341
3.35	55.1	110	166	220	276	331
3.40	53.4	107	161	214	267	321
3.45	51.8	104	156	207	259	311
3.50	50.3	101	151	201	252	302
3.55	48.9	97.8	147	196	244	293
3.60	47.5	95.0	143	190	238	285
3.65	46.1	92.2	139	184	231	277
3.70	44.9	89.8	135	180	225	269
3.75	43.6	87.2	131	174	218	262
3.80	42.4	84.8	128	170	212	255
3.85	41.3	82.6	124	165	207	248
3.90	40.2	80.4	121	161	201	241
3.95	39.1	78.2	118	156	196	235
4.00	38.1	76.2	115	152	191	229
4.05	37.1	74.2	112	148	186	223
4.10	36.2	72.4	109	145	181	217
4.15	35.3	70.6	106	141	177	212
4.20	34.4	68.8	104	138	172	207
4.25	33.6	67.2	101	134	167	201
4.30	32.8	65.6	98.5	131	164	197
4.35	32.0	64.0	96.0	128	160	192
4.40	31.2	62.4	93.5	125	156	187
4.45	30.5	61.0	91.5	122	153	183
4.50	29.8	59.6	89.5	119	149	179
4.55	29.1	58.2	87.0	116	145	174
4.60	28.4	56.6	85.0	114	142	170
4.65	27.8	55.6	83.5	111	139	167
4.70	27.1	54.2	81.5	108	136	163
4.75	26.5	53.0	79.5	106	133	159
4.80	25.9	51.8	78.0	104	130	156
4.85	25.4	50.8	76.0	102	127	152
4.90	24.8	49.6	74.5	99.2	124	149
4.95	24.3	48.6	73.0	97.2	122	146
5.00	23.8	47.6	71.5	95.2	119	143
5.05	23.3	46.6	70.0	93.2	117	140
5.10	22.8	45.6	68.5	91.2	114	137
5.15	22.3	44.6	67.0	89.2	112	134
5.20	21.8	43.6	65.5	87.2	109	131
5.25	21.4	42.8	64.0	85.6	107	128
5.30	20.9	41.8	63.0	83.6	105	126
5.35	20.5	41.0	61.5	82.0	103	123
5.40	20.1	40.2	60.5	80.4	101	121
5.45	19.7	39.4	59.0	78.8	98.5	118
5.50	19.3	38.6	58.0	77.2	96.5	116
5.55	18.9	37.8	57.0	75.6	95.0	114
5.60	18.6	37.2	55.5	74.4	92.5	111
5.65	18.2	36.4	54.5	72.8	90.8	109
5.70	17.8	35.6	53.5	71.2	89.2	107
5.75	17.5	35.0	52.5	70.0	87.5	105
5.80	17.2	34.4	51.5	68.8	85.8	103
5.85	16.8	33.6	50.5	67.2	84.2	101
5.90	16.5	33.0	49.6	66.0	82.5	99.2
5.95	16.2	32.4	48.7	64.8	81.2	97.3
6.00	15.9	31.8	47.8	63.6	79.5	95.5
6.05	15.6	31.2	46.9	62.4	78.0	93.7
6.10	15.3	30.6	46.0	61.2	76.7	92.0
6.15	15.1	30.2	45.2	60.4	75.3	90.3
6.20	14.8	29.6	44.4	59.2	73.8	88.7
6.25	14.5	29.0	43.6	58.0	72.6	87.1
6.30	14.2	28.4	42.8	56.8	71.3	85.5
6.35	14.0	28.0	42.0	56.0	70.0	84.0
6.40	13.7	27.4	41.3	54.8	68.8	82.5
6.45	13.5	27.0	40.5	54.0	67.5	81.0

Index

D

E

F

G

N

O

P

R

S

6912